KT-171-728

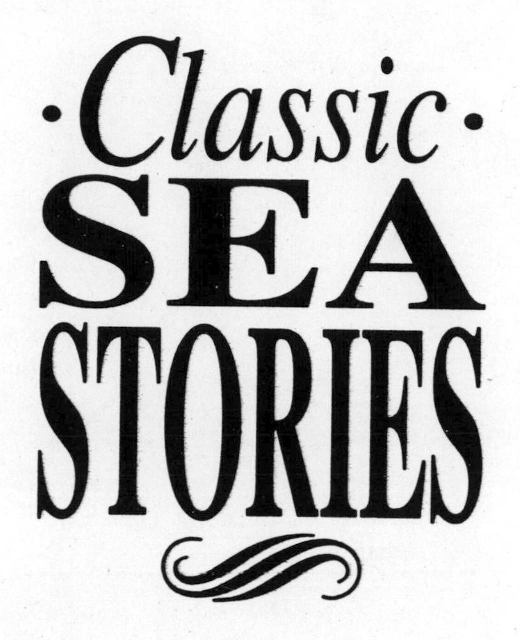
Classic
SEA
STORIES

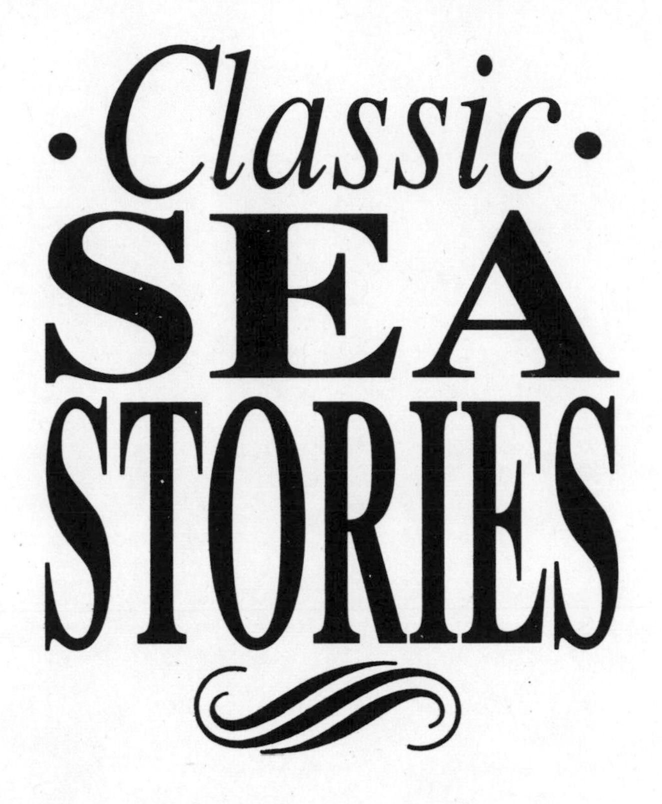

INTRODUCTION BY

BARRY UNSWORTH

BRACKEN BOOKS
LONDON

Classic Sea Stories

This edition published in 1994 by Bracken Books,
an imprint of Studio Editions Ltd, Princess House,
50 Eastcastle Street, London W1N 7AP, England

ISBN 1 85891 134 6

Printed at Thomson Press (India) Ltd.

CONTENTS

UNITED STATES

FRANCE

ITALY

SPAIN

PORTUGAL

NORWAY

SWEDEN

DENMARK

JAPAN

INTRODUCTION

The ocean is the last frontier, the only untamed territory left to us. There are tracts of earth which offer man little in the way of hospitality, but deserts can be made to bloom, mountain peaks can be conquered, jungles can be razed. The sea is another world, uncontrollable, unpredictable, violent in her rages, beguiling in her calms, but always alien. Moreover, she is vast, beyond our scale in her volume and extent and limitless to our imagination. The greater part of our world is water, as is the greater part of our human constitution.

She has been a subject of literature almost since language could be written and read, in all her contradictions, blessed and cursed in equal measure, escape route and prison, friend and foe, bitter exile, and strong defence. For an island people like the British she is an all-pervasive presence both in poetry and prose, just as she is in physical fact – even if we do no more than sit and gaze at her from deckchairs and hotel balconies, or paddle in her shallows. She is a setting for the land, a quality of light, a determiner of weather. But even for landlocked peoples there are always stories – tales of marvels that lie beyond the horizon, regarded as oracles, as people somehow initiated, possessing a special message, like the Ancient Mariner. They have licence to embroider and invent, and so a complex body of true experience and legend and myth has accumulated over centuries and now provides a treasury of reference and association which has moulded our sensibility.

This anthology, ranging widely in place and period, from Ancient Greece to modern America, gives as fair a representation of this diversity and wealth as could be found in one volume. Over great spans of time and across chasms of culture the themes interact and strike echoes. Beowulf's wrestling with the sea-monster Grendel is a heroic struggle with evil expressed in the terms of a savage society half-way between paganism and Christianity. But in thematic terms it is close to the tormented New England conscience we find expressed in the pursuit of the Great White Whale in Moby Dick, an attempt to conquer the beast within as well as the beast without. And both are instinct with that exciting and marvellously realized physical action, that sense of human testing, which all great stories of the sea possess. 'The Gathering of the Waters' in Genesis and the deep fear of engulfment it expresses – a permanent factor of our experience – is echoed again in the terms of the maelstrom in Poe's wonderful story. Conrad's model of the ship at sea as a microcosm of human society, an image of co-operation and solidarity in the face of danger and hardship, is found again and again in classic sea stories from all over the world, amply represented in this collection.

One of the dominant feelings we have about the sea is that it is a source of marvels and this aspect too is given full expression here, from Jonah in the whale's belly to the Clashing Rocks negotiated by the Argonauts to Hans Christian Andersen's story of 'The Little Mermaid'. And in what is perhaps the greatest sea-story of all, Homer's *Odyssey*, the adventures of the wily hero, the dangers and wonders of the deeps that he encounters, form a sort of long postponement to the realization of that desire for a haven, a refuge from storm and stress, which is also one of our deepest feelings, so that the island of Ithaca, so long desired, so much suffered for – and little more in fact than a barren range of rocky slopes rising from the sea – becomes an image of all refuge and safety.

Then there are the great sea-battles and voyages of exploration, episodes of history in which the action itself, though true in fact and carefully documented, becomes half-legendary, so momentous and far-reaching have sometimes been the results: the 'Rounding of the Cape', the Portuguese in their cockle-shell ships sailing into the Pacific, the 'Last Fight of the *Revenge*' in Sir Walter Raleigh's account, the 'Incredible Armada', the battle of Trafalgar from Southey's biography of Nelson, an engagement which established British naval supremacy of more than a century and gave generations of school boys their notion of heroism.

There is an extraordinary range of effects in these stories, from the graphic realism of Richard Henry Dana's account of a storm in the Pacific, the romanticism of Pierre Loti's description of fishermen, the fantasy of Jules Verne with his stories of strange sea-creatures and submerged cities. But perhaps the deepest fascination lies in our sense of the ship as a freightage of human beings, forced into community, obeying rules necessary for survival, subject to time and chance in a way we recognize as true to our condition here below. The sea-story can make us share these vicissitudes, these uncertain destinies, even if we never venture from land, because this is a voyage which in one way or another we are all obliged to make.

Barry Unsworth

ANCIENT GREECE

HOW ODYSSEUS MADE HIMSELF A RAFT, AND HOW POSEIDON, SHAKER OF THE EARTH, OVERWHELMED HIM WITH A STORM[1]

Homer

(c. 1000 B.C.)

SO SOON as early Dawn shone forth, the rosy-fingered, anon Odysseus put on him a mantle and doublet, and the nymph clad her in a great shining robe, light of woof and gracious, and about her waist she cast a fair golden girdle, and a veil withal upon her head. Then she considered of the sending of Odysseus, the great-hearted. She gave him a great axe, fitted to his grasp, an axe of bronze double-edged, and with a goodly handle of olive wood fastened well. Next she gave him a polished adze, and she led the way to the border of the isle where tall trees grew, alder and poplar, and pine that reacheth unto heaven, seasoned long since and sere, that might lightly float for him. Now after she had shown him where the tall trees grew, Calypso, the fair goddess, departed homeward.

And he set to cutting timber, and his work went busily. Twenty trees in all he felled, and then trimmed them with the axe of bronze, and deftly smoothed them, and over them made straight the line. Meanwhile Calypso, the fair goddess, brought him augers, so he bored each piece and jointed them together, and then made all fast with trenails and dowels. Wide as is the floor of a broad ship of burden, which some man well skilled in carpentry may trace him out, of such beam did Odysseus fashion his broad raft. And thereat he wrought, and set up the deckings, fitting them to the close-set uprights, and finished them off with long gunwales, and therein he set a mast, and a yard-arm fitted thereto, and moreover he made him a rudder to guide the craft. And he fenced it with wattled osier withies from stem to stern, to be a bulwark against the wave, and piled up wood to back them. Meanwhile Calypso, the fair goddess, brought him web of cloth to make him sails; and these too he fashioned very skilfully. And he made fast therein braces and halyards and sheets, and at last he pushed the raft with levers down to the fair salt sea.

It was the fourth day when he had accomplished all. And, lo, on the fifth, the fair Calypso sent him on his way from the island, when she had bathed him and clad him in fragrant attire. Moreover, the goddess placed on board the ship two skins, one of dark wine, and another, a great one, of water, and corn too in a wallet,

[1] From *The Odyssey,* translated by S.H. Butcher and Andrew Lang.

and she set therein a store of dainties to his heart's desire, and sent forth a warm and gentle wind to blow. And goodly Odysseus rejoiced as he set his sails to the breeze. So he sate and cunningly guided the craft with the helm, nor did sleep fall upon his eyelids, as he viewed the Pleiads and Boötes, that setteth late, and the Bear, which they likewise call the Wain, which turneth ever in one place, and keepeth watch upon Orion, and alone hath no part in the baths of Ocean. This star, Calypso, the fair goddess, bade him to keep ever on the left as he traversed the deep. Ten days and seven he sailed traversing the deep, and on the eighteenth day appeared the shadowy hills of the land of the Phæacians, at the point where it lay nearest to him; and it showed like a shield in the misty deep.

Now the lord, the shaker of the earth, on his way from the Ethiopians, espied him afar off from the mountains of the Solymi: even thence he saw Odysseus as he sailed over the deep; and he was mightily angered in spirit, and shaking his head he communed with his own heart. "Lo now, it must be that the gods at the last have changed their purpose concerning Odysseus, while I was away among the Ethiopians. And now he is nigh to the Phæacian land, where it is ordained that he escape the great issues of the woe which hath come upon him. But, methinks, that even yet I will drive him far enough in the path of suffering."

With that he gathered the clouds and troubled the waters of the deep, grasping his trident in his hands; and he roused all storms of all manner of winds, and shrouded in clouds the land and sea; and down sped night from heaven. The East Wind and the South Wind clashed, and the stormy West, and the North, that is born in the bright air, rolling onward a great wave. Then were the knees of Odysseus loosened and his heart melted, and heavily he spake to his own great spirit:

"Oh, wretched man that I am! what is to befal me at the last? I fear that indeed the goddess spake all things truly, who said that I should fill up the measure of sorrow on the deep, or ever I came to mine own country; and lo, all these things have an end. In such wise doth Zeus crown the wide heaven with clouds, and hath troubled the deep, and the blasts rush on of all the winds; yea, now is utter doom assured me. Thrice blessed those Danaans, yea, four times blessed, who perished on a time in wide Troy-land, doing a pleasure to the sons of Atreus! Would to God that I too had died, and met my fate on that day when the press of Trojans cast their bronze-shod spears upon me, fighting for the body of the son of Peleus! So should I have gotten my dues of burial, and the Achæans would have spread my fame; but now it is my fate to be overtaken by a pitiful death."

Even as he spake, the great wave smote down upon him, driving on in terrible wise, that the raft reeled again. And far therefrom he fell, and lost the helm from his hand; and the fierce blast of the jostling winds came and brake his mast in the midst, and sail and yard-arm fell afar into the deep. Long time the water kept him under, nor could he speedily rise from beneath the rush of the mighty wave: for the garments hung heavy which fair Calypso gave him. But late and at length he came up, and spat forth from his mouth the bitter salt water, which ran down in streams from his head. Yet even so forgat he not his raft, for all his wretched plight, but made a spring after it in the waves, and clutched it to him, and sat in the midst thereof, avoiding the issues of death; and the great wave swept it hither and thither along the stream. And as the North Wind in the harvest tide sweeps the thistle down along the plain, and close the tufts cling each to other, even so the winds bare the raft hither and thither along the main. Now the South would toss it to the North to carry, and now again the East would yield it to the West to chase.

But the daughter of Cadmus marked him, Ino of the fair ankles, Leucothea, who in time past was a maiden of mortal speech, but now in the depths of the salt sea she had gotten her share of worship from the gods. She took pity on Odysseus in his wandering and travail, and she rose, like a sea-gull on the wing, from the depth of the mere, and sat upon the well-bound raft and spake saying:

"Hapless one, wherefore was Poseidon, shaker of the earth, so wondrous wroth with thee, seeing that he soweth for thee the seeds of many evils? Yet shall he not make a full end of thee, for all his desire. But do even as I tell thee, and methinks thou art not witless. Cast off these garments, and leave the raft to drift before the winds, but do thou swim with thine hands and strive to win a footing on the coast of the Phæacians, where it is decreed that thou escape. Here, take this veil imperishable and wind it about thy breast; so is there no fear that thou suffer aught or perish. But when thou hast laid hold of the mainland with thy hands, loose it from off thee and cast it into the wine-dark deep far from the land, and thyself turn away."

With that the goddess gave the veil, and for her part dived back into the heaving deep, like a sea-gull: and the dark wave closed over her. But the steadfast goodly Odysseus pondered, and heavily he spake to his own brave spirit:

"Ah, woe is me! Can it be that some one of the immortals is weaving a new snare for me, that she bids me quit my raft? Nay, verily, I will not yet obey, for I had sight of the shore yet a long way off, where she told me that I might escape. I am resolved what I will do—and methinks on this wise it is best. So long as the timbers abide in the dowels, so long will I endure steadfast in affliction, but so soon as the wave hath shattered my raft asunder, I will swim, for meanwhile no better counsel may be."

While yet he pondered these things in his heart and soul, Poseidon, shaker of the earth, stirred against him a great wave, terrible and grievous, and vaulted from the crest, and therewith smote him. And as when a great tempestuous wind tosseth a heap of parched husks and scatters them this way and that, even so did the wave scatter the long beams of the raft. But Odysseus bestrode a single beam, as one rideth on a courser, and stript him of the garments which fair Calypso gave him.

And presently he wound the veil beneath his breast, and fell prone into the sea, outstretching his hands as one eager to swim. And the lord, the shaker of the earth, saw him and shook his head, and communed with his own soul. "Even so, after all thy sufferings, go wandering over the deep, till thou shalt come among a people, the fosterlings of Zeus. Yet for all that I deem not that thou shalt think thyself too lightly afflicted." Therewith he lashed his steeds of the flowing manes, and came to Ægea, where is his lordly home.

And Athene, daughter of Zeus, turned to new thoughts. Behold, she bound up the courses of the other winds, and charged them all to cease and be still; but she roused the swift North and brake the waves before him, that so Odysseus, of the seed of Zeus, might mingle with the Phæacians, lovers of the oar, avoiding death and the fates.

So for two nights and two days he was wandering in the swell of the sea, and much his heart boded of death. But when at last the fair-tressed Dawn brought the full light of the third day, thereafter the breeze fell, and lo, there was a breathless calm, and with a quick glance ahead, (he being upborne on a great wave,) he saw the land very near. And even as when most welcome to his children is the sight of a father's life, who lies in sickness and strong pains long wasting away, some angry god assailing him; and to their delight the gods have loosed him from his trouble; so welcome to Odysseus showed land and wood; and he swam onward being eager to set foot on the strand. But when he was within earshot of the shore, and heard now the thunder of the sea against the reefs—for the great wave crashed against the dry land belching in terrible wise, and all was covered with foam of the sea—for there were no harbours for ships nor shelters, but jutting headlands and reefs and cliffs; then at last the knees of Odysseus were loosened and his heart melted, and in heaviness he spake to his own brave spirit:

"Ah me! now that beyond all hope Zeus hath given me sight of land, and withal I have cloven my way through this gulf of the sea, here there is no place to land on from out of the grey water. For without are sharp crags, and round them the wave roars surging, and sheer the smooth rock rises, and the sea is deep thereby, so that in no wise may I find firm foothold and escape my bane, for as I fain would go ashore, the great wave may haply snatch and dash me on the jagged rock—and a wretched endeavour that would be. But if I swim yet further along the coast to find, if I may, spits that take the waves aslant and havens of the sea, I fear lest the storm-winds catch me again and bear me over the teeming deep, making heavy moan; or else some god may even send forth against me a monster from out of the shore water; and many such pastureth the renowned Amphitrite. For I know how wroth against me hath been the great Shaker of the Earth."

Whilst yet he pondered these things in his heart and mind, a great wave bore him to the rugged shore. There would he have been stript of his skin and all his bones been broken, but that the goddess, grey-eyed Athene, put a thought into his heart. He rushed in, and with both his hands clutched the rock, whereto he clung till the great wave went by. So he escaped that peril, but again with backward wash it leapt on him and smote him and cast him forth into the deep. And as when the cuttle-fish is dragged forth from his chamber, the many pebbles clinging to his suckers, even so was the skin stript from his strong hand against the rocks, and the great wave closed over him. There of a truth would luckless Odysseus have perished beyond that which was ordained, had not grey-eyed Athene given him sure counsel. He rose from the line of the breakers that belch upon the shore, and swam outside, ever looking landwards, to find, if he might, spits that take the waves aslant and havens of the sea. But when he came in his swimming over against the mouth of a fair-flowing river, whereby the place seemed best in his eyes, smooth of rocks, and withal there was a covert from the wind, Odysseus felt the river running, and prayed to him in his heart:

"Hear me, O king, whosoever thou art; unto thee am I come, as to one to whom prayer is made, while I flee the rebukes of Poseidon from the deep. Yea, reverend even to the deathless gods is that man who comes as a wanderer, even as I now have come to thy stream and to thy knees after much travail. Nay pity me, O king; for I avow myself thy suppliant."

So spake he, and the god straightway stayed his stream and withheld his waves, and made the water smooth before him, and brought him safely to the mouths of the river. And his knees bowed and his stout hands fell, for his heart was broken by the brine. And his flesh was all swollen and a great stream of sea water gushed up through his mouth and nostrils. So he lay without breath or speech, swooning, such terrible weariness came upon him. But when now his breath returned and his spirit came to him again, he loosed from off him the veil of the goddess, and let it fall into the salt flowing river. And the great wave bare it back down the stream, and lightly Ino caught it in her hands. Then Odysseus turned from the river, and fell back in the reeds, and kissed earth, the grain-giver.

HOW THE GREEKS DEFEATED THE PERSIANS OFF THE ISLE OF SALAMIS[1]

Æschylus

(525 B.C.-456 B.C.)

O YE cities of the whole land of Asia! O realm of Persia, and mighty haven of opulence, how hath the ample weal been demolished by a single stroke, and the flower of the Persians is fallen and gone! The shores of Salamis, and all the adjoining region, are full of the corpses of those who miserably perished. For our bows availed us nought, and our whole host perished, beaten down by the collision of the beaks of the vessels. O name of Salamis, most hateful to our ears! Alas! how I sigh when I remember Athens. Xerxes himself lives, and beholds the light. But Artembares, leader of a myriad of horse, is dashed against the rugged shores of Sileniæ. And Dadaces the chiliarch, beneath the stroke of the spear, bounded a light leap out of his vessel. Tenagon too, the true-born chieftain of the Bactrians, haunts the sea-beat isle of Ajax. Lilæus, and Arsames, and Argestes third, overcome, keep butting against the hard shore around the dove-breeding isle. Arcteus, too, that dwelt near the sources of Egyptian Nile, Adeues, and Pheresseues the third, Pharnuchus, these fell from one vessel. Matallus of Chrysa, commander of a myriad, leader of a body of thirty thousand black cavalry, in his death, tinged his bright auburn beard, changing its colour with a stain of purple. And Arabus the Mage, and Artames the Bactrian, a settler on the rugged land, perished there. Amestris, and Amphistreus who wielded a spear that did great execution, and brave Ariomardus, occasioning grief to Sardis, and Sesames the Mysian; Tharybis, too, commander of five times fifty ships, of Lyrnæan race, a hero of fair form, lies wretched, having died by no means happily. And Syennesis, foremost in gallantry, governor of the Cilicians, that with his single arm occasioned much trouble to the foe, fell gloriously.

So far as numbers are concerned, the barbarians had the advantage with their ships: for the whole number of those of the Greeks amounted to ten squadrons of thirty, and beside these there were ten of surpassing excellence. But Xerxes, for I know this also, had a thousand, the number of those which he led; and those which exceeded in swiftness were two hundred and seven; thus runs report. 'Twas some divinity that thus depressed the balance with a counterpoise of fortune.

A Greek that had come from the host of the Athenians, told thy son Xerxes this, that, when the gloom of murky night should come, the Greeks would not remain, but, springing on the benches of their vessels, would severally, in different

[1] From T.A. Buckley's translation of *The Persians*.

directions, save their lives by stealthy flight. And he, as soon as he heard it, not aware of the stratagem of the Greek, nor of the jealousy of the gods, publishes this order to all his captains, that when the sun should have ceased to illumine the earth with his rays, and darkness tenant the temple of the firmament, they should draw up the squadron of the ships in three lines, to guard the outlets, and the murmuring passes of the sea, and others in a circle around the isle of Ajax; so that if the Greeks should elude fatal destruction by discovering any escape for their ships by stealth, it was decreed that they all should be deprived of their heads. To this effect he spake from a frantic spirit; for he knew not that which was pre-ordained by the gods. And they, without disorder, and with obedient mind, both provided supper for themselves, and the mariner lashed his oar to the well-fitted rowlock. And when the light of the sun had waned, and night had come on, every man, master of an oar, went on board his ship, and everyone that had sway over arms; and one line of ships of war cheered on another line, and they made sail as each had been appointed, and all the live-long night the commanders of the ships were keeping the whole naval host occupied in sailing about.

And night withdrew, and the force of the Greeks by no means made a stealthy escape in any direction. But when Day, drawn by white steeds, had occupied the whole earth, of radiance beautiful to behold, first of all a shout from the Greeks greeted Echo like a song, and Echo from the island-rock at the same instant shouted forth an inspiring cry: and terror fell on all the barbarians, baulked of their purpose; for not as in flight were the Greeks then chaunting the solemn paean, but speeding on to the fight with gallant daring of soul. And the trumpet, with its clang, inflamed their whole line; and forthwith, with the collision of the dashing oar, at the word of command they smote the roaring brine. And quickly were they conspicuous to view. The right wing, well marshalled, led on foremost in good order, and secondly, their whole force was coming forth against us, and we could at the same time hear a mighty shout: SONS OF THE GREEKS! ON! FREE YOUR COUNTRY, AND FREE YOUR CHILDREN, YOUR WIVES, THE ABODES TOO OF THE GODS OF YOUR FATHERS, AND THE TOMBS OF YOUR ANCESTORS; NOW IS THE CONFLICT FOR THEM ALL!

And sooth to say, a murmur of the Persian tongue met them from our line, and no longer was it the moment to delay, but forthwith ship dashed her brazen prow at ship. And a Grecian vessel commenced the engagement, and breaks off the whole of the figure-head of a Phœnician ship: and each commander severally directed his bark against another of the enemy's. At first, indeed, the torrent of the Persian armament bore up against them: but when the multitude of our ships were crowded in the strait, and no assistance could be given to one another, they were struck by their own brazen beaks, and were smashing their entire equipment of oars, and the Grecian vessels, not without science, were smiting them in a circle on all sides, and the hulls of our vessels were upturned, and the sea was no longer to behold, filled as it was with wrecks and the slaughter of men. The shores, too, and the rugged rocks were filled with the dead; and every ship, as many as ever there were in the barbaric armament, was rowed in flight without order. But the Greeks kept striking, hacking us as it were tunnies, or any draught of fishes, with fragments of oars, and splinters of wrecks; and wailing filled the ocean brine with shrieks, until the eye of murky night removed it. But for the multitude of our woes—no, not if I should recite them in order for ten days, could I complete the tale for thee.

HOW THE SHIP *ARGO* PASSED BETWEEN THE CLASHING ROCKS[1]

Apollonius Rhodius
(c. 235 B.C.-)

NOW when the sun, rising from the east, shone upon the dewy hills, and awoke shepherds, in that hour they loosed their cables from the stem of the bay tree, and putting their booty on board, even all that they had need to carry, they steered with the wind along the swirling Bosphorus. Then did a wave like to a steep mountain rush upon them in front as though it were charging them, rearing itself ever above the clouds, and never wouldst thou have said they would escape a horrid fate, for it hung arching right over the middle of the ship in all its fury; but yet even this grows smooth, if but you possess a clever pilot. So then they too came forth, unscathed, though much afeared, through the skill of Tiphys. And on the next day they anchored over against the Bithynian land.

Here Phineus, son of Agenor, had his home beside the sea; he who by reason of the divination that the son of Leto granted him aforetime, suffered most awful woes, far beyond all men; for not one jot did he regard even Zeus himself in foretelling the sacred purpose to men unerringly. Wherefore Zeus granted him a weary length of days, but reft his eyes of the sweet light, nor suffered him to have any joy of all the countless gifts, which those who dwelt around and sought him for oracles, were ever bringing to his house. But suddenly through the clouds the Harpies darted nigh, and kept snatching them from his mouth or hands in their talons. Sometimes never a morsel of food was left him, sometimes a scrap that he might live and suffer.

At once when he heard the sound and noise of a company, he perceived that

[1] From Edward P. Coleridge's translation of *The Argonautica.*

they were the very men now passing by, at whose coming an oracle from Zeus had said that he should enjoy his food. Up from his couch he rose, as it were a lifeless phantom, and leaning on his staff, came to the door on his wrinkled feet, feeling his way along the walls; and as he went, his limbs trembled from weakness and age; and his skin was dry and caked with filth, and nought but the skin held his bones together. So he came forth from his hall, and sat down with heavy knees on the threshold of the court, and a dark mantle wrapped him, and seemed to sweep the ground below all round; and there he sank with never a word, in strengthless lethargy.

But they, when they saw him, gathered round and were astonished. And he, drawing a laboured breath from the bottom of his chest, took up his parable for them, and said:

"Hearken, choice sons of all the Hellenes, if 'tis you in very truth, whom now Jason, at the king's chill bidding, is leading on the ship *Argo* to fetch the fleece. 'Tis surely you. Still doth my mind know each thing by its divining. Wherefore to thee, my prince, thou son of Leto, do I give thanks even in my cruel sufferings. By Zeus, the god of suppliants, most awful god to sinful men, for Phoebus' sake and for the sake of Hera herself, who before all other gods hath had you in her keeping as ye came, help me, I implore; rescue a hapless wretch from misery, and do not heedlessly go hence and leave me thus. For not only hath the avenging fiend set his heel upon my eyes, not only do I drag out to the end a tedious old age, but yet another most bitter pain is added to the tale. Harpies, swooping from some unseen den of destruction, that I see not, do snatch the food from my mouth. Them 'tis heaven's decree that the sons of Boreas shall check; and they shall ward them off, for they are my kinsmen, if indeed I am that Phineus who, in days gone by, had a name amongst men for my wealth and divination, whom Agenor my sire, begat."

So spake the son of Agenor, and deep sorrow took hold on each of the heroes, but especially on the two sons of Boreas. But they wiped away a tear and drew nigh, and thus spake Zetes, taking in his the hand of the suffering old man.

"Ah! poor sufferer, methinks there is no other man more wretched than thee. Why is it that such woes have fastened on thee ? Is it that thou hast sinned against the gods in deadly folly through thy skill in divination ? Wherefore are they so greatly wroth against thee? Lo! our heart within us is sorely bewildered, though we yearn to help thee, if in very truth the god hath reserved for us twain this honour. For plain to see are the rebukes that the immortals send on us men of earth. Nor will we check the coming of the Harpies, for all our eagerness, till that thou swear that we shall not fall from heaven's favour in return for this."

So spake he, and straight that aged man opened his sightless eyes and lifted them up, and thus made answer:

"Hush! Remind me not of those things, my son. The son of Leto be my witness, who of his kindness taught me divination be witness that ill-omened fate that is my lot, and this dark cloud upon my eyes, and the gods below, whose favour may I never find if I die perjured thus, that there shall come no wrath from heaven on you by reason of your aid."

Then were those twain eager to help him by reason of the oath, and quickly did the young men make ready a feast for the old man, a last booty for the Harpies; and the two stood near to strike them with their swords as they swooped down. Soon as ever that aged man did touch the food, down rushed those Harpies with whirr of wings at once, eager for the food, like grievous blasts or like lightning darting suddenly from the clouds. But those heroes, when they saw them in mid air, shouted; and they at the noise sped off afar across the sea. And the two sons of Boreas started in pursuit of them with their swords drawn, for Zeus inspired them with tireless courage and 'twas not without the will of Zeus that they followed them, for they would dart past the breadth of the west wind, what time they went to and from Phineus. As when upon the hilltops dogs skilled in the chase run on the track of horned goats or deer, and straining at full speed just behind, in vain do gnash their teeth upon their lips, even so Zetes and Calais, darting very nigh to them, in vain grazed them with their finger-tips. And now, I trow, they would have torn them in pieces against the will of the gods on the floating islands, after they had come afar, had not swift Iris seen them, and darting down from the clear heaven above stayed them with this word of rebuke:

"Ye sons of Boreas, 'tis not ordained that ye should slay the Harpies, the hounds of mighty Zeus, with your swords, but I, even I, will give you an oath that they will come no more nigh Phineus."

Therewith she sware by the stream of Styx, most dire and awful oath for all the gods, that these should never again draw near unto the house of Phineus, son of Agenor, for even so was it fated. So they yielded to her oath, and turned to hasten back to the ship. And so it is that men call those isles "the isles of turning," though aforetime they called them "the floating isles." And the Harpies and Iris parted; they entered their lair in Crete, the land of Minos, but she sped up to Olympus, soaring on her swift pinions.

Meantime the chieftains sat them down and feasted, and with them Phineus fell a-feasting ravenously, cheering his heart as in a dream. Then when they had taken their fill of food and drink, they sat up all night awaiting the sons of Boreas. And in their midst beside the hearth sat that ancient one himself, telling them of the ends of their voyage and the fulfilment of their journey.

"Hearken then. All ye may not learn of a surety, but as much as is heaven's will I will not hide. First of all, when ye have gone hence from me, ye shall see the two

Cyanean rocks at the place where two seas meet. Through these, I trow, none can win a passage. For they are not fixed on foundations below, but oft they clash together upon each other, and much salt water boils up from beneath, rearing its crest, and loud is the roar round the bluff headland.

"Wherefore now give heed to my exhorting, if in sooth ye make this voyage with cautious mind and due regard for the blessed gods: perish not then senselessly by a death of your own choosing, nor rush on at the heels of youthful rashness. First I bid you let loose from the ship a dove, and send her forth before you to try the way. And if she fly safely on her wings through those rocks to the sea, no longer do ye delay your voyage for any time, but stoutly ply the oars in your hands and cleave through the strait of sea, for now your life will depend not so much on your prayers as on your stalwart arms. Wherefore leave all other things alone and exert yourselves bravely to the utmost, yet ere you start I do not forbid you to entreat the gods. But if the dove be slain right in mid passage, fare ye back again, for far better it is to yield to the deathless gods. For then could ye not escape an evil doom at the rocks, no, not if Argo were made of iron.

"And these things shall be even as they may. But if ye escape the clashing of the rocks and come scathless inside Pontus, forthwith keep the Bithynian land upon your right, and sail cautiously amid the breakers, till that ye round the swift current of the river Rhebas and the Black headland, and be come to a haven in the Thynian isle. Thence return a short stretch across the sea, and beach your ship on the opposite shore of the Mariandyni. There is a path down to Hades, and the headland of Acherusia juts out and stretches itself on high, and swirling Acheron, cutting through the foot of the cliff, pours itself forth from a mighty ravine. Very nigh to it shall ye pass by many hills of the Paphlagonians, over whom Pelops first held sway in Enete, of whose blood they avow them to be. Now there is a certain cliff that fronts the circling Bear, on all sides steep: men call it Carambis; above it the gusty north is parted in twain; in such wise is it turned toward the sea, towering to heaven. At once when a man hath rounded it a wide beach stretches before him, and at the end of that wide beach nigh to a jutting cliff the stream of the river Halys, terribly discharges, and after him, but flowing near, the Iris rolls into the sea, a lesser stream with clear ripples. Here in front a great and towering bend stands out; next, Thermodon's mouth flows into a sleeping bay near the Themiscyrean headland, from its meandering through a wide continent. There is the plain of Doias, and hard by are the triple cities of the Amazons; and after them the Chalybes inhabit a rough and stubborn land, of all men most wretched, labourers they, busied with working of iron. Near them dwell the Tibareni, rich in sheep, beyond the Gentæan headland, where is a temple of Zeus, lord of hospitality. Next beyond this, but nigh thereto, the Mossynæci hold the woody mainland and the foot of the mountain, men that have builded houses. of timber with wooden battlements and chambers deftly finished, which they call Mossynæ, and hence they have their name.

"Coast on past them, and anchor at a smooth isle, after ye have driven off with all the skill ye may those ravening birds, which, men say, do roost upon this desert isle in countless numbers. Therein the queens of the Amazons builded a temple of stone to Ares, even Otrere and Antiope, what time they went forth to battle. Now here shall there come to you from out the bitter sea a help ye looked not for, wherefore of good will I bid you there to stay. But hold! why should I once more offend by telling everything from beginning to end in my divining? In front of the island, on the mainland opposite, dwell the Philyres: higher up, beyond them, are the Macrones: and yet beyond these, the countless tribes of the Becheiri. Next to them dwell the Sapeires, and their neighbours are the Byzeres, and right beyond them come next the warlike Colchians themselves.

"But cleave on your way, until ye come nigh to the inmost sea. There across the Cytæan mainland, from the Amarantian hills afar, and the plain of Circe, the swirling Phasis rolls his broad stream into the sea. Drive your ship into the mouth of that river, and ye shall see the towers of Cytæan Æetes and the shady grove of Ares, where a dragon, dire monster to behold, watches from his ambush round the fleece as it hangs on the top of an oak; nor night nor day doth sweet sleep o'ercome his restless eyes."

So spake he, and as they hearkened, fear fell on them forthwith. Long were they struck with speechlessness: at last spake the hero, the son of Æson, sorely at a loss:

"Old man, lo! now hast thou rehearsed the end of our toilsome voyage, and the sure sign which, if we obey, we shall pass through those loathèd rocks to Pontus; but whether there shall be a return again to Hellas for us, if we do escape them, this too would I fain learn of thee. How am I to act, how shall I come again over so wide a path of sea, in ignorance myself and with a crew alike ignorant? For Colchian Æa lieth at the uttermost end of Pontus and the earth."

So spake he, and to him did that old man make answer:

"My child, as soon as thou hast escaped through those rocks of death, be of good cheer, for a god will guide thee on a different route from Æa; and toward Æa there shall be plenty to guide thee. Yea, friends, bethink you of the crafty aid of the Cyprian goddess. For by her is prepared a glorious end to your toils. But question me no further of these matters."

So spake the son of Agenor, and the two sons of Thracian Boreas came glancing down from heaven, and set their rushing feet upon the threshold beside them. Up sprang the heroes from their seats, when they saw them coming near. And among the eager throng Zetes made harangue, drawing great gasps for breath after his toil, and told them how far they had journeyed, and how Iris prevented them from slaying the Harpies, and how the goddess in her favour gave them an oath, and those others slunk away in terror 'neath the vast cavern of the cliff of Dicte. Glad then were all their comrades in the house, and Phineus himself, at the news.

And anon, in no long space, as they talked the dawn appeared, and the neighbouring folk came round Phineus, they who even aforetime gathered thither day by day, ever bringing a portion of food for him. And unto all of them that aged man with good will gave oracles; wherefore they would visit and care for him. With these came Peræbius, the man most dear to him, and glad was he to hear them in his house. For long before had he himself declared that an expedition of chieftains, on its way from Hellas to the city of Æetes, should fasten its cables to the Thynian land, and they should restrain by Zeus's will the Harpies from coming to him.

And the chiefs abode there by constraint, and every day the Thynians sent forth good store of gifts for the strangers, out of favour for Phineus.

After this, when they had builded an altar to the twelve blessed gods on the edge of the sea opposite, and had offered sacrifice upon it, they went aboard their swift ship to row away, nor did they forget to take with them a timorous dove, but Euphemus clutched her in his hand, cowering with terror, and carried her along, and they loosed their double cables from the shore.

Nor, I ween, had they started ere Athene was ware of them, and forthwith and hastily she stepped upon a light cloud, which should bear her at once for all her weight; and she hasted on her way seaward, with kindly intent to the rowers. As when a man goes wandering from his country, as oft we men do wander in our hardihood, and there is no land too far away, for every path lies open before his eyes, when lo! he seeth in his mind his own home, and withal there appeareth a way to it over land or over sea, and keenly he pondereth this way and that, and searcheth it out with his eyes, even so the daughter of Zeus, swiftly darting on, set foot upon the cheerless strand of Thynia.

Now they, when they came to the strait of the winding passage, walled in with beetling crags on either side, while an eddying current from below washed up against the ship as it went on its way; and on they went in grievous fear, and already on their ears the thud of clashing rocks smote unceasingly, and the dripping cliffs roared; in that very hour the hero Euphemus clutched the dove in his hand, and went to take his stand upon the prow, while they, at the bidding of Tiphys, son of Hagnias, rowed with a will, that they might drive right through the rocks, trusting in their might. And as they rounded a bend, they saw those rocks opening for the last time of all. And their spirit melted at the sight; but the hero Euphemus sent forth the dove to dart through on her wings, and they, one and all, lifted up their heads to see, and she sped through them, but at once the two rocks met again with a clash; and the foam leapt up in a seething mass like a cloud, and grimly roared the sea, and all around the great firmament bellowed. And the hollow caves echoed beneath the rugged rocks as the sea went surging in, and high on the cliffs was the white spray vomited as the billow dashed upon them. Then did the current spin the ship round. And the rocks cut off just the tail-feathers of the dove, but she darted away unhurt. And loudly the rowers cheered, but Tiphys himself shouted to them to row lustily, for once more the rocks were opening.

Then came trembling on them as they rowed, until the wave with its returning wash came and bore the ship within the rocks. Thereon most awful fear seized on all, for above their head was death with no escape; and now on this side and on that lay broad Pontus to their view, when suddenly in front rose up a mighty arching wave, like to a steep hill, and they bowed down their heads at the sight. For it seemed as if it must indeed leap down and whelm the ship entirely. But Tiphys was quick to ease her as she laboured to the rowing, and the wave rolled with all his force beneath the keel, and lifted up the ship herself from underneath, far from the rocks, and high on the crest of the billow she was borne. Then did Euphemus go amongst all the crew, and call to them to lay on to their oars with all their might, and they smote the water at his cry. So she sprang forward twice as far as any other ship would have yielded to rowers, and the oars bent like curved bows as the heroes strained. In that instant the vaulted wave was past them, and she at once was riding over the furious billow like a roller, plunging headlong forward o'er the trough of the sea.

But the eddying current stayed the ship in the midst of the Clashers, and they quaked on either side, and thundered, and the ship-timbers throbbed. Then did Athene with her left hand hold the stubborn rock apart, while with her right she thrust them through upon their course; and the ship shot through the air like a wingèd arrow. Yet the rocks, ceaselessly dashing together, crushed off in passing the tip of the carved stern. And Athene sped back to Olympus, when they were escaped unhurt. But the rocks closed up together, rooted firm for ever; even so was it decreed by the blessed gods, whenso a man should have passed through alive in his ship. And they, I trow, drew breath again after their chilling fear, as they gazed out upon the sky, and the expanse of sea spreading far and wide. For verily they deemed that they were saved from Hades, and Tiphys first made harangue:

"Methinks we have escaped this danger sure enough, we and the ship, and there is no other we have to thank so much as Athene, who inspired the ship with divine courage, when Argus fastened her together with bolts; and it is not right that she should be caught. Wherefore, son of Æson, no more fear at all the bidding of thy king, since God hath granted us to escape through the rocks, for Phineus, son of Agenor, declared that, after this, toils easy to master should be ours."

Therewith he made the ship speed past the Bithynian coast across the sea. But the other answered him with gentle words:

"Ah! Tiphys, why comfort my heavy heart thus? I have sinned, and upon me has come a grievous blindness I may not cope with; for I should have refused this journey outright at once when Pelias ordained it, even though I was to have died, torn ruthlessly limb from limb; but now do I endure exceeding terror, and troubles past bearing, in deadly dread to sail across the chill paths of the deep, in deadly dread whene'er we land. For on all sides are enemies. And ever as the days go by, I watch through the dreary night, and think of all since first ye mustered for my sake; and lightly dost thou speak, caring only for thine own life, while I fear never so little for myself, but for this man and for that, for thee and the rest of my comrades do I fear, if I bring you not safe and sound to Hellas."

So spake he, making trial of the chieftains; but they cried out with words of cheer. And his heart was glad within him at their exhorting, and once more he spake to them outright.

"My friends, your bravery makes me more bold. Wherefore now no more will I let fear fasten on me, even though I must voyage across the gulf of Hades, since ye stand firm amid cruel terrors. Nay, since we have sailed from out the clashing rocks, I trow there will be no other horror in store such as this, if we surely go our way, following the counsel of Phineus."

THE MIGHT OF THE WHALE[1]

Oppian

(fl. c. A.D. 177-A. D. 180)

THE Sea-monsters that are nurtured in the midst of the seas are very many in number and of exceeding size. And not often do they come up out of the brine, but by reason of their heaviness they keep the bottom of the sea below. And they rave for food with unceasing frenzy, being always anhungered and never abating the gluttony of their terrible maw: for what food shall be sufficient to fill the void of their belly or enough to satisfy and give a respite to their insatiable jaws? Moreover, they themselves also destroy one another, the mightier in valour slaying the weaker, and one for the other is food and feast. Often too they bring terror to ships when they meet them in the Iberian sea in the West, where chiefly, leaving the infinite water of the neighbouring Ocean, they roll upon their way, like unto ships of twenty oars. Often also they stray and come nigh the beach where the water is deep inshore: and there one may attack them.

---

[1] From A.W. Mair's translation of *Halieutica*, in the Loeb Classical Library.

For all the great beasts of the sea, save the Dog-fishes, travelling is heavy-limbed and not easy. For they neither see far nor do they travel over all the sea, burdened as they are with their vast limbs, but very tardily they roll upon their way. Wherefore also with all of them there travels a companion fish, dusky to the eye and long of body and with a thin tail: which conspicuously goes before to guide them and show them their path in the sea; for which cause men call it the Guide. But to the Whale it is a companion that hath found wondrous favour, as guide at once and guard; and it easily bringeth him whither he will. For that is the only fish that he follows, the ever-loyal comrade of a loyal friend. And it wheels about near him and close by the eyes of the Whale it extends its tail, which tells the monster everything—whether there is some prey to seize or whether some evil threatens nigh, or if there is a shallow depth of sea which it were better to avoid. Even as if it had a voice, the tail declares all things to him truly, and the burden of the water obeys. For that fish is to the beast champion at once and ears and eyes: by it the Whale hears, by it he sees, to it he entrusts the reins of his life for keeping. Even as a son lovingly entreats his aged father, by anxious care of his years repaying the price of his nurture, and zealously attends and cherishes him, weak now of limb and dim of eye, reaching him his arm in the street and himself in all works succouring him—sons are a new strength to an aged sire: so that fish for love cherishes the monster of the brine, steering as it were a ship by the guiding helm. Surely it had blood akin to his from earliest birth or he took it of his own will and made it his companion. Thus neither valour nor beauty hath such profit as wisdom, and strength with unwisdom is vain. A little man of good counsel sinks or saves the man of might; for even the invincible Whale with its unapproachable limbs takes for its friend a tiny fish. Therefore one should first capture that scouting Guide, entrapping it with might of hook and bait; for while it lives thou shalt never overpower and conquer the monster, but when it is gone, his destruction will be swifter. For he no longer knows surely the paths of the violet brine nor knows to shun the evil that is at hand, but, even as a merchant vessel whose steersman has perished, he wanders idly, defenceless and helpless, wherever the grey water carries him, and is borne in darkling and unguessed ways, widowed of his helpful charioteer. Many a time in his wandering he runs aground on rock or beach: such darkness is spread upon his eyes. Thereupon with eager thoughts the fishers hasten to the labour of the hunt, praying to the blessed gods of whale-killing that they may capture the dread monster of Amphitrite. As when a strong company of foemen, having waited for midnight, stealthily approach their enemy and find by favour of Ares the sentinels asleep before the gates and fall upon them and overcome them: thereupon they haste confidently to the high city and the very citadel, carrying the weapon of fire, the doom of the city, even the brand that wrecks the well-builded walls: even so confidently do the fisher host haste after the beast, unguarded now that his pilot is slain. First they conjecture in their minds his weight and size; and these are the signs that tell the measure of his limbs. If, as he rolls amid the waves of the sea, he rise a little above it, showing the top of his spine and the ridge of his neck, then verily he is a mighty beast and excellent: for not even the sea itself can easily support and carry him. But if some portion of his back also appears, that does not announce so great a weight: for feebler beasts travel a more buoyant path. For these monsters the line is fashioned of many strands of well-woven cord, as thick as the forestay of a ship, neither very large nor very small, and in length suitable to the prey. The well-wrought hook is rough and sharp with barbs projecting alternately on either side, strong enough to take a rock and pierce a cliff and with deadly curve as great as the gape of the beast can cover. A coiled chain is cast about the butt of the dark hook—a stout chain of beaten bronze to withstand the deadly violence of his teeth and the spears of his mouth. In the midst of the chain are set round wheels close together, to stay his wild struggles and prevent him from straightway breaking the iron in his bloody agony, as he tosses in deadly pain, but let him roll and wheel in his fitful course. For fatal banquet they put upon the hook a portion of the black liver of a bull or a bull's shoulder suited to the jaws of the banqueter. To accompany the hunters, as it were for war, are sharpened many strong harpoons and stout tridents and bills and axes of heavy blade and other such weapons as are forged upon the noisy anvil. Swiftly they go on board their well-benched ships, silently nodding to one another as need may be, and set forth. With quiet oars they gently make white the sea, carefully avoiding any noise, lest the great Whale remark aught and dive into the depths for refuge, and the task of the fishers be undertaken in vain. But when they draw nigh to him and close with their task, then boldly from the prow they launch for the giant beast the fatal snare. And when he espies the grievous banquet, he springs and disregards it not, obedient to his shameless belly, and rushing upon the hookèd death he seizes it; and immediately the whetted hook enters within his wide throat and he is impaled upon the barbs. Then, roused by the wound, first, indignant, he shakes his deadly jaw against them and strives to break the brazen cord; but his labour is vain. Then, next, in the anguish of fiery pain he dives swiftly into the nether gulfs of the sea. And speedily the fishers allow him all the length of the line; for there is not in men strength enough to pull him up and to overcome the heavy monster against his will. For easily could he drag them to the bottom, benched ship and all together, when he set himself to rush. Straightway as he dives they let go with him into the water large skins filled with human breath and fastened to the line. And he, in the agony of his pain, heeds not the hides but lightly drags them down, all unwilling and fain for the surface of the foamy sea. But when he comes to the bottom with labouring heart, he halts, greatly foaming in his distress. As some horse when it has accomplished its sweaty labour to the utmost goal, in a bloody foam grinds his teeth in the crooked bit, while the hot panting breath comes through his mouth: so, breathing hard, the Whale rests. But the skins allow him not, even if he would, to remain below, but swiftly speed upward and leap forth from the sea, buoyed by the breath within them; and a new contest arises for the Whale. Then first he makes a vain rush with his jaws, eager to defend himself against the hides which pull him up. But these fly upward and await him not, but flee like living things seeking escape. And he indignant rushes again to the innermost deep of the brine, and many a twist and turn he makes, now perforce, now of his own will, pulling and being pulled in turn. As when woodcutters labour busily at the joint labour of the saw, when they haste to make a keel or other needful matter for mariners: both men in turn draw to them the rough edge of iron pressing on the wood and the row of its teeth is never turned in one path, but urged from either side it sings loudly as it saws and evermore is drawn the other way: even such is the contest between the hides and the deadly beast—he being dragged up, while they are urged the other way. Much bloody spume he discharges over the sea as he struggles in his pain, and his panting breath as he rages resounds under the sea, and the water bubbles and roars around; thou wouldst say that all the blasts of Boreas were housed and hidden beneath the waves: so violently he pants in his fury. And round about many a swirling eddy the swelling waves make a hollow in the waters and the sea is divided in twain. As by the mouth of the Ionian and Tyrrhenian seas the dividing waters of the Strait roll raging under the violent panting of Typhaon and dread straining swirls curve the swift wave and dark Charybdis circles round, drawn by her eddying tides: even so by the panting blasts of the Whale the space of the sea around is lashed and whirled about. Then should one of the whalers row his hollow skiff and come to land and make fast the line to a rock upon the shore and straightway return—even as a man makes fast a ship by cables from the stern. Now when the deadly beast is tired with his struggles and drunk with pain and his fierce heart is bent with weariness and the balance of hateful doom inclines, then first of all a skin comes to the surface, announcing the issue of victory and greatly uplifts the hearts of the fishers. Even as, when a herald returns from dolorous war in white raiment and with cheerful face, his friends exulting follow him, expecting straightway to hear favourable tidings, so do the fishers exult when they behold the hide, the messenger of good news, rising from below. And immediately other skins rise up and emerge from the sea, dragging in their train the huge monster, and the deadly beast is hauled up all unwillingly, distraught in spirit with labour and wounds. Then the courage of the fishers is roused and with hasting blades they row their well-oared boats near. And much noise and much shouting resound upon the sea as they haste and exhort one another to the struggle. Thou wouldst say thou wert beholding the toil of men in war; such valour rises in their hearts and there is such din and such desire for battle.

Far away some goatherd hears their horrid noise, or some shepherd tending his woolly flock in the glens, or woodcutter felling the pine, or hunter slaying wild beasts, and astonished he draws near to sea and shore and standing on a cliff beholds the tremendous toil of the men in this warfare of the sea and the issue of the wondrous hunt, while quenchless lust of war in the water stirs the men. Then one brandishes in his hands the long-barbed trident, another the sharp-pointed lance, others carry the well-bent bill, another wields the two-edged axe. All toil, the hands of all are armed with mighty blade of iron, and close at hand they smite and wound the beast with sweeping blows. And he forgets his mighty valour and is no more able, for all his endeavour, to stay the hasting ships with his jaws, but with heavy sweep of flippers and with the end of his tail he ploughs up the waves of the deep and drives back the ships sternward and turns to naught the work of the oars and the valour of the men, even as a contrary wind that rolls the waves against the prow. The cries of the men resound as they set themselves to work, and all the sea is stained with the gory filth poured forth by his deadly wounds. The infinite water boils with the blood of the beast and the grey sea is reddened. As when in winter a river comes down from the hills of red earth into a billowy gulf and the blood-coloured mud is rolled down by the rush of the water, mingling with the eddying waves; and afar the water is reddened by the ruddy dust and the sea is as if covered with blood: even so in that hour the gory waters are stained with the blood of the beast, rent amid the waves by the shafts of the fishermen. Then they draw and drop into his wounds a bitter stream of bilge-water; and the salt mingling in his sores like fire kindles for him deadliest destruction. As when the fire of heaven smites with the lash of Zeus a bark that is traversing the sea, and the flaming onset that devours the ship is stirred and made yet fiercer by the sea mingling with the torches of heaven: even so his cruel wounds and pains are made more fierce by the cruel water of the putrid evil-smelling bilge. But when, overcome by the pains of many gashes, fate brings him at last to the gates of dismal death, then they take him in tow and joyfully haul him to the land; and he is dragged all unwilling, pierced with many barbs as with nails and nodding as if heavy with wine in the issue of deathly doom. And the fishers, raising the loud paean of victory, while they speed the boat with their oars, make the sea resound, singing their shrill song to hasting blades. As when after the decision of a battle at sea the victors take in tow the ships of the vanquished and haste joyfully to bring to land the foemen who man the ships, shouting loud to the oarsmen the paean of victory in a fight at sea, while the others against their will sorrowfully follow their foe perforce: even so the fishers take in tow the dread monster of the brine and joyfully bring him ashore. But when he comes nigh the land, then destruction real and final rouses him, and he struggles and lashes the sea with his terrible fins, like a bird upon the well-built altar tossing in the dark struggle of death. Unhappy beast!

verily an effort he makes to reach the waves but the strength of his valour is undone and his limbs obey him not and panting terribly he is dragged to land: even as a merchant ship, broad and many-benched, which men draw forth from the sea and haul up on the dry land when winter comes, to rest from its seafaring toil, and heavy is the labour of the sailors: so they bring the mighty-limbed whale to land. And he fills all the beach with his unapproachable limbs as they lie, and he is stretched out dead, terrible to behold.

THE DOLPHIN—LORD OF FISHES[1]

Oppian

(fl. c. A.D. 177-A.D. 180)

NOW all the viviparous denizens of the sea love and cherish their young but diviner than the Dolphin is nothing yet created; for indeed they were aforetime men and lived in cities along with mortals, but by the devising of Dyonysus they exchanged the land for the sea and put on the form of fishes; but even now the righteous spirit of men in them preserves human thought and human deeds. For when the twin offspring of their travail come into the light, straightway, soon as they are born they swim and gambol round their mother and enter within her teeth and linger in the maternal mouth; and she for her love suffers them and circles about her children gaily and exulting with exceeding joy. And she gives them her breasts, one to each, that they may suck the sweet milk; for god has given her milk and breasts of like nature to those of women. Thus for a season she nurses them; but, when they attain the strength of youth, straightway their mother leads them in their eagerness to the way of hunting and teaches them the art of catching fish; nor does she part from her children nor forsake them; until they have attained the fulness of their age in limb and strength, but always the parents attend them to keep watch and ward. What a marvel shalt thou contemplate in thy heart and what sweet delight, when on a voyage, watching when the wind is fair and the sea is calm, thou shalt see the beautiful herds of Dolphins, the desire of the sea; the young go before in a troop like youths unwed, even as if they were going through the changing circle of a mazy dance; behind and not aloof their children come the parents great and splendid, a guardian host, even as in spring the shepherds attend the tender lambs at pasture. As when from the works of the Muses children come trooping while behind there follow, to watch them and to be censors of modesty

[1] From A.W. Mair's translation of *Halieutica*, in the Loeb Classical Library.

and heart and mind, men of older years: for age makes a man discreet; even so also the parent Dolphins attend their children, lest aught untoward encounter them ....

But, notwithstanding, even the Dolphins have foes who meet their encounter, the fish called Amia, which care not for the Dolphin but alone fight them face to face. These have a weaker body than the Tunny and are clothed in feeble flesh, but in their ravenous mouth bristles sharp a dense array of teeth; wherefore also they have great courage and do not cower before the mighty lord of fishes. For when they see one that has wandered away alone from the rest of the herd of Dolphins, then from this quarter and from that, as a great army at command, they gather in a body together and set forth to battle dauntlessly, like shielded warriors against the tower of the foe. And the bearded Dolphin, when the crowd meets him, at first recks not of them but rushes among them, seizing and rending now one and now another, finding a banquet after his heart. But when the ranks of war surround him on every side, and encircle him with their great and dense array, then trouble at length enters his heart and he knows that sheer destruction is upon him, hemmed about as he is, alone among countless foes; and the toil of battle appears. For furiously they fall in a body about the limbs of the Dolphin and fix in him the might of their teeth; everywhere they bite him and cling to him relentlessly, many clutching his head, others his grey jaws, while yet others cleave to his very fins; many in his flanks fix their deadly teeth, others seize the end of his tail, others his belly beneath, others feed upon his back above, others hang from his mane, others from his neck. And, full of manifold distress, he rushes over the sea and his frenzied heart within him is racked with agony and his spirit is afire with pain. Every way he leaps and turns, rushing blindly in the spasms of agony. Like a diver, now he runs over the deep waves like a whirlwind, now he plunges to the nether deeps; and often he springs up and leaps above the foam of the sea, if haply the bold swarm of overweening fishes may let him go. But they, relentless, no wise abate their violence but cling to him all the same; when he dives, they dive along with him; when he leaps up again, they likewise spring forth from the sea in his train. You would say that the Shaker of the Earth had gotten a new and monstrous birth, half Dolphin and half Amia; so grievous the bond of teeth wherewith he is bound. As when a cunning physician drains a swollen wound, within which is gathered much unwholesome blood, and he applies to the flesh of the sufferer the watery brood, the dark-hued reptiles of the marsh to feast on his black blood; and straightway they become arched and rounded and draw the filth and abate not until having drained the strong drink of blood they roll of themselves from the flesh and fall like drunken men; even so the fury of the Amia abates not until they have devoured with the mouth the flesh which they once seize. But when they leave him and the Dolphin gets a breathing-space from toil, then shalt thou behold the rage of the angry lord of fishes and deadly doom appears for the Amia. They flee; and

engagement upon land. The ships that had advanced the foremost of the fight, being thirty in number, were taken with their men. Among these was the General's ship. But Annibal himself found means to get on board a boat, and escaped, though not without the greatest hazard.

The rest of the squadron were now advancing to the fight: but having observed the fate of their companions, they at first turned aside, in order to elude the stroke of the Machines. But as their ships were light, and easy in their motions, they soon resumed their confidence, and began to fall upon the Roman vessels, some in stern, and some upon their sides; being persuaded, that, with this precaution, they should be secure from danger. But when they saw, with great astonishment, that, on which side soever they advanced, the CORVI still hung over them, they were at last content to seek their safety in flight, with the loss of fifty ships.

HOW ÆOLUS, KING OF THE WINDS, SENT FORTH A STORM AGAINST ÆNEAS[1]

Virgil
(70 B.C.-19 B.C.)

SCARCELY had the Trojans, losing sight of Sicily, with joy launched out into the deep, and were ploughing the foaming billows with their brazen prows, when Juno, harbouring everlasting rancour in her breast, thus with herself:

"Shall I then, baffled, desist from my purpose, nor have it in my power to turn away the Trojan king from Italy, because I am restrained by fate? Was Pallas able to burn the Grecian ships, and bury them in the ocean, for the offence of one, and the frenzy of Ajax, Oileus' son? She herself, hurling from the clouds Jove's rapid fire, both scattered their ships, and upturned the sea with the winds; him too she snatched away in a whirlwind, breathing flames from his transfixed breast, and dashed him against the pointed rock. But I, who move majestic, the queen of heaven, both sister and wife of Jove, must maintain a series of wars with one single race for so many years. And who will henceforth adore Juno's divinity, or humbly offer sacrifice on her altars?"

The goddess by herself revolving such thoughts in her inflamed breast, repairs to Æolia, the native land of storms, regions pregnant with boisterous winds. Here, in a vast cave, King Æolus controls with imperial sway the reluctant winds and sounding tempests, and confines them with chains in prison. They roar indignant round their barriers, filling the mountain with loud murmurs. Æolus is seated on

[1] From C. Davidson's translation of *The Æneid* (1866).

a lofty throne, wielding a sceptre, and assuages their fury, and moderates their rage. For, unless he did so, they, in their rapid career, would bear away sea and earth, and the deep heaven, and sweep them through the air. But the almighty Sire, guarding against this, hath pent them in gloomy caves, and thrown over them the ponderous weight of mountains and appointed them a king, who, by fixed laws, and at command, knows both to curb them, and when to relax their reins; whom Juno then in suppliant words thus addressed:

"Æolus (for the sire of gods and the king of men hath given thee power both to smooth the waves and raise them with the wind,) a race by me detested sails the Tuscan Sea, transporting Ilium, and its conquered gods, into Italy. Strike force into thy winds, overset and sink the ships; or drive them different ways, and strew the ocean with carcasses. I have twice seven lovely nymphs, the fairest of whom, Deiopeia, I will join to thee in firm wedlock, and assign to be thine own for ever, that with thee she may spend all her years for this service, and make thee father of a beautiful offspring."

To whom Æolus replies:

"'Tis thy task, O Queen, to consider what you would have done: on me it is incumbent to execute your commands. You conciliate to me whatever of power I have, my sceptre, and Jove. You grant me to sit at the tables of the Gods; and you make me lord of storms and tempests."

Thus having said, whirling the point of his spear, he struck the hollow mountain's side: and the winds, as in a formed battalion, rush forth at every vent, and scour over the lands in a hurricane. They press upon the ocean, and at once, east, and south, and stormy south-west, plough up the whole deep from its lowest bottom, and roll vast billows to the shores. The cries of the seamen succeed, and the cracking of the cordage. In an instant clouds snatch the heavens and day from the eyes of the Trojans; sable night sits brooding on the sea, thunder roars from pole to pole, the sky glares with repeated flashes, and all nature threatens them with immediate death. Forthwith Æneas' limbs are relaxed with cold shuddering fear. He groans, and, spreading out both his hands to heaven, thus expostulates:

"O thrice and four times happy they, who had the good fortune to die before their parents' eyes, under the high ramparts of Troy! O thou, the bravest of the Grecian race, great Tydeus' son, why was I not destined to fall on the Trojan plains, and pour out this soul by thy right hand? where stern Hector lies prostrate by the sword of Achilles; where mighty Sarpedon lies; where Simois rolls along so many shields, and helmets, and bodies of heroes snatched away beneath its waters."

While uttering such words a tempest, roaring from the north, strikes across the sail, and heaves the billows to the stars. The oars are shattered: then the prow turns away, and exposes the side to the waves. A steep mountain of waters follows in a heap. These hang on the towering surge; to whose eyes the wide-yawning deep discloses the earth between two waves; the whirling tide rages with mingled sand. Three other ships the south wind, hurrying away, throws on hidden rocks; rocks in the midst of the ocean, which the Italians call Altars, a vast ridge rising to the surface of the sea. Three from the deep the east wind drives on shoals and flats, a piteous spectacle! and dashing on the shelves, it encloses them with mounds of sand. Before the eyes of Æneas himself, a mighty billow, falling from the height, dashes against the stern of one which bore the Lycian crew, and faithful Orontes: the pilot is tossed out and rolled headlong, prone into the waves: but her the driving surge thrice whirls around in the same place, and the rapid eddy swallows up in the deep. Then floating here and there on the vast abyss, are seen men, their arms, and planks, and the Trojan wealth, among the waves. Now the storm overpowered the stout vessel of Ilioneus, now that of brave Achates, and that in which Abas sailed, and that in which old Alethes; all, at their loosened and disjointed sides, receive the hostile stream, and gape with chinks.

Meanwhile Neptune perceived that the sea was in great uproar and confusion, a storm sent forth, and the depths overturned from their lowest channels. He, in violent commotion, and looking forth from the deep, reared his serene countenance above the waves; sees Æneas' fleet scattered over the ocean, the Trojans oppressed with the waves and the ruin from above. Nor were Juno's wiles and hate unknown to her brother. He calls to him the east and west winds; then thus addresses them:

"And do you thus presume upon your birth? Dare you, winds! without my sovereign leave, to embroil heaven and earth, and raise such mountains? Whom I— But first it is right to assuage the tumultuous waves. A chastisement of another nature from me awaits your next offence. Fly apace, and bear this message to your king: That not to him the empire of the sea, and the awful trident, but to me by lot are given: his dominions are the mighty rocks, your proper mansions, Eurus: in that palace let King Æolus proudly boast and reign in the close prison of the winds."

So he speaks, and, more swiftly than his speech, smooths the swelling seas, disperses the collected clouds, anal brings back the day. With him Cymothoë, and Triton with exerted might, heave the ships from the pointed rock. He himself raised them with his trident; lays open the vast sandbanks, and calms the sea; and in his light chariot glides along the surface of the waves. And as when a sedition has perchance arisen among a mighty multitude, and the minds of the ignoble vulgar rage; now fire brands, now stones fly; fury supplies them with arms: if then, by chance, they espy a man revered in piety and worth, they are hushed, and stand with ears erect; he, by eloquence, rules their passions and calms their breasts. Thus all the raging tumult of the ocean subsides, as soon as the sire, surveying the seas, and wafted through the open sky, guides his steeds, and flying, gives the reins to his easy chariot.

The weary Trojans direct their course towards the nearest shores, and make the coast of Libya. In a long recess, a station lies; an island forms it into a harbour by its jutting sides, against which every wave from the ocean is broken, and divides itself into receding curves. On either side vast cliffs, and two twin-like rocks, threaten the sky; under whose summit the waters all around are calm and still. Above is a sylvan scene with waving woods, and a dark grove with awful shade hangs over. Under the opposite front a cave is of pendant rocks, within which are fresh springs, and seats of living stone, the recess of nymphs. Here neither cables hold, nor anchors with crooked fluke moor the weather-beaten ships. To this retreat Æneas brings seven ships, collected from all his fleet; and the Trojans, longing much for land, disembarking, enjoy the wished-for shore, and stretch their brine-drenched limbs upon the beach.

HOW JULIUS CÆSAR, TAKING FORTUNE FOR HIS COMRADE, PUT OUT INTO THE TUMULT OF THE SEA[1]

Lucan

(39 A.D.-65 A.D.)

ANTONY was the leader, daring in all warfare, even then, in civil war, training for Leucas.[2] Him delaying full oft by threats and by entreaties does Cæsar summon forth:

"O cause of woes so mighty to the world, why dost thou retard the Gods of heaven and the Fates? The rest has been effected by my speed; Fortune demands thee as the finishing hand to the successes of the hastened warfare. Does Libya, sundered with her shoaly quicksands, divide us with uncertain tides? Have I in any way entrusted thy arms to an untried deep, and art thou dragged into dangerous unknown? Sluggard, Cæsar commands thee to come, not to go! I myself, the first, amid the foe touched upon sands in the midst of them, and under the sway of others. Dost thou fear my camp? I lament that the hours of fate are waiting; upon the winds and the waves do I expend my prayers. Keep not those back who desire to go on the shifting deep; if I judge aright, the youths would be willing by shipwreck even to repair to the arms of Cæsar. Now must I employ the language of grief; not on

[1] From H.T. Riley's translation of *The Pharsalia*.

[2] It was off the Leucadian Promontory that Antony fought against Augustus in the Battle of Actium.

equal terms have we divided the World. Cæsar and the whole Senate occupy Epirus; thou alone dost possess Ausonia."

After he sees that he, summoned three or four times in this language, is still delaying, as he believes that it is he himself who is wanting to the Gods, and not the Deities to him, of his accord amid the unsafe shades of night he dares to try the sea, which they, commanded, stand in fear of, having experienced that venturous deeds have prospered under a favouring Divinity; and waves, worthy to be feared by fleets, he hopes to pass over in a little bark.

Night with its languor had now relaxed the wearied care of arms; rest was obtained for the wretched, into whose breasts by sleep a more humble lot inspires strength. Now was the camp silent; now had its third hour brought on the second watch; Cæsar with anxious step amid the vasty silence attempted things hardly by his servants to be dared; and, all left behind, Fortune alone pleased him as his companion. After he had gone through the tents, he passed over the bodies of the sentinels which had yielded to sleep, silently complaining that he was able to elude them. He passed along the winding shore, and at the brink of the waves found a bark attached by a cable to the rocks eaten away.

Not far from thence a house, free from all cares, propped up with no stout timbers, but woven with barren rushes and the reeds of the marsh, and covered on its exposed side with a boat turned bottom upwards, sheltered the pilot and the owner of the bark. Cæsar twice or thrice knocked with his hand at this threshold, that shook the roof. Amyclas arose from the soft couch, which the sea-weed afforded.

"What shipwrecked person, I wonder," said he, "repairs to my abode? Or whom has Fortune compelled to hope for the aid of our cottage?"

Thus having said, the tow now raised from the dense heap of warm ashes, he nourished the small spark into kindled flames; free from care of the warfare, he knew that in civil strife cottages are no prey. O safe the lot of a poor man's life, and his humble home! O gifts of the Deities not yet understood! What temples or what cities could this befall, to be alarmed with no tumult, the hand of Cæsar knocking?

Then, the door being opened, the chieftain says:

"Look for what is greater than thy moderate wishes, and give scope to thy hopes, O youth. If, obeying my commands, thou dost carry me to Hesperia, no more wilt thou be owing everything to thy bark, and by the hands dragging on a needy old age. Hesitate not to entrust thy fate to the God who wishes to fill thy humble abode with sudden wealth."

Thus he says, unable to be taught to speak as a private man, though clad in a plebeian garb. Then says the poor Amyclas:

"Many things indeed forbid me to trust the deep to-night. For the sun did not take down into the seas ruddy clouds, and rays of one hue; one portion of Phœbus invited the southern gales, another, with divided light, the northern. Dimmed, too, and languid in the middle of his orb, he set, not dazzling the eyes that looked on him, with his weakly light. The moon, also, did not rise, shining with slender horn, or hollowed with clear cavities in her mid orb; nor did she describe tapering points on her straitened horn, and with the signs of wind she was red; besides, pallid, she bears a livid aspect, sad with her face about to sink beneath the clouds.

"But neither does the waving of the woods, nor the lashings of the sea-shore, nor the fitful dolphin, that challenges the waves, please me; nor yet that the sea-gull loves the dry land; the fact, too, that the heron ventures to fly aloft, trusting to its hovering wing; and that, sprinkling its head with the waves, as though it would forestall the rain, the crow paces the seashore with infirm step. But if the weight of great events demands, I would not hesitate to lend my aid. Either I will touch the commanded shore, or, on the other hand, the seas and the winds shall deny it."

Thus having said and unmooring his craft, he spreads the canvas to the winds; at the motion of which, not only meteors gliding along the lofty air, as they fall, describe tracks in all quarters of the heavens; but even the stars which are held fixed in the loftiest skies, appear to shake. A dusky swell pervades the surface of the sea; with many a heaving along their lengthened track the threatening waves boil up, uncertain as to the impending blasts; the swelling seas betoken the winds conceived. Then says the master of the quivering bark:

"Behold, how vast dangers the raging sea is preparing. Whether it presages the Zephyrs, or whether the east winds, it is uncertain. On every side the fitful waves are beating against the bark. In the clouds and in the heavens are the southern blasts; if we go by the mumurs of the sea, Corus is skimming along the deep. In a storm thus mighty, neither will bark nor shipwrecked person reach the Hesperian shores. To despair of making our way, and to turn from the forbidden course, is our only safety. Let it be allowed me to make for shore with the tossed bark, lest the nearest land should be too distant."

Cæsar, confident that all dangers will give way for him, says:

"Despise the threats of the deep, and spread sail to the raging winds. If, heaven prompting thee, thou dost decline Italy, myself thy prompter, seek it. This alone is thy reasonable cause for fear, not to have known thy freight; one whom the Deities never forsake; of whom Fortune deserves badly then, when after his wishes expressed she comes. Secure in my protection, burst through the midst of the storms. This is the labour of the heavens and of the sea, not of our bark; that, trod by Cæsar, the freight will protect from the waves. Nor will long duration be granted to the raging fury of the winds; this same bark will advantage the waves. Turn not thy hands; avoid, with thy sails, the neighbouring shores; believe that then thou hast gained the Calabrian port, when no other land can be granted to the ship and to our safety. Art thou ignorant what, amid a tempest so great, is preparing? Amid the tumult of the sea and sky, Fortune is enquiring how she shall favour me."

No more having said, a furious whirlwind, the stern being struck, tears away the shrouds rent asunder, and brings the flapping sails upon the frail mast; the joints overstrained, the vessel groans. Then rush on perils gathered together from the whole universe. First, moving the tides, Corus, thou dost raise thy head from the Atlantic Ocean; now, as thou dost lift it, the sea rages, and uplifts all its billows upon the rocks. The cold Boreas meets it, and beats back the ocean, and doubtful stands the deep, undecided which wind to obey. But the rage of the Scythian north wind conquers and hurls aloft the waves, and makes shallows of the sands entirely concealed. And Boreas does not carry the waves on to the rocks, and he dashes his own seas against the billows of Corus; and the aroused waves, even with the winds lulled, are able to meet in conflict.

I would surmise that the threats of Eurus were not withheld, and that the winds of the South, black with showers, did not lie beneath the dungeons of the Æolian rocks; that all, rushing from their wonted quarters, with violent whirlwinds defended their own regions, and that thus the ocean remained in its place. No small seas do they speak of as having been carried along by the gales; the Tyrrhenian runs into the Ægean waves; the wandering Adriatic echoes in the Ionian sea. O how often did that day overwhelm mountains before beaten in vain by the waves! What lofty summits did the subdued earth permit to be over come! Not on that shore do waves so tremendous rise, and, rolling from another region of the earth, from the vast ocean have they come, and the waves that encircle the world speed on their monstrous billows.

Thus did the ruler of Olympus aid his wearied lightnings against the world with his brother's trident, and the earth was added to the secondary realms of Neptune, when Tethys was unwilling to submit to any shores, content to be bounded by the skies alone. Now as well would the mass of sea so vast have increased to the stars, if the ruler of the Gods of heaven had not kept down the waves with clouds. That was not a night of the heavens; the air lay concealed infected with the paleness of the infernal abodes, and, oppressed with storms, was kept down, and the waves received the showers in the clouds. Even the light so dreadful is lost, and the lightnings flash not with their brilliance, but the cloudy atmosphere obscurely divides for their flashes.

Then do the convex abodes of the Gods of heaven resound, and the lofty skies re-echo, and, the structure strained, the poles re-echo. Nature dreads Chaos, the elements seem to have burst from their concordant repose, and night once more to return about to mingle the shades below with the Gods of heaven. The sole hope of safety is, that not as yet have they perished amid ruin of the universe so great. As far as from the Leucadian heights the calm deep is beheld below, so far do the trembling mariners look down upon the headlong sea from the summits of the waves; and when the swelling billows gape open once again, hardly does the mast stand above the surface. The clouds are touched by the sails, and the earth by the keel. For the sea, in the part where it is at rest, does not conceal the sands; it arises in mountains, and all the waters are in waves. Fears conquer the resources of art, and the pilot knows not which to break, to which wave to give way.

The discord of the sea comes to their aid in their distress, and billow is not able to throw over the vessel against billows; the resisting wave supports the yielding side, and the bark rises upright amid all the winds. They dread not the lowly Sason with its shallows, nor yet the rocky shores of curving Thessaly, and the dangerous harbours of the Ambracian coast; of the summits of rocky Ceraunia the sailors are in dread. Now does Cæsar believe there to be a danger worthy of his destiny.

"Is it a labour so great," says he, "with the Gods above to overwhelm me, who, sitting in a little bark, they have assaulted with seas so vast? If the glory of my end has been granted to the deep, and I am denied to the warfare, fearlessly will I receive whatever death, ye Deities, you send me. Although the day hurried on by the Fates should cut short my mighty exploits, things great enough have I done. The nations of the north have I conquered; hostile arms have I subdued with fear; Rome has beheld Magnus second to me. The commonalty ordered by me, I have obtained by warfare the fasces which were denied unto me. No Roman dignity will be wanting to my titles.

"No one will know this, except thee, Fortune, who alone art conscious of my wishes, that I, although I go loaded with honours and Dictator and Consul, to the Stygian shades, die as a private person. There is need, O Gods of heaven, of no funereal rites for me; retain my mangled carcase in the midst of the waves; let tomb and funeral pile be wanting to me, so long as I shall be always dreaded and looked for by every land."

Him, having thus said, a tenth wave, wondrous to be said, lifts with the frail bark on high; nor again does it hurl it down from the lofty heights of the sea, but the wave bears it along, and casts it on dry land, where the narrow shore is free from rugged cliffs.

BIBLICAL LITERATURE

THE GATHERING TOGETHER OF THE WATERS[1]

IN the beginning God created the heaven and the earth.

And the earth was without form, and void; and darkness was upon the face of the deep. And the Spirit of God moved upon the face of the waters.

And God said, Let there be light: and there was light.

And God saw the light, that it was good: and God divided the light from the darkness.

And God called the light Day, and the darkness he called Night. And the evening and the morning were the first day.

And God said, Let there be a firmament in the midst of the waters, and let it divide the waters from the waters.

And God made the firmament, and divided the waters which were under the firmament from the waters which were above the firmament: and it was so.

And God called the firmament Heaven. And the evening and the morning were the second day.

And God said, Let the waters under the heaven be gathered together unto one place, and let the dry land appear: and it was so.

And God called the dry land Earth; and the gathering together of the waters called he Seas: and God saw that it was good.

THE WATERS OF THE FLOOD[1]

BUT Noah found grace in the eyes of the Lord.

And God looked upon the earth, and, behold, it was corrupt; for all flesh had corrupted his way upon the earth.

And God said unto Noah, The end of all flesh is come before me; for the earth is filled with violence through them; and, behold, I will destroy them with the earth.

Make thee an ark of gopher wood; rooms shalt thou make in the ark, and shalt pitch it within and without with pitch.

And this is the fashion which thou shalt make it of: The length of the ark shall be three hundred cubits, the breadth of it fifty cubits, and the height of it thirty cubits.

A window shalt thou make to the ark, and in a cubit shalt thou finish it above;

[1] From the Book of Genesis.

and the door of the ark shalt thou set in the side thereof; with lower, second, and third stories shalt thou make it.

And, behold, I, even I, do bring a flood of waters upon the earth, to destroy all flesh, wherein is the breath of life, from under heaven; and every thing that is in the earth shall die.

But with thee will I establish my covenant; and thou shalt come into the ark, thou, and thy sons, and thy wife, and thy sons' wives with thee.

And of every living thing of all flesh, two of every sort shalt thou bring into the ark, to keep them alive with thee; they shall be male and female.

Of fowls after their kind, and of cattle after their kind, of every creeping thing of the earth after his kind, two of every sort shall come unto thee, to keep them alive.

And take thou unto thee of all food that is eaten, and thou shalt gather it to thee; and it shall be for food for thee, and for them.

Thus did Noah; according to all that God commanded him, so did he.

And the Lord said unto Noah, Come thou and all thy house into the ark; for thee have I seen righteous before me in this generation.

Of every clean beast thou shalt take to thee by sevens, the male and his female: and of beasts that are not clean by two, the male and his female.

Of fowls also of the air by sevens, the male and the female; to keep seed alive upon the face of all the earth.

For yet seven days, and I will cause it to rain upon the earth forty days and forty nights; and every living substance that I have made will I destroy from off the face of the earth.

And Noah did according unto all that the Lord commanded him.

And Noah was six hundred years old when the flood of waters was upon the earth.

And Noah went in, and his sons, and his wife, and his sons' wives with him, into the ark, because of the waters of the flood.

Of clean beasts, and of beasts that are not clean, and of fowls, and of every thing that creepeth upon the earth.

There went in two and two unto Noah into the ark, the male and the female, as God had commanded Noah.

And it came to pass after seven days, that the waters of the flood were upon the earth.

In the six hundredth year of Noah's life, in the second month, the seventeenth day of the month, the same day were all the fountains of the great deep broken up, and the windows of heaven were opened.

And the rain was upon the earth forty days and forty nights: and the waters increased, and bare up the ark, and it was lift up above the earth.

And the waters prevailed, and were increased greatly upon the earth; and the ark went upon the face of the waters.

And the waters prevailed exceedingly upon the earth; and all the high hills, that were under the whole heaven, were covered.

Fifteen cubits upward did the waters prevail; and the mountains were covered.

And all flesh died that moved upon the earth, both of fowl, and of cattle, and of beast, and of every creeping thing that creepeth upon the earth, and every man:

All in whose nostrils was the breath of life, of all that was in the dry land, died.

And every living substance was destroyed which was upon the face of the ground, both man, and cattle, and the creeping things, and the fowl of the heaven; and they were destroyed from the earth: and Noah only remained alive, and they that were with him in the ark.

And the waters prevailed upon the earth an hundred and fifty days.

And God remembered Noah, and every living thing, and all the cattle that was with him in the ark: and God made a wind to pass over the earth, and the waters asswaged.

The fountains also of the deep and the windows of heaven were stopped, and the rain from heaven was restrained.

And the waters returned from off the earth continually: and after the end of the hundred and fifty days the waters were abated.

And the ark rested in the seventh month, on the seventeenth day of the month, upon the mountains of Ararat.

And the waters decreased continually until the tenth month: in the tenth month, on the first day of the month, were the tops of the mountains seen.

And it came to pass at the end of forty days, that Noah opened the window of the ark which he had made:

And he sent forth a raven, which went forth to and fro, until the waters were dried up from off the earth.

Also he sent forth a dove from him, to see if the waters were abated from off the face of the ground;

But the dove found no rest for the sole of her foot, and she returned unto him into the ark, for the waters were on the face of the whole earth: then he put forth his hand, and took her, and pulled her in unto him into the ark.

And he stayed yet other seven days: and again he sent forth the dove out of the ark;

And the dove came in to him in the evening; and, lo, in her mouth was an olive leaf pluckt off: so Noah knew that the waters were abated from off the earth.

And he stayed yet other seven days; and sent forth the dove; which returned not again unto him any more.

And it came to pass in the six hundredth and first year, in the first month, the first day of the month, the waters were dried up from off the earth: and Noah removed the covering of the ark, and looked, and, behold, the face of the ground was dry.

And in the second month, on the seven and twentieth day of the month, was the earth dried.

And God spake unto Noah, saying:

Go forth of the ark, thou, and thy wife, and thy sons, and thy sons' wives with thee.

Bring forth with thee every living thing that is with thee, of all flesh, both of fowl, and of cattle, and of every creeping thing that creepeth upon the earth: that they may breed abundantly in the earth, and be fruitful, and multiply upon the earth.

And Noah went forth, and his sons, and his wife, and his sons' wives with him:

Every beast, every creeping thing, and every fowl, and whatsoever creepeth upon the earth, after their kinds, went forth out of the ark.

JONAH AND THE WHALE[1]

NOW the word of the Lord came unto Jonah the son of Amittai, saying, Arise, go to Nineveh, that great city, and cry against it, for their wickedness is come up before me,

But Jonah rose up to flee unto Tarshish from the presence of the Lord, and went down to Joppa; and he found a ship going to Tarshish; so he paid the fare thereof, and went down into it, to go with them unto Tarshish from the presence of the Lord.

But the Lord sent out a great wind into the sea, and there was a mighty tempest in the sea, so that the ship was like to be broken. Then the mariners were afraid, and cried every man unto his god, and cast forth the wares that were in the ship into the sea to lighten it of them. But Jonah was gone down into the sides of the ship; and he lay, and was fast asleep.

So the shipmaster came to him, and said unto him,

What meanest thou, O sleeper? Arise, call upon thy God, if so be that God will think upon us, that we perish not.

And they said every one to his fellow,

Come, and let us cast lots, that we may know for whose cause this evil is upon us.

So they cast lots, and the lot fell upon Jonah.

Then said they unto him,

[1] From the Book of Jonah.

Tell us, we pray thee, for whose cause this evil is upon us. What is thine occupation? and whence comest thou? What is thy country? and of what people art thou?

And he said unto them,

I am an Hebrew, and I fear the Lord, the God of Heaven, which hath made the sea and the dry land.

Then were the men exceedingly afraid, and said unto him,

Why hast thou done this?

For the men knew that he fled from the presence of the Lord, because he had told them. Then said they unto him,

What shall we do unto thee, that the sea may be calm unto us?

For the sea wrought and was tempestuous. And he said unto them,

Take me up, and cast me forth into the sea; so shall the sea be calm unto you; for I know that for my sake this great tempest is upon you.

Nevertheless the men rowed hard to bring it to the land; but they could not for the sea wrought and was tempestuous against them. Wherefore they cried unto the Lord, and said,

We beseech thee, O Lord, we beseech thee, let us not perish for this man's life, and lay not upon us innocent blood: for thou, O Lord, hast done as it pleased thee.

So they took up Jonah and cast him forth into the sea, and the sea ceased from her raging. Then the men feared the Lord exceedingly, and offered a sacrifice unto the Lord, and made vows.

Now the Lord had prepared a great fish to swallow up Jonah. And Jonah was in the belly of the fish three days and three nights.

Then Jonah prayed unto the Lord his God out of the fish's belly, and said,

I cried by reason of mine affliction unto the Lord, and he heard me: out of the belly of hell cried I, and thou heardest my voice. For thou hadst cast me into the deep, in the midst of the seas, and the floods compassed me about: all thy billows and thy waves passed over me. Then I said, I am cast out of thy sight, yet I will look again toward thy holy temple. The waters compassed me about, even to the soul: the depth closed me round about: the weeds were wrapped about my head. I went down to the bottoms of the mountains: the earth with her bars was about me for ever; yet hast thou brought up my life from corruption, O Lord my God. When my soul fainted within me I remembered the Lord, and my prayer came in unto thee, into thine holy temple. They that observe lying vanities forsake their own mercy. But I will sacrifice unto thee with the voice of thanksgiving. I will pay that that I have vowed. Salvation is of the Lord.

And the Lord spake unto the fish and it vomited out Jonah upon the dry land.

ARABIA

THE FIRST VOYAGE OF ES-SINDIBÁD OF THE SEA[1]

KNOW, O masters, O noble persons, that I had a father, a merchant, who was one of the first in rank among the people and the merchants, and who possessed abundant wealth and ample fortune. He died when I was a young child, leaving to me wealth and buildings and fields; and when I grew up, I put my hand upon the whole of the property, ate well and drank well, associated with the young men, wore handsome apparel, and passed my life with my friends and companions, feeling confident that this course would continue and profit me; and I ceased not to live in this manner for a length of time. I then returned to my reason, and recovered from my heedlessness, and found that my wealth had passed away, and my condition had changed, and all (the money) that I had possessed had gone. I recovered not to see my situation but in a state of fear and confusion of mind, and remembered a tale that I had heard before, the tale of our lord Suleymán the son of Dáood (on both of whom be peace!), respecting his saying, Three things are better than three: the day of death is better than the day of birth; and a living dog is better than a dead lion; and the grave is better than the palace. Then I arose, and collected what I had, of effects and apparel, and sold them; after which I sold my buildings and all that my hand possessed, and amassed three thousand pieces of silver; and it occurred to my mind to travel to the countries of other people; and I remembered one of the sayings of the poets, which was this:

> In proportion to one's labour, eminences are gained; and he who seeketh eminence passeth sleepless nights.
> He diveth in the sea who seeketh for pearls, and succeedeth in acquiring lordship and good fortune.
> Whoso seeketh eminence without labouring for it, loseth his life in the search of vanity.

Upon this I resolved, and arose, and bought for myself goods and commodities and merchandise, with such other things as were required for travel; and my mind had consented to my performing a sea-voyage. So I embarked in a ship, and it descended to the city of El-Basrah, with a company of merchants; and we traversed the sea for many days and nights. We had passed by island after island, and from sea to sea, and from land to land; and in every place by which we passed we sold and bought and exchanged merchandise. We continued our voyage until we arrived at an island like one of the gardens of Paradise, and at that island the master of the ship brought her to anchor with us. He cast the anchor, and put forth

[1] From E.W. Lane's translation of *The Thousand and One Nights*.

the landing-plank, and all who were in the ship landed upon that island. They had prepared for themselves fire-pots, and they lighted the fires in them; and their occupations were various: some cooked; others washed: and others amused themselves. I was among those who were amusing themselves upon the shores of the island, and the passengers were assembled to eat and drink and play and sport. But while we were thus engaged, lo, the master of the ship, standing upon its side, called out with his loudest voice, O ye passengers, whom may God preserve! come up quickly into the ship, hasten to embark, and leave your merchandise, and flee with your lives, and save yourselves from destruction; for this apparent island, upon which ye are, is not really an island, but it is a great fish that hath become stationary in the midst of the sea, and the sand hath accumulated upon it, so that it hath become like an island, and trees have grown upon it since times of old; and when ye lighted upon it the fire, it felt the heat, and put itself in motion, and now it will descend with you into the sea, and ye will all be drowned: then seek for yourselves escape before destruction, and leave the merchandise!—The passengers, therefore, hearing the words of the master of the ship, hastened to go up into the vessel, leaving the merchandise, and their other goods, and their copper cooking-pots, and their fire-pots; and some reached the ship, and others reached it not. The island had moved, and descended to the bottom of the sea, with all that were upon it, and the roaring sea, agitated with waves, closed over it.

I was among the number of those who remained behind upon the island; so I sank in the sea with the rest who sank. But God (whose name be exalted!) delivered me and saved me from drowning, and supplied me with a great wooden bowl, of the bowls in which the passengers had been washing, and I laid hold upon it and got into it, induced by the sweetness of life, and beat the water with my feet as with oars, while the waves sported with me, tossing me to the right and left. The master of the vessel had caused her sails to be spread, and pursued his voyage with those who had embarked, not regarding such as had been submerged; and I ceased not to look at that vessel until it was concealed from my eye. I made sure of destruction, and night came upon me while I was in this state; but I remained so a day and night, and the wind and the waves aided me until the bowl came to a stoppage with me under a high island, whereon were trees overhanging the sea. So I laid hold upon a branch of a lofty tree, and clung to it, after I had been at the point of destruction; and I kept hold upon it until I landed on the island, when I found my legs be numbed, and saw marks of the nibbling of fish upon their hams, of which I had been insensible by reason of the violence of the anguish and fatigue that I was suffering.

I threw myself upon the island like one dead, and was unconscious of my existence, and drowned in my stupefaction; and I ceased not to remain in this condition until the next day. The sun having then risen upon me, I awoke upon the island, and found that my feet were swollen, and that I had become reduced to the state in which I then was. Awhile I dragged myself along in a sitting posture, and then I crawled upon my knees. And there were in the island fruits in abundance, and springs of sweet water: therefore I ate of those fruits; and I ceased not to continue in this state for many days and nights. My spirit had then revived, my soul had returned to me, and my power of motion was renewed; and I began to meditate, and to walk along the shore of the island, amusing myself among the trees with the sight of the things that God (whose name be exalted!) had created; and I had made for myself a staff from those trees, to lean upon it. Thus I remained until I walked, one day, upon the shore of the island, and there appeared unto me an indistinct object in the distance. I imagined that it was a wild beast, or one of the beasts of the sea; and I walked towards it, ceasing not to gaze at it; and, lo, it was a mare, of superb appearance, tethered in a part of the island by the sea-shore. I approached her; but she cried out against me with a great cry, and I trembled with fear of her, and was about to return, when, behold, a man came forth from beneath the earth, and he called to me and pursued me, saying to me, Who art thou, and whence hast thou come, and what is the cause of thine arrival in this place? So I answered him, O my master, know that I am a stranger, and I was in a ship, and was submerged in the sea with certain others of the passengers; but God supplied me with a wooden bowl, and I got into it, and it bore me along until the waves cast me upon this island. And when he heard my words, he laid hold of my hand and said to me, Come with me. I therefore went with him, and he descended with me into a grotto beneath the earth, and conducted me into a large subterranean chamber, and having seated me at the upper end of that chamber, brought me some food. I was hungry; so I ate until I was satiated and contented, and my soul became at ease. Then he asked me respecting my case, and what had happened to me; wherefore I acquainted him with my whole affair from beginning to end; and he wondered at my story.

And when I had finished my tale, I said, I conjure thee by Allah, O my master, that thou be not displeased with me; I have acquainted thee with the truth of my case and of what hath happened to me, and I desire of thee that thou inform me who thou art, and what is the cause of thy dwelling in this chamber that is beneath the earth, and what is the reason of thy tethering this mare by the sea-side. So he replied, Know that we are a party dispersed in this island, upon its shores, and we are the grooms of the King El-Mihráj, having under our care all his horses; and every month, when moon-light commenceth, we bring the swift mares, and tether them in this island, every mare that has not foaled, and conceal ourselves in this chamber beneath the earth, that they may attract the sea-horses. This is the time of the coming forth of the sea-horse; and afterwards, if it be the will of God (whose name be exalted!), I will take thee with me to the King El-Mihráj, and divert thee with the sight of our country. Know, moreover, that if thou hadst not met with us, thou hadst not seen any one in this place, and wouldst have died in misery, none knowing of thee. But I will be the means of the preservation of thy life, and of thy return to thy country.—I therefore prayed for him, and thanked him for his kindness and beneficence; and while we were thus talking, the horse came forth from the sea, as he had said. And shortly after, his companions came, each leading a mare; and, seeing me with him, they inquired of me my story, and I told them what I had related to him. They then drew near to me, and spread the table, and ate, and invited me: so I ate with them; after which, they arose, and mounted the horses, taking me with them, having mounted me on a mare.

We commenced our journey, and proceeded without ceasing until we arrived at the city of King El-Mihráj, and they went in to him and acquainted him with my story. He therefore desired my presence, and they took me in to him, and stationed me before him; whereupon I saluted him, and he returned my salutation, and welcomed me, greeting me in an honourable manner, and inquired of me respecting my case. So I informed him of all that had happened to me, and of all that I had seen from beginning to end; and he wondered at that which had befallen me and happened to me, and said to me, O my son, by Allah thou hast experienced an extraordinary preservation, and had it not been for the predestined length of thy life, thou hadst not escaped from these difficulties; but praise be to God for thy safety! Then he treated me with beneficence and honour, caused me to draw near to him, and began to cheer me with conversation and courtesy; and he made me his superintendent of the sea-port, and registrar of every vessel that came to the coast. I stood in his presence to transact his affairs, and he favoured me and benefited me in every respect; he invested me with a handsome and costly dress, and I became a person high in credit with him in intercessions, and in accomplishing the affairs of the people. I ceased not to remain in his service for a long time; and whenever I went to the shore of the sea, I used to inquire of the merchants and travellers and sailors respecting the direction of the city of Baghdád, that perchance some one might inform me of it, and I might go with him thither and return to my country; but none knew it, nor knew any one who went to it. At this I was perplexed, and I was weary of the length of my absence from home; and in this state I continued for a length of time, until I went in one day to the King El-Mihráj, and found with him a party of Indians. I saluted them, and they returned my salutations, and welcomed me, and asked me respecting my country; after which, I questioned them as to their country, and they told me that they consisted of various races. Among them are the Shákireeyeh, who are the most noble of their races, who oppress no one, nor offer violence to any. And among them are a class called the Bráhmans, a people who never drink wine; but they are persons of pleasure and joy and sport and merriment, and possessed of camels and horses and cattle. They informed me also that the Indians are divided into seventy-two classes; and I wondered at this extremely. And I saw, in the dominions of the King El-Mihráj, an island, among others, which is called Kásil, in which is heard the beating of tambourines and drums throughout the night, and the islanders and travellers informed us that Ed-Dejjál is in it. I saw too, in the sea in which is that island a fish two hundred cubits long, and the fishermen fear it; wherefore they knock some pieces of wood, and it fleeth from them: and I saw a fish whose face was like that of the owl. I likewise saw during that voyage many wonderful and strange things, such that, if I related them to you, the description would be too long.

I continued to amuse myself with the sight of those islands and the things that they contained, until I stood one day upon the shore of the sea, with a staff in my hand, as was my custom, and, lo, a great vessel approached, wherein were many merchants; and when it arrived at the harbour of the city, and its place of anchoring, the master furled its sails, brought it to an anchor by the shore, and put forth the landing-plank; and the sailors brought out everything that was in that vessel to the shore. They were slow in taking forth the goods, while I stood writing their account, and I said to the master of the ship, Doth ought remain in thy vessel? He answered, Yes, O my master; I have some goods in the hold of the ship; but their owner was drowned in the sea at one of the islands during our voyage hither, and his goods are in our charge; so we desire to sell them, and to take a note of their price, in order to convey it to his family in the city of Baghdád, the Abode of Peace. I therefore said to the master, What was the name of that man, the owner of the goods? He answered, His name was Es-Sindibád of the Sea, and he was drowned on his voyage with us in the sea. And when I heard his words, I looked at him with a scrutinizing eye, and recognized him; and I cried out at him with a great cry, and said, O master, know that I am the owner of the goods which thou hast mentioned, and I am Es-Sindibád of the Sea, who descended upon the island from the ship, with the other merchants who descended; and when the fish that we were upon moved, and thou calledst out to us, some got up into the vessel, and the rest sunk, and I was among those who sank. But God (whose name be exalted!) preserved me and saved me from drowning by means of a large wooden bowl, of those in which the passengers were washing, and I got into it, and began to beat the water with my feet, and the wind and the waves aided me until I arrived at this island, when I landed on it, and God (whose name be exalted!) assisted me, and I met the grooms of the King El-Mihráj, who took me with them and brought me to this city. They then led me in to the King El-Mihráj, and I acquainted him with my story; whereupon he bestowed benefits upon me, and appointed me clerk of the harbour of this city, and I obtained profit in his service, and favour with him. Therefore these goods that thou hast are my goods and my portion.

But the master said, There is no strength nor power but in God the High, the Great! There is no longer faith nor conscience in any one!—Wherefore, O master, said I, when thou hast heard me tell thee my story? He answered, Because thou heardest me say that I had goods whose owner was drowned: therefore thou desirest to take them without price; and this is unlawful to thee; for we saw him when he sank, and there were with him many of the passengers, not one of whom escaped. How then dost thou pretend that thou art the owner of the goods?—So I said to him, O master, hear my story, and understand my words, and my veracity will become manifest to thee; for falsehood is a characteristic of the hypocrites. Then I related to him all that I had done from the time that I went forth with him from the city of Baghdád until we arrived at that island upon which we were submerged in the sea, and I mentioned to him some circumstances that had occurred between me and him. Upon this, therefore, the master and the merchants were convinced of my veracity, and recognized me; and they congratulated me on my safety, all of them saying, By Allah, we believed not that thou hadst escaped drowning; but God hath granted thee a new life. They then gave me the goods, and I found my name written upon them, and nought of them was missing. So I opened them, and took forth from them something precious and costly; the sailors of the ship carried it with me, and I went up with it to the King to offer it as a present, and informed him that this ship was the one in which I was a passenger. I told him also that my goods had arrived all entire, and that this present was a part of them. And the King wondered at this affair extremely; my veracity in all that I had said became manifest to him, and he loved me greatly, and treated me with exceeding honour, giving me a large present in return for mine.

Then I sold my bales, as well as the other goods that I had, and gained upon them abundantly; and I purchased other goods and merchandise and commodities of that city. And when the merchants of the ship desired to set forth on their voyage, I stowed all that I had in the vessel and, going in to the King, thanked him for his beneficence and kindness; after which I begged him to grant me permission to depart on my voyage to my country and my family. So he bade me farewell, and gave me an abundance of things at my departure, of the commodities of that city; and when I had taken leave of him, I embarked in the ship, and we set sail by the permission of God, whose name be exalted! Fortune served us, and destiny aided us, and we ceased not to prosecute our voyage night and day until we arrived in safety at the city of El-Basrah. There we landed, and remained a short time; and I rejoiced at my safety, and my return to my country; and after that, I repaired to the city of Baghdád, the Abode of Peace, with abundance of bales and goods and merchandise of great value. Then I went to my quarter, and entered my house, and all my family and companions came to me. I procured for myself servants and other dependants, and memlooks and concubines and male black slaves, so that

I had a large establishment; and I purchased houses and other immoveable possessions, more than I had at first. I enjoyed the society of my companions and friends, exceeding my former habits, and forgot all that I had suffered from fatigue, and absence from my native country, and difficulty, and the terrors of travel.

PERSIA

THE SAILOR AND THE PEARL MERCHANT[1]

IT IS related that in the city of Basrah there was a man Abu'l Fawaris, who was the chief of the sailors of the town, for in the great ocean there was no port at which he had not landed. One day, as he sat on the seashore, with his sailors round him, an old man arrived in a ship, landed where Abu'l Fawaris was sitting, and said: "Friend, I desire you to give me your ship for six months, and I will pay you whatever you desire." "I demand a thousand gold dinars," said the sailor, and at once received the gold from the old man, who, before departing, said that he would come again on the next day, and warned Abu'l Fawaris that there was to be no holding back.

The sailor took home his gold, made his ship ready, and then, taking leave of his wife and sons, he went down to the shore, where he found the old man waiting for him with a slave and twenty ass-loads of empty sacks. Abu'l Fawaris greeted him, and together they loaded the ship and set sail. Taking a particular star for their mark, they sailed for three months, when an island appeared to one side of them. For this the old man steered, and they soon landed upon it. Having loaded his slave with some sacks, the old man with his companions set out towards a mountain which they could see in the distance. This they reached after some hours of travel, and climbed to the summit, upon which they found a broad plain where more than two hundred pits had been dug. The old man then explained to the sailor that he was a merchant, and that he had, on that spot, found a mine of jewels. "Now that I have given you my confidence," he continued, "I expect faithfulness from you too. I desire you to go down into this pit and send up sufficient pearls to fill these sacks. Half I will give to you, and we shall be able to spend the rest of our lives in luxury." The sailor thereupon asked how the pearls had found their way into these pits, to which the old man replied that there was a passage connecting the pits with the sea. Along this passage oysters swam, and settled in the pits, where by chance he had come upon them. He explained further that he had only brought the sailor because he needed help; but he desired not to disclose the matter to any one else.

With great eagerness then the sailor descended into the pit, and there found oysters in great numbers. The old man let down a basket to him, which he filled again and again, until at last the merchant cried out that the oysters were useless, for they contained no pearls. Abu'l Fawaris therefore left that pit, and descended into another, where he found pearls in great number. By the time night fell he was

[1] From Mr. Reuben Levy's translation of *The Three Dervishes,* in the World's Classics Series.

utterly wearied, and called out to the old man to help him out of the pit. In reply the merchant shouted down that he intended to leave him in the pit, for he feared that Abu'l Fawaris might kill him for the sake of the jewels. With great vehemence the sailor protested that he was innocent of any such intention, but the old man was deaf to his entreaties, and, making his way back to the ship, sailed away.

For three days Abu'l Fawaris remained, hungry and thirsty. As he struggled to find a way out he came upon many human bones, and understood that the accursed old man had betrayed many others in the same fashion. In desperation he dug about, and at last he saw a small opening, which he enlarged with his hands. Soon it was big enough for him to crawl through, and he found himself in the darkness, standing upon mud. Along this he walked carefully, and then felt himself suddenly plunged to his neck in water, which was salt to the taste; and he knew that he was in the passage that led to the sea. He swam along in this for some way, till, in front of him, there appeared a faint light. Greatly heartened by the sight of it, he swam vigorously until he reached the mouth of the passage. On emerging, he found himself facing the sea, and threw himself on his face to give thanks for his delivery. Then he arose, and a little distance from him he found the cloak which he had left behind when he set out for the mountain; but of the old merchant there was no sign, and the ship had disappeared.

Full of trouble and despondency, he sat down at the water's brink, wondering what he was to do. As he gazed at the sea there came into view a ship, and he saw that it was filled with men. At sight of it the sailor leaped from his place; snatching his turban from his head, he waved it with all his might in the air, and shouted at the top of his voice. But as they approached he decided not to tell his rescuers the truth of his presence there; therefore when they landed and asked how he came to be on the island he told them that his ship had been wrecked at sea, that he had clung to a plank and been washed to the shore.

They praised his good fortune at his escape, and in reply to his questions with regard to the place of their origin, told him that they had sailed from Abyssinia, and were then on their way to Hindustan. At this, Abu'l Fawaris hesitated, saying that he had no business in Hindustan. They assured him, however, that they would meet ships going to Basrah, and would hand him over to one of them. He agreed then to go with them, and for forty days they sailed without seeing any inhabited spot. At last he asked them whether they had not mistaken their way, and they admitted that for five days they had been sailing without knowing whither they were going or what direction to follow. All together therefore set themselves to praying, and remained in prayer for some time.

Soon afterwards, as they sailed, something in appearance like a minaret emerged from the sea, and they seemed to behold the flash of a Chinese mirror. Also they perceived that their ship without their rowing, and without any greater

and devours them. We are all merchants whom adverse winds have brought here. That div has seized us and keeps us in this fashion."

With a groan the sailor thought that now at last he was undone. At that moment he saw the shepherd coming, saw him let the sheep into the garden, and then close the gateway with the stone before entering the kiosk. He was carrying a bag full of almonds, dates, and pistachio nuts, with which he approached, and, giving it to the sailor, he told him to share it with the others. Abu'l Fawaris could say nothing, but sat down and ate the food with his companions. When they had finished their meal, the shepherd returned to them, took one of them by the hand, and then in sight of them all, slew, roasted, and devoured him. When he was sated, he brought out a skin of wine and drank until he fell into a drunken sleep.

Then the sailor turned to his companions and said: "Since I am to die, let me first destroy him; if you will give me your help, I will do so." They replied that they had no strength left; but he, seeing the two long spits on which the ogre had roasted his meat, put them into the fire until they were red hot, and then plunged them into the monster's eyes.

With a great cry the shepherd leaped up and tried to seize his tormentor, who sprang away and eluded him. Running to the stone, the shepherd moved it aside and began to let out the sheep one by one, in the hope that when the garden was emptier he could the more easily capture the sailor. Abu'l Fawaris understood his intention: without delay, he slew a sheep, put on the skin and tried to pass through. But the shepherd knew as soon as he felt him that this was not a sheep, and leaped after him in pursuit. Abu'l Fawaris flung off the pelt, and ran like the wind. Soon he came to the sea, and into this he plunged, while the shepherd after a few steps returned to the shore, for he could not swim.

Full of terror the sailor swam till he reached the other side of the mountain. There he met an old man who greeted him, and, after hearing his adventure, fed him and took him to his house. But soon, to his horror, Abu'l Fawaris found that this old man also was an ogre. With great cunning he told the ogre's wife that he could make many useful implements for her house, and she persuaded her husband to save him. After many days in the house, he was sent away to the care of a shepherd, and put to guard sheep. Day by day he planned to escape, but there was only one way across the mountain and that was guarded.

One day, as he wandered in a wood, he found in the hollow trunk of a tree a store of honey, of which he told the shepherd's wife when he went home. The next day, therefore, the woman sent her husband with Abu'l Fawaris, telling him to bring home some of the honey; but, on the way, the sailor leaped upon him and bound him to a tree. Then, taking the shepherd's ring, he returned and told the woman that her husband had given him leave to go, and that he sent his ring in token of this. But the woman was cunning and asked: "Why did not my husband come himself to tell me this?" Seizing him by the cloak, she told him that she would go with him and find out the truth. The sailor, however, tore himself free, and again fled to the sea, where he thought that he might escape death. In haste and terror he swam for many hours, until at last he espied a ship full of men, who steered towards him and took him on board. Full of wonder they asked how he came there, and he related to them all his adventures.

It happened by great good fortune that the ship's captain had business at one place only on the coast, and that from there he was sailing to Basrah. In the space of a month, therefore, Abu'l Fawaris was restored to his family, to the joy of them all.

The many dangers and sufferings of the sailor had turned his hair white. For many days he rested, and then, one day, as he walked by the seashore, that same old man who had before hired his ship again appeared. Without recognizing him, he asked if he would lend his ship on hire for six months. Abu'l Fawaris agreed to do so for a thousand dinars of gold, which the old man at once paid to him, saying that he would come in a boat on the morrow, ready to depart.

When the ancient departed, the sailor took home the money to his wife, who bade him beware not to cast himself again into danger. He replied that he must be avenged not only for himself, but also for the thousand Muslims whom the villainous old man had slain.

The next day, therefore, the sailor took on board the old man and a black slave, and for three months they sailed, until they once more reached the island of pearls. There they made fast the ship on the shore, and taking sacks, they ascended to the top of the mountain. Once arrived there, the old man made the same request to Abu'l Fawaris as before, namely, that he should go down into the pits and send up pearls. The sailor replied that he was unacquainted with the place, and preferred that the old man should go down first, in order to prove that there was no danger. He answered that there was surely no danger; he had never in his life harmed even an ant, and he would of a certainty never send Abu'l Fawaris down into the pits if he knew any peril lay there. But the sailor was obstinate, saying that until he knew how to-carry it out, he could not undertake the task.

Very reluctantly, therefore, the old man allowed himself to be lowered into the first pit by a basket and a rope. He filled the basket with oysters and sent it up, crying out: "You see, there is nothing to do harm in this pit. Draw me up now, for I am an old man and have no more strength left." The sailor replied, "Now that you are there, it were better if you remained there to complete your task. To-morrow I myself will go into another pit and will send up so many pearls as to fill the ship." For a long time the old man worked, sending up pearls, and at last he cried out again, "O my brother, I am utterly wearied, draw me out now." Then the sailor turned upon him with fury, and cried out: "How is it that thou dost see ever thine own trouble and never that of others? Thou misbegotten dog, art thou blind that thou dost not know me? I am Abu'l Fawaris, the sailor, whom long ago you left in one of these pits. By the favor of Allah I was delivered, and now it is your turn. Open your eyes to the truth and remember what you have done to so many men." The old man cried aloud for mercy, but it availed him nothing, for Abu'l Fawaris brought a great stone and covered up the mouth of the pit. The slave too he overwhelmed with threats, and then together they carried down the pearls to the ship, in which they set sail. In three months they arrived at Basrah. There Abu'l Fawaris related his adventures, to the amazement of all. Thenceforward he abandoned the sea and adopted a life of ease. Finally he died, and this story remains in memory of him. And Allah knoweth best.

CELTIC LITERATURE

THE VOYAGE OF MAILDUN[1]

THERE was once an illustrious man of the tribe of Owenaght of Ninus, Allil Ocar Aga by name, a goodly hero, and lord of his own tribe and territory. One time, when he was in his house unguarded, a fleet of plunderers landed on the coast, and spoiled his territory. The chief fled for refuge to the church of Dooclone; but the spoilers followed him thither, slew him, and burned the church over his head.

Not long after Allil's death, a son was born to him. The child's mother gave him the name of Maildun; and, wishing to conceal his birth, she brought him to the queen of that country, who was her dear friend. The queen took him to her, and gave out that he was her own child, and he was brought up with the king's sons, slept in the same cradle with them, and was fed from the same breast and from the same cup. He was a very lovely child; and the people who saw him thought it doubtful if there was any other child living at the time equally beautiful.

As he grew up to be a young man, the noble qualities of his mind gradually unfolded themselves. He was high-spirited and generous, and he loved all sorts of manly exercises. In ball-playing, in running and leaping, in throwing the stone, in chess-playing, in rowing, and in horse racing, he surpassed all the youths that came to the king's palace, and won the palm in every contest.

One day, when the young men were at their games, a certain youth among them grew envious of Maildun; and he said, in an angry and haughty tone of voice:

"It is a cause of much shame to us that we have to yield in every game, whether of skill or of strength, whether on land or on water, to an obscure youth, of whom no one can tell who is his father or his mother, or what race or tribe he belongs to."

On hearing this, Maildun ceased at once from play; for until that moment he believed that he was the son of the king of the Owenaght, and of the queen who had nursed him. And going anon to the queen, he told her what had happened; and he said to her:

"If I am not thy son, I will neither eat nor drink till thou tell me who my father and mother are."

She tried to soothe him, and said:

"Why do you worry yourself searching after this matter? Give no heed to the words of this envious youth. Am I not a mother to you? And in all this country, is there any mother who loves her son better than I love you?"

He answered:

[1] From *Old Celtic Romances,* translated by P.W. Joyce.

Round the room were arranged a number of couches, all pure white and richly ornamented. Abundant food of various kinds was spread on tables, among which they observed a boiled ox and a roast hog, and there were many large drinking horns, full of good, intoxicating ale.

"Is it for us that this food has been prepared?" said Maildun to the cat.

The cat, on hearing the question, ceased from playing, and looked at him; but he recommenced his play immediately. Whereupon Maildun told his people that the dinner was meant for them; and they all sat down, and ate and drank till they were satisfied, after which they rested and slept on the couches.

When they awoke, they poured what was left of the ale into one vessel; and they gathered the remnants of the food to bring them away. As they were about to go, Maildun's eldest foster brother asked him:

"Shall I bring one of those large torques away with me?"

"By no means," said Maildun; "it is well that we have got food and rest. Bring nothing away, for it is certain that this house is not left without some one to guard it."

The young man, however, disregarding Maildun's advice, took down one of the torques and brought it away. But the cat followed him, and overtook him in the middle of the court, and, springing on him like a blazing, fiery arrow, he went through his body, and reduced it in a moment to a heap of ashes. He then returned to the room, and, leaping up on one of the pillars, sat upon it.

Maildun turned back, bringing the torque with him, and, approaching the cat, spoke some soothing words; after which he put the torque back to the place from which it had been taken. Having done this, he collected the ashes of his foster brother, and, bringing them to the shore, cast them into the sea. They all then went on board the curragh, and continued their voyage, grieving for their lost companion, but thanking God for His many mercies to them.

After a time, they came to a sea like green crystal. It was so calm and transparent that they could see the sand at the bottom quite clearly, sparkling in the sunlight. And in this sea they saw neither monsters, nor ugly animals, nor rough rocks; nothing but the clear water and the sunshine and the bright sand. For a whole day they sailed over it, admiring its splendour and beauty.

After leaving this they entered on another sea, which seemed like a clear, thin cloud; and it was so transparent, and appeared so light, that they thought at first it would not bear up the weight of the curragh.

Looking down, they could see, beneath the clear water, a beautiful country, with many mansions surrounded by groves and woods. In one place was a single tree; and, standing on its branches, they saw an animal fierce and terrible to look upon.

Round about the tree was a great herd of oxen grazing, and a man stood near to guard them, armed with shield, and spear, and sword; but when he looked up and saw the animal on the tree, he turned anon and fled with the utmost speed. Then the monster stretched forth his neck, and, darting his head downward, plunged his fangs into the back of the largest ox of the whole herd, lifted him off the ground into the tree, and swallowed him down in the twinkling of an eye; whereupon the whole herd took to flight.

When Maildun and his people saw this, they were seized with great terror; for they feared they should not be able to cross the sea over the monster, on account of the extreme mist-like thinness of the water; but after much difficulty and danger they got across it safely.

The next thing they found after this was an immense silver pillar standing in the sea. It had eight sides, each of which was the width of an oar-stroke of the curragh, so that its whole circumference was eight oar-strokes. It rose out of the sea without any land or earth about it, nothing but the boundless ocean; and they could not see its base deep down in the water, neither were they able to see the top on account of its vast height.

A silver net hung from the top down to the very water, extending far out at one side of the pillar; and the meshes were so large that the curragh in full sail went through one of them. When they were passing through it, Diuran struck the mesh with the edge of his spear, and with the blow cut a large piece off it.

"Do not destroy the net," said Maildun; "for what we see is the work of great men."

"What I have done," answered Diuran, "is for the honour of my God, and in order that the story of our adventures may be more readily believed; and I shall lay this silver as an offering on the altar of Armagh, if I ever reach Erin."

That piece of silver weighed two ounces and a half, as it was reckoned afterwards by the people of the church of Armagh.

After this they heard someone speaking on the top of the pillar, in a loud, clear, glad voice; but they knew neither what he said, nor in what language he spoke.

They came now to a small island with a high wall of fire all round it, and there was a large open door in the wall at one side near the sea. They sailed backward and forward many times and always paused before the door; for whenever they came right in front of it, they could see almost the whole island through it.

And this is what they saw: A great number of people, beautiful and glorious-looking, wearing rich garments adorned and radiant all over; feasting joyously, and drinking from embossed vessels of red gold which they held in their hands. The voyagers heard also their cheerful, festive songs; and they marvelled greatly, and their hearts were full of gladness at all the happiness they saw and heard. But they did not venture to land.

A little time after leaving this, they saw something a long way off towards the south, which at first they took to be a large white bird floating on the sea, and rising and falling with the waves; but on turning their curragh towards it for a nearer view, they found that it was a man. He was very old, so old that he was covered all over with long, white hair, which grew from his body; and he was standing on a broad, bare rock, and kept continually throwing himself on his knees, and never ceased praying.

When they saw that he was a holy man, they asked and received his blessing; after which they began to converse with him; and they inquired who he was, and how he had come to that rock. Then the old man gave them the following account:

"I was born and bred in the island of Tory. When I grew up to be a man, I was cook to the brotherhood of the monastery; and a wicked cook I was; for every day I sold part of the food intrusted to me, and secretly bought many choice and rare things with the money. Worse even than this I did; I made secret passages underground into the church and into the houses belonging to it, and I stole from time to time great quantities of golden vestments, book-covers adorned with brass and gold, and other holy and precious things.

"I soon became very rich, and had my rooms filled with costly couches, with clothes of every colour, both linen and woollen, with brazen pitchers and caldrons, and with brooches and armlets of gold. Nothing was wanting in my house, of furniture and ornament, that a person in a high rank of life might be expected to have; and I became very proud and overbearing.

"One day I was sent to dig a grave for the body of a rustic that had been brought from the mainland to be buried on the island. I went and fixed on a spot in the little graveyard; but as soon as I had set to work, I heard a voice speaking down deep in the earth beneath my feet:

"'Do not dig this grave.'

"I paused for a moment, startled; but, recovering myself, I gave no further heed to the mysterious words, and again I began to dig. The moment I did so, I heard the same voice, even more plainly than before:

"'Do not dig this grave! I am a devout and holy person, and my body is lean and light; do not put the heavy, pampered body of that sinner down upon me!'

"But I answered, in the excess of my pride and obstinacy, 'I will certainly dig this grave; and I will bury this body down on you.'

"'If you put that body down on me, the flesh will fall off your bones, and you will die, and be sent to the infernal pit at the end of three days; and, moreover, the body will not remain where you put it.'

"'What will you give me, ' I asked, 'if I do not bury the corpse on you?'

"'Everlasting life in heaven,' replied the voice.

"'How do you know this; and how am I to be sure of it?' I inquired.

"And the voice answered me, 'The grave you are digging is clay. Observe now whether it will remain so, and then you will know the truth of what I tell you. And you will see that what I say will come to pass, and that you cannot bury that man on me, even if you should try to do so.'

"These words were scarce ended, when the grave was turned into a mass of white sand before my face. And when I saw this I brought the body away, and buried it elsewhere.

"It happened, some time after, that I got a new curragh made, with the hides painted red all over; and I went to sea in it. As I sailed by the shores and islands, I was so pleased with the view of the land and sea from my curragh, that I resolved to live altogether in it for some time; and I brought on board all my treasures—silver cups, gold bracelets, and ornamented drinking horns, and everything else, from the largest to the smallest article.

"I enjoyed myself for a time, while the air was clear and the sea calm and smooth. But one day, the winds suddenly arose and a storm burst upon me, which carried me out to sea, so that I quite lost sight of land, and I knew not in what direction the curragh was drifting. After a time, the wind abated to a gentle gale, the sea became smooth, and the curragh sailed on as before, with a quiet, pleasant movement.

"But suddenly, though the breeze continued to blow, I thought I could perceive that the curragh ceased moving, and, standing up to find out the cause, I saw with great surprise an old man not far off, sitting on the crest of a wave.

"He spoke to me; and, as soon as I heard his voice, I knew it at once, but I could not at the moment call to mind where I had heard it before. And I became greatly troubled, and began to tremble, I knew not why.

"'Whither art thou going?' he asked.

"'I know not,' I replied; 'but this I know, I am pleased with the smooth, gentle motion of my curragh over the waves.'

"'You would not be pleased,' replied the old man, 'if you could see the troops that are at this moment around you.'

"'What troops do you speak of?' I asked. And he answered:

"'All the space round about you, as far as your view reaches over the sea, and upwards to the clouds, is one great towering mass of demons, on account of your avarice, your thefts, your pride, and your other crimes and vices.'

"He then asked, 'Do you know why your curragh has stopped?'

"I answered, 'No'; and he said, 'It has been stopped by me; and it will never move from that spot till you promise me to do what I shall ask of you.'

"I replied that perhaps it was not in my power to grant his demand.

"'It is in your power,' he answered; 'and if you refuse me the torments of hell shall be your doom.'

"He then came close to the curragh, and, laying his hands on me, made me swear to do what he demanded.

"'What I ask is this,' said he; 'that you throw into the sea this moment all the ill-gotten treasures you have in the curragh.'

"This grieved me very much, and I replied, 'It is a pity that all these costly things should be lost.'

"To which he answered, 'They will not go to loss; a person will be sent to take charge of them. Now do as I say.'

"So, greatly against my wishes, I threw all the beautiful precious articles overboard, keeping only a small wooden cup to drink from.

"'You will now continue your voyage,' he said; 'and the first solid ground your curragh reaches, there you are to stay.'

"He then gave me seven cakes and a cup of watery whey as food for my voyage; after which the curragh moved on, and I soon lost sight of him. And now I all at once recollected that the old man's voice was the same as the voice that I had heard come from the ground, when I was about to dig the grave for the body of the rustic. I was so astonished and troubled at this discovery, and so disturbed at the loss of all my wealth, that I threw aside my oars, and gave myself up altogether to the winds and currents, not caring whither I went; and for a long time I was tossed about on the waves, I knew not in what direction.

"At last it seemed to me that my curragh ceased to move; but I was not sure about it, for I could see no sign of land. Mindful, however, of what the old man had told me, that I was to stay wherever my curragh stopped, I looked round more carefully; and at last I saw, very near me, a small rock level with the surface, over which the waves were gently laughing and tumbling. I stepped on to the rock; and the moment I did so, the waves seemed to spring back, and the rock rose high over the level of the water; while the curragh drifted by and quickly disappeared, so that I never saw it after. This rock has been my abode from that time to the present day.

"For the first seven years, I lived on the seven cakes and the cup of whey given me by the man who had sent me to the rock. At the end of that time the cakes were all gone; and for three days I fasted, with nothing but the whey to wet my mouth. Late in the evening of the third day, an otter brought me a salmon out of the sea; but though I suffered much from hunger, I could not bring myself to eat the fish raw, and it was washed back again into the waves.

"I remained without food for three days longer; and in the afternoon of the third day, the otter returned with the salmon. And I saw another otter bring firewood; and when he had piled it up on the rock, he blew it with his breath till it took fire and lighted up. And then I broiled the salmon and ate till I had satisfied my hunger.

"The otter continued to bring me a salmon every day, and in this manner I lived for seven years longer. The rock also grew larger and larger daily, till it became the size you now see it. At the end of seven years, the otter ceased to bring me my salmon, and I fasted for three days. But at the end of the third day, I was sent half a cake of fine wheaten flour and a slice of fish; and on the same day my cup of watery whey fell into the sea, and a cup of the same size, filled with good ale, was placed on the rock for me.

"And so I have lived, praying and doing penance for my sins to this hour. Each day my drinking vessel is filled with ale, and I am sent half a wheat-flour cake and a slice of fish; and neither rain nor wind nor heat nor cold is allowed to molest me on this rock."

This was the end of the old man's history. In the evening of that day, each man of the crew received the same quantity of food that was sent to the old hermit himself, namely, half a cake and a slice of fish; and they found in the vessel as much good ale as served them all.

The next morning he said to them, "You shall all reach your own country in safety. And you, Maildun, you shall find in an island on your way, the very man that slew your father; but you are neither to kill him nor take revenge on him in any way. As God has delivered you from the many dangers you have passed through, though you were very guilty, and well deserved death at His hands; so you forgive your enemy the crime he committed against you."

After this they took leave of the old man and sailed away.

Soon after they saw a beautiful verdant island, with herds of oxen, cows, and sheep browsing all over its hills and valleys; but no houses nor inhabitants were to be seen. And they rested for some time on this island, and ate the flesh of the cows and sheep.

One day, while they were standing on a hill, a large falcon flew by; and two of the crew, who happened to look closely at him, cried out, in the hearing of Maildun:

"See that falcon! He is surely like the falcons of Erin!"

"Watch him closely," cried Maildun, "and observe exactly in what direction he is flying!"

And they saw that he flew to the south-east, without turning or wavering.

They went on board at once; and, having unmoored, they sailed to the south-east after the falcon. After rowing the whole day, they sighted land in the dusk of the evening, which seemed to them like the land of Erin.

On a near approach, they found it was a small island; and now they recognized it as the very same island they had seen in the beginning of their voyage, in which they had heard the man in the great house boast that he had slain Maildun's father, and from which the storm had driven them out into the great ocean.

They turned the prow of their vessel to the shore, landed, and went towards the house. It happened that at this very time the people of the house were seated at their evening meal; and Maildun and his companions, as they stood outside, heard a part of their conversation.

Said one to another, "It would not be well for us if we were now to see Maildun."

"As to Maildun," answered another, "it is very well known that he was drowned long ago in the great ocean."

"Do not be sure," observed a third; "perchance he is the very man that may waken you up some morning from your sleep."

"Supposing he came now," asks another, "what should we do?"

The head of the house now spoke in reply to the last question; and Maildun at once knew his voice:

"I can easily answer that," said he. "Maildun has been for a long time suffering great afflictions and hardships; and if he were to come now, though we were enemies once, I should certainly give him a welcome and a kind reception."

When Maildun heard this, he knocked at the door, and the doorkeeper asked who was there; to which Maildun made answer:-

" It is I, Maildun, returned safely from all my wanderings."

The chief of the house then ordered the door to be opened; and he went to meet Maildun, and brought himself and his companions into the house. They were joyfully welcomed by the whole household; new garments were given to them; and they feasted and rested, till they forgot their weariness and their hardships.

They related all the wonders God had revealed to them in the course of their voyage, according to the word of the sage who says, "It will be a source of pleasure to remember these things at a future time."

After they had remained here for some days, Maildun returned to his own country. And Diuran Lekerd took the five half-ounces of silver he had cut down from the great net at the Silver Pillar, and laid it, according to his promise, on the high altar of Armagh.

GREAT BRITAIN

HOW SCYLD SET FORTH UPON HIS LAST VOYAGE[1]

AT HIS appointed time then Scyld departed, to go into the peace of the Lord; they then, his dear comrades, bore him out to the shore of the sea, as he himself requested, the while that he, the friend of the Scyldings, the beloved chieftain, had power with his words; long he owned it! There upon the beach stood the ring-prowed ship, the vehicle of the noble, shining like ice, and ready to set out. They then laid down the dear prince, the distributer of rings, in the bosom of the ship, the mighty one beside the mast; there was much of treasures, of ornaments, brought from afar. Never heard I of a comelier ship having been adorned with battle-weapons and with war-weeds, with bills and mailed coats. Upon his bosom lay a multitude of treasures which were to depart afar with him, into the possession of the flood. They furnished him not less with offerings, with mighty wealth, than those had done who in the beginning sent him forth in his wretchedness, alone over the waves. Moreover they set up over him a golden ensign, high over head; they let the deep-sea bear him; they gave him to the ocean. Sad was their spirit, mournful their mood. Men know not in sooth to say (men wise of counsel or any man under the heavens) who received the freight.

HOW BEOWULF FOR THE SPACE OF FIVE NIGHTS ABODE IN THE SEA[1]

HUNFERTH, the son of Eglaf, spake, he that sat at the feet of the Lord of the Scyldings.

"Art thou the Beowulf that didst contend with Brecca on the wide sea, in a swimming match, where ye for pride explored the fords, and out of vain glory ventured your lives upon the deep water? Nor might any man, friend or foe, blame your sorrowful expedition: there ye rode upon the sea, there ye two covered the ocean-stream with your arms, measured the sea-streets, whirled them with your hands, glided over the ocean; with the waves of the deep the fury of winter boiled; ye two on the realms of water laboured for a week: he overcame thee in swimming, he had more strength; then at the morning tide the deep sea bore him up on Heathoraemes, whence he sought his own paternal land, dear to his people, the land of the Brondings, where he owned a nation, a town and rings. All his promise to thee, the son of Beanstan truly performed,"

[1] From J.M. Kemble's translation of *Beowulf.*

Beowulf, the son of Ecgtheow, spake:

"Lo! for a long while thou, my friend Hunferth, drunken with beer, hast spoken about Brecca, hast said respecting his journey; I tell thee the truth, that I have greater strength upon the sea, laboriousness upon the waves, than any other man. We two, when we were boys, had said and promised that (we were both of us as yet in early youth) that we could venture with our lives, out upon the ocean: and so we performed it. We had our naked swords, hard in our hands, when we two rode upon the sea; we two thought to defend ourselves against the whale-fishes. He could not float at all far away from me over the waves of the flood, more rapidly on the deep sea, I would not part from him; there were we two together, a space of five nights upon the sea, until the flood drove us asunder; the coldest of storms, darkening night, and a wind from the north, warlike, fierce, turned up the boiling fords; the waves were fierce. The pride of the sea-fishes was excited: there against my foes my bodyshirt, hard, locked by the hand, gave help; my twisted war-dress lay upon my breast, adorned with gold. Me did the many coloured foe drag to the bottom of the sea, he had me fast, grim in his grip: nevertheless it was granted to me to reach the wretch with my point, with my war-bill: the mighty sea-beast received the war-rush through my hand.

"Thus often did my hated foes violently menace me; I served them with my dear sword, as it was fitting; they, the evil-doers, had no joy of the slaughter, in that they attacked me, that they set upon me all together, near the bottom of the sea. But in the morning wounded with knives, they lay aloft beside the leavings of the waves, put to sleep with swords; so that never since, about the boiling ford they have hindered the sea-sailers of their way. The light came from the East, the bright beacon of God, the fierce seas became calm, so that I might see the ocean-promontories, the windy walls. Fate often preserveth a warrior not yet doomed to die, when his valour availeth. Yet I had the fortune to slay with my sword nine nicors: never have I heard of a harder battle by night under the concave of heaven, nor of a man more wretched on the ocean-streams: nevertheless I continued my journey, I escaped with life; weary of my expedition: then did the sea bear me up on Finland, the flood upon the sand, the boiling fords."

THE BATTLE OF ESPAGNOLS-SUR-MER[1]

Sir John Froissart
(1313-1419)

ABOUT this period, there was much ill will between the king of England and the Spaniards, on account of some infractions and pillages committed at sea by the latter. It happened at this season, that the Spaniards who had been in Flanders with their merchandize, were informed they would not be able to return home, without meeting the English fleet. The Spaniards did not pay much attention to this intelligence: however, after they had disposed of their goods, they amply provided their ships from Sluys with arms and artillery, and all such archers, cross-bowmen, and soldiers as were willing to receive pay. The king of England hated these Spaniards greatly, and said publicly:

"We have for a long time spared these people; for which they have done us much harm; without amending their conduct; on the contrary they grow more arrogant; for which reason they must be chastised as they repass our coasts."

When the Spaniards had completed their cargoes, and laden their vessels with linen cloths, and whatever they imagined would be profitable in their own country, they embarked on board their fleet at Sluys. They knew they should meet the English, but were indifferent about it; for they had marvellously provided themselves with all sorts of warlike ammunition; such as bolts for cross-bows, cannon, and bars of forged iron to throw on the enemy, in hopes, with the assistance of great stones, to sink him. When they weighed anchor, the wind was favourable for them: there were forty large vessels of such a size, and so beautiful, it was a fine sight to see them under sail. Near the top of their masts were small castles, full of flints and stones, and a soldier to guard them; and there also was the flag-staff, from whence fluttered their streamers in the wind, that it was pleasant to look at them. If the English had a great desire to meet them, it seemed as if the Spaniards were still more eager for it, as will hereafter appear. The Spaniards were full ten thousand men, including all sorts of soldiers they had enlisted when in Flanders: this made them feel sufficient courage not to fear the combat with the king of England, and whatever force he might have at sea. Intending to meet the English fleet, they advanced with a favourable wind until they came opposite Calais.

The king of England being at sea, had very distinctly explained to all his knights the order of battle he would have them follow: he had appointed the lord Robert de Namur to the command of a ship called *La Salle du Roi,* on board of which was

---

[1] From *The Chronicles of England.*

all his household. The king posted himself in the fore part of his own ship: he was dressed in a black velvet jacket, and wore on his head a small hat of beaver, which became him much. He was that day, as I was told by those who were present, as joyous as he ever was in his life, and ordered his minstrels to play before him a German dance which sir John Chandos had lately introduced. For his amusement, he made the same knight sing with his minstrels, which delighted him greatly. From time to time he looked up to the castle on his mast, where he had placed a watch to inform him when the Spaniards were in sight.

Whilst the king was thus amusing himself with his knights, who were happy in seeing him so gay, the watch, who had observed a fleet, cried out:

"Ho, I spy a ship, and it appears to me to be a Spaniard."

The minstrels were silenced; and he was asked if there were more than one: soon after he replied,

"Yes; I see two, three, four, and so many that, God help me, I cannot count them."

The king and his knights then knew they must be the Spaniards. The trumpets were ordered to sound, and the ships to form a line of battle for the combat; as they were aware that, since the enemy came in such force, it could not be avoided. It was, however, rather late, about the hour of vespers. The king ordered wine to be brought, which he and his knights drank; when each fixed their helmets on their heads. The Spaniards now drew near; they might easily have refused the battle, if they had chosen it, for they were well freighted, in large ships, and had the wind in their favour. They could have avoided speaking with the English, if they had willed, but their pride and presumption made them act otherwise. They disdained to sail by, but bore instantly down on them, and commenced the battle.

When the king of England saw from his ship their order of battle, he ordered the person who managed his vessel, saying:

"Lay me alongside the Spaniard who is bearing down on us; for I will have a tilt with him."

The master dared not disobey the king's order, but laid his ship ready for the Spaniard, who was coming full sail. The king's ship was large and stiff; otherwise she would have been sunk, for that of the enemy was a great one, and the shock of their meeting was more like the crash of a torrent or tempest; the rebound caused the castle in the king's ship to encounter that of the Spaniard: so that the mast of the latter was broken, and all in the castle fell with it into the sea, when they were drowned. The, English vessel, however, suffered, and let in water, which the knights cleared, and stopped the leak, without telling the king any thing of the matter. Upon examining the vessel he had engaged lying before him, he said:

"Grapple my ship with that; for I will have possession of her."

His knights replied:

"Let her go her way; you shall have better than her."

That vessel sailed on, and another large ship bore down, and grappled with chains and hooks to that of the king. The fight now began in earnest, and the archers and cross-bows on each side were eager to shoot and defend themselves. The battle was not in one place, but in ten or twelve at a time. Whenever either party found themselves equal to the enemy, or superior, they instantly grappled, when grand deeds of arms were performed. The English had not any advantage; and the Spanish ships were much larger and higher than their opponents, which gave them a great superiority in shooting and casting stones and iron bars on board their enemy, which annoyed them exceedingly. The knights on board the king's ship were in danger of sinking, for the leak still admitted water: this made them more eager to conquer the vessel they were grappled to: many gallant deeds were done; and at last they gained the ship, and flung all they found in it overboard, having quitted their own ship. They continued the combat against the Spaniards, who fought valiantly, and whose cross-bowmen shot such bolts of iron as greatly distressed the English.

This sea-fight between the English and Spaniards was well and hardly fought: but, as night was coming on, the English exerted themselves to do their duty well, and discomfort their enemies. The Spaniards, who are used to the sea, and were in large ships, acquitted themselves to the utmost of their power.

The young Prince of Wales and his division were engaged apart: his ship was grappled by a great Spaniard, where he and his knights suffered much; for she had so many holes, that the water came in very abundantly, and they could not by any means stop the leaks, which gave the crew fears of her sinking, they therefore did all they could to conquer the enemy's ship, but in vain; for she was very large, and excellently well defended. During this danger of the prince, the duke of Lancaster came near, and, as he approached, saw he had the worst of the engagement, and that his crew had too much on their hands, for they were baling out water: he therefore fell on the other side of the Spanish vessel, with which he grappled, shouting,

"Derby to the rescue!"

The engagement was now very warm, but did not last long, for the ship was taken, and all the crew thrown overboard, not one being saved. The prince, with his men, instantly embarked on board the Spaniard; and scarcely had they done so when his own vessel sunk, which convinced them of the imminent danger they had been in.

The engagement was in other parts well contested by the English knights, who exerted themselves, and need there was of it, for they found those who feared them not. Late in the evening, the *Salle du Roi,* commanded by lord Robert de Namur, was grappled by a large Spaniard, and the fight was very severe. The Spaniards were determined to gain this ship; and, the more effectually to succeed in carrying her off, they set all their sails, took advantage of the wind, and in spite of what lord Robert and his crew could do, towed her out of the battle: for the Spaniard was of a more considerable size than the lord Robert's ship, and therefore she more easily conquered. As they were thus towed, they passed near the king's ship, to whom they cried out,

"Rescue the *Salle du Roi!*"

but were not heard; for it was dark; and, if they were heard, they were not rescued. The Spaniards would have carried away with ease this prize, if it had not been for a gallant act of one Hanequin, a servant to the lord Robert, who, with his drawn sword on his wrist, leaped on board the enemy, ran to the mast, and cut the large cable which held the main sail, by which it became unmanageable; and with great agility, he cut other four principal ropes, so that the sails fell on the deck, and the course of the ship was stopped. Lord Robert, seeing this, advanced with his men, and, boarding the Spaniard, sword in hand, attacked the crew so vigorously that all were slain or thrown overboard, and the vessel won.

I cannot speak of every particular circumstance of this engagement. It lasted a considerable time; and the Spaniards gave the king of England and his fleet enough to do. However, at last, victory declared for the English: the Spaniards lost fourteen ships; the others saved themselves by flight. When it was completely over, and the king saw he had none to fight with, he ordered his trumpets to sound a retreat, and made for England.

HOW SIR LAUNCELOT ENTERED INTO THE SHIP WHERE SIR PERCIVALE'S SISTER LAY DEAD: AND HOW HE MET WITH SIR GALAHAD HIS SON[1]

Sir Thomas Malory

(fl. 1470)

NOW saith the history, that when Launcelot was come to the water of Mortoise, he was in great peril, and so he laid him down and slept, and took the adventure that God would send him.

So when he was asleep, there came a vision unto him and said, Launcelot, arise up, and take thine armour, and enter into the first ship that thou shalt find. And when he had heard these words, he start up and saw great clearness about him. And

[1] From *Morte d'Arthur.*

then he lift up his hand and blessed him, and so took his arms, and made him ready; and so by adventure he came by a strand, and found a ship, the which was without sail or oar. And as soon as he was within the ship, there he felt the most sweetness that ever he felt; and he was fulfilled with all thing that he thought on or desired. Then said he,

Fair sweet Father Jesu Christ, I wot not in what joy I am, for this joy passeth all earthly joys that ever I was in.

And so in this joy he laid him down to the ship's board, and slept till day.

And when he awoke he found there a fair bed, and therein lying a gentlewoman dead, the which was Sir Percivale's sister. And as Launcelot devised her, he espied in her right hand a writ, the which he read, the which told him all the adventures that ye have heard tofore, and of what lineage she was come. So with this gentlewoman Sir Launcelot was a month and more. If ye would ask how he lived, He that fed the people of Israel with manna in the desert, so was he fed. For every day, when he had said his prayers, he was sustained with the grace of the Holy Ghost.

So on a night he went to play him by the water side, for he was somewhat weary of the ship. And then he listened, and heard an horse come, and one riding upon him. And when he came nigh he seemed a knight. And so he let him pass, and went there as the ship was, and there he alight, and took the saddle and the bridle and put the horse from him, and went into the ship.

And then Launcelot dressed unto him and said,

Ye be welcome.

And he answered and saluted him again, and asked him,

What is your name? for much my heart giveth unto you.

Truly, said he, my name is Launcelot du Lake.

Sir, said he, then be ye welcome, for ye were the beginner of me in this world.

Ah, said he, are ye Galahad?

Yea forsooth, said he.

And so he kneeled down and asked him his blessing, and after took off his helm and kissed him. And there was great joy between them, for there is no tongue can tell the joy that they made either of other, and many a friendly word spoken between, as kind would, the which is no need here to be rehearsed. And there every each told other of their adventures and marvels that were befallen to them in many journeys, sith that they departed from the court. Anon as Galahad saw the gentlewoman dead in the bed, he knew her well enough, and told great worship of her, and that she was the best maid living, and it was great pity of her death.

So dwelled Launcelot and Galahad within that ship half a year, and served God daily and nightly with all their power. And often they arrived in isles far from folk, where there repaired none but wild beasts; and there they found many strange adventures and perilous, which they brought to an end. But because the adventures were with wild beasts, and not in the quest of the Sancgreal, therefore the tale maketh here no mention thereof, for it would be too long to tell of all those adventures that befell them.

So after, on a Monday, it befell that they arrived in the edge of a forest, tofore a cross, and then saw they a knight, armed all in white, and was richly horsed, and led in his right hand a white horse. And so he came to the ship, and saluted the two knights on the high Lord's behalf, and said,

Galahad, sir, ye have been long enough with your father, come out of the ship and start upon this horse, and go where the adventures shall lead thee in the quest of the Sancgreal.

Then he went to his father, and kissed him sweetly, and said,

Fair, sweet father, I wot not when I shall see you more, till I see the body of Jesu Christ.

I pray you, said Launcelot, pray ye to the high Father that He hold me in his service.

And so he took his horse; and there they heard a voice that said, Think for to do well, for the one shall never see the other before the dreadful day of doom.

Now, son Galahad, said Launcelot, since we shall depart, and never see other, I pray to the high Father to preserve both me and you both.

Sir, said Galahad, no prayer availeth so much as yours.

And therewith Galahad entered into the forest.

And the wind arose, and drove Launcelot more than a month throughout the sea, where he slept but little, but prayed to God that he might see some tidings of the Sancgreal. So it befell on a night, at midnight he arrived afore a castle, on the back side, which was rich and fair. And there was a postern opened towards the sea, and was open without any keeping, save two lions kept the entry; and the moon shone clear. Anon Sir Launcelot heard a voice that said,

Launcelot, go out of this ship, and enter into the castle, where thou shalt see a great part of thy desire.

Then he ran to his arms, and so armed him, and so he went to the gate, and saw the lions. Then set he hand to his sword, and drew it. Then there came a dwarf suddenly, and smote him on the arm so sore that the sword fell out of his hand. Then heard he a voice say,

Oh man of evil faith and poor belief, wherefore trowest thou more on thy harness than in thy Maker? for He might more avail thee than thine armour, in whose service thou art set.

Then said Launcelot,

Fair Father Jesu Christ, I thank thee of thy great mercy, that thou reprovest me of my misdeed. Now see I well that ye hold me for your servant.

Then took he again his sword, and put it up in his sheath, and made a cross in his forehead, and came to the lions, and they made semblant to do him harm. Notwithstanding he passed by them without hurt, and entered into the castle to the chief fortress, and there were they all at rest. Then Launcelot entered in so armed, for he found no gate nor door but it was open. And at the last he found a chamber whereof the door was shut, and he set his hand thereto to have opened it, but he might not.

Then he enforced him mickle to undo the door. Then he listened, and heard a voice which sang so swetly that it seemed none earthly thing; and him thought the voice said:

Joy and honour be to the Father of Heaven.

Then Launcelot kneeled down tofore the chamber, for well wist he that there was the Sancgreal within that chamber.

THE WORLD ENCOMPASSED BY SIR FRANCIS DRAKE[1]

Richard Hakluyt (1553-1616)

THE 15. day of November, in the yeere of our Lord 1577. M. Francis Drake, with a fleete of five ships and barkes, and to the number of 164 men, gentlemen and sailers, departed from Plimmouth, giving out his pretended voyage for Alexandria: but the wind falling contrary, hee was forced the next morning to put into Falmouth haven in Cornewall, where such and so terrible a tempest tooke us, as few men have seene the like, and was in deed so vehement, that all our ships were like to have gone to wracke: but it pleased God to preserve us from that extremitie, and to afflict us onely for that present with these two particulars: The mast of our Admirall which was the *Pellican,* was cut over boord for the safegard of the ship, and the *Marigold* was driven ashore, and somewhat bruised: for the repairing of which damages wee returned againe to Plimmouth, and having recovered those harmes, and brought the ships againe to good state, we set forth the second time from Plimmouth, and set saile the 13. day of December following.

The 25. day of the same moneth we fell with the Cape Cantin, upon the coast of Barbarie, and coasting along, the 27. day we found an Island called Mogador, lying one mile distant from the maine, betweene which Island and the maine, we

[1] From *The Principal Navigations, Voyages and Discoveries of the English Nation.*

found a very good and safe harbour for our ships to ride in, as also very good entrance, and voyde of any danger.

On this Island our Generall erected a pinnesse, whereof he brought out of England with him foure already framed.

Our pinnesse being finished, wee departed from this place the 30. and last day of December, and coasting along the shore, wee did descrie, not contrary to our expectation, certaine Canters which were Spanish fishermen, to whom we gave chase and tooke three of them, and proceeding further we met with 3. Caravels and tooke them also.

The 17. day of January we arrived at Cape Blanco, where we found a ship riding at anchor, within the Cape, and but two simple Mariners in her, which ship we tooke and caried her further into the harbour, where we remained 4. dayes, and in that space our General mustered, and trayned his men on land in warlike maner, to make them fit for all occasions.

In this place we tooke of the Fishermen such necessaries as wee wanted, and they could yeeld us, and leaving heere one of our litle barkes called the *Benedict,* wee tooke with us one of theirs which they called Canters, being of the burden of 40. tunnes or thereabouts.

All these things being finished, wee departed this harbour the 22. of Januarie, carying along with us one of the Portugall Caravels which was bound to the Islands of Cape Verde for salt, whereof good store is made in one of those Islands.

The master or Pilot of that Caravel did advertise our Generall that upon one of those Islands called Mayo, there was great store of dryed Cabritos, which a few inhabitants there dwelling did yeerly make ready for such of the kings Ships as did there touch, beeing bound for his countrey of Brasile or elsewhere. Wee fell with this Island the 27. of January, but the Inhabitants would in no case traffique with us, being thereof forbidden by the kings Edict: yet the next day our Generall sent to view the Island, and the likelihoodes that might be there of provision of victuals, about threescore and two men under the conduct and government of Master Winter and Master Doughtie, and having travailed to the mountaines the space of three miles, and arriving there somewhat before the day breake, we arrested our selves to see day before us, which appearing, we found the inhabitants to be fled: but the place, by reason that it was manured, wee found to be more fruitfull then the other part, especially the valleys among the hills.

Here we gave our selves a litle refreshing, as by very ripe and sweete grapes, which the fruitfulnesse of the earth at that season of the yeere yeelded us: and that season being with us the depth of Winter, it may seeme strange that those fruites were then there growing.

Being returned to our ships, our Generall departed hence the 31. of this moneth, and sayled by the Island of S. Iago, but farre enough from the danger of the inhabitants, who shot and discharged at us three peeces, but they all fell short of us, and did us no harme.

Being before this Island, we espied two ships under sayle, to the one of which wee gave chase, and in the end boorded her with a ship-boat without resistance, which we found to be a good prize, and she yeelded unto us good store of wine: which prize our Generall committed to the custodie of Master Doughtie, and reteining the Pilot, sent the rest away with his Pinnesse, giving them a Butte of wine and some victuals, and their wearing clothes, and so they departed.

The same night wee came with the Island called by the Portugals, Ilha del Fogo, that is, the burning Island: in the North side whereof is a consuming fire, the matter is sayde to be of Sulphure, but notwithstanding it is like to bee a commodious Island, because the Portugals have built, and doe inhabite there.

Upon the South side thereof lyeth a most pleasant and sweete Island, the trees whereof are alwayes greene and faire to looke upon, in respect whereof they call it Ilha Brava, that is, the brave Island. From the bankes thereof into the sea doe run in many places reasonable streames of fresh waters easie to be come by, but there was no convenient roade for our ships: for such was the depth, that no ground could bee had for anchoring, and it is reported, that ground was never found in that place, so that the tops of Fogo burne not so high in the ayre, but the rootes of Brava are quenched as low in the sea.

Being departed from these Islands, we drew towards the line, where wee were becalmed the space of 3. weekes, but yet subject to divers great stormes, terrible lightnings and much thunder: but with this miserie we had the commoditie of great store of fish, as Dolphins, Bonitos, and flying fishes, whereof some fell into our shippes, wherehence they could not rise againe for want of moisture, for when their wings are drie, they cannot flie.

From the first day of our departure from the Islands of Cape Verde, wee sayled 54. dayes without sight of land, and the first land that we fell with was the coast of Brasil, which we saw the fifth of April in ye height of 33. degrees towards the pole Antarctike, and being discovered at sea by the inhabitants of the countrey, they made upon the coast great fires for a sacrifice (as we learned) to the devils, about which they use conjurations, making heapes of sande and other ceremonies, that when any ship shall goe about to stay upon their coast, not onely sands may be gathered together in shoalds in every place, but also that stormes and tempests may arise, to the casting away of ships and men.

The seventh day in a mightie great storme both of lightning, rayne, and thunder, wee lost the Canter which we called the *Christopher:* but the eleventh day after, by our Generalls great care in dispersing his ships, we found her againe, and the place where we met, our Generall called the Cape of Joy, where every ship tooke in some water. Heere we found a good temperature and sweete ayre, a very faire and pleasant countrey with an exceeding fruitfull soyle, where were great store of large and mightie Deere, but we came not to the sight of any people: but traveiling further into the countrey, we perceived the footing of people in the clay-ground, shewing that they were men of great stature. Being returned to our ships, we wayed anchor, and ranne somewhat further, and harboured our selves betweene a rocke and the maine, where by meanes of the rocke that brake the force of the sea, we rid very safe, and upon this rocke we killed for our provision certaine sea-wolves, commonly called with us Seales,

From hence we went our course to 36. degrees, and entred the great river of Plate, and ranne into 54. and 55. fadomes and a halfe of fresh water, where wee filled our water by the ships side: but the Generall finding here no good harborough, as he thought he should, bare out againe to sea the 27. of April, and in bearing out we lost sight of our Flieboate wherein master Doughtie was, but we sayling along, found a fayre and reasonable good Bay wherein were many, and the same profitable Islands, one whereof had so many Seales, as would at the least have laden all our Shippes, and the rest of the Islands are as it were laden with foules which is wonderfull to see, and they of divers sortes. It is a place very plentifull of victuals, and hath in it no want of fresh water.

The eighteenth day of May our Generall thought it needfull to have a care of such Ships as were absent, and therefore indevouring to seeke the Flieboate wherein master Doughtie was, we espied her againe the next day: and whereas certaine of our ships were sent to discover the coast and to search an harbour, the *Marygold* and the Canter being imployed in that businesse, came unto us and gave us understanding of a safe harbour that they had found, wherewith all our ships bare, and entred it.

Heere our Generall in the Admiral, rid close aboord the Flieboate, and tooke out of her all the provision of victuals and what else was in her, and hailing her to the Lande, set fire to her, and so burnt her to save the iron worke: which being a doing, there came downe of the countrey certaine of the people naked, saving only about their waste the skinne of some beast with the furre or haire on, and every man his bow which was an ell in length, and a couple of arrowes. These people would not of a long time receive any thing at our handes: yet at length our Generall being ashore, and they dauncing after their accustomed manner about him, and hee once turning his backe towards them, one leapt suddenly to him, and tooke his cap with his golde band off his head, and ran a litle distance from him and shared it with his fellow, the cap to the one, and the band to the other.

Having dispatched all our businesse in this place, wee departed and set sayle, and immediately upon our setting foorth we lost our Canter which was absent three or foure dayes: but when our General had her againe, he tooke out the necessaries, and so gave her over neere to the Cape of Good Hope.

The next day after being the twentieth of June, wee harboured our selves againe in a very good harborough, called by Magellan Port S. Julian, where we found a gibbet standing upon the maine; which we supposed to be the place where Magellan did execution upon some of his disobedient and rebellious company.

In this Port our Generall began to enquire diligently of the actions of M. Thomas Doughtie, and found them not to be such as he looked for, but tending rather to contention or mutinie, or some other disorder, whereby (without redresse) the successe of the voyage might greatly have bene hazarded: whereupon the company was called together and made acquainted with the particulars of the cause, which were found partly by master Doughties owne confession, and partly by the evidence of the fact, to be true: which when our Generall saw, although his private affection to M. Doughtie (as hee then in the presence of us all sacredly protested) was great, yet the care he had of the state of the voyage, of the expectation of her Majestie, and of the honour of his countrey did more touch him, (as indeede it ought) then the private respect of one man: so that the cause being throughly heard, and all things done in good order as neere as might be to the course of our lawes in England, it was concluded that M. Doughtie should receive punishment according to the qualitie of the offence: and he seeing no remedie but patience for himselfe, desired before his death to receive the Communion, which he did at the hands of M. Fletcher our Minister, and our Generall himselfe accompanied him in that holy action: which being done, and the place of execution made ready, hee having embraced our Generall and taken his leave of all the companie, with prayer for the Queenes majestie and our realme, in quiet sort laid his head to the blocke, where he ended his life.

The 17. day of August we departed the port of S. Julian, and the 20. day we fell with the streight or freat of Magellan going into the South Sea, at the Cape or headland whereof we found the body of a dead man, whose flesh was cleane consumed.

The 21. day we entred the streight, which we found to have many turnings, and as it were shuttings up, as if there were no passage at all, by meanes whereof we had the wind often against us, so that some of the fleete recovering a Cape or point of land, others should be forced to turne backe againe, and to come to an anchor where they could.

This streight is extreme cold, with frost and snow continually: the trees seeme to stoope with the burden of the weather, and yet are greene continually, and many good and sweete herbes doe very plentifully grow and increase under them. The bredth of the streight is in some place a league, in some other places 2 leagues, and 3 leagues, and in some other 4 leagues, but the narrowest place hath a league over.

The 6. day of September we entred the South sea at the Cape or head shore.

The seventh day we were driven by a great storme from the entring into the South sea two hundred leagues and odde in longitude, and one degree to the Southward of the Streight: in which height, and so many leagues to the Westward, the fifteenth day of September fell out the Eclipse of the Moone at the houre of sixe of the clocke at night: but neither did the Eclipticall conflict of the Moone impayre our state, nor her clearing againe amend us a whit, but the accustomed Eclipse of the Sea continued in his force, wee being darkened more then the Moone seven fold.

From the Bay (which we called The Bay of severing of friends) wee were driven backe to the Southward of the streights in 57. degrees and a terce: in which height we came to an anker among the Islands, having there fresh and very good water, with herbes of singular vertue. Not farre from hence we entred another Bay, where wee found people both men and women in their Canoas, naked, and ranging from one Island to another to seeke their meat, who entered traffique with us for such things as they had.

We returning hence Northward againe, found the 3. of October three Islands, in one of which was such plentie of birdes as is scant credible to report.

The 8. day of October we lost sight of one of our Consorts wherein M. Winter was, who as then we supposed was put by a storme into the streights againe, which at our returne home wee found to be true, and he not perished, as some of our company feared.

Thus being come into the height of the streights againe, we ran, supposing the coast of Chili to lie as the generall Maps have described it, namely Northwest, which we found to lie and trend to the Northeast and Eastwards, whereby it appeareth that this part of Chili hath not bene truely hitherto discovered, or at the least not truely reported for the space of 12. degrees at the least, being set downe either of purpose to deceive, or of ignorant conjecture.

We continuing our course, fell the 29. of November with an Island called la Mocha, where we cast anchor, and our Generall hoysing out our boate, went with ten of our company to shore, where wee found people, whom the cruell and extreme dealings of the Spaniards have forced for their owne safetie and libertie to flee from the maine, and to fortifie themselves in this Island. We being on land, the people came downe to us to the water side with shew of great courtesie, bringing to us potatoes, rootes, and two very fat sheepe, which our Generall received and gave them other things for them, and had promise to have water there: but the next day repayring againe to the shore, and sending two men aland with barrels to fill water, the people taking them for Spaniards (to whom they use to shew no favour if they take them) layde violent hands on them, and as we thinke, slew them.

Our Generall seeing this, stayed here no longer, but wayed anchor, and set sayle towards the coast of Chili, and drawing towards it, we mette neere to the shore an Indian in a Canoa, who thinking us to have bene Spaniards, came to us and tolde us, that at a place called S. Iago, there was a great Spanish ship laden from the kingdome of Peru: for which good newes our Generall gave him divers trifles, wherof he was glad, and went along with us and brought us to the place, which is called the port of Valparizo.

When we came thither, we found indeede the ship riding at anker, having in her eight Spaniards and three Negroes, who thinking us to have bene Spaniards and their friends, welcommed us with a drumme, and made ready a Bottija of wine of Chili to drinke to us: but as soone as we were entred, one of our company called Thomas Moone began to lay about him, and strooke one of the Spanyards, and sayd unto him, Abaxo Perro, that is in English, Goe downe dogge. One of these Spaniards seeing persons of that quality in those seas, all to crossed, and blessed himselfe: but to be short, wee stowed them under hatches all save one Spaniard, who suddenly and desperately leapt over boord into the sea, and swamme ashore to the towne of S. Iago, to give them warning of our arrivall.

They of the towne being not above 9. housholds, presently fled away and abandoned the towne. Our generall manned his boate, and the Spanish ships boate, and went to the Towne, and being come to it, we rifled it, and so being come aboord, we departed the Haven, having first set all the Spaniards on land, saving one John Griego a Greeke borne, whom our Generall caried with him for his Pilot to bring him into the haven of Lima.

When we were at sea, our Generall rifled the ship, and found in her good store of the wine of Chili, and 25000. pezoes of very pure and fine gold of Baldivia, amounting in value to 37000 ducats of Spanish money, and above. So going on our course, wee arrived next at a place called Coquimbo, where our Generall sent 14. of his men on land to fetch water: but they were espied by the Spaniards, who came with 300. horsemen and 200. footemen, and slewe one of our men with a piece, the rest came aboord in safetie, and the Spaniards departed: wee went on shore againe, and buried our man, and the Spaniards came down againe with a flag of truce, but we set sayle and would not trust them.

From hence we went to a certaine port called Tarapaza, where being landed, we found by the Sea side a Spaniard lying asleepe, who had lying by him 13 barres of silver, which weighed 4000. ducats Spanish; we tooke the silver, and left the man.

Not farre from hence going on land for fresh water, we met with a Spaniard and an Indian boy driving 8. Llamas or sheepe of Peru which are as big as asses; every of which sheepe had on his backe 2. bags of leather, each bagge conteining 50. li. weight of fine silver: so that bringing both the sheepe and their burthen to the ships, we found in all the bags 800. weight of silver.

Here hence we sailed to a place called Arica, and being entred the port, we found there three small barkes which we rifled, and found in one of them 57 wedges of silver, each of them weighing about 20 pound weight, and every of these wedges were of the fashion and bignesse of a brickbat. In all these 3. barkes we found not one person: for they mistrusting no strangers, were all gone aland to the Towne, which consisteth of about twentie houses, which we would have ransacked if our company had bene better and more in number. But our Generall contented with the spoyle of the ships, left the Towne and put off againe to sea and set sayle for Lima, and by the way met with a small barke, which he boorded, and found in her good store of linnen cloth, whereof taking some quantitie, he let her goe.

To Lima we came the 13. day of February, and being entred the haven, we found there about twelve sayle of ships lying fast moored at an anker, having all their sayles caried on shore; for the masters and marchants were here most secure, having never bene assaulted by enemies, and at this time feared the approch of none such as we were. Our generall rifled these ships, and found in one of them a chest full of royals of plate, and good store of silkes and linnen cloth, and tooke the chest into his owne ship, and good store of the silkes and linnen. In which ship hee had newes of another ship called the *Cacafuego* which was gone towards Paita, and that the same shippe was laden with treasure: whereupon we staied no longer here, but cutting all the cables of the shippes in the haven, we let them drive whither they would, either to sea or to the shore, and with all speede we followed the *Cacafuego* toward Paita, thinking there to have found her: but before wee arrived there, she was gone from thence towards Panama, whom our Generall still pursued, and by the way met with a barke laden with ropes and tackle for ships, which he boorded and searched, and found in her 80 li. weight of golde, and a crucifixe of gold with goodly great Emerauds set in it which he tooke, and some of the cordage also for his owne ship.

From hence we departed, still following the *Cacafuego,* and our Generall promised our company, that whosoever could first descrie her, should have his chaine of gold for his good news. It fortuned that John Drake going up into the top, descried her about three of the clocke, and about sixe of the clocke we came to her and boorded her, and shotte at her three peeces of ordinance, and strake down her Misen, and being entered, we found in her great riches, as jewels and precious stones, thirteene chests full of royals of plate, foure score pound weight of golde, and sixe and twentie tunne of silver. The place where we tooke this prize, was called Cape de San Francisco, about 150. leagues from Panama.

The Pilots name of this Shippe was Francisco, and amongst other plate that our Generall found in this ship, he found two very faire guilt bowles of silver, which were the Pilots: to whom our Generall sayd: Senior Pilot, you have here two silver cups, but I must needes have one of them: which the Pilot because hee could not otherwise chuse, yeelded unto, and gave the other to the steward of our Generals ships.

When this Pilot departed from us, his boy sayde thus unto our Generall: Captaine, our ship shall be called no more the *Cacafuego,* but the *Cacaplata,* and your shippe shall bee called the *Cacafuego:* which pretie speach of the Pilots boy ministred matter of laughter to us, both then and long after.

When our Generall had done what hee would with this *Cacafuego,* hee cast her off, and wee went on our course still towards the West, and not long after met with a ship laden with linnen cloth and fine China-dishes of white earth, and great store of China-silks, of all which things wee tooke as we listed.

The owner himselfe of this ship was in her, who was a Spanish Gentleman, from whom our Generall tooke a Fawlcon of golde, with a great Emeraud in the breast thereof, and the Pilot of the ship he tooke also with him, and so cast the ship off.

This Pilot brought us to the haven of Guatulco, the towne whereof, as he told us, had but 17. Spaniards in it. As soone as we were entred this haven, wee landed, and went presently to the Towne, and to the Townehouse, where we found a Judge sitting in judgement, being associate with three other officers, upon three Negros that had conspired the burning of the Towne: both which Judges and prisoners we tooke, and brought them a shipboord, and caused the chief Judge to write his letter to the Towne, to command all the Townesmen to avoid, that we might safely water there. Which being done, and they departed, we ransacked the Towne, and in one house we found a pot of the quantitie of a bushell, full of reals of plate, which we brought to our ship.

And here one Thomas Moone one of our company, tooke a Spanish Gentleman as hee was flying out of the towne, and searching him, he found a chaine of golde about him, and other jewels, which he tooke, and so let him goe.

At this place our Generall among other Spaniards, set ashore his Portugal Pilote, which hee tooke at the Islands of Cape Verde, out of a ship of S. Mary port of Portugall: and having set them ashore, we departed hence, and sailed to the Island of Canno, where our Generall landed, and brought to shore his owne ship, and discharged her, mended, and graved her, and furnished our ship with water and wood sufficiently.

And while wee were here, we espied a shippe, and set saile after her, and tooke her, and found in her two Pilots, and a Spanish Governour, going for the Islands of the Philippinas: wee searched the shippe, and took some of her marchandizes, and so let her goe. Our Generall at this place and time, thinking himself both in respect of his private injuries received from the Spaniards, as also of their contempts and indignities offered to our countrey and Prince in generall, sufficiently satisfied, and revenged: and supposing that her Majestie at his returne would rest contented with this service, purposed to continue no longer upon the Spanish coasts, but began to consider and to consult of the best way for his Countrey.

He thought it not good to returne by the Streights, for two speciall causes: the one, lest the Spaniards should there waite, and attend for him in great number and strength, whose hands, hee being left but one ship, could not possibly escape. The other cause was the dangerous situation of the mouth of the streights in the South sea, where continuall stormes reigning and blustering, as he found by experience, besides the shoalds and sands upon the coast, he thought it not a good course to adventure that way: he resolved therefore to avoyde these hazards, to goe forward to the Islandes of the Malucos, and therehence to saile the course of the Portugals by the Cape of Buena Esperanza.

Upon this resolution, hee beganne to thinke of his best way to the Malucos, and finding himselfe where he now was becalmed, he saw that of necessitie hee must be forced to take a Spanish course, namely to sayle somewhat Northerly to get a winde. Wee therefore set saile, and sayled 600. leagues at the least for a winde, and thus much we sailed from the 16. of April, till the 3. of June.

The 5. day of June, being in 43. degrees towards the pole Arcticke, we found the ayre so colde, that our men being grievously pinched with the same, complained of the extremitie thereof, and the further we went, the more the colde increased upon us. Whereupon we thought it best for that time to seeke the land, and did so, finding it not mountainous, but low plaine land, till wee came within 38. degrees towards the line. In which height it pleased God to send us into a faire and good Baye, with a good winde to enter the same.

In this Baye wee anchored, and the people of the Countrey having their houses close by the waters side, shewed themselves unto us, and sent a present to our Generall.

When they came unto us, they greatly wondred at the things that wee brought, but our Generall (according to his naturall and accustomed humanitie) courteously intreated them, and liberally bestowed on them necessary things to cover their nakednesse, whereupon they supposed us to be gods, and would not be perswaded to the contrary: the presents which they sent to our Generall were feathers, and calles of net-worke.

Our Generall called this Countrey Nova Albion, and that for two causes: the one in respect of the white bankes and cliffes, which lie towards the sea: and the other, because it might have some affinitie with our Countrey in name, which sometime was so called.

At our departure hence our Generall set up a monument of our being there, as also of her Majesties right and title to the same, namely a plate, nailed upon a faire great poste, whereupon was ingraven her Majesties name, the day and yeere of our arrivall there, with the free giving up of the province and people into her Majesties hands, together with her hignesse picture and armes, in a peece of sixe pence of current English money under the plate, whereunder was also written the name of our Generall.

It seemeth that the Spaniards hitherto had never bene in this part of the Countrey, neither did ever discover the land by many degrees, to the Southwards of this place.

After we had set saile from hence, wee continued without sight of land till the 13. day of October following, which day in the morning wee fell with certaine Islands 8. degrees to the Northward of the line, from which Islands came a great number of Canoas, having in some of them 4. in some 6. and in some also 14. men, bringing with them cocos, and other fruites. Their Canoas were hollow within, and cut with great arte and cunning, being very smooth within and without, and bearing a glasse as it were a horne daintily burnished, having a prowe, and a sterne of one sort, yeelding inward circle-wise, being of a great height, and full of certaine white shels for a braverie, and on each side of them lie out two peeces of timber about a yard and a halfe long, more or lesse, according to the smalnesse, or bignesse of the boate.

Leaving this Island the night after we fell with it, the 18. of October, we lighted upon divers others, some whereof made a great shew of Inhabitants.

Wee continued our course by the Islands of Tagulada, Zelon, and Zewarra, being friends to the Portugals, the first whereof hath growing in it great store of Cinnamom.

The 14. of November we fell with the Islands of Maluco, which day at night (having directed our course to runne with Tydore) in coasting along the Island of Mutyr, belonging to the King of Ternate, his Deputie or Vice-king seeing us at sea, came with his Canoa to us without all feare, and came aboord, and after some conference with our Generall, willed him in any wise to runne in with Ternate, and not with Tydore, assuring him that the King would bee glad of his comming, and would be ready to doe what he would require, for which purpose he himselfe would that night be with the King, and tell him the newes, with whom if he once dealt, hee should finde that as he was a King, so his word should stand: adding further, that if he went to Tydore before he came to Ternate, the King would have nothing to doe with us, because hee held the Portugall as his enemie: whereupon our General resolved to runne with Ternate, where the next morning early we came to anchor, at which time our Generall sent a messenger to the king with a velvet cloke for a present, and token of his comming to be in peace, and that he required nothing but traffique and exchange of marchandize, whereof he had good store, in such things as he wanted.

In the meane time the Vice-king had bene with the king according to his promise, signifying unto him what good things he might receive from us by traffique: whereby the King was mooved with great liking towards us, and sent to our Generall with speciall message, that hee should have what things he needed, and would requite with peace and friendship, and moreover that hee would yeeld himselfe, and the right of his Island to bee at the pleasure and commandement of so famous a Prince as we served. In token whereof he sent to our Generall a signet, and within short time after came in his owne person, with boates, and Canoas to our ship, to bring her into a better and safer roade then she was in at present.

After that we had heere by the favour of the king received all necessary things that the place could yeeld us: our General considering the great distance, and how farre he was yet off from his Countrey, thought it not best here to linger the time any longer, but waying his anchors, set out of the Island, and sayled to a certaine litle Island to the Southwards of Celebes, where we graved our ship, and continued there in that and other businesses 26. dayes. This Island is throughly growen with wood of a large and high growth, very straight and without boughes, save onely in the head or top, whose leaves are not much differing from our broome in England. Amongst these trees night by night, through the whole land, did shew themselves an infinite swarme of fiery wormes flying in the ayre, whose bodies beeing no bigger then our common English flies, make such a shew and light, as if every twigge or tree had bene a burning candle.

When wee had ended our businesse here, we waied, and set saile to runne for the Malucos: but having at that time a bad winde, and being amongst the Islands, with much difficultie wee recovered to the Northward of the Island of Celebes, where by reason of contrary winds not able to continue our course to runne Westwards, we were inforced to alter the same to the Southward againe, finding that course also to be very hard and dangerous for us, by reason of infinite shoalds which lie off and among the Islands: whereof wee had too much triall to the hazard and danger of our shippe and lives. For of all other dayes upon the 9. of Januarie, in the yeere 1579, wee ranne suddenly upon a rocke, where we stucke fast from 8. of the clocke at night til 4. of the clocke in the afternoone the next day, being indeede out of all hope to escape the danger: but our Generall as hee had alwayes hitherto shewed himself couragious, and of a good confidence in the mercie and protection of God: so now he continued in the same, and lest he should seeme to perish wilfully, both he, and we did our best indevour to save our selves, which it pleased God so to blesse, that in the ende we cleared our selves most happily of the danger.

We lighted our ship upon the rockes of 3. tunne of cloves, 8. peeces of ordinance, and certaine meale and beanes; and then the winde (as it were in a moment by the speciall grace of God) changing from the starreboord to the larboord of the ship, we hoised our sailes, and the happy gale drove our ship off the rocke into the sea againe, to the no litle comfort of all our hearts, for which we gave God such prayse and thanks, as so great a benefite required.

The 8. of Februarie following, wee fell with the fruitfull Island of Barateve, having in the meane time suffered many dangers by windes and shoalds. The people of this Island are comely in body and stature, and of a civill behaviour, just in dealing, and courteous to strangers, whereof we had the experience sundry wayes, they being most glad of our presence, and very ready to releeve our wants in those things which their Countrey did yeelde.

At our departure from Barateve, we set our course for Java Major, where arriving, we found great courtesie, and honourable entertainment. This Island is governed by 5. Kings, whom they call Rajah: as Rajah Donaw, and Rajah Mang Bange, and Rajah Cabuccapollo, which live as having one spirite and one minde.

Of these five we had foure a shipboord at once, and two or three often. They are wonderfully delighted in coloured clothes, as red and greene: their upper parts of their bodies are naked, save their heads, whereupon they weare a Turkish roll as do the Maluccians: from the middle downward they weare a pintado of silke, trailing upon the ground, in colour as they best like. Not long before our departure, they tolde us, that not farre off there were such great Ships as ours, wishing us to beware: upon this our Captaine would stay no longer.

From Java Major we sailed for the cape of Good Hope, which was the first land we fell withall: neither did we touch with it, or any other land, untill we came to Sierra Leona, upon the coast of Guinea; notwithstanding we ranne hard aboord the Cape, finding the report of the Portugals to be most false, who affirme, that it is the most dangerous Cape of the world, never without intolerable stormes and present danger to travailers, which come neere the same.

This Cape is a most stately thing, and the fairest Cape we saw in the whole circumference of the earth, and we passed by it the 18. of June.

From thence we continued our course to Sierra Leona, on the coast of Guinea, where we arrived the 22. of July, and found necessarie provisions, great store of Elephants, Oisters upon trees of one kind, spawning and increasing infinitely, the Oister suffering no budde to grow. We departed thence the 24. day.

We arrived in England the third of November 1580, being the third yeere of our departure.

THE LAST FIGHT OF THE *REVENGE*

A REPORT OF THE TRUTH OF THE FIGHT ABOUT THE AÇORES THIS LAST SUMMER BETWIXT THE "REVENGE," ONE OF HER MAIESTIES SHIPPES, AND AN ARMADA OF THE KING OF SPAINE[1]

Sir Walter Raleigh
(1552(?)-1618)

BECAUSE the rumours are diversely spred, as well in Englande as in the lowe countries and els where, of this late encounter between her maiesties ships and the Armada of Spain; and that the Spaniardes according to their usuall maner, fill the world with their vaine glorious vaunts, making great apparance of victories: when on the contrary, themselves are most commonly and shamefully beaten and dishonoured; thereby hoping to possesse the ignorant multitude by anticipating and forerunning false reports: It is agreeable with all good reason, for manifestation of the truth to overcome falsehood and untruth; that the beginning, continuance and successe of this late honourable encounter of Syr Richard Grinvile, and other her maiesties Captaines, with the Armada of Spaine; should be truely set downe and published without parcialltie or false imaginations.

The L. Thomas Howard, with sixe of her Majesties ships, sixe victualers of London, the barke *Ralegh,* and two or three Pinasses riding at anchor nere unto Flores, one of the Westerlie Islands of the Azores, the last of August in the after noone, had intelligence by one Captaine Midleton, of the approch of the Spanish Armada. Which Midleton being in a verie good Sailer, had kept them companie three daies before, of good purpose, both to discover their forces the more, as also to give advice to my L. Thomas of their approach. He had no sooner delivered the newes but the Fleet was in sight: manie of our shippes companies were on shore in the Iland; some providing balast for their ships; others filling of water and refreshing themselves from the land with such thinges as they coulde either for money, or by force recover. By reason whereof our ships being all pestered and romaging everie thing out of order, verie light for want of balast. And that which was most to our disadvantage, the one halfe part of the men of everie shippe sicke, and utterly unserviceable. For in the *Revenge* there were nintie diseased: in the *Bonaventure,* not so many in health as could handle her maine saile. For had not twentie men been taken out of a Barke of Sir George Caryes, his being commanded to be sunke, and those appointed to her, she had hardly ever recovered England. The rest for the most part were in little better state.

The names of her Majesties shippes were these as followeth: the *Defiaunce,*

---

[1] From *The Last Fight of the "Revenge"* (Arber Reprints).

which was Admirall, the *Revenge* Viceadmirall, the *Bonaventure* commanded by Captaine Crosse, the *Lion* by George Fenner, the *Foresight* by M. Thomas Vavisour, and the *Crane* by Duffield. The *Foresight* and the *Crane* being but small ships; onely the other were of the middle size; the rest, besides the Barke *Ralegh.* commanded by Captaine Thin, were victualers, and of small force or none.

The Spanish fleete having shrouded their approach by reason of the Iland; were now so soone at hand, as our ships had scarce time to waye their anchors, but some of them were driven to let slippe their Cables and set sayle. Sir Richard Grinvile was the last waied, to recover the men that were upon the Iland, which otherwise had been lost. The L. Thomas with the rest verie hardly recovered the winde, which Sir Richard Grinvile not being able to do, was perswaded by the maister and others to cut his maine saile, and cast about, and to trust to the sailing of his shippe: for the squadron of Sivill were on his wether bow. But Sir Richard utterly refused to turne from the enemie, alledging that he would rather chose to dye, then to dishonour him selfe, his countrie, and her Maiesties shippe, perswading his companie that he would passe through the two Squadrons, in despight of them and enforce those of Sivill to give him way. Which he performed upon diverse of the formost, who as the Marriners terme it, sprang their luffe, and fell under the lee of the *Revenge.* But the other course had beene the better, and might right well have beene answered in so great an impossibilitie of prevailing. Notwithstanding out of the greatnesse of his minde, he could not bee perswaded,

In the meane while as hee attended those which were nearest him, the great *San Philip* being in the winde of him, and comming towards him, becalmed his sailes in such sort, as the shippe could neither way nor feele the helme: so huge and high carged was the Spanish ship, being of a thousand and five hundreth tuns. Who after laid the *Revenge* aboord. When he was thus bereft of his sailes, the ships that wer under his lee luffing up, also laid him aboorde: of which the next was the Admirall of the Biscaines, a verie mightie and puysant shippe commanded by Brittan Dona. The said *Philip* carried three tire of ordinance on a side, and eleven peeces in everie tire. She shot eight forth right out of her chase, besides those of her Sterne portes.

After the *Revenge* was intangled with this *Philip,* foure other boorded her; two on her larboord, and two on her starboord. The fight thus beginning at three of the clocke in the after noone, continued verie terrible all that evening. But the great *San Philip* having receyved the lower tire of the *Revenge,* discharged with crossebarshot, shifted hir selfe with all diligence from her sides, utterly misliking hir first entertainment. Some say that the shippe foundred, but wee cannot report it for truth, unlesse we were assured. The Spanish ships were filled with companies of souldiers, in some two hundred besides the Marriners; in some five, in others eight hundreth. In ours there were none at all, beside the Marriners, but the servants of the commanders and some fewe voluntarie Gentlemen only. After many enterchanged voleies of great ordinance and small shot, the Spaniards deliberated to enter the *Revenge,* and made divers attempts, hoping to force her by the multitudes of their armed souldiers and Musketiers, but were still repulse againe and againe, and at all times beaten backe, into their owne shippes, or into the seas.

In the beginning of the fight, the *George Noble* of London, having received some shot thorow her by the Armados, fell under the Lee of the *Revenge,* and asked Syr Richard what he would command him, being but one of the victulers and of small force: Syr Richard bid him save himselfe, and leave him to his fortune. After the fight had thus without intermission, continued while the day lasted and some houres of the night, many of our men were slaine and hurt, and one of the great Gallions of the Armada, and the Admirall of the Hulkes both sunke, and in many other of the Spanish ships great slaughter was made. Some write that sir Richard was verie dangerously hurt almost in the beginning of the fight, and laie speechlesse for a time ere he recovered. But two of the *Revenges* owne companie, brought home in a ship of Lime from the Ilandes, examined by some of the Lordes, and others: affirmed that he was never so wounded as that hee forsooke the upper decke, til an houre before midnight; and then being shot into the bodie with a Musket as hee was a dressing, was againe shot into the head, and withall his Chirugion wounded to death. This agreeth also with an examination taken by Syr Francis Godolphin, of 4 other Marriners of the same shippe being returned, which examination the said Syr Francis sent unto maister William Killigrue of her Maiesties privie Chamber.

But to return to the fight, the Spanish ships which attempted to board the *Revenge,* as they were wounded and beaten of, so alwaies others came in their places, she having never lesse then two mightie Gallions by her sides, and aboard her. So that ere the morning from three of the clocke the day before, there had fifteene severall Armados assailed her; and all so ill approved their entertainment, as they were by the break of day, far more willing to harken to a composition, then hastily to make any more assaults or entries. But as the day encreased, so our men decreased: and as the light grew more and more, by so much more grew our discomforts. For none appeared in sight but enemies, saving one small ship called the *Pilgrim,* commanded by Jacob Whiddon, who hovered all night to see the successe: but in the mornyng bearing with the *Revenge,* was hunted like a hare amongst many ravenous houndes but escaped.

All the powder of the *Revenge* to the last barrell was now spent, all her pikes broken, fortie of her best men slaine, and the most part of the rest hurt. In the beginning of the fight she had but one hundreth free from sicknes, and fourescore and ten sicke, laid in hold upon the Ballast. A small troupe to man such a ship, and a weake Garrison to resist so mighty an Army. By those hundred all was sustained, the voleis, bourdings, and entrings of fifteene shippes of warre, besides those which beat her at large. On the contrarie, the Spanish were alwaies supplied with souldiers brought from everie squadron: all maner of Armes and pouder at will. Unto ours there remained no comfort at all, no hope, no supply either of ships, men, or weapons; the mastes all beaten over board, all her tackle cut a sunder, her upper worke altogither rased, and in effect evened shee was with the water, but the very foundation or bottom of a ship, nothing being left over head either for flight or defence.

Syr Richard finding himselfe in this distresse, and unable anie longer to make resistance, having endured in this fifteene houres fight the assault of fifteene severall Armadoes, all by tornes aboorde him, and by estimation eight hundred shot of great artillerie, besides manie assaults and entries. And that himselfe and the shippe must needes be possessed by the enemie, who were now all cast in a ring round about him; The *Revenge* not able to move one way or other, but as she was moved with the waves and billow of the sea: commanded the maister Gunner, whom he knew to be a most resolute man, to split and sinke the shippe; that thereby nothing might remaine of glorie or victorie to the Spaniards: seeing in so many houres fight, and with so great a Navie they were not able to take her, having had fifteene houres time, fifteene thousand men, and fiftie and three saile of men of warre to performe it withall. And perswaded the companie, or as manie as he could induce, to yeelde themselves unto God, and to the mercie of none els; but as they had like valiant resolute men, repulsed so manie enimies, they should not now shorten the honour of their nation by prolonging their owne lives for a few houres, or a few daies.

The maister Gunner readilie condescended and divers others; but the Captaine and the Maister were of an other opinion, and besought Sir Richard to have care of them: alleaging that the Spaniard would be as readie to entertaine a composition as they were willing to offer the same: and that there being diverse sufficient and valiant men yet living, and whose woundes were not mortall, they might doe their countrie and prince acceptable service hereafter. And (that where Sir Richard had alleaged that the Spaniards should never glorie to have taken one shippe of her Maiesties, seeing that they had so long and so notably defended them selves) they answered, that the shippe had sixe foote water in hold, three shot under water which were so weakly stopped, as with the first working of the sea, she must needes sinke, and was besides so crusht and brused, as she could never be removed out of the place.

And as the matter was thus in dispute, and Sir Richard refusing to hearken to any of those reasons: the maister of the *Revenge* (while the Captaine wan unto him the greater part) was convoyde aborde the Generall Don Alfonso Bassan. Who finding none over hastie to enter the *Revenge* againe, doubting least Sir Richard would have blowne them up and himselfe, and perceiving by the report of the maister of the *Revenge* his daungerous disposition: yeelded that all their lives should be saved, the companie sent for England, and the better sorte to pay such reasonable ransome as their estate would beare, and in the meane season to be free from Gally or imprisonment. To this he so much the rather condescended as well as I have saide, for feare of further losse and mischiefe to them selves, as also for the desire hee had to recover Sir Richard Grinvile; whom for his notable valure he seemed greatly to honour and admire.

When this answer was returned, and that safetie of life was promised, the common sort being now at the end of their perill, the most drew backe from Sir Richard and the maister Gunner, being no hard matter to diswade men from death to life. The maister Gunner finding him selfe and Sir Richard thus prevented and maistered by the greater number, would have slain him selfe with a sword, had he not beene by force withheld and locked into his Cabben. Then the Generall sent manie boates abord the *Revenge,* and diverse of our men fearing Sir Richards disposition, stole away aboord the Generall and other shippes. Sir Richard thus overmatched, was sent unto by Alonso Bassan to remove out of the *Revenge,* the shippe being marvellous unsaverie, filled with bloud and bodies of deade, and wounded men like a slaughter house. Sir Richard answered that he might do with his bodie what he list, for he esteemed it not, and as he was carried out of the shippe he swounded, and reviving againe desired the companie to pray for him. The Generall used Sir Richard with all humanitie, and left nothing unattempted that tended to his recoverie, highly commendinghis valour and worthines, and greatly bewailed the daunger wherein he was, beeing unto them a rare spectacle, and a resolution sildome approved, to see one ship turne toward so many enemies, to endure the charge and boording of so many huge Armados, and to resist and repell the assaults and entries of so many souldiers. All which and more, is confirmed by a Spanish Captaine of the same Armada, and a present actor in the fight, who being severed from the rest in a storm, was by the *Lyon* of London a small ship taken, and is now prisoner in London.

The generall commander of the Armada, was Don Alphonso Bassan, brother to the Marquesse of Santa Cruce. The Admirall of the Biscaine squadron, was Britan Dona. Of the squadron of Sivill, Marques of *Arumburch.* The Hulkes and Flybotes were commanded by Luis Cutino. There were slaine and drowned in this fight, well neere two thousand of the enemies, and two especiall commanders Don Luis de Sant John and Don George de Prunaria de Mallaga, as the Spanish Captaine confesseth, besides divers others of speciall account, whereof as yet report is not made.

The Admirall of the Hulkes and the Ascention of Sivill, were both suncke by the side of the *Revenge;* one other recovered the rode of Saint Michels, and suncke also there; a fourth ranne herselfe with the shore to save her men.

Sir Richard died as it is said, the second or third day aboard the Generall, and was by them greatly bewailed. What became of his bodie, whether it were buried in the sea or on the lande wee know not: the comfort that remaineth to his friendes is, that he hath ended his life honourably in respect of the reputation wonne to his nation and country, and of the same to his posteritie, and that being dead, he hath not outlived his owne honour.

A fewe daies after the fight was ended, and the English prisoners dispersed into the Spanish and Indy ships, there arose so great a storme from the West and Northwest, that all the fleet was dispersed, as well the Indian fleet which were then come unto them as the rest of the Armada that attended their arrivall, of which 14 saile togither with the *Revenge,* and her 200 Spaniards, were cast away upon the Isle of S. Michaels. So it pleased them to honor the buriall of that renowned ship the *Revenge,* not suffring her to perish alone for the great honour she achieved in her life time.

THE LAST VOYAGE OF HENRY HUDSON[1]

Abacuk Pricket

WE BEGAN our Voyage for the North-west passage; the seventeenth of April, 1610. Thwart of Shepey, our Master sent Master Colbert backe to the Owners with his Letter. The next day we weighed from hence, and stood for Harwich, and came thither the eight and twentieth of Aprill. From Harwich we set sayle the first of May, along the Coast to the North, till we came to the Iles of Orkney, from thence to the Iles of Faro, and from thence to Island: on which we fell in a fogge, hearing the Rut of the Sea, ashoare, but saw not the Land whereupon our Master came to an Anchor. Heere we were embayed in the Southeast part of the Land. Wee weighed and stood along the Coast, on the West side towards the North: but one day being calme, we fell a fishing, and caught good store of fish, as Cod and Ling, and Butte, with some other sorts that we knew not. The next day, we had a good gale of wind at South-west, and raysed the Iles of Westmonie, where the King of Denmarke hath a Fortresse, by which we passed to rayse the Snow Hill foot, a Mountayne so called on the North-west part of the Land. But in our course we saw that famous Hill, Mount Hecla, which cast out much fire, a signe of foule weather to come in short time. Wee leave Island a sterne of us, and

[1] From *Purchas His Pilgrimes.*

met a Mayne of Ice, which did hang on the North part of Island, and stretched downe to the West, which when our Master saw, he stood backe for Island to find an Harbour, which we did on the North-west part, called Derefer,[1] where wee killed good store of Fowle. From hence wee put to Sea againe, but (neither wind nor weather serving) our Master stood backe for this Harbour againe, but could not reach it, but fell with another to the South of that, called by our Englishmen, Louise Bay: where on the shoare we found an hot Bath, and heere all our Englishmen bathed themselves: the water was so hot that it would scald a Fowle.

From hence the first of June we put to Sea for Groneland, but to the West wee saw Land as we thought, for which we beare the best part of a day, but it proved but a foggie bank. So wee gave it over, and made for Gronland, which we raysed the fourth of June. Upon the Coast thereof hung good store of Ice, so that our Master could not attayne to the shoare by any meanes. The Land in this part is very Mountaynous, and full of round Hils, like to Sugar-loaves, covered with snow. We turned the Land on the South side, as neere as the Ice would suffer us. Our course for the most part was betweene the West and North-west, till we raysed the Desolations, which is a great Iland in the West part of Groneland. On this Coast we saw store of Whales, and at one time three of them came close by us, so as wee could hardly shunne them: then two passing very neere, and the third going under our ship, wee received no harme by them, praysed bee God.

From the Desolations our Master made his way North-west, the wind being against him, who else would have gone more to the North: but in this course we saw the first great Iland or Mountayne of Ice, whereof after we saw store. About the latter end of June, we raysed Land to the North of us, which our Master tooke to bee that Iland which Master Davis setteth downe in his Chart. On the West side of his Streight, our Master would have gone to the North of it, but the wind would not suffer him: so we fell to the South of it, into a great Rippling or over-fall of current, the which setteth to the West. Into the current we went, and made our way to the North of the West, till we met with Ice which hung on this Iland. Wherefore our Master casting about, cleered himselfe of this Ice, and stood to the South, and then to the West, through store of floting Ice, and upon the Ice store of Scales. We gained a cleere Sea, and continued our course till wee meete Ice; first, with great Ilands, and then with store of the smaller sort. Betweene them we made our course Northwest, till we met with Ice againe. But, in this our going betweene the Ice, we saw one of the great Ilands of Ice overturne which was a good warning to us, not to come nigh them, nor within their reach. Into the Ice wee put ahead, as betweene two Lands. The next day we had a storme, and the wind brought the Ice so fast upon us, that in the end we were driven to put her into the chiefest of the

[1] Or Diraford.

Ice, and there to let her lie. Some of our men this day fell sicke, I will not say it was for feare, although I saw small signe of other griefe.

The storme ceasing, we stood out of the Ice, where wee saw any cleere Sea to goe to: which was sometime more, and sometime lesse. Our course was as the Ice did lye, sometime to the North, then to the North-west, and then to the West, and to the South-west: but still inclosed with Ice. Which when our Master saw, he made his course to the South, thinking to cleere himselfe of the Ice that way: but the more he strove, the worse he was, and the more inclosed, till we could goe no further. Here our Master was in despaire, and (as he told me after) he thought he should never have got out of this Ice, but there have perished. Therefore hee brought forth his Card, and shewed all the company, that hee was entred above an hundred leagues further than ever any English was: and left it to their choice, whether they would proceed any further; yea, or nay. Whereupon, some were of one minde, and some of another, some wishing themselves at home, and some not caring where, so they were out of the Ice: but there were some who then spake words, which were remembred a great while after.

There was one who told the Master, that if he had an hundred pounds, hee would give fourescore and ten to be at home: but the Carpenter made answere, that if hee had an hundred, hee would not give ten upon any such condition, but would thinke it to be as good money as ever he had any, and to bring it as well home, by the leave of God. After many words to no purpose, to worke we must on all hands, to get our selves out, and to cleere our ship. After much labour and time spent, we gained roome to turne our ship in, and so by little and little, to get cleere in the Sea a league or two off, our course being North and North-west.

In the end, we raysed Land to the South-west, high Land and covered with Snow. Our Master named this Land, Desire provokes. Lying here, wee heard the noyse of a great over-fall of a tyde, that came out of the Land: for now we might see well, that wee had beene embayed before, and time had made us know, being so well acquainted with the Ice, that when night, or foggie, or foule weather tooke us, we would seeke out the broadest Iland of Ice, and there come to anchor and runne, and sport, and fill water that stood on the Ice in Ponds, both sweete and good. But after we had brought this Land to beare South of us, we had the tyde and the current to open the Ice, as being carried first one way, and then another: but in Bayes they lye as in a pond without moving. In this Bay where wee were thus troubled with Ice, wee saw many of those Mountaynes of Ice aground, in sixe or sevenscore fathome water. In this our course we saw a Beare upon a piece of Ice by it selfe, to the which our men gave chase with their Boat: but before they came nigh her, the tyde had carried the Ice and the Beare on it, and joyned it with the other Ice: so they lost their labour, and came aboord againe.

We continued our course to the North-west, and raysed Land to the North of our course, toward which we made, and comming nigh it, there hung on the Eastermost point, many Ilands of floting Ice, and a Beare on one of them, which from one to another came towards us, till she was readie to come aboord. But when she saw us looke at her, she cast her head betweene her hinder legges, and then dived under the Ice: and so from one piece to another, till she was out of our reach. We stood along by the Land on the Southside ahead of us, wee met with Ice that hung on a point of Land that lay to the South, more than this that we came up by: which when our Master saw, he stood in for the shoare. At the West end of this Iland (for so it is) we found an Harbour, and came in (at a full Sea) over a Rocke, which had two fathome and an halfe on it, and was so much bare at a low water. But by the great mercie of God, we came to an Anchor cleere of it: and close by it, our Master named them, the Iles of Gods Mercie.

From hence we stood to the South-west, to double the Land to the West of us, through much floting Ice: In the end wee found a cleere Sea, and continued therein, till wee raysed Land to the Northwest. Then our Master made his course more to the South then before: but it was not long ere we met with Ice which lay ahead of us. Our Master would have doubled this Ice to the North, but could not; and in the end put into it downe to the South-west through much Ice, and then to the South, where we were embayed againe. Our Master strove to get the shoare, but could not, for the great store of Ice that was on the coast. From out of this Bay, we stood to the North, and were soone out of the Ice: then downe to the South-west, and so to the West, where we were enclosed (to our sight) with Land and Ice. For wee had Land from the South to the North-west on one side, and from the East to the West on the other side: but the Land that was to the North of us, and lay by East and West, was but an Iland. On we went till we could goe no further for Ice: so we made our ship fast to the Ice which the tide brought upon us, but when the ebbe came, the Ice did open, and made way; so as in seven or eight houres we were cleere from the Ice, till we came to weather; but onely some of the great Ilands, that were carried along with us to the North-west.

Having a cleere Sea, our Master stood to the West along by the South shoare, and raysed three Capes or Head-lands, lying one above another. The middlemost is an Iland, and maketh a Bay or Harbour, which (I take) will prove a good one. Our Master named them Prince Henries Cape, or Fore-land. When we had layd this we raised another, which was the extreme point of the Land, looking towards the North: upon it are two Hills, but one (above the rest) like an Hay-cocke; which our Master named, King James his Cape. To the North of this, lie certaine llands, which our Master named, Queene Annes Cape, or Fore-land. Wee followed the North shoare still. Beyond the Kings Cape there is a Sound or Bay, that hath some Ilands in it: and this is not to be forgotten, if need be. Beyond this, lieth some broken Land, close to the Mayne, but what it is I know not: because we passed by it in the night.

Wee stood to the North to double this Land, and after to the West againe, till wee fell with Land that stretched from the Mayne, like a shewer from the South to the North, and from the North to the West, and then downe to the South againe. Being short of this Land, a storme tooke us, the wind at West, we stood to the North, and raised Land: which when our Master saw, he stood to the South againe; for he was loath at any time that wee should see the North shoare. The storme continuing, and comming to the South shoare againe, our Master found himselfe shot to the West, a great way, which made him muse, considering his Leeward way. To the South-west of this Land, on the Mayne, there is an high Hill, which our Master named Mount Charles. To the North and beyond this, lieth an Iland, that to the East hath a faire head, and beyond it to the West other broken Land, which maketh a Bay within, and a good Road may be found there for ships. Our Master named the first, Cape Salsburie.

When we had left this to the North-east, we fell into a Rippling or Over-fall of a Current, which (at the first) we tooke to bee a Shoald: but the Lead being cast, wee had no ground. On we passed still in sight of the South shoare, till we raised Land lying from the Mayne some two leagues. Our Master tooke this to bee a part of the Mayne of the North Land; but it is an Iland, the North side stretching out to the West more then the South. This Iland hath a faire Head to the East, and very high Land, which our Master named Deepes Cape: and the Land on the South side, now falling away to the South, makes another Cape or Head-land, which our Master named, Worsenhams Cape. When wee were nigh the North or Iland Cape, our Master sent the Boat ashoare, with my selfe (who had the charge) and the Carpenter, and divers others, to discover to the West and North-west, and to the South-west: but we had further to it then we thought; for the Land is very high, and we were overtaken with a storme of Raine, Thunder, and Lightning. But to it we came on the North-east side, and up we got from one Rocke to another, till we came to the highest of that part. Here we found some plaine ground, and saw some Deere; as first, foure or five, and after a dozen or sixteene in an Herd, but could not come nigh them with a Musket shot.

Thus, going from one place to another, wee saw to the West of us an high Hill above all the rest, it being nigh us: but it proved further off then we made account; for, when wee came to it, the Land was so steepe on the East and North-east parts, that wee could not get unto it. To the South-west we saw that wee might, and towards that part wee went along by the side of a great Pond of water, which lieth under the East side of this Hill: and there runneth out of it a streame of water, as much as would drive an over-shot Mill: which falleth downe from an high Cliffe into the Sea on the South side. In this place great store of Fowle breed, and there is the best Grasse that I had seene since we came from England.

Our Master (in this time) came in betweene the two Lands, and shot off some Peeces to call us aboord; for it was a fogge. Wee came aboord, and told him what we had seene, and perswaded him to stay a day or two in this place, telling him what refreshing might there bee had: but by no meanes would he stay, who was not pleased with the motion. So we left the Fowle, and lost our way downe to the South-west, before they went in sight of the Land, which now beares to the East from us, being the same mayne Land that wee had all this while followed. Now, we had lost the sight of it, because it falleth away to the East, after some five and twenty or thirty leagues. Now we came to the shallow water, wherewith wee were not acquainted since we came from Island; now we came into broken ground and Rockes, through which we passed downe to the South. In this our course we had a storme, and the water did shoald apace. Our Master came to an anchor in fifteene fathoms water.

Wee weighed and stood to the South-east, because the Land in this place did lie so. When we came to the point of the West Land (for we now had Land on both sides of us) we came to an anchor. Our Master sent the Boat ashoare, to see what that Land was, and whether there were any way through. They soone returned, and shewed that beyond the point of Land to the South, there was a large Sea. This Land on the West side, was a very narrow Point. Wee weighed from hence, and stood in for this Sea betweene the two Lands, which (in this place) is not two leagues broad downe to the South, for a great way in sight of the East shoare. In the end we lost sight thereof, and saw it not till we came to the bottome of the Bay, into sixe or seven fathomes water. Hence we stood up to the North by the West shoare, till wee came to an Iland in 53. where we tooke in water and ballast.

From hence wee passed towards the North: but some two or three dayes after (reasoning concerning our comming into this Bay, and going out) our Master tooke occasion to revive old matters, and to displace Robert Juet from being his Mate, and the Boatswaine from his place, for words spoken in the first great Bay of Ice. Then hee made Robert Billet his Mate, and William Wilson our Boatswaine. Up to the North wee stood, till we raised Land, then downe to the South, and up to the North, then downe againe to the South: and on Michaelmasse day came in, and went out of certaine Lands: which our Master sets downe by the name of Michaelmasse Bay, because we came in and went out on that day. From hence wee stood to the North, and came into shoald water; and the weather being thicke and foule, wee came to an anchor in seven or eight fathome water, and there lay eight dayes: in all which time wee could not get one houre to weigh our anchor. But the eight day, the wind beginning to cease, our Master would have the anchor up, against the mind of all who knew what belonged thereunto. Well, to it we went, and when we had brought it to a peake, a Sea tooke her, and cast us all off from the Capstone, and hurt divers of us. Here wee lost our Anchor, and if the Carpenter had not beene, we had lost our Cable too: but he (fearing such a matter) was ready with his Axe, and so cut it.

From hence we stood to the South, and to the South-west, through a cleere Sea of divers sounding, and came to a Sea of two colours, one blacke, and the other white, sixteene or seventeene fathome water, betweene which we went foure or five leagues. But the night comming, we tooke in our Top-sayles, and stood afore the wind with our Maine-sayle and Fore-sayl, and came into five or sixe fathomes, and saw no Land for it was darke. Then we stood to the East, and had deepe water againe, then to the South and Southwest, and so came to our Westermost Bay of all, and came to an anchor neerest to the North shoare. Out went our Boat to the Land that was next us, when they came neere it, our Boat could not flote to the shoare it was so shallow: yet ashoare they got. Here our men saw the footing of a man and a Ducke in the snowy Rockes, and Wood good store, whereof they tooke some and returned aboord. Being at anchor in this place, we saw a ledge of Rockes to the South of.us, some league of length; It lay North and South, covered at a full Sea; for a strong tide setteth in here. At mid-night wee weighed, and stood to goe out as we came in; and had not gone long, but the Carpenter came and told the Master, that if he kept that course he would be upon the Rockes: the Master conceived that he was past them, when presently wee ranne on them, and there stucke fast twelve houres: but (by the mercy of God) we got off unhurt, though not unscarred.

Wee stood up to the East and raysed three Hills, lying North and South: wee went to the furthermost, and left it to the North of us, and so into a Bay, where wee came to an anchor. Here our Master sent out our Boat, with my selfe and the Carpenter to seeke a place to winter in: and it was time; for the nights were long and cold, and the earth covered with Snow. Having spent three moneths in a Labyrinth without end, being now the last of October, we went downe to the East, to the bottome of the Bay: but returned without speeding of that we went for. The next day we went to the South, and the South-west, and found a place, whereunto we brought our ship, and haled her aground: and this was the first of November, By the tenth thereof we were frozen in: but now we were in, it behooved us to have care of what we had; for, that we were sure of; but what we had not, was uncertaine.

Wee were victualled for sixe moneths in good proportion, and of that which was good: if our Master would have had more, he might have had it at home and in other places. Here we were now, and therefore it behoved us so to spend, that wee might have (when time came) to bring us to the Capes where the Fowle bred, for that was all the hope wee had to bring us home. Wherefore our Master tooke order, first for the spending of that wee had, and then to increase it, by propounding a reward to them that killed either Beast, Fish, or Fowle. About the middle of this moneth of November, dyed John Williams our Gunner: God pardon the Masters uncharitable dealing with this man. Now for that I am come to speake of him, out of whose ashes (as it were) that unhappy deed grew which brought a scandall upon all that are returned home, and upon the action it selfe, the multitude (like the dog) running after the stone, but not at the caster: therefore, not to wrong the living, nor slander the dead, I will (by the leave of God) deliver the truth as neere as I can.

You shall understand, that our Master kept (in his house at London) a young man, named Henrie Greene, borne in Kent, of Worshipfull Parents, but by his leud life and conversation hee had lost the good will of all his friends, and had spent all that hee had. This man, our Master would have to Sea with him, because hee could write well: our Master gave him meate, and drinke, and lodging, and by meanes of one Master Venson, with much adoe got foure pounds of his mother to buy him clothes, wherewith Master Venson would not trust him: but saw it laid out himselfe. This Henrie Greene was not set downe in the owners booke, nor any wages made for him. Hee came first aboord at Gravesend, and at Harwich should have gone into the field, with one Wilkinson. At Island the Surgeon and hee fell out in Dutch, and hee beat him a shoare in English, which set all the company in a rage: so that wee had much adoe to get the Surgeon aboord. I told the Master of it, but hee bade mee let it alone, for (said hee) the Surgeon had a tongue that would wrong the best friend hee had. But Robert Juet (the Masters Mate) would needs burne his finger in the embers, and told the Carpenter a long tale (when hee was drunke) that our Master had brought in Greene to cracke his credit that should displease him: which words came to the Masters eares, who when hee understood it, would have gone backe to Island, when he was fortie leagues from thence, to have sent home his Mate Robert Juet in a Fisher-man. But, being otherwise perswaded, all was well. So Henry Greene stood upright, and very inward with the Master, and was a serviceable man every way for manhood: but for Religion he would say, he was cleane paper whereon he might write what hee would. Now, when our Gunner was dead, and (as the order is in such cases) if the company stand in need of any thing that belonged to the man deceased, then is it brought to the Mayne Mast, and there sold to them that will give most for the same: This Gunner had a gray cloth gowne, which Greene prayed the Master to friend him so much as to let him have it, paying for it as another would give: the Master saith hee should, and thereupon hee answered some, that sought to have it, that Greene should have it, and none else, and so it rested.

Now out of season and time, the Master calleth the Carpenter to goe in hand with an house on shoare, which at the beginning our Master would not heare, when it might have beene done. The Carpenter told him, that the Snow and Frost were such, as hee neither could, nor would goe in hand with such worke. Which when our Master heard, hee ferreted him out of his Cabbin to strike him, calling him by many foule names, and threatning to hang him. The Carpenter told him that hee knew what belonged to his place better than himselfe, and that hee was no House Carpenter. So this passed, and the house was (after) made with much labour, but to no end. The next day after the Master and the Carpenter fell out, the Carpenter tooke his Peece and Henry Greene with him, for it was an order that none should goe out alone, but one with a Peece, and another with a Pike. This did move the Master so much the more against Henry Greene, that Robert Billet his Mate must have the gowne, and had it delivered unto him; which when Henry Greene saw, he challenged the Masters promise: but the Master did so raile on Greene, with so many words of disgrace, telling him, that all his friends would not trust him with twenty shillings, and therefore why should he? As for wages he had none, nor none should have, if he did not please him well. Yet the Master had promised him to make his wages as good, as any mans in the Ship; and to have him one of the Princess guard when we came home. But you shall see how the devil out of this so wrought with Green, that he did the Master what mischiefe hee could in seeking to discredit him, and to thrust him and many other honest men out of the Ship in the end. To speake of all our trouble in this time of Winter (which was so cold, as it lamed the most of our Company, and my selfe doe yet feele it) would bee too tedious.

But I must not forget to shew, how mercifully God dealt with us in this time; for the space of three moneths wee had such store of Fowle of one kinde (which were Partridges as white as milke) that wee killed above an hundred dozen, besides others of sundry sorts: for all was fish that came to the net. The Spring comming, this Fowle left us, yet they were with us all the extreame cold. Then in their places came divers sort of other Fowle, as Swanne, Geese, Duck, and Teale, but hard to come by. Our Master hoped they would have bred in those broken grounds, but they doe not: but came from the South, and flew to the North, further then we were this Voyage: yet if they be taken short with the wind at North, or North-west, or North-east, then they fall and stay till the winde serve them, and then flye to the North.

About this time, when the Ice began to breake out of the Bayes, there came a Savage to our Ship, as it were to see and to bee seene, being the first that we had seene in all this time: whom our Master intreated well, and made much of him, promising unto himselfe great matters by his meanes, and therefore would have all the Knives and Hatchets (which any man had) to his private use, but received none but from John King the Carpenter, and my selfe. To this Savage our Master gave a Knife, a Looking-glasse, and Buttons, who received them thankefully, and made signes that after hee had slept hee would come againe, which hee did. When hee came, hee brought with him a Sled, which hee drew after him, and upon it two Deeres skinnes, and two Beaver skinnes. Hee had a scrip under his arme, out of which hee drew those things which the Master had given him. Hee tooke the Knife and laid it upon one of the Beaver skinnes, and his Glasses and Buttons upon the other, and so gave them to the Master, who received them; and the Savage tooke those things which the Master had given him, and put them up into his script againe. Then the Master shewed him an Hatchet, for which hee would have given the Master one of his Deere skinnes, but our Master would have them both, and so hee had, although not willingly. After many signes of people to the North, and to the South, and that after so many sleepes he would come againe, he went his way, but never came more.

Now the Ice being out of the Sounds, so that our Boat might go from one place unto another, a company of men were appointed by the Master to go a fishing with our net; their names were as followeth: William Wilson, Henry Greene, Michael Perce, John Thomas, Andrew Moter, Bennet Matthewes, and Arnold Lodlo. These men, the first day they went, caught five hundred fish, as big as good Herrings, and some Troutes: which put us all in some hope to have our wants supplied, and our Commons amended: but these were the most that ever they got in one day, for many dayes they got not a quarter so many. In this time of their fishing, Henry Green and William Wilson, with some others plotted to take the net and the shallop, which the Carpenter had now set up, and so to shift for themselves. But the shallop being readie, our Master would goe in it himselfe, to the South and South-west, to see if hee could meete with the people; for, to that end was it set up, and (that way) wee might see the Woods set on fire by them. So the Master tooke the Sayve and the Shallop, and so much victuall as would serve for eight or nine dayes, and to the South hee went. They that remained aboord, were to take in water, wood and ballast, and to have all things in a readiness against hee came backe. But hee set no time of his returne; for he was perswaded, if he could meet with the people, hee should have flesh of them, and that good store; but he returned worse than hee went forth. For, hee could by no meanes meete with the people, although they were neere them, yet they would set the woods on fire in his sight.

Being returned, hee fitted all things for his returne, and first, delivered all the bread out of the bread roome (which came to a pound a piece for every mans share) and delivered also a Bill of Returne, willing them to have that to shew, if it pleased God, that they came home: and he wept when hee gave it unto them. But to helpe us in this poore estate with some reliefe, the Boate and Sayve went to worke on Friday morning, and stayed till Sunday noone: at which time they came aboord, and brought fourescore small Fish, a poore reliefe for so many hungry bellies. Then we wayed, and stood out of our wintering place, and came to an Anchor without, in the mouth of the Bay: from whence we wayed and came to an anchor without in the Sea, where our bread being gone, that store of cheese we had was to stop a gap, whereof there were five, whereat the company grudged, because they made account of nine. But those that were left, were equally divided by the Master, although he had counsell to the contrarie: for there were some who having it, would make hast to bee rid thereof, because they could not governe it. I knew when Henrie Greene gave halle his bread, which hee had for fourteene dayes, to one to keepe, and prayed him not to let him have any untill the next Monday: but before Wednesday at night, hee never left till hee had it againe, having eaten up his first weeks bread before. So Wilson the Boatswaine hath eaten (in one day) his fortnights bread, and hath beene two or three dayes sicke for his labour. The cause that moved the Master to deliver all the Cheese, was because they were not all of one goodnesse, and therefore they should see that they had no wrong done them: but every man should have alike the best and the worst together, which was three pounds and a halfe for seven dayes.

The wind serving, we weighed and stood to the North-west, and on Munday at night (the eighteenth day of June) wee fell into the Ice, and the next day the wind being at West, we lay there till Sunday in sight of Land. Now being here, the Master told Nicholas Simmes, that there would be a breaking up of chests, and a search for bread, and willed him (if hee had any) to bring it to him, which hee did, and delivered to the Master thirty cakes in a bagge. This deed of the Master (if it bee true) hath made mee marvell, what should bee the reason that hee did not stop the breach in the beginning, but let it grow to that height, as that it overthrew himselfe and many other honest men: but there are many devices in the heart of man, yet the counsell of the Lord shall stand.

Being thus in the Ice on Saturday, the one and twentieth of June at night, Wilson the Boatswayne, and Henry Greene came to mee lying (in my Cabbin) lame, and told mee that they and the rest of their Associates, would shift the Company, and turne the Master, and all the sicke men into the shallop, and let them shift for themselves. For, there was not fourteen daies victual left for all the Company, at that poore allowance they were at, and that there they lay, the Master not caring to goe one way or other: and that they had not eaten any thing these three dayes, and therefore were resolute, either to mend or end, and what they had begun they would goe through with it, or dye. When I heard this, I told them I marvelled to heare so much from them, considering that they were married men, and had wives and children, and that for their sakes they should not commit so foule a thing in the sight of God and man, as that would bee; for why should they banish themselves from their native Countrie? Henry Greene bad me hold my peace, for he knew the worst, which was, to be hanged when hee came home, and therefore of the two he would rather he hanged at home then starved abroad: and for the good will they bare me, they would have mee stay in the Ship. I gave them thankes, and told them that I came into her, not to forsake her, yet not to hurt my selfe and others by any such deed. Henry Greene told me then, that I must take my fortune in the Shallop. If there bee no remedie (said I) the will of God bee done.

Away went Henry Greene in a rage, swearing to cut his throat that went about to disturbe them, and left Wilson by me, with whom I had some talke, but to no good: for he was so perswaded, that there was no remedie now, but to goe on while it was hot, least their partie should faile them, and the mischiefe they had intended to others, should light on themselves. Henry Greene came againe, and demanded of him what I said. Wilson answered, He is in his old song, still patient. Then I spake to Henry Greene to stay three dayes, in which time I would so deale with the Master, that all should be well. So I dealt with him to forbeare but two dayes, nay twelve houres; there is no way then (say they) but out of hand. Then I told them that if they would stay till Munday, I would joyne with them to share all the victuals in the ship, and would justifie it when I came home; but this would not serve their turnes. Wherefore I told them, it was some worse matter they had in hand then they made shew of, and that it was bloud and revenge hee sought, or else he would not at such a time of night undertake such a deed. Henry Greene (with that) taketh my Bible which lay before me, and sware that hee would doe no man harme, and what hee did was for the good of the voyage, and for nothing else; and that all the rest should do the like. The like did Wilson sweare.

Henry Greene went his way, and presently came Juet, who because hee was an ancient man, I hoped to have found some reason in him; but hee was worse than Henry Greene, for hee sware plainely that he would justifie this deed when he came home. After him came John Thomas, and Michel Perce, as birds of one feather: but because they are not living I will let them goe, as then I did. Then came Moter and Bennet, of whom I demanded, if they were well advised what they had taken in hand. They answered, they were, and therefore came to take their oath.

Now, because I am much condemned for this oath, as one of them that plotted with them, and that by an oath I should bind them together to performe what they had begun, I thought good heere to set downe to the view of all, how well their oath and deedes agreed: and thus it was. You shall sweare truth to God, your Prince and Countrie: you shall doe nothing, but to the glory of God, and the good of the action in hand, and harme to no man. This was the oath, without adding or diminishing. I looked for more of these companions (although these were too many) but there came no more. It was darke, and they in a readinesse to put this deed of darknesse in execution. I called to Henry Greene and Wilson, and prayed them not to goe in hand with it in the darke, but to stay till the morning. Now, everie man (I hope) would goe to his rest, but wickednesse sleepeth not; for Henry Greene keepeth the Master company all night (and gave mee bread, which his Cabbin-mate gave him) and others are as watchfull as he. Then I asked Henrie Greene, whom he would put out with the Master? he said, the Carpenter, John King, and the sicke men. I said, they should not doe well to part with the Carpenter, what need soever they should have. Why the Carpenter was in no more regard amongst them, was; first, for that he and John King were condemned for wrong done in the victuall. But the chiefest cause was, for that the Master loved him, and made him his Mate, upon his returne out of our wintering place, thereby displacing Robert Billet, whereat they did grudge, because hee could neither write nor read. And therefore (said they) the Master and his ignorant Mate would carry the Ship whither the Master pleased: the Master forbidding any man to keepe account or reckoning, having taken from all men whatsoever served for that purpose. Well, I obtained of Henrie Greene and Wilson, that the Carpenter should stay, by whose meanes I hoped (after they had satisfied themselves) that the Master, and the poore man might be taken into the Ship againe. Or, I hoped, that some one or other would give some notice, either to the Carpenter John King, or the Master; for so it might have come to passe by some of them that were the most forward.

Now, it shall not bee amisse to shew how we were lodged, and to begin in the Cooke roome; there lay Bennet and the Cooper lame; without the Cooke roome, on the steere-board side, lay Thomas Wydhouse sicke; next to him lay Sydrack Funer lame, then the Surgeon, and John Hudson with him; next to them lay Wilson the Boatswaine, and then Arnold Lodlo next to him in the Gun-roome lay Robert Juet and John Thomas; on the Larboord side, lay Michael Bute and Adria Moore, who had never beene well since wee lost our anchor; next to them lay Michael Perce and Andrew Moter. Next to them without the Gun-roome, lay John King, and with him Robert Billet: next to them my selfe, and next to me Francis Clements: In the mid-ship, betweene the Capstone and the Pumpes, lay Henrie Greene and Nicholas Simmes. This night John King was late up, and they thought he had been with the Master, but he was with the Carpenter, who lay on the Poope, and comming downe from him, was met by his Cabbin-mate, as it were by chance, and so they came to their Cabbin together. It was not long ere it was day: then came Bennet for water for the Kettle, hee rose and went into the Hold: when hee was in, they shut the Hatch on him (but who kept it downe I know not) up upon the Deck went Bennet.

In the meane time Henrie Greene, and another went to the Carpenter, and held him with a talke, till the Master came out of his Cabbin (which hee soone did) then came John Thomas and Bennet before him, while Wilson bound his armes behind him. He asked them what they meant? they told him, he should know when he was in the Shallop. Now Juet, while this was a doing, came to John King into the Hold, who was provided for him, for he had got a sword of his own, and kept him at a bay, and might have killed him, but others came to helpe him: and so he came up to the Master. The master called to the Carpenter, and told him that he was bound; but, I heard no answere he made. Now Arnold Lodlo, and Michael Bute rayled at them, and told them their knaverie would shew it selfe. Then was the Shallop haled up to the Ship side, and the poore, sicke, and lame men were called upon to get them out of their Cabbins into the Shallop. The Master called to me, who came out of my Cabbin as well as I could, to the Hatch way to speake with him: where, on my knees I besought them, for the love of God, to remember themselves, and to doe as they would be done unto. They bad me keepe my selfe well, and get me into my Cabbin; not suffering the Master to speake with me. But when I came into my Cabbin againe, hee called to me at the Horne, which gave light into my Cabbin, and told mee that Juet would overthrow us all; nay (said I) it is that villaine Henry Greene, and I spake it not softly.

Now was the Carpenter at libertie, who asked them, if they would bee hanged when they came home: and as for himselfe, hee said, hee would not stay in the Ship unlesse they would force him: they bad him goe then, for they would not stay him: I will (said hee) so I may have my chest with mee, and all that is in it: they said, hee should, and presently they put it into the Shallop. Then hee came downe to mee, to take his leave of mee, who perswaded him to stay, which if he did, he might so worke that all should bee well: hee said, hee did not thinke, but they would be glad to take them in againe. For he was so perswaded by the Master, that there was not one in all the ship, that could tell how to carrie her home; but (saith he) if we must part (which wee will not willingly doe, for they would follow the ship) hee prayed me, if wee came to the Capes before them, that I would leave some token that wee had beene there, neere to the place where the Fowles bred, and hee would doe the like for us: and so (with teares) we parted. Now were the sicke men driven out of their Cabbins into the Shallop; but John Thomas was Francis Clements friend, and Bennet was the Coopers, so as there were words betweene them and Henrie Greene, one saying, that they should goe, and the other swearing that they should not goe, but such as were in the shallop should returne. When Henrie Greene heard that, he was compelled to give place, and to put out Arnold Lodlo, and Michael Bute, which with much adoe they did.

In the meane time, there were some of them that plyed their worke, as if the Ship had beene entred by force, and they had free leave to pillage, breaking up Chests, and rifling all places. One of them came by me, who asked me, what they should doe. I answered, hee should make an end of what hee had begun; for I saw him doe nothing but sharke up and downe. Now, were all the poore men in the Shallop, whose names are as followeth; Henrie Hudson, John Hudson, Arnold Lodlo, Sidrack Faner, Phillip Staffe, Thomas Woodhouse, or Wydhouse, Adam Moore, Henrie King, Michael Bute. The Carpenter got of them a Pcccc, and Powder, and Shot, and some Pikes, an Iron Pot, with some meale, and other things. They stood out of the Ice, the Shallop being fast to the Sterne of the Shippe, and so (when they were nigh out, for I cannot say, they were cleane out) they cut her head fast from the Sterne of our Ship, then out with their Top-sayles, and towards the East they stood in a cleere Sea. In the end they tooke in their Top-sayles, righted their Helme, and lay under their Fore-sayle till they had ransacked and searched all places in the Ship. In the Hold they found one of the vessels of meale whole, and the other halfe spent, for wee had but two; wee found also two firkins of Butter, some twentie seven piece of Porke, halfe a bushell of Pease, but in the Masters Cabbin we found two hundred of bisket Cakes, a pecke of Meale, of Beere to the quantitie of a Butt, one with another. Now, it was said, that the Shallop was come within sight, they let fall the Mainsayle, and out with their Top-sayles, and flye as from an Enemy.

Then I prayed them yet to remember themselves: but William Wilson (more then the rest) would heare of no such matter. Comming nigh the East shoare they cast about, and stood to the West and came to an Iland, and anchored in sixteene or seventeene fathome water. So they sent the Boat, and the Net ashoare to see if they could have a Draught: but could not for Rocks and great stones. Michael Perse killed two Fowle, and heere they found good store of that Weede, which we called Cockle grasse in our wintering place, whereof they gathered store, and came aboard againe. Heere we lay that night, and the best part of the next day, in all which time we saw not the shallop, or ever after.

SOME ADVENTURES OF CRUSOE[1]

Daniel Defoe

(1661(?)-1731)

I

He Is Saved from the Wreck

THE ship being fitted out, and the cargo furnished, and all things done, as by agreement, by my partners in the voyage, I went on board in an evil hour, the Ist of September, 1659, being the same day eight years that I went from my father and mother at Hull, in order to act the rebel to their authority, and the fool to my own interests.

Our ship was about one hundred and twenty tons burden, carried six guns, and fourteen men, besides the master, his boy, and myself. We had on board no large cargo of goods, except of such toys as were fit for our trade with the Negroes, such as beads, bits of glass, shells, and other trifles, especially little looking-glasses, knives, scissors, hatchets and the like.

The same day I went on board we set sail, standing away to the northward upon our own coast, with design to stretch over for the African coast when we came

[1] From *Robinson Crusoe*.

about ten or twelve degrees of northern latitude, which, it seems, was the manner of course in those days. We had very good weather, only excessively hot, all the way upon our own coast, till we came to the height of Cape St Augustino; from whence, keeping further off at sea, we lost sight of land, and steered as if we were bound for the isle Fernando de Noronha, holding our course N.E. by N., and leaving those isles on the east. In this course we passed the line in about twelve days' time, and were, by our last observation, in seven degrees twenty-two minutes northern latitude, when a violent tornado, or hurricane, took us quite out of our knowledge. It began from the south-east, came about to the north-west, and then settled in the north-east; from whence it blew in such a terrible manner, that for twelve days together we could do nothing but drive, and, scudding away before it, let it carry us whither ever fate and the fury of the winds directed; and, during these twelve days, I need not say that I expected every day to be swallowed up; nor, indeed, did any in the ship expect to save their lives.

In this distress we had, besides the terror of the storm, one of our men die of the calenture, and one man and the boy washed overboard. About the twelfth day, the weather abating a little, the master made an observation as well as he could, and found that he was in about eleven degrees north latitude, but that he was twenty-two degrees of longitude difference west from Cape St Augustino; so that he found he was upon the coast of Guiana, or the north part of Brazil, beyond the river Amazons, towards that of the river Oroonoque, commonly called the Great River; and began to consult with me what course he should take, for the ship was leaky, and very much disabled, and he was going directly back to the coast of Brazil.

I was positively against that; and looking over the charts of the seacoast of America with him, we concluded there was no inhabited country for us to have recourse to, till we came within the circle of the Caribbee Islands, and therefore resolved to stand away for Barbadoes; which, by keeping off at sea, to avoid the indraft of the Bay or Gulf of Mexico, we might easily perform, as we hoped, in about fifteen days' sail; whereas we could not possibly make our voyage to the coast of Africa without some assistance both to our ship and to ourselves.

With this design we changed our course, and steered away N.W. by W., in order to reach some of our English islands, where I hoped for relief. But our voyage was otherwise determined; for, being in the latitude of twelve degrees eighteen minutes, a second storm came upon us, which carried us away with the same impetuosity westward, and drove us so out of the way of all human commerce, that, had all our lives been saved as to the sea, we were rather in danger of being devoured by savages than ever returning to our own country.

In this distress, the wind still blowing very hard, one of our men early in the morning cried out, "Land!" and we had no sooner run out of the cabin to look out, in hopes of seeing whereabouts in the world we were, than the ship struck upon a sand, and in a moment, her motion being so stopped, the sea broke over her in such a manner, that we expected we should all have perished immediately; and we were immediately driven into our close quarters, to shelter us from the very foam and spray of the sea.

It is not easy for any one who has not been in the like condition to describe or conceive the consternation of men in such circumstances. We knew nothing where we were, or upon what land it was we were driven—whether an island or the main, whether inhabited or not inhabited. As the rage of the wind was still great, though rather less than at first, we could not so much as hope to have the ship hold many minutes without breaking into pieces, unless the winds, by a kind of miracle, should turn immediately about. In a word, we sat looking upon one another, and expecting death every moment, and every man, accordingly, preparing for another world; for there was little or nothing more for us to do in this. That which was our present comfort, and all the comfort we had, was that, contrary to our expectation, the ship did not break yet, and that the master said the wind began to abate.

Now, though we thought that the wind did a little abate, yet the ship having thus struck upon the sand, and sticking too fast for us to expect her getting off we were in a dreadful condition indeed and had nothing to do but to think of saving our lives as well as we could. We had a boat at our stern just before the storm, but she was first staved by dashing against the ship's rudder, and in the next place, she broke away, and either sunk, or was driven off to sea; so there was no hope from her. We had another boat on board, but how to get her off into the sea was a doubtful thing. However, there was no time to debate, for we fancied the ship would break in pieces every minute, and some told us she was actually broken already.

In this distress, the mate of our vessel laid hold of the boat, and with the help of the rest of the men, got her slung over the ship's side; and getting all into her, let go, and committed ourselves, being eleven in number, to God's mercy and the wild sea; for though the storm was abated considerably, yet the sea ran dreadfully high upon the shore, and might be well called *den wild zee,* as the Dutch call the sea in a storm.

And now our case was very dismal indeed; for we all saw plainly, that the sea went so high that the boat could not live, and that we should be inevitably drowned. As to making sail, we had none, nor, if we had, could we have done anything with it; so we worked at the oar towards the land, though with heavy hearts, like men going to execution; for we all knew that when the boat came nearer the shore, she would be dashed in a thousand pieces by the breach of the sea. However, we committed our souls to God in the most earnest manner; and the wind driving us towards the shore, we hastened our destruction with our own hands, pulling as well as we could towards land.

What the shore was, whether rock or sand, whether steep or shoal, we knew not. The only hope that could rationally give us the least shadow of expectation, was, if we might find some bay or gulf, or the mouth of some river, where by great chance we might have run our boat in, or got under the lee of the land, and perhaps made smooth water. But there was nothing like this appeared; but as we made nearer and nearer the shore, the land looked more frightful than the sea.

After we had rowed or rather driven about a league and a half, as we reckoned it, a raging wave, mountain-like, came rolling astern of us, and plainly bade us expect the *coup de grace*. In a word, it took us with such a fury, that it overset the boat at once; and separating us, as well from the boat as from one another, gave us not time to say, "O God!" for we were all swallowed up in a moment.

Nothing can describe the confusion of thought which I felt, when I sunk into the water; for though I swam very well, yet I could not deliver myself from the waves so as to draw breath, till that wave having driven me, or rather carried me, a vast way on towards the shore, and having spent itself, went back, and left me upon the land almost dry, but half dead with the water I took in. I had so much presence of mind, as well as breath left, that seeing myself nearer the main land than I expected, I got upon my feet, and endeavoured to make on towards the land as fast as I could, before another wave should return and take me up again; but I soon found it was impossible to avoid it; for I saw the sea come after me as high as a great hill, and as furious as an enemy, which I had no means or strength to contend with; my business was to hold my breath, and raise myself upon the water, if I could; and so, by swimming, to preserve my breathing and pilot myself towards the shore, if possible, my greatest concern now being, that the sea, as it would carry me a great way towards the shore when it came on, might not carry me back again with it when it gave back towards the sea.

The wave that came upon me again, buried me at once twenty or thirty feet deep in its own body, and I could feel myself carried with a mighty force and swiftness towards the shore a very great way; but I held my breath, and assisted myself to swim still forward with all my might. I was ready to burst with holding my breath, when as I felt myself rising up, so, to my immediate relief, I found my head and hands shoot out above the surface of the water; and though it was not two seconds of time that I could keep myself so, yet it relieved me greatly, gave me breath and new courage. I was covered again with water a good while, but not so long but I held it out; and, finding the water had spent itself and began to return, I struck forward against the return of the waves, and felt ground again with my feet. I stood still a few moments to recover breath and till the waters went from me, and then took to my heels and ran, with what strength I had, further towards the shore. But neither would this deliver me from the fury of the sea, which came pouring in after me again; and twice more I was lifted up by the waves and carried forwards as before, the shore being very flat.

The last time of these two had well-nigh been fatal to me, for the sea having hurried me along, as before, landed me, or rather dashed me, against a piece of rock, and that with such force, that it left me senseless, and indeed helpless, as to my own deliverance; for the blow taking my side and breast, beat the breath, as it were, quite out of my body; and had it returned again immediately, I must have been strangled in the water; but I recovered a little before the return of the waves, and seeing I should be covered again with the water, I resolved to hold fast by a piece of the rock, and so to hold my breath, if possible, till the wave went back. Now, as the waves were not so high as at first, being nearer land, I held my hold till the wave abated, and then fetched another run, which brought me so near the shore, that the next wave, though it went over me, yet did not so swallow me up as to carry me away; and the next run I took, I got to the main land, where, to my great comfort, I clambered up the cliffs of the shore, and sat me down upon the grass, far from danger and quite out of the reach of the water.

II

And Attempts to Escape from the Island

My thoughts ran many times upon the prospect of land which I had seen from the other side of the island; and I was not without secret wishes that I were on shore there, fancying that, seeing the main land, and an inhabited country, I might find some way or other to convey myself farther, and perhaps at last find some means of escape.

But all this while I made no allowance for the dangers of such an undertaking, and how I might fall into the hands of savages, and perhaps such as I might have reason to think far worse than the lions and tigers of Africa: that if I once came in their power, I should run a hazard of more than a thousand to one of being killed, and perhaps of being eaten, for I had heard that the people of the Caribbean coast were cannibals, or man-eaters, and I knew by the latitude that I could not be far from that shore.

Now I wished for my boy Xury, and the long-boat with the shoulder-of-mutton sail, with which I sailed above a thousand miles on the coast of Africa; but this was in vain: then I thought I would go and look at our ship's boat, which, as I have said, was blown up upon the shore a great way, in the storm, when we were first cast away. She lay almost where she did at first, but not quite; and was turned, by the force of the waves and the winds, almost bottom upward, against a high ridge of beachy rough sand, but no water about her. If I had had hands to have refitted her, and to have launched her into the water, the boat would have done well enough, and I might have gone back into the Brazils with her easily enough; but I might have foreseen that I could no more turn her and set her upright upon her bottom, than I could remove the island; however, I went to the woods, and cut levers and rollers, and brought them to the boat, resolving to try what I could do; suggesting to myself, that if I could but turn her down, I might repair the damage she had received, and she would be a very good boat, and I might go to sea in her very easily.

I spared no pains, indeed, in this piece of fruitless toil, and spent, I think, three or four weeks about it; at last, finding it impossible to heave it up with my little strength, I fell to digging away the sand, to undermine it, and so to make it fall down, setting pieces of wood to thrust and guide it right in the fall.

But when I had done this I was unable to stir it up again, or to get under it, much less to move it forward towards the water; so I was forced to give it over; and yet, though I gave over the hopes of the boat, my desire to venture over for the main increased, rather than decreased, as the means for it seemed impossible.

This at length put me upon thinking whether it was not possible to make myself a canoe, or periagua, such as the natives of those climates make, even without tools, or, as I might say, without hands, of the trunk of a great tree. This I not only thought possible, but easy, and pleased myself extremely with the thoughts of making it, and with my having much more convenience for it than any of the Negroes or Indians; but not at all considering the particular inconveniences which I lay under more that the Indians did, viz. want of hands to move it, when it was made, into the water—a difficulty much harder for me to surmount than all the consequences of want of tools could be to them; for what was it to me, if when I had chosen a vast tree in the woods, and with much trouble cut it down, if I had been able with my tools to hew and dub the outside into the proper shape of a boat, and burn or cut out the inside to make it hollow, so as to make a boat of it—if, after all this, I must leave it just there where I found it, and not be able to launch it into the water?

One would have thought I could not have had the least reflection upon my mind of my circumstances while I was making this boat, but I should have immediately thought how I should get it into the sea; but my thoughts were so intent upon my voyage over the sea in it, that I never once considered how I should get it off the land: and it was really, in its own nature, more easy for me to guide it over forty-five miles in sea, than about forty-five fathoms of land, where it lay, to set it afloat in the water.

I went to work on this boat the most like a fool that ever man did, who had any of his senses awake. I pleased myself with the design, without determining whether I was ever able to undertake it; not but that the difficulty of launching my boat came often into my head; but I put a stop to my inquiries into it, by this foolish answer, which I gave myself: "Let me first make it; I warrant I will find some way or other to get it along when it is done."

This was a most preposterous method; but the eagerness of my fancy prevailed, and to work I went. I felled a cedar tree, and I question much whether Solomon ever had such a one for the building of the Temple of Jerusalem; it was five feet ten inches diameter at the lower part next the stump, and four feet eleven inches diameter at the end of twentytwo feet; after which it lessened for a while, and then parted into branches. It was not without infinite labour that I felled this tree; I was twenty days hacking and hewing at it at the bottom; I was fourteen more getting the branches and limbs, and the vast spreading head cut off, which I hacked and hewed through with axe and hatchet, and inexpressible labour: after this, it cost me a month to shape it and dub it to a proportion, and to something like the bottom of a boat, that it might swim upright as it ought to do. It cost me near three months more to clear the inside, and work it out so as to make an exact boat of it; this I did, indeed, without fire, by mere mallet and chisel, and by the dint of hard labour, till I had brought it to be a very handsome periagua, and big enough to have carried six and twenty men, and consequently big enough to have carried me and all my cargo.

When I had gone through this work, I was extremely delighted with it. The boat was really much bigger than ever I saw a canoe or periagua, that was made of one tree in my life. Many a weary stroke it had cost, you may be sure; and had I gotten it into the water, I make no question but I should have begun the maddest voyage, and the most unlikely to be performed that ever was undertaken.

But all my devices to get it into the water failed me; though they cost me infinite labour too. It lay about one hundred yards from the water, and not more; but the first inconvenience was, it was uphill towards the creek. Well, to take away this discouragement, I resolved to dig into the surface of the earth, and so make a declivity: this I began, and it cost me a prodigious deal of pains (but who grudge pains that have their deliverance in view?); but when this was worked through, and this difficulty managed, it was still much the same, for I could no more stir the canoe than I could the other boat. Then I measured the distance of ground, and resolved to cut a dock or canal, to bring the water up to the canoe, seeing I could not bring the canoe down to the water. Well, I began this work; and when I began to enter upon it, and calculate how deep it was to be dug, how broad, how the stuff was to be thrown out, I found that, by the number of hands I had, being none but my own, it must have been ten or twelve years before I could have gone through with it; for the shore lay so high, that at the upper end it must have been at least twenty feet deep; so at length, though with great reluctancy, I gave this attempt over also.

In the middle of this work, I finished my fourth year in this place, and kept my anniversary with the same devotion, and with as much comfort as ever before; for, by a constant study and serious application to the Word of God, and by the assistance of His grace, I gained a different knowledge from what I had before. I entertained different notions of things. I looked now upon the world as a thing remote, which I had nothing to do with, no expectation from, and, indeed, no desires about: in a word, I had nothing indeed to do with it, nor was ever likely to have.

I cannot say, after this, for five years, any extraordinary thing happened to me, but I lived on in the same course, in the same posture and place, as before; the chief things I was employed in, besides my yearly labour of planting my barley and rice, and curing my raisins, of both which I always kept up just enough to have sufficient stock of one year's provision beforehand; I say, besides this yearly labour, and my daily pursuit of going out with my gun, I had one labour, to make a canoe, which at last I finished: so that, by digging a canal to it of six feet wide and four feet deep, I brought it into the creek, almost half a mile. As for the first, which was so vastly big, for I made it without considering beforehand, as I ought to have done, how I should be able to launch it, so, never being able to bring it into the water, or bring the water to it, I was obliged to let it lie where it was as a memorandum to teach me to be wiser the next time: indeed, the next time, though I could not get a tree proper for it, and was in a place where I could not get the water to it at any less distance than, as I have said, near half a mile, yet, as I saw it was practicable at last, I never gave it over; and though I was near two years about it, yet I never grudged my labour, in hopes of having a boat to go off to sea at last.

However, though my little periagua was finished, yet the size of it was not at all answerable to the design which I had in view when I made the first; I mean of venturing over to the *terra firma,* where it was above forty miles broad; accordingly, the smallness of my boat assisted to put an end to that design, and now I thought no more of it. As I had a boat, my next design was to make a cruise round the island; for as I had been on the other side in one place, crossing, as I have already described it, over the land, so the discoveries I made in that little journey made me very eager to see other parts of the coast; and now I had a boat, I thought of nothing but sailing round the island.

For this purpose, that I might do everything with discretion and consideration, I fitted up a little mast in my boat, and made a sail too out of some of the pieces of the ship's sails which lay in store, and of which I had a great stock by me. Having fitted my mast and sail, and tried the boat, I found she would sail very well: then I made little lockers, or boxes, at each end of my boat, to put provisions, necessaries, ammunition, etc. into, to be kept dry, either from rain or the spray of the sea; and a little, long, hollow place I cut in the inside of the boat, where I could lay my gun, making a flap to hang down over it, to keep it dry.

I fixed my umbrella also in a step at the stern, like a mast, to stand over my head, and keep the heat of the sun off me, like an awning; and thus I ever now and then took a little voyage upon the sea; but never went far out, nor far from the little creek. At last, being eager to view the circumference of my little kingdom, I resolved upon my cruise; and accordingly I victualled my ship for the voyage, putting in two dozen of loaves (cakes I should rather call them) of barley bread, an earthen pot full of parched rice (a food I ate a great deal of) a little bottle of rum, half a goat, and powder and shot for killing more, and two large watchcoats, of those which, as I mentioned before, I had saved out of the seamen's chests; these I took, one to lie upon, and the other to cover me in the night.

It was the 6th of November, in the sixth year of my reign, or my captivity, which you please, that I set out on this voyage, and I found it much longer than I expected; for though the island itself was not very large, yet when I came to the east side of it, I found a great ledge of rocks lie out about two leagues into the sea, some above water, some under it; and beyond that a shoal of sand, lying dry half a league more, so that I was obliged to go a great way out to sea to double the point.

When I first discovered them, I was going to give over my enterprise, and come back again, not knowing how far it might oblige me to go out to sea: and, above all, doubting how I should get back again: so I came to an anchor; for I had made a kind of an anchor with a piece of a broken grappling which I got out of the ship.

Having secured my boat, I took my gun and went on shore, climbing up a hill, which seemed to overlook that point where I saw the full extent of it, and resolved to venture.

In my viewing the sea from that hill where I stood, I perceived a strong and, indeed, a most furious current, which ran to the east, and even came clost to the point; and I took the more notice of it, because I saw there might be some danger, that when I came into it, I might be carried out to sea by the strength of it, and not be able to make the island again; and, indeed, had I not got first upon this hill, I believe it would have been so; for there was the same current on the other side of the island, only that it set off at a farther distance, and I saw there was a strong eddy under the shore; so I had nothing to do but to get out of the first current, and I should presently be in an eddy.

I lay here, however, two days, because the wind blowing pretty fresh at E.S.E., and that being just contrary to the current, made a great breach of the sea upon the point; so that it was not safe for me to keep too close to the shore for the beach, nor to go too far off, because of the stream.

The third day, in the morning, the wind having abated overnight, the sea w calm, and I ventured: but I am a warning to all rash and ignorant pilots; fc sooner was I come to the point, when I was not even my boat's length from the shore, but I found myself in a great depth of water, and a current like the sluice of a mill: it carried my boat along with it with such violence that all I could do could not keep her so much as on the edge of it; but I found it hurried me farther and farther out from the eddy which was on my left hand. There was no wind stirring to help me, and all I could do with my paddles signified nothing: and now I began to give myself over for lost; for as the current was on both sides of the island, I knew in a few leagues' distance they must join again, and then I was irrecoverably gone; nor did I see any possibility of avoiding it; so that I had no prospect before me but of perishing, not by the sea, for that was calm enough, but of starving from hunger. I had indeed found a tortoise on the shore, as big almost as I could lift, and had tossed it into the boat; and I had a great jar of fresh water, that is to say, one of my earthen pots; but what was all this to being driven into the vast ocean, where, to be sure, there was no shore, no main land or island, for a thousand leagues at least?

And now I saw how easy it was for the providence of God to make even the most miserable condition of mankind worse. Now I looked back upon my desolate, solitary island, as the most pleasant place in the world, and all the happiness my heart could wish for was to be but there again. I stretched out my hands to it, with eager wishes: "O happy desert!" said I, "I shall never see thee more. O miserable creature! Whither am I going?" Then I reproached myself with my unthankful temper, and that I had repined at my solitary condition; and now what would I give to be on shore there again! Thus, we never see the true state of our condition till it is illustrated to us by its contraries, nor know how to value what we enjoy, but by the want of it. It is scarcely possible to imagine the consternation I was now in, being driven from my beloved island (for so it appeared to me now to be) into the wide ocean, almost two leagues, and in the utmost despair of ever recovering it again. However, I worked hard till indeed my strength was almost exhausted, and kept my boat as much to the northward, that is, towards the side of the current which the eddy lay on, as possible I could; when about noon, as the sun passed the meridian I thought I felt a little breeze of wind in my face, springing up from S.S.E. This cheered my heart a little, and especially when, in about half an hour more, it blew a pretty gentle gale. By this time, I had got at a frightful distance from the island, and had the least cloudy or hazy weather intervened, I had been undone another way, too; for I had no compass on board, and should never have known how to have steered towards the island, if I had but once lost sight of it; but the weather continuing clear, I applied myself to get up my mast again, and spread my sail, standing away to the north as much as possible, to get out of the current.

Just as I had set my mast and sail, and the boat began to stretch away, I saw even the clearness of the water some alteration of the current was near; for where the current was so strong the water was foul; but perceiving the water clear, I found the current abate; and presently I found to the east, at about half a mile, a breach of the sea upon some rocks: these rocks I found caused the current to part again, and as the main stress of it ran away more southerly, leaving the rocks to the northeast, so the other returned by the repulse of the rocks, and made a strong eddy, which ran back again to the north-west, with a very sharp stream.

They who know what it is to have a reprieve brought to them upon the ladder, or to be rescued from thieves just going to murder them, or who have been in such extremities, may guess what my present surprise of joy was, and how gladly I put my boat into the stream of the eddy; and the wind also freshening, how gladly I spread my sail to it, running cheerfully before the wind, and with a strong tide or eddy under foot.

This eddy carried me about a league in my way back again, directly towards the island, but about two leagues more to the northward than the current which carried me away at first; so that when I came near the island, I found myself open to the northern shore of it, that is to say, the other end of the island, opposite to that which I went out from.

When I had made something more than a league of way by the help of this current or eddy, I found it was spent, and served me no farther. However, I found that being between two great currents, viz. that on the south side, which had hurried me away, and that on the north, which lay about a league on the other side; I say, between these two, in the wake of the island, I found the water at least still, and running no way; and having still a breeze of wind fair for me, I kept on steering directly for the island, though not making such fresh way as I did before.

About four o'clock in the evening, being then within a league of the island, I found the point of the rocks which occasioned this disaster, stretching out, as is described before, to the southward, and casting off the current more southerly, had, of course, made another eddy to the north; and this I found very strong, but not directly setting the way my course lay, which was due west, but almost full north. However, having a fresh gale, I stretched across this eddy, slanting north-west; and in about an hour came within about a mile of the shore, where, it being smooth water, I soon got to land.

When I was on shore, I fell on my knees, and gave God thanks for my deliverance, resolving to lay aside all thoughts of my deliverance by my boat; and refreshing myself with such things as I had, I brought my boat close to the shore, in a little cove that I had spied under some trees, and laid me down to sleep, being quite spent with the labour and fatigue of the voyage.

I was now at a great loss which way to get home with my boat! I had run so much hazard, and knew too much of the case, to think of attempting it by the way I went out; and what might be at the other side (I mean the west side) I knew not, nor had

I any mind to run any more ventures: so I resolved on the next morning to make my way westward along the shore, and to see if there was no creek where I might lay up my frigate in safety, so as to have her again, if I wanted her. In about three miles, or thereabouts, coasting the shore, I came to a very good inlet or bay, about a mile over, which narrowed till it came to a very little rivulet or brook, where I found a very convenient harbour for my boat, and where she lay as if she had been in a little dock made on purpose for her. Here I put in, and having stowed my boat very safe, I went on shore to look about me, and see where I was.

I soon found I had but a little passed by the place where I had been before, when I travelled on foot to that shore; so taking nothing out of my boat but my gun and umbrella, for it was exceedingly hot, I began my march. The way was comfortable enough after such a voyage as I had been upon, and I reached my old bower in the evening, where I found every thing standing as I left it; for I always kept it in good order, being, as I said before, my country-house.

I got over the fence, and laid me down in the shade to rest my limbs, for I was very weary, and fell asleep; but judge you, if you can, that read my story, what a surprise I must be in when I was awaked out of my sleep by a voice, calling me by my name several times, "Robin, Robin, Robin Crusoe: poor Robin Crusoe! Where are you, Robin Crusoe? Where are you? Where have you been?"

I was so dead asleep at first, being fatigued with rowing, or paddling as it is called, the first part of the day, and with walking the latter part that I did not wake thoroughly; but dozing between sleeping and waking, thought I dreamed that somebody spoke to me; but as the voice continued to repeat, "Robin Crusoe, Robin Crusoe," at last I began to wake more perfectly and was at first dreadfully frightened, and started up in the utmost consternation; but no sooner were my eyes open, but I saw my Poll sitting on the top of the hedge; and immediately knew that it was he that spoke to me; for just in such bemoaning language I had used to talk to him, and teach him; and he had learned it so perfectly that he would sit upon my finger, and lay his bill close to my face, and cry, "Poor Robin Crusoe! Where are you? Where have you been? How came you here?" and such things as I had taught him.

However, even though I knew it was the parrot, and that indeed it could be nobody else, it was a good while before I could compose myself. First, I was amazed how the creature got thither; and then, how he should just keep about the place, and nowhere else; but as I was well satisfied it could be nobody but honest Poll, I got over it; and holding out my hand, and calling him by his name, "Poll," the sociable creature came to me, and sat upon my thumb, as he used to do, and continued talking to me, "Poor Robin Crusoe! And how did I come here? and where had I been?" just as if he had been overjoyed to see me again; and so I carried him home along with me.

GULLIVER AT LILLIPUT AND BROBDINGNAG[1]

Jonathan Swift
(1667-1745)

I

How He was Wrecked upon the Shores of Lilliput

MY FATHER had a small estate in Nottinghamshire; I was the third of five sons. He sent me to Emanuel college in Cambridge, at fourteen years old, where I resided three years, and applied myself close to my studies; but the charge of maintaining me, although I had a very scanty allowance, being too great for a narrow fortune, I was bound apprentice to Mr James Bates, an eminent surgeon in London, with whom I continued four years; and my father now and then sending me small sums of money, I laid them out in learning navigation, and other parts of the mathematics, useful to those who intend to travel, as I always believed it would be, some time or other, my fortune to do. When I left Mr Bates, I went down to my father; where, by the assistance of him and my uncle John, and some other relations, I got forty pounds, and a promise of thirty pounds a year to maintain me at Leyden; there I studied physic two years and seven months, knowing it would be useful in long voyages.

Soon after my return from Leyden, I was recommended by my good master, Mr Bates, to be surgeon to the *Swallow,* Captain Abraham Pannell, commander: with whom I continued three years and a half, making a voyage or two into the Levant, and some other parts. When I came back I resolved to settle in London: to which Mr Bates, my master, encouraged me, and by him I was recommended to several patients. I took part of a small house in the Old Jewry; and being advised to alter my condition, I married Mrs Mary Burton, second daughter to Mr Edmund Burton, hosier, in Newgate-street, with whom I received four hundred pounds for a portion.

But my good master Bates dying in two years after, and I having few friends, my business began to fail; for my conscience would not suffer me to imitate the bad practice of too many among my brethren. Having therefore consulted with my wife, and some of my acquaintance, I determined to go again to sea. I was surgeon successively in two ships, and made several voyages, for six years, to the East and West Indies, by which I got some addition to my fortune. My hours of leisure I spent in reading the best authors, ancient and modern, being always provided with a good number of books; and when I was ashore, in observing the manners and

[1] From *Gulliver's Travels.*

dispositions of the people, as well as learning their language; wherein I had a great facility, by the strength of my memory.

The last of these voyages not proving very fortunate, I grew weary of the sea and intended to stay at home with my wife and family. I removed from the Old Jewry to Fetter-lane, and from thence to Wapping, hoping to get business among the sailors, but it would not turn to account. After three years' expectation that things would mend, I accepted an advantageous offer from Captain William Prichard, master of the *Antelope,* who was making a voyage to the South Sea. We set sail from Bristol, May 4, 1699, and our voyage at first was very prosperous.

It would not be proper, for some reasons, to trouble the reader with the particulars of our adventures in those seas; let it suffice to inform him, that in our passage from thence to the East Indies, we were driven by a violent storm to the north-west of Van Diemen's Land. By an observation, we found ourselves in the latitude of 30 degrees 2 minutes south. Twelve of our crew were dead by immoderate labour and ill food; the rest were in a very weak condition. On the 5th of November, which was the beginning of summer in those parts, the weather being very hazy, the seamen spied a rock within half a cable's length of the ship; but the wind was so strong, that we were driven directly upon it, and split. Six of the crew, of whom I was one, having let down the boat into the sea, made shift to get clear of the ship and the rock. We rowed, by my computation, about three leagues, till we were able to work no longer, being already spent with labour while we were in the ship. We therefore trusted ourselves to the mercy of the waves, and in about half an hour the boat was overset by a sudden flurry from the north. What became of my companions in the boat, as well as of those who escaped on the rock, or were left in the vessel, I cannot tell; but conclude they were all lost.

For my own part, I swam as fortune directed me, and was pushed forward by the wind and tide. I often let my legs drop, and could feel no bottom; but when I was almost gone, and able to struggle no longer, I found myself within my depth; and by this time the storm was so much abated. The declivity was so small, that I walked near a mile before I got to the shore, which I conjectured was about eight o'clock in the evening. I then advanced forward near half a mile, but could not discover any sign of houses or inhabitants; at least I was in so weak a condition, that I did not observe them. I was extremely tired, and with that, and the heat of the weather, and about half a pint of brandy that I drank as I left the ship, I found myself much inclined to sleep. I lay down on the grass, which was very short and soft, where I slept sounder than I ever remembered to have done in my life, and, as I reckoned, about nine hours; for when I awaked, it was just day-light. I attempted to rise, but was not able to stir; for as I happened to lie on my back, I found my arms and legs were strongly fastened on each side to the ground; and my hair, which was long and thick, tied down in the same manner. I likewise felt several slender ligatures across my body, from my arm-pits to my thighs. I could only look upwards, the sun began to grow hot, and the light offended my eyes. I heard a confused noise about me; but in the posture I lay, could see nothing except the sky. In a little time I felt something alive moving on my left leg, which advancing gently forward over my breast came almost up to my chin; when bending my eyes downward as much as I could, I perceived it to be a human creature not six inches high, with a bow and arrow in his hands, and a quiver at his back. In the mean time, I felt at least forty more of the same kind (as I conjectured) following the first. I was in the utmost astonishment, and roared so loud, that they all ran back in a fright; and some of them, as I was afterwards told, were hurt with the falls they got by leaping from my sides upon the ground. However, they soon returned, and one of them, who ventured so far as to get a full sight of my face, lifting up his hands and eyes by way of admiration, cried out in a shrill but distinct voice, *Hekinah degul!*

II

How He Captured the Blefuscu Fleet

The Empire of Blefuscu is an island situated to the north-east of Lilliput, from which it is parted only by a channel of eight hundred yards wide. I had not yet seen it, and upon this notice of an intended invasion, I avoided appearing on that side of the coast, for fear of being discovered by some of the enemy's ships, who had received no intelligence of me; all intercourse between the two empires having been strictly forbidden during the war, upon pain of death, and an embargo laid by our emperor upon all vessels whatsoever. I communicated to his majesty a project I had formed, of seizing the enemy's whole fleet; which as our scouts assured us lay at anchor in the harbour, ready to sail with the first fair wind. I consulted the most experienced seamen upon the depth of the channel, which they had often plumbed; who told me, that in the middle at high water it was seventy *glumgluffs* deep, which is about six feet of European measure; and the rest of it fifty *glumgluffs* at most.

I walked towards the north-east coast, over against Blefuscu; where, lying down behind a hillock, I took out my small perspective glass, and viewed the enemy's fleet at anchor, consisting of about fifty men of war, and a great number of transports: I then came back to my house, and gave orders (for which I had a warrant) for a great quantity of the strongest cable and bars of iron. The cable was about as thick as packthread, and the bars of the length and size of a knitting-needle. I trebled the cable to make it stronger, and for the same reason I twisted three of the iron bars together, bending the extremities into a hook. Having thus fixed fifty hooks to as many cables, I went back to the north-east coast, and putting off my coat, shoes, and stockings, walked into the sea, in my leathern jerkin, about half an hour before high water. I waded with what haste I could, and swam in the middle about thirty yards, till I felt ground. I arrived at the fleet in less than half an hour. The enemy were so frightened when they saw me, that they leaped out of their ships and swam to shore, where there could not be fewer than thirty thousand souls: I then took my tackling, and fastening a hook to the hole at the prow of each, I tied all the cords together at the end.

While I was thus employed, the enemy discharged several thousand arrows, many of which stuck in my hands and face; and, besides the excessive smart, gave me much disturbance in my work. My greatest apprehension was for mine eyes, which I should have infallibly lost, if I had not suddenly thought of an expedient. I kept, among other little necessaries, a pair of spectacles, in a private pocket, which, as I observed before, had escaped the emperor's searchers. These I took out, and fastened as strongly as I could upon my nose, and thus armed, went on boldly with my work, in spite of the enemy's arrows, many of which struck against the glasses of my spectacles, but without any other effect than a little to discompose them. I had now fastened all the hooks, and taking the knot in my hand, began to pull; but not a ship would stir, for they were all too fast held by their anchors; so that the boldest part of my enterprise remained. I therefore let go the cord, and leaving the hooks fixed to the ships, I resolutely cut with my knife the cables that fastened the anchors, receiving about two hundred shots in my face and hands; then I took up the knotted end of the cables, to which my hooks were tied, and with the greatest ease drew fifty of the enemy's largest men-of-war after me.

The Blefuscudians, who had not the least imagination of what I intended, were at first confounded with astonishment. They had seen me cut the cables, and thought my design was only to let the ships run adrift, or fall foul of each other, but when they perceived the whole fleet moving in order, and saw me pulling at the end, they set up such a scream of grief and despair as it is almost impossible to describe or conceive. When I had got out of danger, I stopped awhile to pick out the arrows that stuck in my hands and face; and rubbed on some of the same ointment that was given me on my first arrival, as I have formerly mentioned. I then took off my spectacles, and waiting about an hour, till the tide was a little fallen, I waded through the middle with my cargo, and arrived safe at the royal port of Lilliput.

The emperor and his whole court stood on the shore, expecting the issue of this great adventure. They saw the ships move forward in a large half-moon, but could not discern me, who was up to my breast in water. When I advanced to the middle of the channel, they were yet in pain, because I was under water to my neck. The emperor concluded me to be drowned, and that the enemy's fleet was approaching in a hostile manner; but he soon eased of his fears; for the channel growing shallower every step I made, I came in a short time within hearing, and holding up the end of the cable, by which the fleet was fastened, I cried in a loud voice, "Long live the most puissant king of Lilliput!" This great prince received me at my landing with all possible encomiums, and created me a *nardac* upon the spot, which is the highest title of honour among them.

III

How He Voyaged to Brobdingnag

Having been condemned, by nature and fortune, to an active and restless life, in two months after my return, I again left my native country, and took shipping in the Downs, on the 20th day of June, 1702, in the *Adventure,* captain John Nicholas, a Cornishman, commander, bound for Surat. We had a very prosperous gale, till we arrived at the Cape of Good Hope, where we landed for fresh water; but discovering a leak, we unshipped our goods, and wintered there; for the captain falling sick of an ague, we could not leave the Cape till the end of March. We then set sail, and had a good voyage till we passed the Straits of Madagascar; but having got northward of that island, and to about five degrees south latitude, the winds, which in those seas are observed to blow a constant equal gale between the north and west, from the beginning of December to the beginning of May, on the 19th of April began to blow with much greater violence, and more westerly than usual, continuing so for twenty days together: during which time, we were driven a little to the east of Molucca Islands, and about three degrees northward of the line, as our captain found by an observation he took the 2nd of May, at which time the wind ceased, and it was a perfect calm, whereat I was not a little rejoiced. But he, being a man well experienced in the navigation of those seas, bid us all prepare against a storm, which accordingly happened the day following; for the southern wind, called the southern monsoon, began to set in.

Finding it was likely to overblow, we took in our sprit-sail, and stood by to hand the fore-sail, but, making foul weather, we looked the guns were all fast and handed the mizen. The ship lay very broad off, so we thought it better spooning before the sea, than trying or hulling. We reefed the foresail, and set him, and hauled aft the fore-sheet; the helmwas hard a-weather. The ship wore bravely. We belayed the fore downhaul; but the sail was split, and we hauled down the yard, and got the sail into the ship, and unbound all the things clear of it. It was a very fierce storm; and the sea broke strange and dangerous. We hauled off upon the laniard of the whip-staff, and helped the man at the helm. We would not get down our top-mast, but let all stand, because she scudded before the sea very well, and we knew that the top-mast being aloft, the ship was the wholesomer, and made better way through the sea, seeing we had sea-room. When the storm was over, we set fore-sail and main-sail, and brought the ship to. Then we set the mizen, main-topsail, and the fore-top-sail. Our course was east-north-east, the wind was at south-west. We got the starboard tacks aboard;we cast off our weather bowlings, weather-braces and lifts; we set in the lee-braces, and hauled them tight, and belayed them; and hauled over the mizen and hauled forward by tack to windward, and kept her full and by as near as she would lie.

During this storm, which was followed by a strong wind west-southwest, we were carried, by my computation, about five hundred leagues to the east, so that the oldest sailor on board could not tell in what part of the world we were. Our provisions held out well; our ship was staunch, and our crew all in good health; but we lay in the utmost distress for water. We thought it best to hold on the same course, rather than turn more northerly, which might have brought us to the north-west part of great Tartary, and into the Frozen Sea.

On the 16th day of June, 1703, a boy on the topmast discovered land. On the 17th, we came in full view of a great island or continent (for we knew not whether); on the south side whereof was a small neck of land jutting out into the sea, and a creek too shallow to hold a ship of above one hundred tons. We cast anchor within a league of this creek, and our captain sent a dozen of his men well armed in the long boat, with vessels for water, if any could be found. I desired his leave to go with them, that I might see the country, and make what discoveries I could. When we came to land, we saw no river, or spring, nor any sign of inhabitants. Our men therefore wandered on the shore to find out some fresh water near the sea, and I walked alone about a mile on the other side, where I observed the country all barrenland rocky. I now began to be weary, and seeing nothing to entertain my curiosity, I returned gently down towards the creek; and the sea being full in my view, I saw our men already got into the boat, and rowing for life to the ship. I was going to holla after them, although it had been to little purpose, when I observed a huge creature walking after them in the sea, as fast as he could: he waded not much deeper than his knees, and took prodigious strides: but our men had the start of him half a league, and the sea thereabouts being full of sharp-pointed rocks, the monster was not able to overtake the boat. This I was afterwards told, for I durst not stay to see the issue of the adventure; and ran as fast as I could the way I first went, and then climbed up a steep hill, which gave me some prospect of the country. I found it fully cultivated; but that which first surprised me was the length of the grass, which, in those grounds that seemed to be kept for hay, was about twenty feet high.

I fell into a high road, for so I took it to be, though it served to the inhabitants only as a foot-path, through a field of barley. Here I walked on for some time, but could see little on either side, it being now near harvest, and the corn rising at least forty feet. I was an hour walking to the end of this field, which was fenced in with a hedge of at least one hundred and twenty feet high, and the trees so lofty that I could make no computation of their altitude. There was a stile to pass from this field into the next. It had four steps, and a stone to cross over when you came to the uppermost. It was impossible for me to climb this stile, because every step was six feet high, and the upper stone about twenty.

I was endeavouring to find some gap in the hedge, when I discovered one of the inhabitants in the next field, advancing towards the stile, of the same size with him whom I saw in the sea pursuing our boat. He appeared as tall as an ordinary spire steeple, and took about ten yards at every stride, as near as I could guess. I was struck with the utmost fear and astonishment, and ran to hide myself in the corn, whence I saw him at the top of the stile, looking back into the next field on the right hand, and heard him call in a voice many degrees louder than a speaking trumpet; but the noise was so high in the air, that at first I certainly thought it was thunder. Whereupon seven monsters, like himself, came towards him, with reaping hooks in their hands, each hook about the largeness of six scythes. These people were not so well clad as the first, whose servants or labourers they seemed to be; for, upon some words he spoke, they went to reap the corn in the field where I lay. I kept from them at as great a distance as I could, but was forced to move with extreme difficulty, for the stalks of the corn were sometimes not above a foot distant, so that I could hardly squeeze my body betwixt them. However I made a shift to go forward, till I came to a part of the field where the corn had been laid by the rain and wind. Here it was impossible for me to advance a step; for the stalks were so interwoven, that I could not creep through, and the beards of the fallen ears so strong and pointed, that they pierced through my clothes into my flesh. At the same time I heard the reapers not above a hundred yards behind me.

Being quite dispirited with toil, and wholly overcome by grief and despair, I lay down between two ridges, and heartily wished I might there end my days. I bemoaned my desolate widow and fatherless children. I lamented my own folly and wilfulness, in attempting a second voyage, against the advice of all my friends and relations. In this terrible agitation of mind, I could not forbear thinking of Lilliput, whose inhabitants looked upon me as the greatest prodigy that ever appeared in the world; where I was able to draw an imperial fleet in my hand, and perform those other actions which will be recorded for ever in the chronicles of that empire; while posterity shall hardly believe them, although attested by millions. I reflected what a mortification it must prove to me to appear as inconsiderable in this nation, as one single Lilliputian would be among us. But this I conceived was to be the least of my misfortunes; for, as human creatures are observed to be more savage and cruel in proportion to their bulk, what could I expect but to be a morsel in the mouth of the first among these enormous barbarians who should happen to seize me? Undoubtedly philosophers are in the right, when they tell us nothing is great or little otherwise than by comparison. It might have pleased fortune, to have let the Lilliputians find some nation where the people were as diminutive with respect to them, as they were to me. And who knows but that even this prodigious race of mortals might be equally overmatched in some distant part of the world, whereof we have yet no discovery.

Feared and confounded as I was, I could not forbear going on with these reflections, when one of the reapers approaching within ten yards of the ridge where I lay, made me apprehend that with the next step I should be squashed to death under his foot, or cut in two with his reaping hook. And therefore, when he was again about to move, I screamed as loud as fear could make me; whereupon the huge creature trod short, and looking round about under him for some time, at last espied me as I lay on the ground. He considered awhile, with the caution of one who endeavours to lay hold on a small dangerous animal in such a manner that it shall not be able either to scratch or bite him, as I myself had sometimes done with a weasel in England. At length he ventured to take me behind, by the middle, between his fore-finger and thumb, and brought me within three yards of his eyes, that he might behold my shape more perfectly. I guessed his meaning, and my good fortune gave me so much presence of mind, that I resolved not to struggle in the least as he held me in the air, above sixty feet from the ground, although he grievously pinched my sides, for fear I should slip through his fingers. All I ventured was to raise mine eyes towards the sun, and place my hands together in a supplicating posture, and to speak some words in an humble melancholy tone, suitable to the condition I then was in: for I apprehended every moment that he would dash me against the ground, as we usually do any little hateful animal which we have a mind to destroy. But my good star would have it, that he appeared pleased with my voice and gestures, and began to look upon me as a curiosity, much wondering to hear me pronounce articulate words, although he could not understand them. In the mean time I was not able to forbear groaning and shedding tears, and turning my head towards my sides; letting him know, as well as I could, how cruelly I was hurt by the pressure of his thumb and finger. He seemed to apprehend my meaning; for, lifting up the lappet of his coat, he put me gently into it.

IV

And of His Escape Therefrom

The king thought proper to pass a few days at a palace he has near Flanflasnic, a city within eighteen English miles of the seaside. Glumdalclitch and I were much fatigued, I had gotten a small cold, but the poor girl was so ill as to be confined to her chamber. I longed to see the ocean, which must be the only scene of my escape, if ever it should happen. I pretended to be worse than I really was, and desired leave to take the fresh air of the sea, with a page whom I was very fond of, and who had sometimes been trusted with me. I shall never forget with what unwillingness Glumdalclitch consented, nor the strict charge she gave the page to be careful of me, bursting at the same time into a flood of tears, as if she had some foreboding of what was to happen. The boy took me out in my box, about half an hour's walk from the palace, towards the rocks on the sea-shore. I ordered him to set me down, and lifting up one of my sashes, cast many a wistful melancholy look towards the sea. I found myself not very well, and told the page that I had a mind to take a nap in my hammock, which I hoped would do me good. I got in, and the boy shut the window close down to keep out the cold. I soon fell asleep, and all I conjecture is, while I slept, the page, thinking no danger could happen, went among the rocks to look for birds' eggs, having before observed him from my window searching about, and picking up one or two in the clefts. Be that as it will, I found myself suddenly awaked with a violent pull upon the ring, which was fastened at the top of my box, for the convenience of carriage. I felt my box raised very high in the air, and then borne forward with prodigious speed. The first jolt had like to have shaken me out of my hammock, but afterward the motion was easy enough. I called out several times as loud as I could raise my voice, but all to no purpose. I looked towards my windows, and could see nothing but the clouds and sky. I heard a noise just over my head, like the clapping of wings, and then began to perceive the woeful condition I was in; that some eagle had got the ring of my box in his beak, with an intent to let it fall on a rock, like a tortoise in a shell, and then pick out my body, and devour it: for the sagacity and smell of this bird enables him to discover his quarry at a great distance, though better concealed than I could be within a two-inch board.

In a little time, I observed the noise and flutter of wings to increase very fast, and my box was tossed up and down like a sign on a windy day. I heard several bangs or buffets, as I thought, given to the eagle (for such I am certain it must have been that held the ring of my box in his beak), and then, all on a sudden, felt myself falling perpendicularly down, for above a minute, but with such incredible swiftness that I almost lost my breath. My fall was stopped by a terrible squash, that sounded louder to my ears than the cataract of Niagara; after which, I was quite in the dark for another minute, and then my box began to rise so high, that I could see light from the tops of the windows. I now perceived I was fallen into the sea. My box, by the weight of my body, the goods that were in, and the broad plate of iron fixed for strength at the four corners of the top and bottom, floated about five feet deep in water. I did then, and do now suppose that the eagle which flew away with my box was pursued by two or three others, and forced to let me drop, while he defended himself against the rest, who hoped to share in the prey. The plates of iron fastened at the bottom of the box (for those were the strongest) preserved the balance while it fell, and hindered it from being broken on the surface of the water. Every joint of it was well grooved; and the door did not move on hinges, but up and down like a sash, which kept *my* closet so tight that very little water came in. I got with much difficulty out of my hammock, having first ventured to draw back the slip-board on the roof already mentioned, contrived on purpose to let in air, for want of which I found myself almost stifled.

How often did I then wish myself with my dear Glumdalclitch, from whom one single hour had so far divided me! And I may say with truth, that in the midst of my own misfortunes, I could not forbear lamenting my poor nurse, the grief she would suffer for my loss, the displeasure of the queen, and the ruin of her fortune. Perhaps many travellers have not been under greater difficulties and distress than I was at this juncture, expecting every moment to see my box dashed to pieces, or at least overset by the first violent blast, or rising wave. A breach in one pane of glass would have been immediate death: nor could anything have preserved the windows, but the strong lattice wires on the outside, against accidents in travelling. I saw the water ooze in at several crannies, although the leaks were not considerable, and I endeavoured to stop them as well as I could. I was not able to lift up the roof of my closet, which otherwise I certainly should have done, and sat on the top of it; where I might at least preserve myself some hours longer, than by being shut up (as I may call it) in the hold. Or if I escaped these dangers for a day or two, what could I expect but a miserable death of cold and hunger? I was four hours under these circumstances, expecting and indeed wishing, every moment to be my last.

I have already told the reader that there were two strong staples fixed upon that side of my box which had no window, and into which the servant who used to carry me on horseback would put a leathern belt, and buckle it about his waist. Being in this disconsolate state, I heard, or at least thought I heard, some kind of grating noise on that side of my box where the staples were fixed; and soon after I began to fancy that the box was pulled or towed along the sea; for I now and then felt a sort of tugging, which made the waves rise near the tops of my windows, leaving me almost in the dark. This gave me some faint hopes of relief, although I was not able to imagine how it could be brought about. I ventured to unscrew one of my chairs, which were always fastened to the floor; and having made a hard shift to screw it down again, directly under the slipping-board that I had lately opened, I mounted on the chair, and putting my mouth as near as I could to the hole, I called for help in a loud voice, and in all the languages I understood. I then fastened my handkerchief to a stick I usually carried, and thrusting it up the hole, waved it several times in the air, that if any boat or ship were near, the seamen might conjecture some unhappy mortal to be shut up in the box.

I found no effect from all I could do, but plainly perceived my closet to be moved along; and in the space of an hour, or better, that side of the box where the staples were, and had no windows, struck against something that was hard. I apprehended it to be a rock, and found myself tossed more than ever. I plainly heard a noise upon the cover of my closet, like that of a cable, and the grating of it as it passed through the ring. I then found myself hoisted up, by degrees, at least three feet higher than I was before. Whereupon I again thrust up my stick and handkerchief, calling for help till I was almost hoarse. In return to which, I heard a great shout repeated three times, giving me such transports of joy, as are not to be conceived but by those who feel them. I now heard a trampling over my head, and somebody calling through the hole with a loud voice, in the English tongue, "If there be anybody below, let them speak." I answered, "I was an Englishman drawn by ill-fortune into the greatest calamity that ever any creature underwent, and begged, by all that was moving, to be delivered of the dungeon I was to." The voice replied, "I was safe, for my box was fastened to their ship; and the carpenter should immediately come and saw a hole in the cover, large enough to pull me out." I answered, "that was needless, and would take up too much time; for there was no more to be done, but to let one of the crew put his finger into the ring, and take the box out of the sea into the ship, and so into the captain's cabin." Some of them, upon hearing me talk so wildly, thought I was mad; others laughed; for indeed it never came into my head, that I was now got among people of my own stature and strength. The carpenter came, and in a few minutes sawed a passage of about four feet square, then let down a small ladder, upon which I mounted, and thence was taken into the ship in a very weak condition.

The sailors were all in amazement, and asked me a thousand questions which I had no inclination to answer. I was equally confounded at the sight of so many pigmies, for such I took them to be, after having so long accustomed mine eyes to the monstrous objects I had left. But the Captain, Mr. Thomas Wilcocks, an honest, worthy Shropshire man, observing I was ready to faint, took me into his cabin, gave me a cordial to comfort me, and made me turn in upon his own bed, advising me to take a little rest, of which I had great need.

I slept some hours, but perpetually disturbed with dreams of the place I had left, and the dangers I had escaped. However, upon waking, I found myself much recovered. It was now about eight o'clock at night, and the captain ordered supper immediately, thinking I had already fasted too long. He entertained me with great kindness, observing me not to look wildly, or talk inconsistently; and, when we were left alone, desired I would give him a relation of my travels, and by what accident I came to be set adrift, in that monstrous wooden chest. He said, "that about twelve o'clock at noon, as he was looking through his glass, he espied it at a distance, and thought it was a sail, which he had a mind to make, being not much out of his course, in hopes of buying some biscuit, his own beginning to fall short. That upon coming nearer and finding his error, his sent out his long boat, to discover what it was; that his men came back in a fright, swearing they had seen a swimming house. That he laughed at their folly, and went himself in the boat, ordering his men to take a strong cable along with them. That the weather being calm, he rowed round me several times, observed my windows and wire lattices that defended them. That he discovered two staples upon one side, which was all of boards, without any passage for light. He then commanded his men to row up to that side, and fastening a cable to one of the staples, ordered them to tow my chest, as they called it, towards the ship. When it was there, he gave directions to fasten another cable to the ring fixed in the cover, and to raise up my chest with pulleys, which all the sailors were not able to do above two or three feet. He said, they saw my stick and handkerchief thrust out of the hole, and concluded that some unhappy man must be shut up in the cavity."

I asked "whether he or the crew had seen any prodigious birds in the air, about the time he first discovered me." To which he answered, "that discoursing this matter with the sailors while I was asleep, one of them said, he had observed three eagles flying towards the north, but remarked nothing of their being larger than the usual size"; which I suppose must be imputed to the great height they were at; and he could not guess the reason of my question. I then asked the captain "how far he reckoned we might be from land?" He said, "by the best computation he could make, we were at least a hundred leagues." I assured him he must be mistaken by almost half, for I had not left the country from whence I came above two hours before I dropped into the sea. Whereupon he began to think that my brain was disturbed, of which he gave me a hint and advised me to go to bed in a cabin he had provided. I assured him, "I was well refreshed with his good entertainment and company, and as much in my senses as ever I was in my life." He then grew serious, and desired to ask me freely, whether I were not troubled in my mind by the consciousness of some enormous crime, for which I was punished, at the command of some prince, by exposing me in that chest; as great criminals, in other countries, have been forced to sea in a leaky vessel, without provisions: for although he would be sorry to have taken so ill a man into his ship, yet he would engage his word to set me safe ashore, in the first port where we arrived. He added, "that his suspicions were much increased by some very absurd speeches I had delivered at first to his sailors, and afterwards to himself, in relation to my closet or chest, as well as by my odd looks and behaviour while I was at supper."

I begged his patience to hear me tell my story, which I faithfully did, from the last time I left England to the moment he first discovered me. And as truth always forces its way into rational minds, so this honest, worthy gentleman, who had some tincture of learning, and very good sense, was immediately convinced of my candour and veracity and said, "he hoped when we returned to England, I would oblige the world by putting it on paper, and making it public." My answer was, "that I thought we were overstocked with books of travels: that nothing could now pass which was not extraordinary; wherein I doubted some authors less consulted truth than their own vanity, or interest, or the diversion of ignorant readers; that my story could contain little beside common events, without those ornamental descriptions of strange plants, trees, birds, and other animals; or of the barbarous customs and idolatry of savage people, with which most writers abound." However, I thanked him for his good opinion, and promised to take the matter into my thoughts.

The captain having been at Tonquin, was, in his return to England, driven north-eastward to the latitude of 44 degrees, and longitude of 143. But meeting a trade wind two days after I came on board him, we sailed southward a long time, and coasting New-Holland kept our course west-south-west, and then south-south-west, till we doubled the Cape of Good Hope. Our voyage was very prosperous, and I shall not trouble the reader with a journal of it. The captain called in at one or two ports, and sent in his long-boat for provisions and fresh water; but I never went out of the ship till we came into the Downs, which was on the third day of June 1706, about nine months after my escape. I offered to leave my goods in security for payment of my freight, but the captain protested he would not receive one farthing. We look a kind leave of each other, and I made him promise he would come and see me at my house in Redriff. I hired a horse and guide for five shillings, which I borrowed of the captain.

As I was on the road, observing the littleness of the houses, the trees, the cattle, and the people, I began to think myself in Lilliput. I was afraid of trampling upon every traveller I met, and often called aloud to have them stand out of the way, so that I had liked to have gotten one or two broken heads for my impertinence.

When I came to my own house, for which I was forced to inquire, one of the servants opening the door, I bent down to go in (like a goose under a gate), for fear of striking my head. My wife ran out to embrace me, but I stooped lower than her knees, thinking she could otherwise never be able to reach my mouth. My daughter kneeled to ask my blessing, but I could not see her till she rose, having been so long used to stand with my head and eyes erect to above sixty feet; and then I went to take her up with one hand by the waist. I looked down upon the servants, and one or two friends who were in the house, as if they had been pigmies, and I a giant. I told my wife, "she had been too thrifty, for I found she had starved herself and her daughter to nothing." In short, I behaved myself so unaccountably, that they were all of the Captain's opinion when he first saw me and concluded I had lost my wits. This I mention as an instance of the great power of habit and prejudice.

In a little time, I and my family and friends came to a right understanding: but my wife protested I should never go to sea any more.

TRAFALGAR[1]

Robert Southey
(1774-1843)

THE station which Nelson had chosen was some fifty or sixty miles to the west of Cadiz, near Cape St Mary. At this distance he hoped to decoy the enemy out, while he guarded against the danger of being caught with a westerly wind near Cadiz, and driven within the Straits. The blockade of the port was rigorously enforced, in hopes that the combined fleets might be forced to sea by want. The Danish vessels therefore, which were carrying provisions from the French ports in the bay, under the name of Danish property, to all the little ports from Ayamonte to Algeziras, from whence they were conveyed in coasting boats to Cadiz, were seized. Without this proper exertion of power the blockade would have been rendered nugatory by the advantage thus taken of the neutral flag. The supplies from France were thus effectually cut off. There was now every indication that the enemy would speedily venture out; officers and men were in the highest spirits at the prospect of giving them a decisive blow—such, indeed, as would put an end to all further contests upon the seas.

On the 9th Nelson sent Collingwood what he called in his diary the "Nelson touch." "I send you," said he, "my plan of attack, as far as a man dare venture to guess at the very uncertain position the enemy may be found in; but it is to place you perfectly at ease respecting my intentions, and to give full scope to your judgment for carrying them into effect. We can, my dear Coll, have no little jealousies. We have only one great object in view, that of annihilating our enemies, and getting a glorious peace for our country. No man has more confidence in another than I have in you, and no man will render your services more justice than your very old friend, Nelson and Bronte."

The order of sailing was to be the order of battle—the fleet in two lines, with an advanced squadron of eight of the fastest sailing twodeckers. The second in command, having the entire direction of his line, was to break through the enemy, about the twelfth ship from their rear; he would lead through the centre, and the advanced squadron was to cut off three or four ahead of the centre. This plan was to be adapted to the strength of the enemy, so that they should always be one-fourth

[1] From *The Life of Nelson.*

superior to those whom they cut off. Nelson said that "his admirals and captains, knowing his precise object to be that of a close and decisive action, would supply any deficiency of signals and act accordingly. In case signals cannot be seen or clearly understood, no captain can do wrong if he places his ship alongside that of an enemy."

About half-past nine in the morning of the 19th the *Mars,* being the nearest to the fleet of the ships which formed the line of communication with the frigates inshore, repeated the signal that the enemy were coming out of port. The wind was at this time very light, with partial breezes, mostly from the S.S.W. Nelson ordered the signal to be made for a chase in the south-east quarter. About two the repeating ships announced that the enemy were at sea. All night the British fleet continued under all sail, steering to the south-east. At daybreak they were in the entrance of the Straits, but the enemy were not in sight. About seven, one of the frigates made signal that the enemy were bearing north. Upon this the *Victory* hove to, and shortly afterwards Nelson made sail again to the northward. In the afternoon the wind blew fresh from the south-west, and the English began to fear that the foe might be forced to return to port.

A little before sunset, however, Blackwood, in the *Euryalus,* telegraphed that they appeared determined to go to the westward. "And that," said the Admiral in his diary, "they shall not do, if it is the power of Nelson and Bronte to prevent them." Nelson had signified to Blackwood that he depended upon him to keep sight of the enemy. They were observed so well that all their motions were made known to him, and as they wore twice, he inferred that they were aiming to keep the port of Cadiz open, and would retreat there as soon as they saw the British fleet; for this reason he was very careful not to approach near enough to be seen by them during the night. At daybreak the combined fleets were distinctly seen from the *Victory's* deck, formed in a close line of battle ahead, on the starboard tack, about twelve miles to leeward, and standing to the south. Our fleet consisted of twenty-seven sail of the line and four frigates; theirs of thirty-three and seven large frigates. Their superiority was greater in size and weight of metal than in numbers. They had four thousand troops on board, and the best riflemen that could be procured, many of them Tyrolese, were dispersed through the ships.

Soon after daylight Nelson came upon deck. The 21st of October was a festival in his family, because on that day his uncle, Captain Suckling, in the *Dreadnought,* with two other line-of-battle ships, had beaten off a French squadron of four sail of the line and three frigates. Nelson, with that sort of superstition from which few persons are entirely exempt, had more than once expressed his persuasion that this was to be the day of his battle also, and he was well pleased at seeing his prediction about to be verified. The wind was now from the west—light breezes, with a long heavy swell. Signal was made to bear down upon the enemy in two lines, and the fleet set all sail. Collingwood, in the *Royal Sovereign,* led the lee line of thirteen ships; the *Victory* led the weather line of fourteen. Having seen that all was as it should be, Nelson retired to his cabin, and wrote the following prayer—

"May the great God whom I worship, grant to my country, and for the benefit of Europe in general, a great and glorious victory, and may no misconduct in any one tarnish it, and may humanity after victory be the predominant feature in the British fleet! For myself individually, I commit my life to Him that made me, and may His blessing alight on my endeavours for serving my country faithfully! To Him I resign myself, and the just cause which is entrusted to me to defend. Amen, Amen, Amen."

Blackwood went on board the *Victory* about six. He found him in good spirits, but very calm; not in that exhilaration which he felt upon entering into battle at Aboukir and Copenhagen; he knew that his own life would be particularly aimed at, and seems to have looked for death with almost as sure an expectation as for victory. His whole attention was fixed upon the enemy. They tacked to the northward, and formed their line on the larboard tack; thus bringing the shoals of Trafalgar and St. Pedro under the lee of the British, and keeping the port of Cadiz open for themselves. This was judiciously done; and Nelson, aware of all the advantages which he gave them, made signal to prepare to anchor.

Villeneuve was a skilful seaman, worthy of serving a better master and a better cause. His plan of defence was as well conceived and as original as the plan of attack. He formed the fleet in a double line, every alternate ship being about a cable's length to windward of her second ahead and astern. Nelson, certain of a triumphant issue to the day, asked Blackwood what he should consider as a victory. That officer answered that, considering the handsome way in which battle was offered by the enemy, their apparent determination for a fair trial of strength, and the situation of the land, he thought it would be a glorious result if fourteen were captured. He replied: "I shall not be satisfied with less than twenty." Soon afterwards he asked him if he did not think there was a signal wanting. Captain Blackwood made answer that he thought the whole fleet seemed very clearly to understand what they were about. These words were scarcely spoken before that signal was made which will be remembered as long as the language or even the memory of England shall endure—"ENGLAND EXPECTS EVERY MAN WILL DO HIS DUTY!" It was received throughout the fleet with a shout of answering acclamation, made sublime by the spirit which it breathed and the feeling which it expressed. "Now," said Lord Nelson, "I can do no more. We must trust to the great Disposer of all events and the justice of our cause. I thank God for this great opportunity of doing my duty."

He wore that day, as usual, his admiral's frock-coat, bearing on the left breast four stars of the different orders with which he was invested. Ornaments which rendered him so conspicuous a mark for the enemy were beheld with ominous apprehension by his officers. It was known that there were riflemen on board the French ships, and it could not be doubted but that his life would be particularly aimed at. They communicated their fears to each other, and the surgeon, Mr Beatty, spoke to the chaplain, Dr Scott, and to Mr Scott, the public secretary, desiring that some person would entreat him to change his dress or cover the stars; but they knew that such a request would highly displease him. "In honour I gained them," he had said when such a thing had been hinted to him formerly, "and in honour I will die with them." Mr Beatty, however, would not have been deterred by any fear of exciting his displeasure from speaking to him himself upon a subject in which the weal of England, as well as the life of Nelson, was concerned; but he was ordered from the deck before he could find an opportunity. This was a point upon which Nelson's officers knew that it was hopeless to remonstrate or reason with him; but both Blackwood and his own captain, Hardy, represented to him how advantageous to the fleet it would be for him to keep out of action as long as possible, and he consented at last to let the *Leviathan* and the *Temeraire,* which were sailing abreast of the *Victory,* be ordered to pass ahead.

Yet even here the last infirmity of this noble mind was indulged, for these ships could not pass ahead if the *Victory* continued to carry all her sail; and so far was Nelson from shortening sail, that it was evident he took pleasure in pressing on, and rendering it impossible for them to obey his own orders. A long swell was setting into the Bay of Cadiz. Our ships, crowding all sail, moved majestically before it, with light winds from the south-west. The sun shone on the sails of the enemy, but their well-formed line, with their numerous three-deckers, made an appearance which any other assailants would have thought formidable, but the British sailors only admired the beauty and the splendour of the spectacle, and in full confidence of winning what they saw, remarked to each other what a fine sight yonder ships would make at Spithead!

The French admiral, from the *Bucentaure,* beheld the new manner in which his enemy was advancing—Nelson and Collingwood, each leading his line; and pointing them out to his officers, he is said to have exclaimed that such conduct could not fail to be successful. Yet Villeneuve had made his own dispositions with the utmost skill, and the fleets under his command waited for the attack with perfect coolness. Ten minutes before twelve they opened their fire. Eight or nine of the ships immediately ahead of the *Victory,* and across her bows, fired single guns at her to ascertain whether she was yet within their range. As soon as Nelson perceived that their shot passed over him, he desired Blackwood and Captain Prowse, of the *Sirius,* to repair to their respective frigates, and on their way to tell all the captains of the line-of-battle ships that he depended on their exertions, and that, if by the prescribed mode of attack they found it impracticable to get into action immediately, they might adopt whatever they thought best, provided it led them quickly and closely alongside an enemy. As they were standing on the poop, Blackwood took him by the hand, saying he hoped soon to return and find him in possession of twenty prizes. He replied, "God bless you, Blackwood; I shall never see you again."

Nelson's column was steered about two points more to the north than Collingwood's, in order to cut off the enemy's escape into Cadiz. The lee line, therefore, was first engaged. "See," cried Nelson, pointing to the *Royal Sovereign,* as she steered right for the centre of the enemy's line, cut through it astern of the *Santa Anna,* three-decker, and engaged her at the muzzle of her guns on the starboard side; "see how that noble fellow Collingwood carries his ship into action!" Collingwood, delighted at being first in the heat of the fire, and knowing the feelings his commander and old friend, turned to his captain and exclaimed: "Rotherham, what would Nelson give to be here!" Both these brave officers, perhaps, at this moment thought of Nelson with gratitude for a circumstance which had occurred on the preceding day. Admiral Collingwood, with some of the captains, having gone on board the *Victory* to receive instructions, Nelson inquired of him where his captain was, and was told in reply that they were not upon good terms with each other. "Terms!" said Nelson; "good terms with each other!" Immediately he sent a boat for Captain Rotherham, led him, so soon as he arrived, to Collingwood, and saying, "Look, yonder are the enemy!" bade them shake hands like Englishmen.

The enemy continued to fire a gun at a time at the *Victory* till they saw that a shot had passed through her main-topgallant sail; then they opened their broadsides, aiming chiefly at her rigging, in the hope of disabling her before she could close with them. Nelson as usual had hoisted several flags, lest one should be shot away. The enemy showed no colours till late in the action, when they began to feel the necessity of having them to strike. For this reason the *Santissima Trinidad,* Nelson's old acquaintance, as he used to call her, was distinguishable only by her four decks, and to the bow of this opponent he ordered the *Victory* to be steered. Meantime an incessant raking fire was kept up upon the *Victory.* The Admiral's secretary was one of the first who fell; he was killed by a cannon shot while conversing with Hardy. Captain Adair, of the marines, with the help of a sailor, endeavoured to remove the body from Nelson's sight, who had a great regard for Mr Scott, but he anxiously asked, "Is that poor Scott that's gone?" and being informed that it was indeed so, exclaimed, "Poor fellow!"

Presently a double-headed shot struck a party of marines who were drawn up on the poop, and killed eight of them, upon which Nelson immediately desired Captain Adair to disperse his men round the ship, that they might not suffer so much from being together. A few minutes afterwards a shot struck the fore-brace bits on the quarter-deck, and passed between Nelson and Hardy, a splinter from the bit tearing off Hardy's buckle and bruising his foot. Both stopped, and looked anxiously at each other: each supposed the other to be wounded. Nelson then smiled, and said: "This is too warm work, Hardy, to last long."

The *Victory* had not yet returned a single gun; fifty of her men had by this time been killed or wounded, and her main top mast, with all her studding sails and their booms, shot away. Nelson declared that in all his battles he had seen nothing which surpassed the cool courage of his crew on this occasion. At four minutes after twelve she opened her fire from both sides of her deck. It was not possible to break the enemy's lines without running on board one of their ships; Hardy informed him of this, and asked him which he would prefer. Nelson replied: "Take your choice, Hardy; it does not signify much." The master was ordered to put the helm to port, and the *Victory* ran on board the *Redoubtable* just as her tiller-ropes were shot away. The French ship received her with a broadside, then instantly let down her lower-deck ports for fear of being boarded through them, and never afterwards fired a great gun during the action. Her tops, like those of all the enemy's ships, were filled with riflemen. Nelson never placed musketry in his tops; he had a strong dislike to the practice, not merely because it endangers setting fire to the sails, but also because it is a murderous sort of warfare, by which individuals may suffer and a commander now and then be picked off, but which never can decide the fate of a general engagement.

Captain Harvey, in the *Temeraire,* fell on board the *Redoubtable* on the side; another enemy was in like manner on board the *Temeraire;* so that these four ships formed as compact a tier as if they had been moored together, their heads all lying the same way. The lieutenants of the *Victory* seeing this, depressed their guns of the middle and lower decks, and fired with a diminished charge, lest the shot should pass through and injure the *Temeraire;* and because there was danger that the *Redoubtable* might take fire from the lower deck guns, the muzzles of which touched her side when they were run out, the fireman of each gun stood ready with a bucket of water, which, as soon as the gun was discharged, he dashed into the hole made by the shot. An incessant fire was kept up from the *Victory* from both sides, her larboard guns playing upon the *Bucentaure* and the huge *Santissima Trinidad.*

It had been part of Nelson's prayer that the British fleet should be distinguished by humanity in the victory he expected. Setting an example himself, he twice gave orders to cease firing upon the *Redoubtable,* supposing that she had struck, because her great guns were silent; for, as she carried no flag, there was no means of instantly ascertaining the fact. From this ship, which he had thus twice spared, he received his death. A ball fired from her mizzen-top, which in the then situation of the two vessels was not more than fifteen yards from that part of the deck where he was standing, struck the epaulette on his left shoulder, about a quarter after one, just in the heat of action. He fell upon his face, on the spot which was covered with his poor secretary's blood. Hardy, who was a few steps from him, turning round, saw three men raising him up. "They have done for me at last, Hardy!" said he. "I hope not!" cried Hardy. "Yes," he replied, "my backbone is shot through!"

Yet even now, not for a moment losing his presence of mind, he observed as they were carrying him down the ladder, that the tiller-ropes, which had been shot away, were not yet replaced, and ordered that new ones should be rove immediately. Then, that he might not be seen by the crew, he took out his handkerchief and covered his face and his stars. Had he but concealed these badges of honour from the enemy, England perhaps would not have cause to receive with sorrow the news of the battle of Trafalgar. The cockpit was crowded with wounded and dying men, over whose bodies he was with some difficulty conveyed, and laid upon a pallet in the midshipmen's berth. It was soon perceived, upon examination, that the wound was mortal. This, however, was concealed from all except Captain Hardy, the chaplain, and the medical attendants. He himself being certain, from the sensation in his back and the gush of blood he felt momently within his breast, that no human care could avail him, insisted that the surgeon should leave him, and attend to those to whom he might be useful, "for," said he, "you can do nothing for me."

All that could be done was to fan him with paper, and frequently give him lemonade to alleviate his intense thirst. He was in great pain, and expressed much anxiety for the event of the action, which now began to declare itself. As often as a ship struck, the crew of the *Victory* hurrahed, and at every hurrah a visible expression of joy gleamed in the eyes and marked the countenance of the dying hero. But he became impatient to see Captain Hardy, and as that officer, though often sent for, could not leave the deck, Nelson feared that some fatal cause prevented him, and repeatedly cried, "Will no one bring Hardy to me? He must be killed! He is surely dead!"

An hour and ten minutes elapsed from the time when Nelson received his wound before Hardy could come to him. They shook hands in silence; Hardy in vain struggling to express the feelings of that most painful and yet sublimest moment. "Well, Hardy," said Nelson, "how goes the day with us?"—"Very well," replied Hardy; "ten ships have struck, but five of the van have tacked, and show an intention to bear down upon the *Victory*. I have called two or three of our fresh ships round, and have no doubt of giving them a drubbing."—"I hope," said Nelson, "none of our ships have struck." Hardy answered, "There was no fear of that." Then, and not till then, Nelson spoke of himself. "I am a dead man, Hardy," said he; "I am going fast; it will be all over with me soon. Come nearer to me." Hardy observed that he hoped Mr Beatty could yet hold out some prospect of life.

"Oh no!" he replied, "it is impossible; my back is shot through. Beatty will tell you so." Captain Hardy then once more shook hands with him, and with a heart almost bursting hastened upon deck.

By this time, all feeling below the breast was gone; and Nelson, having made the surgeon ascertain this, said to him: "You know I am gone. I know it. I feel something rising in my breast"—putting his hand on his left side—"which tells me so." And upon Beatty's inquiring whether his pain was very great, he replied, "So great that he wished he was dead." "Yet," said he in a lower voice, "one would like to live a little longer too!" Captain Hardy, some fifty minutes after he had left the cockpit, returned, and again taking the hand of his dying friend and commander, congratulated him on having gained a complete victory. How many of the enemy were taken he did not know, as it was impossible to perceive them distinctly; but fourteen or fifteen at least. "That's well!" cried Nelson; "but I bargained for twenty." And then in a stronger voice he said, "Anchor, Hardy, anchor." Hardy upon this hinted that Admiral Collingwood would take upon himself the direction of affairs. "Not while I live, Hardy," said the dying Nelson, ineffectually endeavouring to raise himself from the bed; "Do you anchor."

His previous order for preparing to anchor had shown how clearly he foresaw the necessity of this. Presently calling Hardy back, he said to him in a low voice: "Don't throw me overboard"; and he desired that he might be buried by his parents, unless it should please the king to order otherwise. Then turning to Hardy: "Kiss me, Hardy," said he. Hardy knelt down and kissed his cheek, and Nelson said: "Now I am satisfied. Thank God, I have done my duty!" Hardy stood over him in silence for a moment or two, then knelt again and kissed his forehead. "Who is that?" said Nelson; and being informed, he replied: "God bless you, Hardy." And Hardy then left him for ever.

Nelson now desired to be turned upon his right side, and said: "I wish I had not left the deck, for I shall soon be gone." Death was indeed rapidly approaching. He said to the chaplain: "Doctor, I have *not* been a *great* sinner." His articulation now became difficult, but he was distinctly heard to say: "Thank God, I have done my duty!" These words he repeatedly pronounced. And they were the last words that he uttered. He expired at thirty minutes after four, three hours and a quarter after he had received his wound.

THE PHANTOM SHIP[1]

Captain Frederick Marryat
(1792-1848)

A BANK of clouds rose up from the eastward, with a rapidity that to the seamen's eyes was unnatural, and it soon covered the whole firmament; the sun was obscured, and all was one deep and unnatural gloom; the wind subsided; and the ocean was hushed. It was not exactly dark, but the heavens were covered with one red haze, which gave an appearance as if the world was in a state of conflagration.

In the cabin the increased darkness was first observed by Philip, who went on deck; he was followed by the captain and passengers, who were in a state of amazement. It was unnatural and incomprehensive.

"Now, Holy Virgin, protect us! what can this be?" exclaimed the captain, in a fright. "Holy Saint Antonio, protect us!but this is awful."

"There—there!" shouted the sailors, pointing to the beam of the vessel. Every eye looked over the gunnel to witness what had occasioned such exclamations. Philip, Schriften, and the captain were side by side. On the beam of the ship, not more than two cables' length distant, they beheld slowly rising out of the water the tapering masthead and spars of another vessel. She rose, and rose, gradually; her top-masts and topsail yards, with the sails set, next made their appearance; higher and higher she rose up from the element. Her lower masts and rigging, and, lastly, her hull showed itself above the surface. Still she rose up, till her ports, with her guns, and at last the whole of her floatage was above water, and there she remained close to them, with her main yard squared, and hove to.

"Holy Virgin!" exclaimed the captain, breathless. "I have known ships to *go down,* but never to *come up* before. Now will I give one thousand candles, of ten ounces each, to the shrine of the Virgin, to save us in this trouble. One thousand wax candles!Hear me, blessed lady, ten ounces each!Gentlemen," cried the captain to the passengers, who stood aghast, "why don't you promise?—promise, I say *promise,* at all events."

"The Phantom Ship—the *Flying Dutchman,"* shrieked Schriften. "I told you so, Philip Vanderdecken. There is your father. He, he!"

Philip's eyes had remained fixed on the vessel; he perceived that they were lowering down a boat from her quarter. "It is possible," thought he, "I shall now be permitted," and put his hand into his bosom and grasped the relic.

The gloom now increased, so that the strange vessel's hull could but just be discovered through the murky atmosphere. The seamen and passengers threw

---

[1] From *The Phantom Ship.*

themselves down on their knees, and invoked their saints. The captain ran down for a candle, to light before the image of St Antonio, which he took out of its shrine and kissed with much apparent affection and devotion, and then replaced.

Shortly afterwards, the splash of oars was heard alongside, and a voice calling out, "I say, my good people, give us a rope from forward."

No one answered, or complied with the request. Schriften only went up to the captain, and told him that if they offered to send letters they must not be received, or the vessel would be doomed, and all would perish.

A man now made his appearance from over the gunnel, at the gangway. "You might as well have let me have a side-rope, my hearties," said he, as he stepped on deck. "Where is the captain?"

"Here," replied the captain, trembling from head to foot. The man who accosted him appeared a weather-beaten seaman, dressed in a fur cap and canvas petticoats; he held some letters in his hand.

"What do you want?" at last screamed the captain.

"Yes—what do you want?" continued Schriften. "He! he!"

"What, you here, pilot?" observed the man. "Well—I thought you had gone to Davy's locker long enough ago."

"He! he!" replied Schriften, turning away.

"Why, the fact is, captain, we have had very foul weather, and we wish to send letters home; I do believe that we shall never get round this cape."

"I can't take them," cried the captain.

"Can't take them! well, it's very odd, but every ship refuses to take our letters. It's very unkind; seamen should have a feeling for brother seamen, especially in distress. God knows, we wish to see our wives and families again; and it would be a matter of comfort to them if they only could hear from us."

"I cannot take your letters—the saints preserve us!" replied the captain.

"We have been a long while out," said the seaman, shaking his head.

"How long?" inquired the captain; not knowing what to say.

"We can't tell; our almanack was blown overboard, and we have lost our reckoning. We never have our latitude exact now, for we cannot tell the sun's declination for the right day."

"Let *me* see your letters," said Philip, advancing and taking them out of the seaman's hands.

"They must not be touched," screamed Schriften.

"Out, monster!" replied Philip, "who dares interfere with me?"

"Doomed—doomed—doomed!" shrieked Schriften, running up and down the deck, and then breaking into a wild fit of laughter.

"Touch not the letters," said the captain, trembling as if in an ague fit.

Philip made no reply, but held his hand out for the letters.

"Here is one from our second mate to his wife at Amsterdam, who lives on Waser Quay."

"Waser Quay has long been gone, my good friend; there is now a large dock for ships where it once was," replied Philip.

"Impossible!" replied the man. "Here is another from the boatswain to his father, who lives in the old market-place."

"The old market-place has long been pulled down, and there now stands a church upon the spot."

"Impossible!" replied the seaman. *"Here* is another from myself to my sweetheart, Vrow Ketser—with money to buy her a new brooch."

Philip shook his head. "I remember seeing an old lady of that name buried some thirty years ago."

"Impossible! I left her young and blooming. Here's one for the house of Slutz and Co., to whom the ship belongs."

"There's no such house now," replied Philip, "but I have heard that, many years ago, there was a firm of that name."

"Impossible! you must be laughing at me. Here is a letter from our captain to his son—"

"Give it me," cried Philip, seizing the letter.

He was about to break the seal, when Schriften snatched it out of his hand, and threw it over the lee gunnel.

"That's a scurvy trick for an old shipmate," observed the seaman.

Schriften made no reply, but catching up the other letters, which Philip had laid down on the capstan, he hurled them after the first. The strange seaman shed tears, and walked again to the side.

"It's very hard—very unkind," observed he, as he descended; "the time may come when you may wish that your family should know your situation."

So saying, he disappeared. In a few seconds was heard the sound of the oars, retreating from the ship.

"Holy Saint Antonio!" exclaimed the captain. "I am lost in wonder and fright. Steward, bring me up the arrack."

The steward ran down for the bottle; being so much alarmed as his captain, he helped himself before he brought it up to his commander.

"Now," said the captain, after keeping his mouth for two minutes to the bottle, and draining it to the bottom, "what is to be done next?"

"I'll tell you," said Schriften, going up to him. "That man there has a charm hung round his neck. Take it from him, and throw it overboard, and your ship will be saved. If not, it will be lost, with every soul on board."

"Yes, yes, it's all right, depend upon it," cried the sailors.

"Fools!" replied Philip, "do you believe that wretch? Did you not hear the man who came on board recognize him, and call him shipmate? He is the party whose presence on board will prove so unfortunate."

"Yes, yes," cried the sailors, "it's all right; the man did call him shipmate."

"I tell you it's all wrong," cried Schriften. "That is the man. Let him give up the charm."

"Yes, yes; let him give up the charm," cried the sailors, and they rushed upon Philip.

Philip started back to where the captain stood.

"Madmen, know ye what ye are about? It is the holy cross that I wear round my neck. Throw it overboard if you dare, and your souls are lost for ever," and he took the relic from his bosom and showed it to the captain.

"No, no, men," exclaimed the captain, who was now more settled in his nerves, "that won't do—the saints protect us."

The seamen, however, became clamorous; one portion were for throwing Schriften overboard, the other for throwing Philip. At last, the point was decided by the captain, who directed the small skiff hanging astern to be lowered down, and ordered both Philip and Schriften to get into it. The seamen approved of this arrangement, as it satisfied both parties. Philip made no objection; Schriften screamed and fought, but he was tossed into the boat. There he remained trembling in the stern-sheets, while Philip, who had seized the sculls, pulled away from the vessel in the direction of the Phantom Ship.

In a few minutes, the vessel which Philip and Schriften had left was no longer to be discerned through the thick haze; the Phantom Ship was still in sight, but at a much greater distance from them than she was before. Philip pulled hard towards her, but although hove to, she appeared to increase her distance from the boat. For a short time he paused on his oars, to regain his breath, when Schriften rose up and took his seat in the stern-sheets of the boat.

"You may pull and pull, Philip Vanderdecken," observed he, "but you will not gain that ship. No, no, that cannot be. We may have a long cruise together, but you will be as far from your object at the end of it, as you are now at the commencement. Why don't you throw me overboard again? You would be all the lighter. He!he!"

"I threw you overboard in a state of frenzy," replied Philip, "when you attempted to force from me my relic."

"And have I not endeavoured to make others take it from you this very day? Have I not? He! he!"

"You have," rejoined Philip, "but I am now convinced that you are as unhappy as myself, and that in what you are doing, you are only following your destiny, as I am mine. Why and wherefore I cannot tell, but we are both engaged in the same mystery; if the success of my endeavours depends upon guarding the relic, the success of yours depends upon your obtaining it, and defeating my purpose by so doing. In this matter we are both agents, and you have been, as far as my mission is concerned, my most active enemy. But, Schriften, I have not forgotten, and never will, that you kindly *did advise* my poor Amine; that you prophesied to her what would be her fate, if she did not listen to your counsel; that you were no enemy of hers, although you have been and are still mine. Although my enemy, for her sake I *forgive you,* and will not attempt to harm you."

"You do then forgive your enemy, Philip Vanderdecken?" replied Schriften, mournfully, "for such I acknowledge myself to be."

"I do, *with all my heart, with all my soul,"* replied Philip.

"Then have you conquered me, Philip Vanderdecken; you have now made me your friend, and your wishes are about to be accomplished. You would know who I am. Listen. When your father, defying the Almighty's will, in his rage took my life, he was vouchsafed a chance of his doom being cancelled, through the merits of his son. I had also my appeal, which was for *vengeance.* It was granted that I should remain on earth, and thwart your will. That as long as we were enemies, you should not succeed; but that when you had conformed to the highest attribute of Christianity, proved on the holy cross, that *of forgiving your enemy,* your task should be fulfilled. Philip Vanderdecken, you have forgiven your enemy, and both our destinies are now accomplished."

As Schriften spoke, Philip's eyes were fixed on him. He extended his hand to Philip—it was taken; and as it was pressed, the form of the pilot wasted as it were into the air, and Philip found himself alone.

"Father of mercy, I thank thee," said Philip, "that my task is done, and that I again may meet my Amine."

Philip then pulled towards the Phantom Ship, and found that she no longer appeared to leave: on the contrary, every minute he was nearer and nearer, and, at last, he threw in his oars, climbed up her side and gained her deck.

The crew of the vessel crowded round him.

"Your captain," said Philip, "I must speak with your captain."

"Who shall I say, sir?" demanded one who appeared to be the first mate.

"Who?" replied Philip. "Tell him his son would speak to him, his son, Philip Vanderdecken."

Shouts of laughter from the crew followed this answer of Philip's; and the mate, as soon as they ceased, observed, with a smile.

"You forget, sir; perhaps you would say his father."

"Tell him his son, if you please," replied Philip. "Take no note of grey hairs."

"Well, sir, here he is coming forward," replied the mate, stepping aside, and pointing to the captain.

"What is all this?" inquired the captain.

"Are you Philip Vanderdecken, the captain of this vessel?"

"I am, sir," replied the other.

"You appear not to know me! But how can you? You saw me but when I was only three years old; yet may you remember a letter which you gave to your wife."

"Ha!" replied the captain; "and who, then, are you?"

"Time has stopped with you, but with those who live in the world he stops not; and for those who pass a life of misery, he hurries on still faster. In me behold your son, Philip Vanderdecken, who has obeyed your wishes; and, after a life of such peril and misery as few have passed, has at last fulfilled his vow, and now offers to his father the precious relic that he required to kiss."

Philip drew out the relic, and held it towards his father. As if a flash of lightning had passed through his mind, the captain of the vessel started back, clasped his hands, fell on his knees, and wept.

"My son, my son!" exclaimed he, rising and throwing himself into Philip's arms; "my eyes are opened—the Almighty knows how long they have been obscured."

Embracing each other, they walked aft, away from the men, who were still crowded at the gangway.

"My son, my noble son, before the charm is broken—before we resolve, as we must, into the elements, oh!let me kneel in thanksgiving and contrition; my son, my noble son, receive a father's thanks," exclaimed Vanderdecken. Then with tears of joy and penitence he humbly addressed himself to that Being whom he once so awfully defied.

The elder Vanderdecken knelt down; Philip did the same; still embracing each other with one arm, while they raised on high the other, and prayed.

For the last time the relic was taken from the bosom of Philip and handed to his father—and his father raised his eyes to heaven and kissed it. And as he kissed it, the long tapering upper spars of the Phantom vessel, the yards and sails that were set, fell into dust, fluttered in the air, and sank upon the wave. The mainmast, foremast, bowsprit, everything above the deck, crumbled into atoms and disappeared.

Again he raised the relic to his lips, and the work of destruction continued—the heavy iron guns sank through the decks and disappeared; the crew of the vessel (who were looking on) crumbled down into skeletons, and dust, and fragments of ragged garments; and there were none left on board the vessel in the semblance of life but the father and son.

Once more did he put the sacred emblem to his lips, and the beams and timbers separated, the decks of the vessel slowly sank, and the remnants of the hull floated upon the water; and as the father and son—the one young and vigorous, the other old and decrepit—still kneeling, still embracing, with their hands raised to heaven, sank slowly under the deep blue wave, the lurid sky was for a moment illuminated by a lightning cross.

Then did the clouds which obscured the heavens roll away swift as thought—the sun again burst out in all its splendour—the rippling waves appeared to dance with joy. The screaming sea-gull again whirled in the air, and the scared albatross once more slumbered on the wing. The porpoise tumbled and tossed in his sportive play, the albicore and dolphin leaped from the sparkling sea. All nature smiled as if it rejoiced that the charm was dissolved for ever, and that THE PHANTOM SHIP WAS NO MORE.

WHITBY WHALERS[1]

Elizabeth Gaskell
(1810-1865)

I

The Press Gang

SYLVIA scampered across the rough farm-yard in the wetting, drizzling rain to the place where she expected to find Kester; but he was not there, so she had to retrace her steps to the cow-house, and, making her way up a rough kind of ladder-staircase fixed against the wall she surprised Kester as he sat in the wool-loft, looking over the fleeces reserved for the home-spinning.

"Kester, feyther's just tiring hissel' wi' weariness an' vexation, sitting by t' fireside wi' his hands afore him, an' nought to do. An' mother and me can't think on aught as'll rouse him up to a bit of a laugh, or aught more cheerful than a scolding. Now, Kester, thou mun just be off, and find Harry Donkin th' tailor, and bring him here; it's gettin' on for Martinmas, an' he'll be coming his rounds, and he may as well come here first as last, and feyther's clothes want a deal o' mending up, and Harry's always full of his news, and anyhow he'll do for feyther to scold, and be a new person too, and that's somewhat for all on us. Now go, like a good old Kester as yo' are."...

The next morning Sylvia's face was a little redder than usual when Harry Donkin's bow-legs were seen circling down the path to the house door.

"Here's Donkin, for sure!" exclaimed Bell, when she caught sight of him a minute after her daughter. "Well, I just call that lucky!for he'll be company for thee while Sylvia and me has to turn th' cheeses."

[1] From *Sylvia's Lovers.*

"That's all t' women know about it. Wi' them it's 'coompany, coompany, coompany,' an' they think a man' s no better than theirsels. A'd have yo' to know a've a vast o' thoughts in mysel', as I'm noane willing to lay out for t' benefit o' every man. A've niver gotten time for meditation sin' a were married; leastways, sin' a left t' sea. Aboard ship, wi' niver a woman we' in leagues o' hail, and upo' t' masthead, in special, a could .... Come in, Harry, come in, and talk a bit o' sense to me, for a've been shut up wi' women these four days, and a'm a'most a nateral by this time."

So Harry took off his coat, and seated himself professional-wise on the hastily cleared dresser, so that he might have all the light afforded by the long, low casement window. Then he blew in his thimble, sucked his finger, so that they might adhere tightly together, and looked about for a subject for opening conversation, while Sylvia and her mother might be heard opening and shutting drawers and box-lids before they could find the articles that needed repair, or that were required to mend each other.

"Women's well enough i' their way," said Daniel. . . . He had taken his pipe out of the square hollow in the fireside wall, where he usually kept it, and was preparing to diversify his remarks with satisfying interludes of puffing. "Why, look ye; this very baccy ... came ashore sewed up neatly enough i' a woman's stays, as was wife to a fishing-smack down at t' bay yonder. She were a lean thing as iver you saw when she went for t' see her husband aboard t' vessel; but she coom back lustier by a deal, and wi' many a thing on her, here and theere, beside baccy. An' that were i' t' face o' coast-guard and yon tender, an' a'."

"Speaking of t' tender, there's been a piece o' wark i' Monkshaven this week wi' t' press-gang," said Harry. "Folk had gotten to think nought o' t' tender, she lay so still, an' t' leftenant paid such a good price for all he wanted for t' ship. But o' Thursday t' *Resolution,* first whaler back this season, came in port, and t' press gang showed their teeth, and carried off four as good able-bodied seamen as iver I made trousers for; and t' place were all up like a nest o' wasps, when yo've set your foot in t' midst. They were so mad, they were ready for t' fight t' very pavin' stones."

"A wish a'd been there! A just wish a had! A've a score for t' reckon up wi' t' press-gang!"

And the old man lifted up his right hand—his hand on which the forefinger and thumb were maimed and useless—partly in denunciation, and partly as a witness of what he had endured to escape from the service, abhorred because it was forced. His face became a totally different countenance with the expression of settled and unrelenting indignation, which his words called out.

"G'on, man, g'on," said Daniel, impatient with Donkin for the little delay occasioned by the necessity of arranging his work more fully.

"Ay! ay! all in good time; for a've a long tale to tell yet, an' a mun have some'un to iron out my seams, and look me out my bits, for there's none here fit for my purpose."

"Dang thy bits! Here, Sylvie! Sylvie! come and be tailor's man, and let t' chap get settled sharp, for a'm fain t' hear his story."

Sylvia took her directions, and placed her irons in the fire, and ran upstairs for the bundle which had been put aside by her careful mother for occasions like the present. Daniel grew angry before Donkin had selected his patterns and settled the work to his own mind.

"Well," said he at last; "a mought be a young man a-goin' a-wooin', by t' pains thou'st taken for t' match my oud clothes. I don't care if they're patched wi' scarlet, a tell thee; so as thou'lt work away at thy tale wi' thy tongue, same time as thou works at thy needle wi' thy fingers."

"Then, as a were saying, all Monkshaven were like a nest o' wasps, flyin' hither and thither, and makin' sich a buzzin' and a talkin' as niver were; and each wi' his sting out ready for t' vent his venom o' rage and revenge. And women cryin' and sobbin' i' t' streets—when, Lord help us!o' Saturday came a worse thing than iver! for all Friday there had been a kind o' expectation an' dismay about t' *Good Fortune,* as t' mariners had said was off St Abb's Head o' Thursday, when t' *Resolution* came in!and there was wives and maids wi' husbands an' sweethearts aboard t' *Good Fortune* ready to throw their eyes out on their heads wi' gazin', gazin', nor'ards over t' sea, as were all one haze o' blankness wi' t' rain; and when t' afternoon tide comed in, an' niver a line on her to be seen, folk were oncertain as t' whether she were holding off for fear o' t' tender—as were out o' sight, too—or what were her mak' o' goin' on. An' t' poor, wet, draggled women folk came up t' town, some slowly cryin', as if their hearts was sick, an' others just bent their heads to t' wind, and went straight to their homes, nother looking nor speaking to ony one; but barred their doors, and stiffened theirsels up for a night o' waiting. Saturday morn—yo'll mind Saturday morn, it were stormy and gusty, downreet dirty weather—there stood t' folk again by dayhght, a-watching an', a-straining, and by that tide t' *Good Fortune* came o' er t' bar. But t' excisemen had sent back her news by t' boat as took 'em there. They'd a deal of oil, and a vast o' blubber. But for all that her flag was drooping i' t' rain, half mast high, for mourning and sorrow, an' they'd a dead man aboard—a dead man as was living and strong last sunrise. An' there was another as lay between life an' death, and there was seven more as should ha' been there as wasn't, but was carried off by t' gang. T' frigate as we'n a' heard tell on, as lying off Hartlepool, got tidings fra' t' tender as captured t' seamen o' Thursday: and *t' Aurora,* as they ca'ed her, made off for t' nor'ard; and nine leagues off St Abb's Head, t' *Resolution* thinks she were, she seed t' frigate, and knowed by her build she were a man-o'-war, and guessed she were bound on king's kidnapping. I seen t' wounded man mysen wi' my own eyes; and he'll live!he'll live! Niver a man died yet, wi' such a strong purpose o' vengeance in him. He could barely speak, for he were badly shot, but his colour coome and went, as t' master's mate an' t' captain telled me and some others how t' *Aurora* fired at 'em and how t' innocent whaler hoisted her colours, but afore they were fairly run up, another shot coome close in t' shrouds, and then t' Greenland ship being t' windward, bore down on t' frigate; but as they knew she were an oud fox, and bent on mischief, Kinraid (that's he who lies a-dying, only he'll noane die, a'se bound), the specksioneer, bade t' men go down between decks, and fasten t' hatches well, and he'd stand guard, he an' captain, and t' oud master's mate being left upo' deck for t' give a welcome just skin-deep to t' boat's crew fra' t' *Aurora,* as they could see coming t'wards them o'er t' watter, wi' their reg'lar man-o'-war's rowing—"

"Damn 'em!" said Daniel in soliloquy, and under his breath. Sylvia stood, poising her iron, and listening eagerly, afraid to give Donkin the hot iron for fear of interrupting the narrative, unwilling to put it into the fire again, because that action would perchance remind him of his work, which now the tailor had forgotten, so eager was he in telling his story.

"Well, they coome on over t' watters wi' great bounds, and up t' sides they coome like locusts, all armed men; an' t' captain says he saw Kinraid hide away his whaling-knife under some tarpaulin, an' he knew he meant mischief, an' he would no more ha' stopped him wi' a word nor he would ha' stopped him fra' killing a whale. And when t' *Aurora's* men were aboard, one on 'em runs to t' helm; and at that t' captain says he felt as if his wife were kissed afore his face; but says he, 'I bethought me on t' men as were shut up below hatches, an' I remembered t' folk at Monkshaven as were looking out for us even then; an' I said to mysel', I would speak fair as long as I could, more by token o' the whaling-knife, as I could see glinting bright under t' black tarpaulin.' So he spoke quite fair and civil though he see'd they was nearing t' *Aurora* and t' *Aurora* was nearing them. Then t' navy captain hailed him thro' t' trumpet, wi' a great rough blast, and, says he, 'Order your men to come on deck.' And t' captain o' t' whaler says, his men cried up from under t' hatches as they'd niver be gi'en up wi'out bloodshed, and he sees Kinraid take out his pistol, and look well to t' priming; so he says to t' navy captain, 'We're protected Greenlandmen, and you have no right t' meddle wi' us.' But t' navy captain only bellows t' more, 'Order your men t' come on deck. If they won't obey you, and you have lost the command of your vessel, I reckon you're in a state of mutiny, and you may come aboard t' *Aurora* and such men as are willing t' follow you, and I'll fire int' the rest.' To' see, that were t' depth o' the man: he were for pretending and pretexting as t' captain could na manage his own ship, and as he'd help him. But our Greenland captain were none so poor-sighted, and says he, 'She's full of oil, and I ware you of consequences if you fire into her. Anyhow, pirate or no pirate' (for word pirate stuck in his gizzard), 'I'm an honest Monkshaven man, an' come fra' a land where there's great icebergs and many a deadly danger, but niver a press-gang, thank God!and that's what you are, I reckon.' Them's the words he told me, but whether he spoke 'em out so bold at t' time, I'se not so sure; they were in his mind for t' speak, only maybe prudence got t' better on him, for he said he prayed i' his heart to bring his cargo safe to t' owners, come what might. Well t' *Aurora's* men aboard t' *Good Fortune* cried out, 'might they fire down t' hatches, and bring t' men out that a way?' and then t' specksioneer, he speaks, an' he says he stands ower t' hatches, and he has two good pistols, an' summut besides, and he don't care for his life, bein' a bachelor, but all below are married men, yo' see, and he'll put an end to t' first two chaps as come near t' hatches. An' they say he picked two off as made for t' come near, and then just as he were stooping for t' whaling-knife, an' it's as big as a sickle—"

"Teach folk as don't know a whaling-knife," cried Daniel. "I were a Greenland man mysel '."

"They shot him through t' side, and dizzied him, and kicked him aside for dead; and fired down t' hatches, and killed one man, and disabled two, and then t' rest cried for quarter, for life is sweet, e'en aboard a king's ship; and t' *Aurora* carried 'em off, wounded men, an' able men, an' all; leaving Kinraid for dead, as wasn't dead, and Darley for dead, as was dead, an' t' captain and master's mate as were too old for work; and t' captain, as loves Kinraid like a brother, poured rum down his throat, and bandaged him up, and has sent for t' first doctor in Monkshaven for to get t' slugs out; for they say there's niver such a harpooner in a' t' Greenland Seas; an' I can speak fra' my own seeing he's a fine young fellow where he lies theere, all stark and wan for weakness and loss o' blood. But Darley's dead as a door-nail; and there's to be such a burying of him as niver was seen afore i' Monkshaven, come Sunday. And now gi' us t' iron, wench, and let's lose no more time a-talking."

"It's noane loss o' time," said Daniel, moving himself heavily in his chair, to feel how helpless he was once more. "If a were as young as once a were—nay, lad, if a had na these sore rheumatics, now—a reckon as t' press-gang 'ud find out as 't shouldn't do such things for nothing. Bless thee, man! it's waur nor i' my youth i' th' Ameriky war, and then 't were bad enough."

"And Kinraid?" said Sylvia, drawing a long breath, after the effort of realising it all; her cheeks had flushed up, and her eyes had glittered during the progress of the tale.

"Oh, he'll do. He'll not die. Life's stuff is in him yet."

II

The Manners of Whales

Farmer Robson left Haytersbank betimes, on a longish day's journey, to purchase a horse. Sylvia and her mother were busied with a hundred household things, and the early winter's evening closed in upon them almost before they were aware.

The mother and daughter hardly spoke at all when they sat down at last. The cheerful click of the knitting-needles made a pleasant home sound; and in the occasional snatches of slumber that overcame her mother, Sylvia could hear the long-rushing boom of the waves, down below the rocks, for the Haytersbank gulley allowed the sullen roar to come up so far inland. It might have been about eight o'clock—though from the monotonous course of the evening it seemed much later—when Sylvia heard her father's heavy step cranching down the pebbly path. More unusual, she heard his voice talking to some companion.

Curious to see who it could be, with a lively instinctive advance towards any event which might break the monotony she had begun to find somewhat dull, she sprang up to open the door. Half a glance into the grey darkness outside made her suddenly timid, and she drew back behind the door as she opened it wide to admit her father and Kinraid.

Daniel Robson came in bright and boisterous. He was pleased with his purchase, and had had some drink to celebrate his bargain. He had ridden the new mare into Monkshaven, and left her at the smithy there until morning, to have her feet looked at, and to be new shod. On his way from the town he had met Kinraid wandering about in search of Haytersbank Farm itself, so he had just brought him along with him; and here they were, ready for bread and cheese, and aught else the mistress would set before them.

To Sylvia the sudden change into brightness and bustle occasioned by the entrance of her father and the specksioneer was like that which you may effect any winter's night, when you come into a room where a great lump of coal lies hot and slumbering on the fire; just break it up with a judicious blow from the poker, and the room, late so dark, and dusk, and lone, is full of life, and light, and warmth.

She moved about with pretty, household briskness, attending to all her father's wants. Kinraid's eyes watched her as she went backwards and forwards, to and fro, into the pantry, the back-kitchen, out of light into shade, out of the shadow into the broad firelight where he could see and note her appearance. She wore the high-crowned, linen cap of that day, surmounting her lovely masses of golden brown hair, rather than concealing them, and tied firm to her head by a broad blue ribbon. A long curl hung down on each side of her neck—her throat rather, for her neck was concealed by a little spotted handkerchief carefully pinned across at the waist of her brown stuff gown . . . .

By the time she could sit down, her father and Kinraid had their glasses filled, and were talking of the relative merits of various kinds of spirits; that led on to tales of smuggling, and the different contrivances by which they or their friends had eluded the preventive service; the nightly relays of men to carry the goods inland; the kegs of brandy found by certain farmers whose horses had gone so far in the night that they could do no work the next day ....

From smuggling adventures it was easy to pass on to stories of what had happened to Robson, in his youth a sailor in the Greenland seas, and to Kinraid, now one of the best harpooners in any whaler that sailed off the coast.

"There's three things to be afeared on," said Robson, authoritatively: "there's t' ice, that's bad; there's dirty weather, that's worse; and there's whales theirselves, as is t' worst of all; leastways, they was i' my days; t' darned brutes may ha' larnt better manners sin'. When I were young, they could niver be got to let theirsels be harpooned wi'out flounderin' and makin' play wi' their tails and their fins, till t' say were all in a foam, and t' boats' crews as all o'er wi' spray, which i' them latitudes is a kind o' shower-bath not needed."

"Th' whales hasn't mended their manners, as you call it," said Kinraid; "but th' ice is not to be spoken lightly on. I were once in th' ship *John,* of Hull, and we were in good green water, and were keen after whales; and ne'er thought harm of a great grey iceberg as were on our lee-bow, a mile or so off; it looked as if it had been there from the days of Adam, and were likely to see th' last man out, and it ne'er a bit bigger nor smaller in all them thousands and thousands o' years. Well, the fast boats were out after a fish, and I were specksioneer in one; and we were so keen after capturing our whale, that none on us ever saw that we were drifting away from them right into deep shadow o' th' iceberg. But we were set upon our whale, and I harpooned it; and as soon as it were dead we lashed its fins together, and fastened its tail to our boat; and then we took breath and looked about us, and away from us a little space were th' other boats, wi' two other fish making play, and as likely as not to break loose, for I may say as I were th' best harpooner on board the *John,* wi'out saying great things o' mysel'. So I says, 'My lads, one o' you stay i' th' boat by this fish,' the fins o' which, as I said, I'd reeved a rope through mysel', and which was as dead as Noah's grandfather—'and th' rest on us shall go off and help th' other boats wi' their fish.' For, you see, we had another boat close by in order to sweep th' fish. (I suppose they swept fish i' your time, master?)"

"Ay, ay!" said Robson; "one boat lies still holding t' end o' t' line; t' other makes a circuit round t' fish."

"Well! luckily for us we had our second boat, for we all got into it, ne'er a man on us was left i' th' fast-boat. And says I, 'But who's to stay by t' dead fish?' And no man answered, for they were all as keen as me for to go and help our mates;

and we thought as we could come back to our dead fish, as had a boat for a buoy, once we had helped our mate. So off we rowed, every man Jack on us, out o' the black shadow o' th' iceberg, as looked as steady as th' pole-star. Well! We had na' been a dozen fathoms away fra th' boat as we had left, when crash!down wi' a roaring noise, and then a gulp of the deep waters, and then a shower o' blinding spray; and when we had wiped our eyes clear, and getten our hearts down agen fra our mouths, there were never a boat nor a glittering belly o' e'er a great whale to be seen; but th' iceberg were there, still and grim, as if a hundred ton or more had fallen off all in a mass, and crushed down boat, and fish, and all, into th' deep water, as goes half through the earth in them latitudes. Th' coal-miners round about Newcastle way may come upon our good boat if they mine deep enough, else ne'er another man will see her. And I left as good a clasp-knife in her as ever I clapt eyes on."

"But what a mercy no man stayed in her," said Bell.

"Why, mistress, I reckon we a' must die some way; and I'd as soon go down into the deep waters as be choked up wi' moulds."

"But it must be so cold," said Sylvia, shuddering and giving a little poke to the fire to warm her fancy.

"Cold!" said her father, "what do ye stay-at-homes know about cold, a should like to know? If yo'd been where a were once, north latitude 81, in such a frost as ye ha' niver known, no, not i' deep winter, and it were June i' them seas, and a whale i' sight, and a were off in a boat after her; an' t' ill-mannered brute, as soon as she were harpooned, ups wi' her big, awkward tail, and struck th' boat i' her stern, and chucks me out into t' watter. That were cold, a can tell the'! First, I smarted all ower me, as if my skin were suddenly stript off me; and next, ivery bone i' my body had getten t' toothache, and there were a great roar i' my ears, an' a great dizziness i' my eyes; an' t' boat's crew kept throwin' out their oars, an' a kept clutchin' at 'em, but a could na' make out where they was, my eyes dazzled so wi' t' cold, an' I thought I were bound for 'kingdom come,' an' a tried to remember t' Creed, as a might die a Christian. But all a could think on was, 'What is your name, M. or N?' an' just as a were giving up both words and life, they heaved me aboard. But, bless ye, they had but one oar; for they'd thrown a' t' others after me; so yo' may reckon it were some time afore we could reach t' ship; an', a've heard tell, a were a precious sight to look on, for my clothes was just hard frozen to me, an' my hair a'most as big a lump o' ice as yon iceberg he was a-telling us on; they rubbed me as missus theere was rubbing t' hams yesterday, and gav' me brandy; an' a've niver getten t' frost out o' my bones for a' their rubbin', and a deal o' brandy as I 'ave ta'en sin'. Talk o' cold! it's little yo' women known o' cold!"

"But there's heat, too, i' some places," said Kinraid. "I was once a voyage i' an American. They goes for th' most part south, to where you come round to th' cold again; and they'll stay there for three year at a time, if need be, going into winter harbour i' some o' th' Pacific Islands. Well, we were i' th' southern seas, a-seeking for good whaling-ground; and, close on our larboard beam, there were a great wall o' ice, as much as sixty feet high. And says our captain—as were a dare-devil, if ever a man were—'There'll be an opening in yon dark grey wall, and into that opening I'll sail, if I coast along it till th' day o' judgment.' But, for all our sailing, we never seemed to come nearer to th' opening. The waters were rocking beneath us, and the sky were steady above us; and th' ice rose out o' the waters, and seemed to reach up into the sky. We sailed on, and we sailed on, for more days nor I could count. Our captain were a strange, wild man, but once he looked a little pale when he came upo' deck after his turn-in, and saw the green-grey ice going straight up on our beam. Many on us thought as the ship were bewitched for th' captain's words; and we got to speak low, and to say our prayers o' nights, and a kind o' dull silence came into th' very air; our voices did na' rightly seem our own. And we sailed on, and we sailed on. All at once, th' man as were on watch gave a cry; he saw a break in the ice, as we'd begun to think were everlasting; and we all gathered towards the bows, and the captain called to th' man at the helm to keep her course, and cocked his head, and began to walk the quarter-deck, jaunty again. And we came to a great cleft in th' long, weary rock of ice; and the sides o' th' cleft were not jagged, but went straight sharp down into th' foaming waters. But we took but one look at what lay inside, for our captain, with a loud cry to God, bade the helmsman steer nor'ards away fra' th' mouth o' hell. We all saw wi' our own eyes, inside that fearsome wall o' ice—seventy mile long, as we could swear to—inside that grey, cold ice, came leaping flames, all red and yellow wi' heat o' some unearthly kind out o' th' very waters o' the sea; making our eyes dazzle wi' their scarlet blaze, that shot up as high, nay, higher than th' ice around, yet never so much as shred on 't was melted. They did say that some beside our captain saw the black devils dart hither and thither, quicker than the very flames themselves; anyhow, *he* saw them. And as he knew it were his own daring as had led him to have that peep at terrors forbidden to any on us afore our time, he just dwined away, and we hadn't taken but one whale afore our captain died, and first mate took th' command. It were a prosperous voyage; but, for all that, I'll never sail those seas again, nor ever take wage aboard an American again."

"Eh, dear! but it's awful t' think o' sitting wi' a man that has seen th' doorway into hell," said Bell aghast.

Sylvia had dropped her work, and sat gazing at Kinraid with fascinated wonder.

Daniel was just a little annoyed at the admiration which his own wife and daughter were bestowing on the specksioneer's wonderful stories, and he said—

"Ay, ay. If a'd been a talker, ye'd ha' thought a deal more on me nor ye've iver done yet. A've seen such things, and done such things."

"Tell us father!" said Sylvia, greedy and breathless.

"Some on 'em is past telling," he replied, "an some is not to be had for t' asking, seeing as how they might bring a man into trouble. But, as a said, if a had a fancy to reveal all as is on my mind a could make t' hair on your heads lift up your caps—well, we'll say an inch, at least. Thy mother, lass, has heerd one or two on 'em. Thou minds the story o' my ride on a whale's back, Bell? That'll maybe be within this young fellow's comprehension o' t' danger; thou's heerd me tell it, hastn't ta?"

"Yes" said Bell; "but it's a long time ago; when we was courting."

"An' 'that's afore' this young lass were born, as is a'most up to woman's estate. But sin' those days a ha' been o'er busy to tell stories to my wife, an' as a'll warrant she's forgotten it; an' as Sylvia here niver heerd it, if yo'll fill your glass, Kinraid, yo' shall ha' t' benefit o't.

"A were a specksioneer mysel', though, after that, a rayther directed my talents int' t' smuggling branch o' my profession; but a were once a-whaling aboord t' *Aimwell* of Whitby. An' we was anchored off t' coast o' Greenland one season; an we'd getten a cargo o' seven whales; but our captain he were a keen-eyed chap, an' niver above doin' any man's work; an' once seein' a whale he throws himself int' a boat an' goes off to it, makin' signals to me, an' another specksioneer as were off for diversion i' another boat, for to come after him sharp. Well, afore we comes alongside, captain had harpooned t' fish; an says he, 'Now, Robson, all ready! give into her again when she comes to t' top; an I stands up, right leg foremost, harpoon all ready, as soon as iver I cotched a sight o' t' whale, but niver a fin could a see. 'Twere no wonder, for she were right below t' boat in which a were; and when she wanted to rise, what does t' great, ugly brute do but come wi' her head, as is like cast iron, up bang again t' bottom o' t' boat. I were thrown up in t' air like a shuttle-cock, me an' my line an' my harpoon—up we goes, an' many a good piece o' timber wi' us, an' many a good fellow too; but I had t' look after mysel', an' a were up high i' t' air, afore I could say Jack Robinson, an' a thowt a were safe for another dive int' saut water; but i'stead a comes down plump on t' back o' t' whale. Ay! yo' may stare, master, but theere a were, an' main an' slippery it were, only a sticks my harpoon intil her, an' steadies mysef', an' looks abroad o'er t' vast o' waves, and gets sea-sick in a manner, an' puts up a prayer as she mayn't dive, and it were as good a prayer for wishin' it might come true as iver t' clergyman an' t' clerk too puts up i' Monkshaven Church. Well, a reckon it were heerd, for all a were i' them north latitudes, for she keeps steady, an' a does my best for t' keep steady; an' 'deed a was too steady, for a was fast wi' t' harpoon line, all knotted and tangled about me T' captain, he sings out for me to cut it; but it's easy singin' out, and it's noane so easy fumblin' for your knife i' t' pocket o' your drawers, when yo've t' hold hard wi' t' other hand on t' back of a whale, swimmin' fourteen knots an hour. At last a thinks to mysel' a can't get free o' t' line, and t' line is fast to t' harpoon, and t' harpoon is fast to t' whale; and t' whale may go down fathoms deep wheniver t' maggot stirs i' her head; and t' watter's cold, an' noane good for drownin' in; a can't get free o' t' line, and a cannot get my knife out o' my breeches pocket, though t' captain should ca' it mutiny to disobey orders, and t' line's fast to t' harpoon—let's see if t' harpoon's fast to t' whale. So a tugged, an' a lugged, and t' whale didn't mistake it for ticklin', but she cocks up her tail, and throws out showers o' water as were ice or iver it touched me; but a pulls on at t' shank, an' a were only afeard as she wouldn't keep at t' top wi' it sticking in her; but at last t' harpoon broke, an' just i' time, for a reckon she was near as tired o' me as a were on her, and down she went; and a had hard work to make for t' boats as was near enough to catch me; for what wi' t' whale's being but slippery an' t' watter being cold, an' me hampered wi' t' line an' t' piece o' harpoon, it's a chance, missus, as thou had stopped an oud maid."

"Eh dear a' me!" said Bell, "how well I mind yo'r telling me that tale! It were twenty-four year ago come October. I thought I never could think enough on a man as had rode on a whale's back."

"Yo' may learn t' way of winnin' t' women," said Daniel, winking at the specksioneer.

And Kinraid immediately looked at Sylvia.

IN THE STEERAGE[1]

Charles Dickens
(1812-1870)

A DARK and dreary night; people nestling in their beds, or circling late about the fire; Want, colder than Charity, shivering at the street corners; church-towers humming with the faint vibration of their own tongues, but newly resting from the ghostly preachment "One!" The earth covered with a sable pall as for the burial of yesterday; the clumps of dark trees, its giant plumes of funeral feathers, waving sadly to and fro: all hushed, all noiseless, and in deep repose, save the swift clouds that skim across the moon, and the cautious wind, as, creeping after them upon the ground, it stops to listen, and goes rustling on, and stops again, and follows, like a savage on the trail.

[1] From *Martin Chuzzlewit.*

Whither go the clouds and wind so eagerly? If, like guilty spirits, they repair to some dread conference with powers like themselves, in what wild regions do the elements hold council, or where unbend in terrible disport?

Here! Free from that cramped prison called the earth, and out upon the waste of waters. Here, roaring, raging, shrieking, howling, all night long. Hither come the sounding voices from the caverns on the coast of that small island, sleeping, a thousand miles away, so quietly in the midst of angry waves; and hither, to meet them, rush the blasts from unknown desert places of the world. Here, in the fury of their unchecked liberty, they storm and buffet with each other, until the sea, lashed into passion like their own, leaps up, in ravings mightier than theirs, and the whole scene is madness.

On, on, on, over the countless miles of angry space roll the long heaving billows. Mountains and caves are here, and yet are not; for what is now the one, is now the other; then all is but a boiling heap of rushing water. Pursuit, and flight, and mad return of wave on wave, and savage struggle ending in a sporting-up of foam that whitens the black night; incessant change of place, and form, and hue; constancy in nothing, but eternal strife; on, on, on, they roll, and darker grows the night, and louder howls the wind, and more clamorous and fierce become the million voices in the sea, when the wild cry goes forth upon the storm "A ship!"

Onward she comes, in gallant combat with the elements, her tall masts trembling, and her timbers starting on the strain; onward she comes, now high upon the curling billows, now low down in the hollows of the sea, as hiding for the moment from its fury; and every stormvoice in the air and water cries more loudly yet, "A ship!"

Still she comes striving on: and at her boldness and the spreading cry, the angry waves rise up above each other's hoary heads to look; and round about the vessel, far as the mariners on the decks can pierce into the gloom, they press upon her, forcing each other down, and starting up, and rushing forward from afar, in dreadful curiosity. High over her they break; and round her surge and roar; and giving place to others, moaningly depart, and dash themselves to fragments in their baffled anger. Still she comes onward bravely. And though the eager multitude crowd thick and fast upon her all the night, and dawn of day discovers the untiring train yet bearing down upon the ship in an eternity of troubled water, onward she comes, with dim lights burning in her hull, and people there, asleep; as if no deadly element were peering in at every seam and chink, and no drowned seaman's grave, with but a plank to cover it, were yawning in the unfathomable depths below.

Among these sleeping voyagers were Martin and Mark Tapley, who, rocked into a heavy drowsiness by the unaccustomed motion, were as insensible to the foul air in which they lay, as to the uproar without. It was broad day, when the latter awoke with a dim idea that he was dreaming of having gone to sleep in a four-post bedstead which had turned bottom upwards in the course of the night. There was more reason in this too, than in the roasting of eggs; for the first objects Mr Tapley recognized when he opened his eyes were his own heels—looking down to him, as he afterwards observed, from a nearly perpendicular elevation.

"Well!" said Mark, getting himself into a sitting posture, after various ineffectual struggles with the rolling of the ship. "This is the first time as ever I stood on my head all night."

"You shouldn't go to sleep upon the ground with your head to leeward then," growled a man in one of the berths.

"With my head to *where?*" asked Mark.

The man repeated his previous sentiment.

"No, I won't another time," said Mark, "when I know whereabouts on the map that country is. In the meanwhile I can give you a better piece of advice. Don't you nor any other friend of mine never go to sleep with his head in a ship any more."

The man gave a grunt of discontented acquiescence, turned over in his berth, and drew his blanket over his head.

"—For," said Mr Tapley, pursuing the theme by way of soliloquy, in a low tone of voice: "the sea is as nonsensical a thing as any going. It never knows what to do with itself. It hasn't got no employment for its mind, and is always in a state of vacancy. Like them Polar bears in the wild-beast shows as is constantly a-nodding their heads from side to side, it never *can* be quiet. Which is entirely owing to its uncommon stupidity."

"Is that you, Mark?" asked a faint voice from another berth.

"It's as much of me as is left, sir, after a fortnight of this work," Mr Tapley replied. "What with leading the life of a fly, ever since I've been aboard—for I've been perpetually holding-on to something or other, in a upside-down position—what with that, sir, and putting a very little into myself, and taking a good deal out of myself, there an't too much of me to swear by. How do *you* find yourself this morning, sir?"

"Very miserable," said Martin, with a peevish groan. "Ugh! This is wretched, indeed!"

"Creditable," muttered Mark, pressing one hand upon his aching head and looking round him with a rueful grin. "That's the great comfort. It *is* creditable to keep up one's spirits here. Virtue's its own reward. So's jollity."

Mark was so far right, that unquestionably any man who retained his cheerfulness among the steerage accommodations of that noble and fast-sailing line-of-packet ship, *The Screw,* was solely indebted to his own resources, and shipped his good humour, like his provisions, without any contribution or assistance from the owners. A dark, low, stifling cabin, surrounded by berths all filled to overflowing with men, women, and children, in various stages of sickness and misery, is not the liveliest place of assembly at any time; but when it is so crowded (as the steerage cabin of *The Screw* was, every passage out), that mattresses and beds are heaped upon the floor, to the extinction of everything like comfort, cleanliness, and decency, it is liable to operate not only as a pretty strong barrier against amiability of temper, but as a positive encourager of selfish and rough humours. Mark felt this, as he sat looking about him; and his spirits rose proportionately.

There were English people, Irish people, Welsh people, and Scotch people there; all with their little store of coarse food and shabby clothes; and nearly all with their families of children. There were children of all ages; from the baby at the breast, to the slattern-girl who was as much a grown woman as her mother. Every kind of domestic suffering that is bred in poverty, illness, banishment, sorrow, and long travel in bad weather, was crammed into the little space; and yet was there infinitely less of complaint and querulousness, and infinitely more of mutual assistance and general kindness to be found in that unwholesome ark, than in many brilliant ball-rooms.

Mark looked about him wistfully, and his face brightened as he looked. Here an old grandmother was crooning over a sick child, and rocking it to and fro, in arms hardly more wasted than its own young limbs; here a poor woman with an infant in her lap, mended another little creature's clothes, and quieted another who was creeping up about her from their scanty bed upon the floor. Here were old men awkwardly engaged in little household offices, wherein they would have been ridiculous but for their good-will and kind purpose; and here were swarthy fellows-giants in their way—doing such little acts of tenderness for those about them, as might have belonged to gentlest-hearted dwarfs. The very idiot in the corner who sat mowing there, all day, had his faculty of imitation roused by what he saw about him; and snapped his fingers to amuse a crying child.

"Now, then," said Mark, nodding to a woman who was dressing her three children at no great distance from him: and the grin upon his face had by this time spread from ear to ear: "Hand over one of them young uns according to custom."

"I wish you'd get breakfast, Mark, instead of worrying with people who don't belong to you," observed Martin, petulantly.

"All right," said Mark. *"She'll* do that. It's a fair division of labour, sir. I wash her boys, and she makes our tea. I never *could* make tea, but any one can wash a boy."

The woman, who was delicate and ill, felt and understood his kindness, as well she might, for she had been covered every night with his great-coat, while he had had for his own bed the bare boards and a rug. But Martin, who seldom got up or looked about him, was quite incensed by the folly of this speech, and expressed his dissatisfaction by an impatient groan.

"So it is, certainly," said Mark, brushing the child's hair as coolly as if he had been born and bred a barber.

"What are you talking about, now?" asked Martin.

"What you said," replied Mark; "or what you meant, when you gave that there dismal vent to your feelings. I quite go along with it, sir. It *is* very hard upon her."

"What is?"

"Making this voyage by herself along with these young impediments here, and going such a way at such a time of the year to join her husband. If you don't want to be driven mad with yellow soap in your eye, young man," said Mr Tapley to the second urchin, who was by this time under his hands at the basin, "you'd better shut it."

"Where does she join her husband?" asked Martin, yawning.

"Why, I'm very much afraid," said Mr Tapley, in a low voice, "that she don't know. I hope she mayn't miss him. But she sent her last letter by hand, and it don't seem to have been very clearly understood between 'em without it, and if she don't see him a-waving his pocket handkerchief on the shore, like a pictur out of a song-book, my opinion is she'll break her heart."

"Why, how, in Folly's name, does the woman come to be on board ship on such a wild-goose venture!" cried Martin.

Mr Tapley glanced at him for a moment as he lay prostrate in his berth, and then said, very quietly:

"Ah! How indeed! I can't think! He's been away from her for two year: she's been very poor and lonely in her own country; and has always been a-looking forward to meeting him. It's very strange she should be here. Quite amazing! A little mad perhaps! There can't be no other way of accounting for it."

Martin was too far gone in the lassitude of sea-sickness to make any reply to these words, or even to attend to them as they were spoken. And the subject of their discourse returning at this crisis with some hot tea, effectually put a stop to any resumption of the theme by Mr Tapley; who, when the meal was over and he had adjusted Martin's bed, went up on deck to wash the breakfast service, which consisted of two halfpint tin mugs, and a shaving-pot of the same metal.

It is due to Mark Tapley to state that he suffered at least as much from sea-sickness as any man, woman, or child, on board; and that he had a peculiar faculty of knocking himself about on the smallest provocation, and losing his legs at every lurch of the ship. But resolved, in his usual phrase, to "come out strong" under disadvantageous circumstances, he was the life and soul of the steerage, and made no more of stopping in the middle of a facetious conversation to go away and be excessively ill by himself, and afterwards come back in the very best and gayest of tempers to resume it, than if such a course of proceeding had been the commonest in the world.

It cannot be said that as his illness wore off, his cheerfulness and good nature increased, because they would hardly admit of augmentation; but his usefulness among the weaker members of the party was much enlarged; and at all times and seasons there he was exerting it. If a gleam of sun shone out of the dark sky, down Mark tumbled into the cabin, and presently up he came again with a woman in his arms, or half-a-dozen children, or a man, or a bed, or a saucepan, or a basket, or something animate or inanimate, that he thought would be the better for the air. If an hour or two of fine weather in the middle of the day tempted those who seldom or never came on deck at other times to crawl into the long-boat, or lie down upon the spare spars, and try to eat, there, in the centre of the group, was Mr Tapley, handing about salt beef and biscuit, or dispensing tastes of grog, or cutting up the children's provisions with his pocket-knife, for their greater ease and comfort, or reading aloud from a venerable newspaper, or singing some roaring old song to a select party, or writing the beginnings of letters to their friends at home for people who couldn't write, or cracking jokes with the crew, or nearly getting blown over the side, or emerging, half-drowned, from a shower of spray, or lending a hand somewhere or other: but always doing something for the general entertainment. At night, when the cooking-fire was lighted on the deck, and the driving sparks that flew among the rigging, and the cloud of sails, seemed to menace the ship with certain annihilation by fire, in case the elements of air and water failed to compass her destruction; there, again, was Mr Tapley, with his coat off and his shirt sleeves turned up to his elbows, doing all kinds of culinary offices; compounding the strangest dishes; recognized by every one as an established authority; and helping all parties to achieve something which, left to themselves, they never could have done, and never would have dreamed of. In short, there never was a more popular character than Mark Tapley became, on board that noble and fast-sailing line-of-packet ship, *The Screw;* and he attained at last to such a pitch of universal admiration that he began to have grave doubts within himself whether a man might reasonably claim any credit for being jolly under such exciting circumstances.

"If this was going to last," said Tapley, "there'd be no great difference as I can perceive, between *The Screw* and the Dragon. I never *am* to get credit, I think. I begin to be afraid that the Fates is determined to make the world easy to me."

"Well, Mark," said Martin, near whose berth he had ruminated to this effect. "When will this be over?"

"Another week, they say, sir," returned Mark, "will most likely bring us into port. The ship's a-going along at present, as sensible as a ship can, sir; though I don't mean to say as that's any very high praise."

"I don't think it is, indeed," groaned Martin.

"You'd feel all the better for it, sir, if you was to turn out," observed Mark.

"And be seen by the ladies and gentlemen on the after-deck," returned Martin, with a scornful emphasis upon the words, "mingling with the beggarly crowd that are stowed away in this vile hole. I should be greatly the better for that, no doubt!"

"I'm thankful that I can't say from my own experience what the feelings of a gentleman may be," said Mark, "but I should have thought, sir, as a gentleman would feel a deal more uncomfortable down here than up in the fresh air, especially when the ladies and gentlemen in the after-cabin know just as much about him as he does about them, and are likely to trouble their heads about him in the same proportion. I should have thought that, certainly."

"I tell you, then," rejoined Martin, "you would have thought wrong, and do think wrong."

"Very likely, sir," said Mark, with imperturbable good temper. "I often do."

"As to lying here," cried Martin, raising himself on his elbow, and looking angrily at his follower. "Do you suppose it's a pleasure to lie here?"

"All the madhouses in the world," said Mr Tapley, "couldn't produce such a maniac as the man must be who could think that."

"Then why are you for ever goading and urging me to get up?" asked Martin. "I lie here because I don't wish to be recognized, in the better days to which I aspire, by any purse-proud citizen, as the man who came over with him among the steerage passengers. I lie here because I wish to conceal my circumstances and myself, and not to arrive in a new world badged and ticketed as an utterly poverty-stricken man. If I could have afforded a passage in the after-cabin, I should have held up my head with the rest. As I couldn't, I hide it. Do you understand that?"

"I am very sorry, sir," said Mark. "I didn't know you took it so much to heart as this comes to."

"Of course you didn't know," returned his master. "How should you know, unless I told you? It's no trial to *you,* Mark, to make yourself comfortable, and to bustle about. It's as natural for you to do so under the circumstances as it is for me not to do so. Why, you don't suppose there is a living creature in this ship who can by possibility have half so much to undergo on board of her as I have? Do you?" he asked, sitting upright in his berth and looking at Mark, with an expression of great earnestness not unmixed with wonder.

Mark twisted his face into a tight knot, and with his head very much on one side pondered upon this question as if he felt it an extremely dificult onc to answer. He was relieved from his embarrassment by Martin himself, who said, as he stretched himself upon his back again and resumed the book he had been reading:

"But what is the use of my putting such a case to you, when the very essence of what I have been saying is, that you cannot by possibility understand it!Make me a little brandy-and-water, cold and very weak, and give me a biscuit, and tell your friend, who is a nearer neighbour of ours than I could wish, to try and keep her children a little quieter to-night than she did last night; that's a good fellow."

Mr Tapley set himself to obey these orders with great alacrity, and pending their execution, it may be presumed his flagging spirits revived: inasmuch as he several times observed, below his breath, that in respect of its power of imparting a credit to jollity, *The Screw* unquestionably had some decided advantages over the Dragon. He also remarked that it was a high gratification to him to reflect that he would carry its main excellence ashore with him, and have it constantly beside him wherever he went; but what he meant by these consolatory thoughts he did not explain.

And now a general excitement began to prevail on board; and various predictions relative to the precise day, and even the precise hour at which they would reach New York, were freely broached. There was infinitely more crowding on deck and looking over the ship's side than there had been before; and an epidemic broke out for packing up things every morning, which required unpacking again every night. Those who had any letters to deliver, or any friends to meet, or any settled plans of going anywhere or doing anything, discussed their prospects a hundred times a day; and as this class of passengers was very small, and the number of those who had no prospects whatever was very large, there were plenty of listeners and few talkers. Those who had been ill all along, got well now, and those who had been well, got better. An American gentleman in the after-cabin, who had been wrapped up in fur and oilskin the whole passage, unexpectedly appeared in a very shiny, tall, black hat, and constantly overhauled a very little valise of pale leather, which contained his clothes, linen, brushes, shaving apparatus, books, trinkets, and other baggage. He likewise stuck his hands deep into his pockets, and walked the deck with his nostrils dilated, as already inhaling the air of Freedom which carries death to all tyrants, and can never (under any circumstances worth mentioning) be breathed by slaves. An English gentleman who was strongly suspected of having run away from a bank, with something in his possession belonging to its strong-box besides the key, grew eloquent upon the subject of the rights of man, and hummed the Marseillaise Hymn constantly. In a word, one great sensation pervaded the whole ship, and the soil of America lay close before them: so close at last, that, upon a certain starlight night, they took a pilot on board, and within a few hours afterwards lay to until the morning, awaiting the arrival of a steamboat in which the passengers were to be conveyed ashore.

Off she came, soon after it was light next morning, and lying alongside an hour or more during which period her very firemen were objects of hardly less interest and curiosity than if they had been so many angels, good or bad—took all her living freight aboard. Among them Mark, who still had his friend and her three children under his close protection: and Martin, who had once more dressed himself in his usual attire, but wore a soiled, old cloak above his ordinary clothes, until such time as he should separate for ever from his late companions.

The steamer—which, with its machinery on deck, looked, as it worked its long slim legs, like some enormously magnified insect or antediluvian monster—dashed at great speed up a beautiful bay; and presently they saw some heights, and islands, and a long, flat, straggling city.

"And this," said Mr Tapley, looking far ahead, "is the Land of Liberty, is it? Very well. I'm agreeable. Any land will do for me after so much water!"

HOW AMYAS THREW HIS SWORD INTO THE SEA[1]

Charles Kingsley
(1819-1875)

YES, it is over; and the great Armada is vanquished.

Yes, as the medals struck on the occasion said, "It came, it saw, and it fled." And whither? Away and northward, like a herd of frightened deer, past the Orkneys and Shetlands, catching up a few hapless fishermen as guides, past the coast of Norway, there, too, refused water and food by the brave descendants of the Vikings; and on northward ever towards the lonely Faroes, and the everlasting dawn which heralds round the Pole the midnight sun.

Their water is failing; the cattle must go overboard; and the wild northern sea echoes to the shrieks of drowning horses. They must homeward at least, somehow, each as best he can. Let them meet again at Cape Finisterre, if indeed they ever meet. Medina Sidonia, with some five-and-twenty of the soundest and best victualled ships, will lead the way, and leave the rest to their fate. He is soon out of sight; and forty more, the only remnant of that mighty host, come wandering wearily behind, hoping to make the south-west coast of Ireland, and have help, or, at least, fresh water there, from their fellow Romanists. Alas from them!—

Make Thou their way dark and slippery,
And follow them up ever with Thy storm.

For now comes up from the Atlantic, gale on gale; and few of that hapless remnant reached the shoes of Spain.

And where are Amyas and the *Vengeance* all this while?

At the fifty-seventh degree of latitude, the English fleet, finding themselves

[1] From *Westward Ho!*

growing short of provisions, and having been long since out of powder and ball, turn southward toward home, "thinking it best to leave the Spaniard to those uncouth and boisterous northern seas." A few pinnaces are still sent onward to watch their course; and the English fleet, caught in the same storms which scattered the Spaniards, "with great danger and industry reached Harwich port, and there provide themselves of victuals and ammunition," in case the Spaniard should return; but there is no need for that caution. Parma, indeed, who cannot believe that the idol at Halle, after all his compliments to it, will play him so scurvy a trick, will watch for weeks on Dunkirk dunes, hoping against hope for the Armada's return, casting anchors, and spinning rigging to repair their losses.

> But lang, lang may his ladies sit,
> With their fans intill their hand,
> Before they see Sir Patrick Spens
> Come sailing to the land.

The Armada is away on the other side of Scotland, and Amyas is following in its wake.

For when the Lord High Admiral determined to return, Amyas asked leave to follow the Spaniard; and asked, too, of Sir John Hawkins, who happened to be at hand, such ammunition and provision as could be afforded him, promising to repay the same like an honest man, out of his plunder if he lived, out of his estate if he died; lodging for that purpose bills in the hands of Sir John, who, as a man of business, took them, and put them in his pocket among the thimbles, string, and tobacco; after which Amyas, calling his men together, reminded them once more of the story of the Rose of Torridge and Don Guzman de Soto, and then asked:

"Men of Bideford, will you follow me? There will be plunder for those who love plunder; revenge for those who love revenge; and for all of us (for we all love honour) the honour of having never left the chase as long as there was a Spanish flag in English seas."

And every soul on board replied, that they would follow Sir Amyas Leigh around the world.

There is no need for me to detail every incident of that long and weary chase; how they found the *Sta Catharina,* attacked her, and had to sheer off, she being rescued by the rest; how when Medina's squadron left the crippled ships behind, they were all but taken or sunk, by thrusting into the midst of the Spanish fleet to prevent her escaping with Medina; how they crippled her, so that she could not beat to windward out into the ocean, but was fain to run south, past the Orkneys, and down through the Minch, between Cape Wrath and Lewis; how the younger hands were ready to mutiny, because Amyas, in his stubborn haste, ran past two or three noble prizes which were all but disabled, among others one of the great galliasses, and the two great Venetians, *La Ratta* and *La Belanzaza—which* were afterwards, with more than thirty other vessels, wrecked on the west coast of Ireland; how he got fresh water, in spite of certain "Hebridean Scots" of Skye, who, after reviling him in an unknown tongue, fought with him a while, and then embraced him and his men, with howls of affection, and were not much more decently clad, nor more civilized than his old friends of California; how he pacified his men by letting them pick the bones of a great Venetian which was going on shore upon Islay, (by which they got booty enough to repay them for the whole voyage), and offended them again by refusing to land and plunder two great Spanish wrecks on the Mull of Cantire (whose crews, by-the-bye, James tried to smuggle off secretly into Spain in ships of his own, wishing to play, as usual, both sides of the game at once; but the Spaniards were stopped at Yarmouth till the council's pleasure was known—which was, of course, to let the poor wretches go on their way, and be hanged elsewhere); how they passed a strange island, half black, half white, which the wild people called Raghery, but Cary christened it "the drowned magpie"; how the *Sta Catharina* was near lost on the Isle of Man, and then put into Castleton (where the Manxmen slew a whole boat's-crew with their arrows), and then put out again, when Amyas fought with her a whole day, and shot away her mainyard; how the Spaniard blundered down the coast of Wales, not knowing whither he went; how they were both nearly lost on Holyhead, and again on Bardsey Island; how they got on a lee shore in Cardigan Bay, before a heavy westerly gale, and the *Sta Catharina* ran aground on Sarn David, one of those strange subaqueous pebble-dykes which are said to be the remnants of the lost land of Gwalior, destroyed by the carelessness of Prince Seithenin, the drunkard, at whose name each loyal Welshman spits; how she got off again at the rising of the tide, and fought with Amyas a fourth time; how the wind changed, and she got round St David's Head;—these, and many more moving accidents of this eventful voyage, I must pass over without details, and go on to the end; for it is time that the end should come.

It was now the sixteenth day of the chase. They had seen, the evening before, St David's Head, and then the Welsh coast round Milford Haven, looming out black and sharp before the blaze of the inland thunderstorm; and it had lightened all round them during the fore part of the night, upon a light south-western breeze.

In vain they had strained their eyes through the darkness, to catch, by the fitful glare of the flashes, the tall masts of the Spaniard. Of one thing at least they were certain, that with the wind as it was, she could not have gone far to the westward; and to attempt to pass them again, and go northward, was more than she dare do. She was probably lying-to ahead of them, perhaps between them and the land; and when, a little after midnight, the wind chopped up to the west, and blew stiffly till daybreak, they felt sure that, unless she had attempted the desperate expedient of running past them, they had her safe in the mouth of the Bristol Channel. Slowly and wearily broke the dawn, on such a day as often follows heavy thunder, a sunless, drizzly day, roofed with low dingy cloud, barred, and netted, and festooned with black, a sign that the storm is only taking breath a while before it bursts again; while all the narrow horizon is dim and spongy with vapour drifting before a chilly breeze. As the day went on, the breeze died down, and the sea fell to a long glassy foam-flecked roll, while overhead brooded the inky sky, and round them the leaden mist shut out alike the shore and the chase.

Amyas paced the sloppy deck fretfully and fiercely. He knew that the Spaniard could not escape; but he cursed every moment which lingered between him and that one great revenge which blackened all his soul. The men sate sulkily about the deck, and whistled for a wind; the sails flapped idly against the masts; and the ship rolled in the long troughs of the sea, till her yard-arm almost dipped right and left.

"Take care of those guns. You will have something loose next," growled Amyas.

"We will take care of the guns, if the Lord will take care of the wind," said Yeo.

"We shall have plenty before night," said Cary, "and thunder too."

"So much the better," said Amyas. "It may roar till it splits the heavens, if it does but let me get my work done."

"He's not far off, I warrant," said Cary. "One lift of the cloud, and we should see him."

"To windward of us, as likely as not," said Amyas. "The devil fights for him, I believe. To have been on his heels sixteen days, and not sent this through him yet!" And he shook his sword impatiently.

So the morning wore away, without a sign of a living thing, not even a passing gull; and the black melancholy of the heaven reflected itself in the black melancholy of Amyas. Was he to lose his prey after all? The thought made him shudder with rage and disappointment. It was intolerable. Anything but that.

"No, God!" he cried, "let me but once feel this in his accursed heart, and then—strike me dead, if Thou wilt!"

"The Lord have mercy on us," cried John Brimblecombe. "What have you said?"

"What is that to you, sir? There, they are piping to dinner. Go down. I shall not come."

And Jack went down, and talked in a half-terrified whisper of Amyas's ominous words.

All thought that they portended some bad luck, except old Yeo.

"Well, Sir John," said he, "and why not? What better can the Lord do for a man, than take him home when he has done his work? Our captain is wilful and spiteful, and must needs kill his man himself; while for me, I don't care how the Don goes, provided he does go. I owe him no grudge, nor any man. May the Lord give him repentance, and forgive him all his sins; but if I could but see him once safe ashore, as he may be ere nightfall, on the Morestone, or the back of Lundy, I would say, 'Lord, now lettest Thou Thy servant depart in peace,' even if it were the lightning which was sent to fetch me."

"But, Master Yeo, a sudden death?"

"And why not a sudden death, Sir John? Even fools long for a short life and a merry one, and shall not the Lord's people pray for a short death and a merry one? Let it come as it will to old Yeo. Hark! there's the captain's voice."

"Here she is!" thundered Amyas from the deck; and in an instant all were scrambling up the hatchway as fast as the frantic rolling of the ship would let them.

Yes. There she was. The cloud had lifted suddenly, and to the south a ragged bore of blue sky let a long stream of sunshine down on her tall masts and stately hull, as she lay rolling some four or five miles to the eastward; but as for land, none was to be seen.

"There she is; and here we are," said Cary; "but where is here? and where is there? How is the tide, master?"

"Running up Channel by this time, sir."

"What matters the tide?" said Amyas, devouring the ship with terrible and cold blue eyes. "Can't we get at her?"

"Not unless some one jumps out and shoves behind," said Cary. "I shall down again and finish that' mackerel, if this roll has not chucked it to the cockroaches under the table."

"Don't jest, Will! I can't stand it," said Amyas, in a voice which quivered so much that Cary looked at him. His whole frame was trembling like an aspen. Cary took his arm, and drew him aside.

"Dear old lad," said he as they leaned over the bulwarks, "what is this? You are not yourself, and have not been these four days."

"No. I am not Amyas Leigh. I am my brother's avenger. Do not reason with me, Will: when it is over, I shall be merry old Amyas again," and he passed his hand over his brow.

"Do you believe," said he, after a moment, "that men can be possessed by devils?"

"The Bible says so."

"If my cause were not a just one, I should fancy I had a devil in me. My throat and heart are as hot as the pit. Would to God it were done, for done it must be!Now go."

Cary went away with a shudder. As he passed down the hatchway he looked back. Amyas had got the hone out of his pocket, and was whetting away again at his sword-edge, as if there was some dreadful doom on him, to whet, and whet for ever.

The weary day wore on. The strip of blue sky was curtained over again, and all was dismal as before, though it grew sultrier every moment; and now and then a distant mutter shook the air to westward. Nothing could be done to lessen the distance between the ships, for the *Vengeance* had had all her boats carried away but one, and that was much too small to tow her; and while the men went down again to finish dinner, Amyas worked on at his sword, looking up every now and then suddenly at the Spaniard, as if to satisfy himself that it was not a vision which had vanished.

About two Yeo came up to him.

"He is ours safely now, sir. The tide has been running to the eastward for this two hours."

"Safe as a fox in a trap. Satan himself cannot take him from us."

"But God may," said Brimblecombe simply.

"Who spoke to you, sir? If I thought that He—There comes the thunder at last!"

And as he spoke, an angry growl from the westward heavens seemed to answer his wild words, and rolled and loudened nearer and nearer, till right over their heads it crashed against some cloud-cliff far above, and all was still.

Each man looked in the other's face: but Amyas was unmoved.

"The storm is coming," said he, "and the wind in it. It will be Eastward-ho now, for once, my merry men all!"

"Eastward-ho never brought us luck," said Jack in an undertone to Cary. But by this time all eyes were turned to the north-west, where a black line along the horizon began to define the boundary of sea and air, till now all dim in mist.

"There comes the breeze."

"And there the storm, too."

And with that strangely accelerating pace which some storms seem to possess, the thunder, which had been growling slow and seldom far away, now rang peal on peal along the cloudy floor above their heads.

"Here comes the breeze. Round with the yards, or we shall be taken aback."

The yards creaked round; the sea grew crisp around them; the hot air swept their cheeks, tightened every rope, filled every sail, bent her over. A cheer burst from the men as the helm went up, and they staggered away before the wind, right down upon the Spaniard, who lay still becalmed.

"There is more behind, Amyas," said Cary. "Shall we not shorten sail a little?"

"No. Hold on every stitch," said Amyas. "Give me the helm, man. Boatswain, pipe away to clear for fight."

It was done, and in ten minutes the men were all at quarters while the thunder rolled louder and louder overhead, and the breeze freshened fast.

"The dog has it now. There he goes!" said Cary.

"Right before the wind. He has no liking to face us."

"He is running into the jaws of destruction," said Yeo. "An hour more will send him either right up the Channel, or smack on shore somewhere."

"There! he has put his helm down. I wonder if he sees land?"

"He is like a March hare beat out of his country," said Cary, "and don't know whither to run next."

Cary was right. In ten minutes more the Spaniard fell off again, and went away dead down wind, while the *Vengeance* gained on him fast. After two hours more, the four miles had diminished to one, while the lightning flashed nearer and nearer as the storm came up; and from the vast mouth of a black cloud-arch poured so fierce a breeze that Amyas yielded unwillingly to hints which were growing into open murmurs, and bade shorten sail.

On they rushed with scarcely lessened speed, the black arch following fast, curtained by one flat grey sheet of pouring rain, before which the water was boiling in a long white line; while every moment, behind the watery veil, a keen blue spark leapt down into the sea, or darted zigzag through the rain.

"We shall have it now, and with a vengeance; this will try your tackle, Master," said Cary.

The functionary answered with a shrug, and turned up the collar of his rough frock, as the first drops flew stinging round his ears. Another minute, and the squall burst full upon them in rain, which cut like hail—hail which lashed the sea into froth, and wind which whirled off the heads of the surges, and swept the waters into one white seething waste. And above them, and behind them, and before them, the lightning leapt and ran, dazzling and blinding, while the deep roar of the thunder was changed to sharp ear-piercing cracks.

"Get the arms and ammunition under cover, and then below with you all," shouted Amyas from the helm.

"And heat the pokers in the galley fire," said Yeo, "to be ready if the rain puts our linstocks out. I hope you'll let me stay on deck, sir, in case—"

"I must have some one, and who better than you? Can you see the chase?"

No; she was wrapped in the grey whirlwind. She might be within half-a-mile of them for ought they could have seen of her.

And now Amyas and his old liegeman were alone. Neither spoke; each knew the other's thoughts, and knew that they were his own. The squall blew fiercer and fiercer, the rain poured heavier and heavier. Where was the Spaniard?

"If he has laid-to, we may overshoot him, sir!"

"If he has tried to lay-to, he will not have a sail left in the bolt-ropes, or perhaps a mast on deck. I know the stiff-neckedness of those Spanish tubs. Hurrah! there he is, right on our larboard bow!"

There she was indeed, two musket-shots off, staggering away with canvas split and flying.

"He has been trying to hull, sir, and caught a buffet," said Yeo, rubbing his hands. "What shall we do now?"

"Range alongside, if it blow live imps and witches, and try our luck once more. Pah! how this lightning dazzles!"

On they swept, gaining fast on the Spaniard.

"Call the men up, and to quarters; the rain will be over in ten minutes."

Yeo ran forward to the gangway; and sprang back again, with a face white and wild—

"Land right ahead! Port your helm, sir! For the love of God, port your helm!"

Amyas, with the strength of a bull, jammed the helm down, while Yeo shouted to the men below.

She swung round. The masts bent like whips; crack went the foresail like a cannon. What matter? Within two hundred yards of them was the Spaniard; in front of her, and above her, a huge dark bank rose through the dense hail, and mingled with the clouds; and at its foot, plainer every moment, pillars and spouts of leaping foam.

"What is it? Morte? Hartland?"

It might be anything for thirty miles.

"Lundy!" said Yeo. "The south end! I see the head of the Shutter in the breakers! Hard a-port yet, and get her close-hauled as you can, and the Lord may have mercy on us still! Look at the Spaniard!"

Yes, look at the Spaniard!

On their left hand, as they broached-to, the wall of granite sloped down from the clouds toward an isolated peak of rock, some two hundred feet in height. Then a hundred yards of roaring breaker upon a sunken shelf, across which the race of the tide poured like a cataract; then, amid a column of salt smoke, the Shutter, like a huge black fang, rose waiting for its prey; and between the shutter and the land, the great galleon loomed dimly through the storm.

He, too, had seen his danger, and tried to broach-to. But his clumsy mass refused to obey the helm; he struggled a moment, half hid in foam; fell away again, and rushed upon his doom.

"Lost! lost! lost!" cried Amyas madly, and throwing up his hands, let go the tiller. Yeo caught it just in time.

"Sir! sir! What are you at? We shall clear the rock yet."

"Yes!" shouted Amyas in his frenzy; "But he will not!"

Another minute. The galleon gave a sudden jar, and stopped. Then one long heave and bound, as if to free herself. And then her bows lighted clean upon the Shutter.

An awful silence fell on every English soul. They heard not the roaring of wind and surge; they saw not the blinding flashes of lightning; but they heard one long ear-piercing wail to every saint in heaven rise from from five hundred human throats; they saw the mighty ship heel over from the wind, and sweep headlong down the cataract of the race, plunging her yards into the foam, and showing her whole black side even to her keel, till she rolled clean over, and vanished for ever and ever.

"Shame!" cried Amyas, hurling his sword far into the sea, "to lose my right, my right!when it was in my very grasp!Unmerciful!"

A crack which rent the sky, and made the granite ring and quiver; a bright world of flame, and then a blank of utter darkness, against which stood out, glowing red-hot, every mast, and sail, and rock, and Salvation Yeo as he stood just in front of Amyas, the tiller in his hand All red-hot, transfigured into fire; and behind, the black, black night.

THE MAN WITH THE BELT OF GOLD[1]

Robert Louis Stevenson
(1850-1894)

MORE than a week went by, in which the ill-luck that had hitherto pursued the *Covenant* upon this voyage grew yet more strongly marked. Some days she made a little way; others, she was driven actually back. At last we were beaten so far to the south that we tossed and tacked to and fro the whole of the ninth day, within sight of Cape Wrath and the wild, rocky coast on either hand of it. There followed on that a council of the officers, and some decision which I did not rightly understand, seeing only the result: that we had made a fair wind of a foul one and were running south.

The tenth afternoon, there was a falling swell and a thick, wet, white fog that hid one end of the brig from the other. All afternoon, when I went on deck, I saw men and officers listening hard over the bulwarks—"for breakers," they said; and though I did not so much as understand the word, I felt danger in the air, and was excited.

Maybe about ten at night, I was serving Mr Riach and the captain at their supper, when the ship struck something with a great sound, and we heard voices singing out. My two masters leaped to their feet.

"She's struck," said Mr Riach.

[1] From *Kidnapped.*

"No, sir," said the captain. "We've only run a boat down."

And they hurried out.

The captain was in the right of it. We had run down a boat in the fog, and she had parted in the midst and gone to the bottom with all her crew, but one. This man (as I heard afterwards) had been sitting in the stern as a passenger, while the rest were on the benches rowing. At the moment of the blow, the stern had been thrown into the air, and the man (having his hands free, and for all he was encumbered with a frieze overcoat that came below his knees) had leaped up and caught hold of the brig's bowsprit. It showed he had luck and much agility and unusual strength, that he should have thus saved himself from such a pass. And yet, when the captain brought him into the round-house, and I set eyes on him for the first time, he looked as cool as I did.

He was smallish in stature, but well set and as nimble as a goat; his face was of a good open expression, but sunburnt very dark, and heavily freckled and pitted with the small-pox; his eyes were unusually light and had a kind of dancing madness in them, that was both engaging and alarming; and when he took off his great-coat, he laid a pair of fine silver-mounted pistols on the table, and I saw that he was belted with a great sword. His manners, besides, were elegant, and he pledged the captain handsomely. Altogether I thought of him, at the first sight, that here was a man I would rather call my friend than my enemy.

The captain, too, was taking his observations, but rather of the man's clothes than his person. And to be sure, as soon as he had taken off the great coat, he showed forth mighty fine for the round-house of a merchant brig: having a hat with feathers, a red waistcoat, breeches of black plush, and a blue coat with silver buttons and handsome silver lace: costly clothes, though somewhat spoiled with the fog and being slept in.

"I'm vexed, sir, about the boat," says the captain.

"There are some pretty men gone to the bottom," said the stranger, "that I would rather see on the dry land again than half a score of boats."

"Friends of yours?" said Hoseason.

"You have none such friends in your country," was the reply. "They would have died for me like dogs."

"Well, sir," said the captain, still watching him, "there are more men in the world than boats to put them in."

"And that's true too," cried the other, "and ye seem to be a gentleman of great penetration."

"I have been in France, sir," says the captain, so that it was plain he meant more by the words than showed upon the face of them.

"Well, sir," says the other, "and so has many a pretty man, for the matter of that."

"No doubt, sir," says the captain; "and fine coats."

"Oho!" says the stranger, "is that how the wind sets?" And he laid his hand quickly on his pistols.

"Don't be hasty," said the captain. "Don't do a mischief, before ye see the need for it. Ye've a French soldier's coat upon your back and a Scotch tongue in your head, to be sure; but so has many an honest fellow in these days, and I dare say none the worse of it."

"So?" said the gentleman in the fine coat: "are ye of the honest party?" (meaning, Was he a Jacobite? for each side, in these sort of civil broils, takes the name of honesty for its own.)

"Why, sir," replied the captain, "I am a true-blue Protestant, and I thank God for it." (It was the first word of any religion I had ever heard from him, but I learnt afterwards he was a great church-goer while on shore.) "But, for all that," says he, "I can be sorry to see another man with his back to the wall."

"Can ye so indeed?" asks the Jacobite "Well, sir, to be quite plain with ye, I am one of those honest gentlemen that were in trouble about the years forty-five and six; and (to be still quite plain with ye) if I got into the hands of any of the red-coated gentry, it's like it would go hard with me. Now, sir, I was for France; and there was a French ship cruising here to pick me up; but she gave us the go-by in the fog—as I wish from the heart ye had done yoursel'! And the best that I can say is this; If ye can set me ashore where I was going, I have that upon me will reward you highly for your trouble."

"In France?" says the captain. "No, sir; that I cannot do. But where ye come from—we might talk of that."

And then, unhappily, he observed me standing in my corner, and packed me off to the galley to get supper for the gentleman. I lost no time I promise you; and when I came back into the round-house, I found the gentleman had taken a money-belt from about his waist, and poured out a guinea or two upon the table. The captain was looking at the guineas, and then at the belt, and then at the gentleman's face; and I thought he seemed excited.

"Half of it," he cried, "and I'm your man!"

The other swept back the guineas into the belt, and put it on again under his waistcoat. "I have told ye, sir," said he, "that not one doit of it belongs to me. It belongs to my chieftain"—and here he touched his hat—" and while I would be but a silly messenger to grudge some of it that the rest might come safe, I should show myself a hound indeed if I bought my own carcase any too dear. Thirty guineas on the seaside, or sixty if ye set me on the Linnhe loch. Take it, if ye will; if not, ye can do your worst."

"Ay," said Hoseason. "And if I give ye over to the soldiers?"

"Ye would make a fool's bargain," said the other. "My chief, let me tell you, sir, is forfeited, like every honest man in Scotland. His estate is in the hands of the man they call King George; and it is his officers that collect the rents, or try to collect them. But for the honour of Scotland, the poor tenant bodies take a thought upon their chief lying in exile; and his money is a part of that very rent for which King George is looking. Now, sir, ye seem to me to be a man that understands things: bring this money within the reach of Government, and how much of it 'll come to you?"

"Little enough, to be sure," said Hoseason; and then, "If they knew," he added, dryly. "But I think, if I was to try, that I could hold my tongue about it."

"Ah, but I'll begowk[1] ye there," cried the gentleman. "Play me false, and I'll play you cunning. If a hand's laid upon me, they shall ken what money it is."

"Well," returned the captain, "what must be must. Sixty guineas, and done. Here's my hand upon it."

"And here's mine," said the other.

And thereupon the captain went out (rather hurriedly, I thought), and left me alone in the round-house with the stranger.

At that period (so soon after the forty-five) there were many exiled gentlemen coming back at the peril of their lives, either to see their friends or to collect a little money; and as for the Highland chiefs that had been forfeited, it was a common matter of talk how their tenants would stint themselves to send them money, and their clansmen outface the soldiery to get it in, and run the gauntlet of our great navy to carry it across. All this I had, of course, heard tell of; and now I had a man under my eyes whose life was forfeit on all these counts and upon one more; for he was not only a rebel and a smuggler of rents, but had taken service with King Louis of France. And as if all this were not enough, he had a belt full of golden guineas round his loins. Whatever my opinions, I could not look on such a man without a lively interest.

"And so you're a Jacobite?" said I, as I set meat before him.

"Ay," said he, beginning to eat. "And you, by your long face, should be a Whig."

"Betwixt and between," said I, not to annoy him; for indeed I was as good a Whig as Mr Campbell could make me.

"And that's naething," said he. "But I'm saying, Mr. Betwixt-and-Between," he added, "this bottle of yours is dry; and it's hard if I'm to pay sixty guineas and be grudged a dram upon the back of it."

"I'll go and ask for the key," said I, and stepped on deck.

The fog was as close as ever, but the swell almost down. They had laid the brig to, not knowing precisely where they were, and the wind (what little there was of

[1] Befool.

it) not serving well for their true course. Some of the hands were still hearkening for breakers; but the captain and the two officers were in the waist with their heads together. It struck me, I don't know why, that they were after no good; and the first word I heard, as I drew softly near, more than confirmed me.

It was Mr Riach, crying out as if upon a sudden thought.

"Couldn't we wile him out of the round-house?"

"He's better where he is," returned Hoseason; "He hasn't room to use his sword."

"Well, that's true," said Riach; "but he's hard to come at."

"Hut!" said Hoseason. "We can get the man in talk, one upon each side, and pin him by the two arms; or if that'Il not hold, sir, we can make a run by both the doors and get him under hand before he has the time to draw."

At this hearing, I was seized with both fear and anger at these treacherous, greedy, bloody men that I sailed with. My first mind was to run away; my second was bolder.

"Captain," said I, "the gentleman is seeking a dram, and the bottle's out. Will you give me the key?"

They all started and turned about.

"Why, here's our chance to get the firearms!" Riach cried; and then to me: "Hark ye, David," he said, "do ye ken where the pistols are?"

"Ay, ay," put in Hoseason. "David kens; David's a good lad. Ye see, David my man, yon wild Hielandman is a danger to the ship, besides being a rank foe to King George, God bless him!"

I had never been so be-Davided since I came on board; but I said yes, as if all I heard were quite natural.

"The trouble is," resumed the captain, "that all our firelocks great and little, are in the round-house under this man's nose; likewise the powder. Now, if I, or one of the officers, was to go in and take them, he would fall to thinking. But a lad like you, David, might snap up a horn and a pistol or two without remark. And if ye can do it cleverly, I'll bear it in mind when it'll be good for you to have friends; and that's when we come to Carolina."

Here Mr Riach whispered him a little.

"Very right, sir," said the captain; and then to myself: "And see here, David, yon man has a beltful of gold, and I give you my word that you shall have your fingers in it."

I told him I would do as he wished, though indeed I had scarce breath to speak with; and upon that he gave me the key of the spirit-locker, and I began to go slowly back to the round-house. What was I to do? They were dogs and thieves; they had stolen me from my own country; they had killed poor Ransome; and was I to hold the candle to another murder? But then, upon the other hand, there was the fear of death very plain before me; for what could a boy and a man, if they were as brave as lions, against a whole ship's company.

I was still arguing it back and forth, and getting no great clearness, when I came into the round-house and saw the Jacobite eating his supper under the lamp; and at that my mind was made up all in a moment. I have no credit by it; it was by no choice of mine, but as if by compulsion, that I walked right up to the table and put my hand on his shoulder.

"Do ye want to be killed?" said I.

He sprang to his feet, and looked a question at me as clear as if he had spoken.

"Oh!" cried I, "they're all murderers here; it's a ship full of them! They've murdered a boy already. Now it's you."

"Ay, ay," said he; "but they haven't got me yet." And then looking at me curiously, "Will ye stand with me?"

"That will I!" said I. "I am no thief, nor yet murderer. I'll stand by you."

"Why, then," said he, "what's your name?"

"David Balfour," said I; and then thinking that a man with so fine a coat must like fine people, I added for the first time, "of Shaws."

It never occurred to him to doubt me, for a Highlander is used to see great gentlefolk in great poverty; but as he had no estate of his own, my words nettled a very childish vanity he had.

"My name is Stewart," he said, drawing himself up. "Alan Breck, they call me. A king's name is good enough for me, though I bear it plain and have the name of no farm-midden to clap to the hind-end of it."

And having administered this rebuke as though it were something of a chief importance, he turned to examine our defences.

The round-house was built very strong, to support the breaching of the seas. Of its five apertures, only the skylight and the two doors were large enough for the passage of a man. The doors, besides, could be drawn close; they were of stout oak, and ran in grooves, and were fitted with hooks to keep them either shut or open, as the need arose. The one that was already shut, I secured in this fashion; but when I was proceeding to slide to the other, Alan stopped me.

"David," said he—" for I cannae bring to mind the name of your landed estate, and so will make so bold as call you David—that door, being open, is the best part of my defences."

"It would be better shut," says I.

"Not so, David," says he. "Ye see, I have but one face; but so long as that door is open and my face to it, the best part of my enemies will be in front of me, where I would aye wish to find them."

Then he gave me from the rack a cutlass (of which there were a few besides the firearms), choosing it with great care, shaking his head and saying he had never in all his life seen poorer weapons; and next he set me down to the table with a powder-horn, a bag of bullets, and all the pistols, which he bade me charge.

"And that will be better work, let me tell you," said he, "for a gentleman of decent birth, than scraping plates and raxing[1] drams to a wheen tarry sailors."

Thereupon he stood up in the midst with his face to the door, and drawing his great sword, made trial of the room he had to wield it in.

"I must stick to the point," he said, shaking his head; "And that's a pity, too. It doesn't set my genius, which is all for the upper guard. And now," said he, "do you keep on charging the pistols, and give heed to me."

I told him I would listen closely. My chest was tight, my mouth dry, the light dark to my eyes; the thought of the numbers that were soon to leap in upon us kept my heart in a flutter; and the sea, which I heard washing round the brig, and where I thought my dead body would be cast ere morning, ran in my mind strangely.

"First of all," said he, "how many are against us?"

I reckoned them up; and such was the hurry of my mind, I had to cast the numbers twice. "Fifteen," said I.

Alan whistled. "Well," said he, "that can't be cured. And now follow me. It is my part to keep this door, where I look for the main battle. In that, ye have no hand. And mind and dinna fire to this side unless they get me down; for I would rather have ten foes in front of me than one friend like you cracking pistols at my back."

I told him, indeed, I was no great shot.

"And that's very bravely said," he cried, in a great admiration of my candour. "There's many a pretty gentleman that wouldnae dare to say it."

"But then, sir," said I, "there is the door behind you, which they may perhap break in."

"Ay," said he, "and that is a part of your work. No sooner the pistols charged, than ye must climb up into yon bed where ye're handy at the window; and if they lift hand against the door, ye're to shoot. But that's not all. Let's make a bit of a soldier of ye, David. What else have ye to guard?"

"There's the skylight," said I. "But indeed, Mr Stewart, I would need to have eyes upon both sides to keep the two of them; for when my face is at the one, my back is to the other."

"And that's very true," said Alan. "But have ye no ears to your head?"

"To be sure!" cried I. "I must hear the bursting of the glass!"

"Ye have some rudiments of sense," said Alan, grimly.

But now our time of truce was come to an end. Those on deck had waited for my coming till they grew impatient; and scarce had Alan spoken, when the captain showed face in the open door.

---

[1] Reaching.

"Stand!" cried Alan, and pointed his sword at him.

The captain stood, indeed; but he neither winced nor drew back a foot.

"A naked sword?" says he. "This is a strange return for hospitality."

"Do ye see me?" said Alan. "I am come of kings; I bear a king's name. My badge is the oak. Do ye see my sword? It has slashed the heads off mair Whigamores than you have toes upon your feet. Call up your vermin to your back, sir, and fail on! The sooner the clash begins, the sooner ye'll taste this steel throughout your vitals."

The captain said nothing to Alan, but he looked over at me with an ugly look. "David," said he, "I'll mind this"; and the sound of his voice went through me with a jar.

Next moment he was gone.

"And now," said Alan, "let your hand keep your head, for the grip is coming."

Alan drew a dirk, which he held in his left hand in case they should run in under his sword. I, on my part, clambered up into the berth with an armful of pistols, and something of a heavy heart, and set open the window where I was to watch. It was a small part of the deck that I could overlook, but enough for our purpose. The sea had gone down, and the wind was steady and kept the sails quiet; so that, there was a great stillness in the ship, in which I made sure I heard the sound of muttering voices. A little after, and there came a clash of steel upon the deck, by which I knew they were dealing out the cutlasses and one had been let fail; and after that, silence again.

I do not know if I was what you call afraid; but my heart beat like a bird's, both quick and little; and there was a dimness came before my eyes which I continually rubbed away, and which continually returned. As for hope, I had none; but only a darkness of despair and a sort of anger against all the world that made me long to sell my life as dear as I was able. I tried to pray, I remember, but that same hurry of my mind, like a man running, would not suffer me to think upon the words; and my chief wish was to have the thing begin and be done with it.

It came all of a sudden when it did, with a rush of feet and a roar, and then a shout from Alan, and a sound of blows and some one crying out as if hurt. I looked back over my shoulder, and saw Mr Shuan in the doorway, crossing blades with Alan.

"That's him that killed the boy!" I cried.

"Look to your window!" said Alan, and as I turned back to my place, I saw him pass his sword through the mate's body.

It was none too soon for me to look to my own part; for my head was scarce back at the window, before five men carrying a spare yard for a battering-ram, ran past me and took post to drive the door in. I had never fired with a pistol in my life, and not often with a gun; far less against a fellow-creature. But it was now or never; and just as they swang the yard, I cried out, "Take that!" and shot into their midst.

I must have hit one of them, for he sang out and gave back a step, and the rest stopped as if a little disconcerted. Before they had time to recover, I sent another ball over their heads; and at my third shot (which went as wide as the second) the whole party threw down the yard and ran for it.

Then I looked round again into the deck-house. The whole place was full of the smoke of my own firing, just as my ears seemed to be burst with the noise of the shots. But there was Alan, standing as before; only now his sword was running blood to the hilt, and himself so swelled with triumph and fallen into so fine an attitude, that he looked to be invincible. Right before him on the floor was Mr Shuan, on his hands and knees; the blood was pouring from his mouth, and he was sinking slowly lower, with a terrible, white face; and just as I looked, some of those from behind caught hold of him by the heels and dragged him bodily out of the round-house. I believe he died as they were doing it.

"There's one of your Whigs for ye!" cried Alan; and then turning to me, he asked if I had done much execution.

I told him I had winged one, and thought it was the captain.

"And I've settled two," says he. "No, there's not enough blood let; they'll be back again. To your watch, David. This was but a dram before meat."

I settled back to my place, re-charging the three pistols I had fired, and keeping watch with both eye and ear.

Our enemies were disputing not far off upon the deck, and that so loudly that I could hear a word or two above the washing of the seas.

"It was Shuan bauchled[1] it," I heard one say.

And another answered him with a "Wheesht, man! He's paid the piper."

After that the voices fell again into the same muttering as before. Only now, one person spoke most of the time, as though laying down a plan, and first one and then another answered him briefly, like men taking orders. By this, I made sure they were coming on again, and told Alan.

"It's what we have to pray for," said he. "Unless we can give them a good distaste of us, and done with it, there'll be nae sleep for either you or me. But this time, mind, they'll be in earnest."

By this, my pistols were ready, and there was nothing to do but listen and wait. While the brush lasted, I had not the time to think if I was frighted; but now, when all was still again, my mind ran upon nothing else. The thought of the sharp swords and the cold steel was strong in me; and presently, when I began to hear stealthy steps and a brushing of men's clothes against the round-house wail, and knew they

[1] Bungled.

were taking their places in the dark, I could have found it in my mind to cry out aloud.

All this was upon Alan's side; and I had begun to think my share of the fight was at an end, when I heard some one drop softly on the roof above me.

Then there came a single call on the sea-pipe, and that was the signal. A knot of them made one rush of it, cutlass in hand, against the door; and at the same moment, the glass of the skylight was dashed in a thousand pieces, and a man leaped through and landed on the floor. Before he got his feet, I had clapped a pistol to his back, and might have shot him, too; only at the touch of him (and him alive) my whole flesh misgave me, and I could no more pull the trigger than I could have flown.

He had dropped his cutlass, as he jumped, and when he felt the pistol, whipped straight round and laid hold of me, roaring out an oath; and at that either my courage came again, or I grew so much afraid as came to the same thing; for I gave a shriek and shot him in the midst of the body. He gave the most horrible ugly groan and fell to the floor. The foot of a second fellow, whose legs were dangling through the skylight, struck me at the same time upon the head; and at that I snatched another pistol and shot this one through the thigh, so that he slipped through and tumbled in a lump on his companion's body. There was no talk of missing, any more than there was time to aim; I clapped the muzzle to the very place and fired.

I might have stood and stared at them for long, but I heard Alan shout as if for help, and that brought me to my senses.

He had kept the door so long; but one of the seamen, while he was engaged with others, had run in under his guard and caught him about the body. Alan was dirking him with his left hand, but the fellow clung like a leech. Another had broken in and had his cutlass raised. The door was thronged with their faces. I thought we were lost, and catching up my cutlass, fell on them in flank.

But I had not time to be of help. The wrestler dropped at last; and Alan, leaping back to get his distance, ran upon the others like a bull, roaring as he went. They broke before him like water, turning, and running, and falling one against another in their haste. The sword in his hand flashed like quicksilver into the huddle of our fleeing enemies; and at every flash there came the scream of a man hurt. I was still thinking we were lost, when lo! they were all gone, and Alan was driving them along the deck as a sheepdog chases sheep.

Yet he was no sooner out than he was back again, being as cautious as he was brave; and meanwhile the seamen continued running and crying out as if he was still behind them; and we heard them tumble one upon another into the forecastle, and clap-to the hatch upon the top.

The round-house was like a shambles; three were dead inside, another lay in his death agony across the threshold; and there were Alan and I victorious and unhurt.

He came up to me with open arms. "Come to my arms!" he cried, and embraced and kissed me hard upon both cheeks. "David," said he, "I love you like a brother. And oh, man," he cried in a kind of ecstasy, "am I no a bonny fighter?"

Thereupon he turned to the four enemies, passed his sword clean through each of them, and tumbled them out of doors one after the other. As he did so, he kept humming and singing and whistling to himself, like a man trying to recall an air; only what *he* was trying, was to make one. All the while, the flush was in his face, and his eyes were as bright as a five-year-old child's with a new toy. And presently he sat down upon the table, sword in hand; the air that he was making all the time began to run a little clearer, and then clearer still; and then out he burst with a great voice into a Gaelic song.

I have translated it here, not in verse (of which I have no skill) but at least in the king's English. He sang it often afterwards, and the thing became popular; so that I have heard it, and had it explained to me, many's the time.

This is the song of the sword of Alan:
The smith made it,
The fire set it;
Now it shines in the hand of Alan Breck.

Their eyes were many and bright,
Swift were they to behold,
Many the hands they guided:
The sword was alone.

The dun deer troop over the hill,
They are many, the hill is one;
The dun deer vanish,
The hill remains.

Come to me from the hills of heather,
Come from the isles of the sea.
O far-beholding eagles,
Here is your meat.

ABANDONING SHIP[1]

Joseph Conrad
(1857-1924)

THE skipper lingered disconsolately, and we left him to commune alone for a while with his first command. Then I went up again and brought him away at last. It was time. The ironwork on the poop was hot to the touch.

Then the painter of the long-boat was cut, and the three boats, tied together, drifted clear of the ship. It was just sixteen hours after the explosion when we abandoned her. Mahon had charge of the second boat, and I had the smallest—the 14-foot thing. The long-boat would have taken the lot of us; but the skipper said we must save as much property as we could—for the underwriters—and so I got my first command. I had two men with me, a bag of biscuits, a few tins of meat, and a breaker of water. I was ordered to keep close to the long-boat, that in case of bad weather we might be taken into her.

And do you know what I thought? I thought I would part company as soon as I could. I wanted to have my first command all to myself. I wasn't going to sail in a squadron if there were a chance for independent cruising. I would make land by myself. I would beat the other boats. Youth! All youth! The silly, charming, beautiful youth.

But we did not make a start at once. We must see the last of the ship. And so the boats drifted about that night, heaving and setting on the swell. The men dozed, waked, sighed, groaned. I looked at the burning ship.

Between the darkness of earth and heaven she was burning fiercely upon a disc of purple sea shot by the blood-red play of gleams; upon a disc of water glittering and sinister. A high, clear flame, an immense and lonely flame, ascended from the ocean, and from its summit the black smoke poured continuously at the sky. She burned furiously, mournful and imposing like a funeral pile kindled in the night, surrounded by the sea, watched over by the stars. A magnificent death had come like a grace, like a gift, like a reward to that old ship at the end of her laborious days. The surrender of her weary ghost to the keeping of stars and sea was stirring like the sight of a glorious triumph. The masts fell just before daybreak, and for a moment there was a burst and turmoil of sparks that seemed to fill with flying fire the night patient and watchful, the vast night lying silent upon the sea. At daylight she was only a charred shell, floating still under a cloud of smoke and bearing a glowing mass of coal within.

Then the oars were got out, and the boats forming in a line moved round her remains as if in procession—the long-boat leading. As we pulled across her stern

[1] From *Youth.*

a slim dart of fire shot out viciously at us, and suddenly she went down, head first, in a great hiss of steam. The unconsumed stern was the last to sink; but the paint had gone, had cracked, had peeled off, and there were no letters, there was no word, no stubborn device that was like her soul, to flash at the rising sun her creed and her name.

We made our way north. A breeze sprang up, and about noon all the boats came together for the last time. I had no mast or sail in mine, but I made a mast out of a spare oar and hoisted a boat-awning for a sail, with a boat-hook for a yard. She was certainly over-masted, but I had the satisfaction of knowing that with the wind aft I could beat the other two. I had to wait for them. Then we all had a look at the captain's chart, and, after a sociable meal of hard bread and water, got our last instructions. These were simple: steer north, and keep together as much as possible. "Be careful with that jury-rig, Marlow," said the captain; and Mahon, as I sailed proudly past his boat, wrinkled his curved nose and hailed, "You will sail that ship of yours under water, if you don't look out, young fellow." He was a malicious old man—and may the deep sea where he sleeps now rock him gently, rock him tenderly to the end of time!

Before sunset a thick rain-squall passed over the two boats, which were far astern, and that was the last I saw of them for a time. Next day I sat steering my cockle-shell—my first command—with nothing but water and sky around me. I did sight in the afternoon the upper sails of a ship far away, but said nothing, and my men did not notice her. You see I was afraid she might be homeward bound, and I had no mind to turn back from the portals of the East. I was steering for Java—another blessed name—like Bankok, you know. I steered many days.

I need not tell you what it is to be knocking about in an open boat. I remember nights and days of calm when we pulled, we pulled, and the boat seemed to stand still, as if bewitched within the circle of the sea horizon. I remember the heat, the deluge of rain-squalls that kept us baling for dear life (but filled our water-cask), and I remember sixteen hours on end with a mouth dry as a cinder and a steering-oar over the stern to keep my first command head on to a breaking sea. I did not know how good a man I was till then. I remember the drawn faces, the dejected figures of my two men, and I remember my youth and the feeling that will never come back any more—the feeling that I could last for ever, outlast the sea, the earth, and all men; the deceitful feeling that lures us on to joys, to perils, to love, to vain effort—to death; the triumphant conviction of strength, the heat of life in the handful of dust, the glow in the heart that with every year grows dim, grows cold, grows small, and expires—and expires, too soon, too soon—before life itself.

And this is how I see the East. I have seen its secret places and have looked into its very soul; but now I see it always from a small boat, a high outline of mountains, blue and afar in the morning; like faint mist at noon; a jagged wall of purple at sunset. I have the feel of the oar in my hand, the vision of a scorching blue sea in my eyes. And I see a bay, a wide bay, smooth as glass and polished like ice, shimmering in the dark. A red light burns far off upon the gloom of the land, and the night is soft and warm. We drag at the oars with aching arms, and suddenly a puff of wind, a puff faint and tepid and laden with strange odours of blossoms, of aromatic wood, comes out of the still night—the first sigh of the East on my face. That I can never forget. It was impalpable and enslaving, like a charm, like a whispered promise of mysterious delight.

We had been pulling this finishing spell for eleven hours. Two pulled, and he whose turn it was to rest sat at the tiller. We had made out the red light in that bay and steered for it, guessing it must mark some small coasting port. We passed two vessels, outlandish and high-sterned, sleeping at anchor, and, approaching the light, now very dim, ran the boat's nose against the end of a jutting wharf. We were blind with fatigue. My men dropped the oars and fell off the thwarts as if dead. I made fast to a pile. A current rippled softly. The scented obscurity of the shore was grouped into vast masses, a density of colossal clumps of vegetation, probably—mute and fantastic shapes. And at their foot the semicircle of beach gleamed faintly, like an illusion. There was not a light, not a stir, not a sound. The mysterious East faced me, perfumed like a flower, silent like death, dark like a grave.

And I sat weary beyond expression, exulting like a conqueror, sleepless and entranced as if before a profound, a fateful enigma.

A splashing of oars, a measured dip reverberating on the level of water, intensified by the silence of the shore into loud claps, made me jump up. A boat, a European boat, was coming in. I invoked the name of the dead; I hailed: *Judea* ahoy. A thin shout answered.

It was the captain.I had beaten the flagship by three hours, and I was glad to hear the old man's voice again, tremulous and tired. "Is it you, Marlow?" "Mind the end of that jetty, sir," I cried.

He approached cautiously, and brought up with the deep-sea leadline which we had saved—for the underwriters. I eased my painter and fell alongside. He sat, a broken figure at the stern, wet with dew, his hands clasped in his lap. His men were asleep already. "I had a terrible time of it," he murmured. "Mahon is behind—not very far." We conversed in whispers, in low whispers, as if afraid to wake up the land. Guns, thunder, earthquakes would not have awakened the men just then.

THE VOYAGE OF THE *JAMES CAIRD*[1]

Sir Ernest Shackleton
(1874-1922)

I DISCUSSED with Wild and Worsley the chances of reaching South Georgia before the winter locked the seas against us. Some effort had to be made to secure relief. Privation and exposure had left their mark on the party, and the health and mental condition of several men were causing me serious anxiety. Then the food-supply was a vital consideration. We had left ten cases of provisions in the crevice of the rocks at our first camping-place on the island. An examination of our stores showed that we had full rations for the whole party for a period of five weeks. The rations could be spread over three months on a reduced allowance and probably would be supplemented by seals and sea-elephants to some extent. I did not dare to count with full confidence on supplies of meat and blubber, for the animals seemed to have deserted the beach and the winter was near. Our stocks included three seals and two and a half skins (with blubber attached). We were mainly dependent on the blubber for fuel, and, after making a preliminary survey of the situation, I decided that the party must be limited to one hot meal a day.

A boat journey in search of relief was necessary and must not be delayed. That conclusion was forced upon me. The nearest port where assistance could certainly be secured was Port Stanley, in the Falkland Islands, 540 miles away, but we could scarcely hope to beat up against the prevailing north-westerly wind in a frail and weakened boat with a small sail area. South Georgia was over 800 miles away, but lay in the area of the west winds, and I could count upon finding whalers at any of the whaling-stations on the east coast. A boat party might make the voyage and be back with relief within a month, provided that the sea was clear of ice and the boat survive the great seas. It was not difficult to decide that South Georgia must be the objective, and I proceeded to plan ways and means. The hazards of a boat journey across 800 miles of stormy sub-Antarctic ocean were obvious, but I calculated that at worst the venture would add nothing to the risks of the men left on the island. There would be fewer mouths to feed during the winter and the boat would not require to take more than one month's provisions for six men, for if we did not make South Georgia in that time we were sure to go under. A consideration that had weight with me was that there was no chance at all of any search being made for us on Elephant Island.

The case required to be argued in some detail, since all hands knew that the perils of the proposed journey were extreme. The risk was justified solely by our

[1] From *South.*

urgent need of assistance. The ocean south of Cape Horn in the middle of May is known to be the most tempestuous stormswept area of water in the world. The weather then is unsettled, the skies are dull and overcast, and the gales are almost unceasing. We had to face these conditions in a small and weather-beaten boat, already strained by the work of the months that had passed. Worsley and Wild realized that the attempt must be made, and they both asked to be allowed to accompany me on the voyage. I told Wild at once that he would have to stay behind. I relied upon him to hold the party together while I was away, and to make the best of his way to Deception Island with the men in the spring in the event of our failure to bring help. Worsley I would take with me, for I had a very high opinion of his accuracy and quickness as a navigator, and especially in the snapping and working out of positions in difficult circumstances—an opinion that was only enhanced during the actual journey. Four other men would be required and I decided to call for volunteers, although, as a matter of fact, I pretty well knew which of the people I would select. Crean I proposed to leave on the island as a right-hand man for Wild, but he begged so hard to be allowed to come in the boat that, after consultation with Wild, I promised to take him. I called the men together, explained my plan, and asked for volunteers. Many came forward at once. Some were not fit enough for the work that would have to be done, and others would not have been much use in the boat since they were not seasoned sailors, though the experiences of recent months entitled them to some consideration as seafaring men. I finally selected McNeish, McCarthy, and Vincent in addition to Worsley and Crean. The crew seemed a strong one, and as I looked at the men I felt confidence increasing.

The decision made, I walked through the blizzard with Worsley and Wild to examine the *James Caird.* The 20-ft. boat had never looked big; she appeared to have shrunk in some mysterious way when I viewed her in the light of our new undertaking. She was an ordinary ship's whaler, fairly strong, but showing signs of the strains she had endured since the crushing of the *Endurance.* Where she was holed in leaving the pack was, fortunately, about the water-line and easily patched. Standing beside her, we glanced at the fringe of the storm-swept, tumultuous sea that formed our path. Clearly, our voyage would be a big adventure. I called the carpenter and asked him if he could do anything to make the boat more seaworthy. He first inquired if he was to go with me, and seemed quite pleased when I said "Yes." He was over fifty years of age, and not altogether fit, but he had a good knowledge of sailing boats and was very quick. McCarthy said that he could contrive some sort of covering for the *James Caird* if he might use the lids of the cases and the four sledge-runners that we had lashed inside the boat for use in the event of a landing on Graham Land at Wilhelmina Bay. This bay, at one time the goal of our desire, had been left behind in the course of our drift, but we had retained the runners. The carpenter proposed to complete the covering with some of our canvas, and he set about making his plans at once.

Noon had passed and the gale was more severe than ever. We could not proceed with our preparations that day. The tents were suffering in the wind and the sea was rising. The gale was stronger than ever on the following morning (April 20). No work could be done. Blizzard and snow, snow and blizzard, sudden lulls and fierce returns. During the lulls we could see on the far horizon to the north-east bergs of all shapes and sizes driving along before the gale, and the sinister appearance of the swiftmoving masses made us thankful indeed that instead of battling with the storm amid the ice, we were required only to face the drift from the glaciers and the inland heights. The gusts might throw us off our feet, but at least we fell on solid ground and not on rocking floes.

There was a lull in the bad weather on April 21, and the carpenter started to collect material for the decking of the *James Caird.* He fitted the mast of the *Stancomb Wills* fore and aft inside the *James Caird* as a hog-back, and thus strengthened the keel with the object of preventing our boat "hogging"—that is, buckling in heavy seas. He had not sufficient wood to provide a deck, but by using the sledge-runners and boxlids he made a framework extending from the forecastle aft to a well. It was a patched-up affair, but it provided a base for a canvas covering. He had a bolt of canvas frozen stiff, and this material had to be cut and then thawed out over the blubber-stove, foot by foot, in order that it might be sewn into the form of a cover. When it had been nailed and screwed into position it certainly gave an appearance of safety to the boat, though I had an uneasy feeling that it bore a strong likeness to stage scenery, which may look like a granite wall and is in fact nothing better than canvas and lath. As events proved, the covering served its purpose well. We certainly could not have lived through the voyage without it.

Another fierce gale was blowing on April 22, interfering with our preparations for the voyage. We were setting aside stores for the boat journey and choosing, the essential equipment from the scanty stock at our disposal. Two ten-gallon casks had to be filled with water melted down from ice collected at the foot of the glacier. This was rather a slow business.

The weather was fine on April 23, and we hurried forward our preparations. It was on this day I decided finally that the crew for the *James Caird* should consist of Worsley, Crean, McNeish, McCarthy, Vincent, and myself. A storm came on about noon, with driving snow and heavy squalls. Occasionally the air would clear for a few minutes, and we could see a line of pack-ice, five miles out, driving across from west to east. The sight increased my anxiety to get away quickly. Winter was advancing, and soon the pack might close completely round the island and stay our departure for days, or even weeks.

Worsley, Wild, and I climbed to the summit of the seaward rocks and examined the ice from a better vantage-point than the beach offered. The belt of pack outside appeared to be sufficiently broken for our purposes, and I decided that, unless the conditions forbade it, we would make a start in the *James Caird* on the following morning. Obviously the pack might close at any time. This decision made, I spent the rest of the day looking over the boat, gear, and stores, and discussing plans with Worsley and Wild.

Our last night on the solid ground of Elephant Island was cold and uncomfortable. We turned out at dawn and had breakfast. Then we launched the *Stancomb Wills* and loaded her with stores, gear, and ballast, which would be transferred to the *James Caird* when the heavier boat had been launched. The ballast consisted of bags made from blankets and filled with sand, making a total weight of about 1000 lb. In addition we had gathered a number of round boulders and about 250 lb. of ice, which would supplement our two casks of water.

The swell was slight when the *Stancomb Wills* was launched and the boat got under way without any difficulty; but half an hour later, when we were pulling down the *James Caird,* the swell increased suddenly. Apparently the movement of the ice outside had made an opening and allowed the sea to run in without being blanketed by the line of pack. The swell made things difficult. Many of us got wet to the waist while dragging the boat out—a serious matter in that climate. When the *James Caird* was afloat in the surf she nearly capsized among the rocks before we could get her clear, and Vincent and the carpenter, who were on the deck, were thrown into the water. This was really bad luck for the two men would have small chance of drying their clothes after we had got under way.

The *James Caird* was soon clear of the breakers. We used all the available ropes as a long painter to prevent her drifting away to the northeast, and then the *Stancomb Wills* came alongside, transferred her load, and went back to the shore for more.

By midday the *James Caird* was ready for the voyage. Vincent and the carpenter had secured some dry clothes by exchange with members of the shore party (I heard afterwards that it was a full fortnight before the soaked garments were finally dried), and the boat's crew was standing by waiting for the order to cast off. A moderate westerly breeze was blowing, I went ashore in the *Stancomb Wills* and had a last word with Wild, who was remaining in full command, with directions as to his course of action in the event of our failure to bring relief, but I practically left the whole situation and scope of action and decision to his own judgment, secure in the knowledge that he would act wisely. I told him that I trusted the party to him, and said good-bye to the men. Then we pushed off for the last time, and within a few minutes I was aboard the *James Caird.* The crew of the *Stancomb Wills* shook hands with us as the boats bumped together and offered us the last good wishes. Then, setting our jib, we cut the painter and moved away to the north-east. The men who were staying behind made a pathetic little group on the beach, with the grim heights of the island behind them and the sea seething at their feet, but they waved to us and gave three hearty cheers. There was hope in their hearts and they trusted us to bring the help that they needed.

I had all sails set, and the *James Caird* quickly dipped the beach and its line of dark figures. The westerly wind took us rapidly to the line of pack, and as we entered it I stood up with my arm around the mast, directing the steering, so as to avoid the great lumps of ice that were flung about in the heave of the sea. The pack thickened and we were forced to turn almost due east, running before the wind towards a gap I had seen in the morning from the high ground. I could not see the gap now, but we had come out on its bearing and I was prepared to find that it had been influenced by the easterly drift. At four o'clock in the afternoon we found the channel, much narrower than it had seemed in the morning but still navigable. Dropping sail we rowed through without touching the ice anywhere, and by 5.30 P.M. we were clear of the pack with open water before us. We passed one more piece of ice in the darkness an hour later, but the pack lay behind, and with a fair wind swelling the sails we steered our little craft through the night, our hopes centered on our distant goal. The swell was very heavy now, and when the time came for our first evening meal we found great difficulty in keeping the Primus lamp alight and preventing the hoosh splashing out of the pot. Three men were needed to attend to the cooking, one man holding the lamp and two men guarding the aluminium cooking-pot, which had to be lifted clear of the Primus whenever the movement of the boat threatened to cause a disaster. Then the lamp had to be protected from water, for sprays were coming over the bows and our flimsy decking was by no means water-tight. All these operations were conducted in the confined space under the decking, where the men lay or knelt and adjusted themselves as best they could to the angles of our cases and ballast. It was uncomfortable, but we found consolation in the reflection that without the decking we could not have used the cooker at all.

The tale of the next sixteen days is one of supreme strife amid heaving waters. The sub-Antarctic Ocean lived up to its evil winter reputation. I decided to run north for at least two days while the wind held and so get into warmer weather before turning to the east and laying a course for South Georgia. We took two-hourly spells at the tiller. The men who were not on watch crawled into the sodden sleeping-bags and tried to forget their troubles for a period; but there was no comfort in the boat. The bags and cases seemed to be alive in the unfailing knack of presenting their most uncomfortable angles to our rest-seeking bodies. A man might imagine for a moment that he had found a position of ease, but always discovered quickly that some unyielding point was impinging on muscle or bone.

The first night aboard the boat was one of acute discomfort for us all, and we were heartily glad when the dawn came and we could set about the preparation of a hot breakfast.

By running north for the first two days I hoped to get warmer weather and also to avoid lines of pack that might be extending beyond the main body. We needed all the advantage that we could obtain from the higher latitude for sailing on the great circle, but we had to be cautious regarding possible ice streams. Cramped in our narrow quarters and continually wet by the spray, we suffered severely from cold throughout the journey. We fought the seas and the winds, and at the same time had a daily struggle to keep ourselves alive. At times we were in dire peril. Generally we were upheld by the knowledge that we were making progress towards the land where we would be, but there were days and nights when we lay hove to, drifting across the storm-whitened seas and watching, with eyes interested rather than apprehensive, the uprearing masses of water, flung to and fro by Nature in the pride of her strength. Deep seemed the valleys when we lay between the reeling seas. High were the hills when we perched momentarily on the tops of giant combers. Nearly always there were gales. So small was our boat and so great were the seas that often our sail flapped idly in the calm between the crests of two waves. Then we would climb the next slope and catch the full fury of the gale where the wool-like whiteness of the breaking water surged around us.

The wind came up strong and worked into a gale from the north-west on the third day out. We stood away to the east. The increasing seas discovered the weakness of our decking. The continuous blows shifted the box-lids and sledge-runners so that the canvas sagged down and accumulated water. Then icy trickles, distinct from the driving sprays, poured fore and aft into the boat. The nails that the carpenter had extracted from cases at Elephant Island and used to fasten down the battens were too short to make firm the decking. We did what we could to secure it, but our means were very limited, and the water continued to enter the boat at a dozen points. Much bailing was necessary, and nothing that we could do prevented our gear from becoming sodden. The searching runnels from the canvas were really more unpleasant than the sudden definite douches of the sprays. Lying under the thwarts during watches below, we tried vainly to avoid them. There were no dry places in the boat, and at last we simply covered our heads with our Burberrys and endured the all-pervading water. The bailing was work for the watch. Real rest we had none. The perpetual motion of the boat made repose impossible; we were cold, sore, and anxious. We moved on hands and knees in the semi-darkness of the day under the decking. The darkness was complete by 6 P.M. and not until 7 A.M. of the following day could we see one another under the thwarts. We had a few scraps of candle, and they were preserved carefully in order that we might have light at meal-times. There was one fairly dry spot in the boat, under the solid original decking at the bows, and we managed to protect some of our biscuit from the saltwater; but I do not think any of us got the taste of salt out of our mouths during the voyage.

The difficulty of movement in the boat would have had its humorous side if it had not involved us in so many aches and pains. We had to crawl under the thwarts in order to move along the boat, and our knees suffered considerably. When a watch turned out it was necessary for me to direct each man by name when and where to move, since if all hands had crawled about at the same time the result would have been dire confusion and many bruises. Then there was the trim of the boat to be considered. The order of the watch was four hours on and four hours off, three men to the watch. One man had the tiller-ropes, the second man attended to the sail, and the third bailed for all he was worth. Sometimes when the water in the boat had been reduced to reasonable proportions, our pump could be used. This pump, which Hurley had made from the Flinders bar case of our ship's standard compass, was quite effective, though its capacity was not large. The man who was attending to the sail could pump into the big outer cooker, which was lifted and emptied overboard when filled. We had a device by which the water could go direct from the pump into the sea through a hole in the gunwale, but this hole had to be blocked at an early stage of the voyage, since we found that it admitted water when the boat rolled.

While a new watch was shivering in the wind and spray, the men who had been relieved groped hurriedly among the soaked sleeping-bags and tried to steal a little of the warmth created by the last occupants; but it was not always possible for us to find even this comfort when we went off watch. The boulders that we had taken aboard for ballast had to be shifted continually in order to trim the boat and give access to the pump, which became choked with hairs from the moulting sleeping-bags and finneskoe. The four reindeer-skin sleeping-bags shed their hair freely owing to the continuous wetting, and soon became quite bald in appearance. The moving of the boulders was very weary and painful work. We came to know every one of the stones by sight and touch, and I have vivid memories of their angular peculiarities even to-day. They might have been of considerable interest as geological specimens to a scientific man under happier conditions. As ballast they were useful. As weights to be moved about in cramped quarters they were simply appalling. They spare no portion of our poor bodies.

Our meals were regular in spite of the gales. Breakfast, at 8 A.M., consisted of a pannikin of hot hoosh made from Bovril sledging ration, two biscuits, and some lumps of sugar. Lunch came at 1 P.M. and comprised Bovril sledging ration, eaten raw, and a pannikin of hot milk for each man. Tea, at 5 P.M., had the same menu. Then during the night we had a hot drink, generally of milk. The meals were the bright beacons in those cold and stormy days. The glow of warmth and comfort produced by the food and drink made optimists of us all.

A severe south-westerly gale on the fourth day out forced us to heave to. I would have liked to have run before the wind, but the sea was very high and the *James Caird* was in danger of broaching to and swamping. The delay was vexatious, since up to that time we had been making sixty or seventy miles a day; good going with our limited sail area. We hove to under double-reefed mainsail and our little jigger, and waited for the gale to blow itself out. During that afternoon we saw bits of wreckage, the remains probably of some unfortunate vessel that had failed to weather the strong gales south of Cape Horn. The weather conditions did not improve, and on the fifth day out the gale was so fierce that we were compelled to take in the double-reefed mainsail and hoist our small jib instead. We put out a sea-anchor to keep the *James Caird's* head up to the sea. This anchor consisted of a triangular canvas bag fastened to the end of the painter and allowed to stream out from the bows. The boat was high enough to catch the wind, and as she drifted to leeward the drag of the anchor kept her head to windward. Thus our boat took most of the seas more or less end on. Even then the crests of the waves often would curl right over us and we shipped a great deal of water, which necessitated unceasing bailing and pumping. Looking out abeam, we would see a hollow like a tunnel formed as the crest of a big wave toppled over on to the swelling body of water. A thousand times it appeared as though the *James Caird* must be engulfed; but the boat lived. The south-westerly gale had its birthplace above the Antarctic Continent and its freezing breath lowered the temperature far towards zero. The sprays froze upon the boat, and gave bows, sides, and decking a heavy coat of mail. This accumulation of ice reduced the buoyancy of the boat, and to that extent was an added peril; but it possessed a notable advantage from one point of view. The water ceased to drop and trickle from the canvas, and the spray came in solely at the well in the after part of the boat. We could not allow the load of ice to grow beyond a certain point, and in turns we crawled about the decking forward, chipping and picking at it with the available tools.

When daylight came on the morning of the sixth day out, we saw and felt that the *James Caird* had lost her resiliency. She was not rising to the oncoming seas. The weight of the ice that had formed in her and upon her during the night was having its effect, and she was becoming more like a log than a boat. The situation called for immediate action. We first broke away the spare oars, which were encased in ice and frozen to the sides of the boat, and threw them overboard. We retained two oars for use when we got inshore. Two of the fur sleeping-bags went over the side; they were thoroughly wet, weighing probably 40 lb. each, and they had frozen stiff during the night. Three men constituted the watch below, and when a man went down it was better to turn into the wet bag just vacated by another man than to thaw out a frozen bag with the heat of his unfortunate body. We now had four bags, three in use, and one for emergency use in case a member of the party should break down permanently. The reduction of weight relieved the boat to some extent, and vigorous chipping and scraping did more. We had to be very careful not to put axe or knife through the frozen canvas of the decking as we crawled over it, but gradually we got rid of a lot of ice. The *James Caird* lifted to the endless waves as though she lived again.

About 11 A.M. the boat suddenly fell off into the trough of the sea. The-painter had parted and the sea-anchor had gone. This was serious. The *James Caird* went away to leeward, and we had no chance at all of recovering the anchor and our valuable rope, which had been our only means of keeping the boat's head up to the seas without the risk of hoisting sail in a gale. Now we had to set the sail and trust to its holding. While the *James Caird* rolled heavily in the trough, we beat the frozen canvas until the bulk of the ice had cracked off it, and then hoisted it. The frozen gear worked protestingly, but after a struggle our little craft came up to the wind again, and we breathed more freely.

We held the boat up to the gale during that day, enduring as best we could discomforts that amounted to pain. The boat tossed interminably on the big waves under grey, threatening skies. Our thoughts did not embrace much more than the necessities of the hour. Every surge of the sea was an enemy to be watched and circumvented. We ate our scanty meals, treated our frost-bites, and hoped for the improved conditions that the morrow might bring. Night fell early, and in the lagging hours of darkness we were cheered by a change for the better in the weather. The wind dropped, the snow-squalls became less frequent, and the sea moderated. When the morning of the seventh day dawned, there was not much wind. We shook the reef out of the sail and laid our course once more for South Georgia. The sun came out bright and clear, and presently Worsley got a snap for longitude. We hoped that the sky would remain clear until noon, so that we could get the latitude. We had been six days out without an observation, and our dead reckoning naturally was uncertain. The boat must have presented a strange appearance that morning. All hands basked in the sun. We hung our sleeping-bags to the mast and spread our socks and other gear all over the deck. Some of the ice had melted off the *James Caird* in the early morning after the gale began to slacken, and dry patches were appearing in the decking. Porpoises came blowing round the boat, and Cape pigeons wheeled and swooped within a few feet of us. These little black-and-white birds have an air of friendliness that is not possessed by the great circling albatross. They had looked grey against the swaying sea during the storm as they darted about over our heads and uttered their plaintive cries. The albatrosses, of the black or sooty variety, had watched with hard, bright eyes, and seemed to have a quite impersonal interest in our struggle to keep afloat amid the battering seas. In addition to the Cape pigeons an occasional stormy petrel flashed overhead. Then there was a small bird, unknown to me, that appeared always to be in a fussy, bustling state, quite out of keeping with the surroundings. It irritated me. It had practically no tail, and it flitted about vaguely as though in search of the lost member. I used to find myself wishing it would find its tail and have done with the silly fluttering.

We revelled in the warmth of the sun that day. Life was not so bad, after all. We felt we were well on our way. Our gear was drying, and we could have a hot meal in comparative comfort. The swell was still heavy, but it was not breaking and the boat rode easily. At noon Worsley balanced himself on the gunwale and clung with one hand to the stay of the mainmast while he got a snap of the sun. The result was more than encouraging. We had done over 380 miles and were getting on for halfway to South Georgia. It looked as though we were going to get through.

The wind freshened to a good stiff breeze during the afternoon, and the *James Caird* made satisfactory progress. I had not realized until the sunlight came how small our boat really was. There was some influence in the light and warmth, some hint of happier days, that made us revive memories of other voyages, when we had stout deeks beneath our feet, unlimited food at our command, and pleasant cabins for our ease. Now we clung to a battered little boat, "alone, alone, all, all alone, alone on a wide, wide, sea." So low in the water were we that each succeeding swell cut off our view of the sky-line. We were a tiny speck in the vast vista of the sea—the ocean that is open to all, and merciful to none, that threatens even when it seems to yield, and that is pitiless always to weakness. For a moment the consciousness of the forces arrayed against us would be almost overwhelming. Then hope and confidence would rise again as our boat rose to a wave and tossed aside the crest in a sparkling shower like the play of prismatic colours at the foot of a waterfall. My double-barrelled gun and some cartridges had been stowed aboard the boat as an emergency precaution against a shortage of food, but we were not disposed to destroy our little neighbours, the Cape pigeons, even for the sake of fresh meat. We might have shot an albatross, but the wandering king of the ocean aroused in us something of the feeling that inspired, too late, the Ancient Mariner. So the gun remained among the stores and sleeping-bags in the narrow quarters beneath our leaking deck, and the birds followed us unmolested.

The eighth, ninth, and tenth days of the voyage had few features worthy of special note. The wind blew hard during those days, and the strain of navigating the boat was unceasing, but always we made some advance towards our goal. No bergs showed on our horizon, and we knew that we were clear of the ice-fields. Each day brought its little round of troubles, but also compensation in the form of food and growing hope. We felt that we were going to succeed. The odds against us had been great, but we were winning through. We still suffered severely from the cold, for, though the temperature was rising, our vitality was declining owing to shortage of food, exposure, and the necessity of maintaining our cramped positions day and night. I found that it was now absolutely necessary to prepare hot milk for all hands during the night, in order to sustain life till dawn. This meant lighting the Primus lamp in the darkness and involved an increased drain on our small store of matches. It was the rule that one match must serve when the Primus was being lit. We had no lamp for the compass, and during the early days of the voyage we would strike a match when the steersman wanted to see the course at night; but later the necessity for strict economy impressed itself upon us, and the practice of striking matches at night was stopped. We had one water-tight tin of matches. I had stowed away in a pocket, in readiness for a sunny day, a lens from one of the telescopes, but this was of no use during the voyage. The sun seldom shone upon us. The glass of the compass got broken one night, and we contrived to mend it with adhesive tape from the medicine-chest. One of the memories that comes to me from those days is of Crean singing at the tiller. He always sang while he was steering, and nobody ever discovered what the song was. It was devoid of tune and as monotonous as the chanting of a Buddhist monk at his prayers; yet somehow it was cheerful. In moments of inspiration Crean would attempt "The Wearing of the Green."

On the tenth night Worsley could not straighten his body after his spell at the tiller. He was thoroughly cramped, and we had to drag him beneath the decking and massage him before he could unbend himself and get into a sleeping-bag. A hard north-westerly gale came up on the eleventh day (May 5) and shifted to the south-west in the late afternoon. The sky was overcast and occasional snow squalls added to the discomfort produced by a tremendous cross-sea—the worst, I thought, that we had experienced. At midnight I was at the tiller and suddenly noticed a line of clear sky between the south and south-west. I called to the other men that the sky was clearing, and then a moment later I realized that what I had seen was not a rift in the clouds. but the white crest of an enormous wave. During twenty-six years' experience of the ocean in all its moods I had not encountered a wave so gigantic. It was a mighty upheaval of the ocean, a thing quite apart from the big whitecapped seas that had been our tireless enemies for many days. I shouted, "For God's sake, hold on! It's got us!" Then came a moment of suspense that seemed drawn out into hours. White surged the foam of the breaking sea around us. We felt our boat lifted and flung forward like a cork in breaking surf. We were in a seething chaos of tortured water; but somehow the boat lived through it, half-full of water, sagging to the dead weight and shuddering under the blow. We bailed with the energy of men fighting for life, flinging the water over the sides with every receptacle that came to our hands, and after ten minutes of uncertainty we felt the boat renew her life beneath us. She floated again and ceased to lurch drunkenly as though dazed by the attack of the sea. Earnestly we hoped that never again would we encounter such a wave.

The conditions in the boat, uncomfortable before, had been made worse by the deluge of water. All our gear was thoroughly wet again. Our cooking-stove had been floating about in the bottom of the boat, and portions of our last hoosh seemed to have permeated everything. Not until 3 A.M., when we were all chilled almost to the limit of endurance, did we manage to get the stove alight and make ourselves hot drinks. The carpenter was suffering particularly, but he showed grit and spirit. Vincent had for the past week ceased to be an active member of the crew, and I could not easily account for his collapse. Physically he was one of the strongest men in the boat. He was a young man, he had served on North Sea trawlers, and he should have been able to bear hardships better than McCarthy, who, not so strong, was always happy.

The weather was better on the following day (May 6), and we got a glimpse of the sun. Worsley's observation showed that we were not more than a hundred miles from the north-west corner of South Georgia. Two more days with a favourable wind and we would sight the promised land. I hoped that there would be no delay, for our supply of water was running very low. The hot drink at night was essential, but I decided that the daily allowance of water must be cut down to half a pint per man. The lumps of ice we had taken aboard had gone long ago. We were dependent upon the water we had brought from Elephant Island, and our thirst was increased by the fact that we were now using the brackish water in the breaker that had been slightly stove in in the surf when the boat was being loaded. Some sea-water had entered at that time.

Thirst took possession of us. I dared not permit the allowance of water to be increased since an unfavourable wind might drive us away from the island and lengthen our voyage by many days. Lack of water is always the most severe privation that men can be condemned to endure, and we found, as during our earlier boat voyage, that the salt water in our clothing and the salt spray that lashed our faces made our thirst grow quickly to a burning pain. I had to be very firm in refusing to allow anyone to anticipate the morrow's allowance, which I was sometimes begged to do. We did the necessary work dully and hoped for the land. I had altered the course to the east so as to make sure of our striking the island, which would have been impossible to regain if we had run past the northern end. The course was laid on our scrap of chart for a point some thirty miles down the coast. That day and the following day passed for us in a sort of nightmare. Our mouths were dry and our tongues were swollen. The wind was still strong and the heavy sea forced us to navigate carefully, but any thought of our peril from the waves was buried beneath the consciousness of our raging thirst. The bright moments were those when we each received our one mug of hot milk during the long, bitter watches of the night. Things were bad for us in those days, but the end was coming. The morning of May 8 broke thick and stormy, with squalls from the north-west. We searched the waters ahead for a sign of land, and though we could see nothing more than had met our eyes for many days, we were cheered by a sense that the goal was near at hand. About ten o'clock that morning we passed a little bit of kelp, a glad signal of the proximity of land. An hour later we saw two shags sitting on a big mass of kelp, and knew then that we must be within ten or fifteen miles of the shore. These birds are as sure an indication of the proximity of land as a lighthouse is, for they never venture far to sea. We gazed ahead with increasing eagerness, and at 12.30 P.M., through a rift in the clouds, McCarthy caught a glimpse of the black cliffs of South Georgia, just fourteen days after our departure from Elephant Island. It was a glad moment. Thirst-ridden, chilled, and weak as we were, happiness irradiated us. The job was nearly done.

We stood in towards the shore to look for a landing-place, and presently we could see the green tussock-grass on the ledges above the surfbeaten rocks. Ahead of us and to the south, blind rollers showed the presence of uncharted reefs along the coast. Here and there the hungry rocks were close to the surface, and over them the great waves broke, swirling viciously and spouting thirty and forty feet into the air. The rocky coast appeared to descend sheer to the sea. Our need of water and rest was wellnigh desperate, but to have attempted a landing at that time would have been suicidal. Night was drawing near, and the weather indications were not favourable. There was nothing for it but to haul off till the following morning, so we stood away on the starboard tack until we had made what appeared to be a safe offing. Then we hove to in the high westerly swell. The hours passed slowly as we waited the dawn, which would herald, we fondly hoped, the last stage of our journey. Our thirst was a torment and we could scarcely touch our food; the cold seemed to strike right through our weakened bodies. At 5 A.M. the wind shifted to the north-west and quickly increased to one of the worst hurricanes any of us had ever experienced. A great cross-sea was running, and the wind simply shrieked as it tore the tops off the waves and converted the whole seascape into a haze of driving spray. Down into valleys, up to tossing heights, straining until her seams opened, swung our little boat, brave still but labouring heavily. We knew that the wind and set of the sea was driving us ashore, but we could do nothing. The dawn showed us a storm-torn ocean, and the morning passed without bringing us a sight of the land; but at 1 P.M., through a rift in the flying mists, we got a glimpse of the huge crags of the island and realized that our position had become desperate. We were on a dead lee shore, and we could gauge our approach to the unseen cliffs by the roar of the breakers against the sheer walls of rock. I ordered the double-reefed mainsail to be set in the hope that we might claw off, and this attempt increased the strain upon the boat. The *James Caird* was bumping heavily, and the water was pouring in everywhere. Our thirst was forgotten in the realization of our imminent danger, as we bailed unceasingly, and adjusted our weights from time to time; occasional glimpses showed that the shore was nearer. I knew that Annewkow Island lay to the south of us, but our small and badly marked chart showed uncertain reefs in the passage between the island and the mainland, and I dared not trust it, though as a last resort we could try to lie under the lee of the island. The afternoon wore away as we edged down the coast, with the thunder of the breakers in our ears. The approach of evening found us still some distance from Annewkow Island, and, dimly in the twilight, we could see a snow-capped mountain looming above us. The chance of surviving the night, with the driving gale and the implacable sea forcing us on to the lee shore, seemed small. I think most of us had a feeling that the end was very near. Just after 6 P.M., in the dark, as the boat was in the yeasty backwash from the seas flung from this iron-bound coast, then, just when things looked their worst, they changed for the best. I have marvelled often at the thin line that divides success from failure and the sudden turn that leads from apparently certain disaster to comparative safety. The wind suddenly shifted, and we were free once more to make an offing. Almost as soon as the gale eased, the pin that locked the mast to the thwart fell out. It must have been on the point of doing this throughout the hurricane, and if it had gone nothing could have saved us; the mast would have snapped like a carrot. Our backstays had carried away once before when iced up, and were not too strongly fastened now. We were thankful indeed for the mercy that had held that pin in its place throughout the hurricane.

We stood off shore again, tired almost to the point of apathy. Our water had long been finished. The last was about a pint of hairy liquid, which we strained through a bit of gauze from the medicine chest. The pangs of thirst attacked us with redoubled intensity, and I felt that we must make a landing on the following day at almost any hazard. The night wore on. We were very tired. We longed for day. When at last the dawn came on the morning of May 10 there was practically no wind, but a high cross-sea was running. We made slow progress towards the shore. About 8 A.M. the wind backed to the northwest and threatened another blow. We had sighted in the meantime a big indentation which I thought must be King Haakon Bay, and I decided that we must land there. We set the bows of the boat towards the bay and ran before the freshening gale. Soon we had angry reefs on either side. Great glaciers came down to the sea and offered no landing-place. The sea spouted on the reefs and thundered against the shore. About noon we sighted a line of jagged reef, like blackened teeth, that seemed to bar the entrance to the bay. Inside, comparatively smooth water stretched eight or nine miles to the head of the bay. A gap in the reef appeared, and we made for it. But the fates had another rebuff for us. The wind shifted and blew from the east right out of the bay. We could see the way through the reef, but we could not approach it directly. That afternoon we bore up, tacking five times in the strong wind. The last tack enabled us to get through, and at last we were in the wide mouth of the bay. Dusk was approaching. A small cove, with a boulder-strewn beach guarded by a reef, made a break in the cliffs on the south side of the bay, and we turned in that, direction. I stood in the bows directing the steering as we ran through the kelp and made the passage of the reef. The entrance was so narrow that we had to take in the oars, and the swell was piling itself right over the reef into the cove; but in a minute or two we were inside, and in the gathering darkness the *James Caird* ran in on a swell and touched the beach. I sprang ashore with the short painter and held on when the boat went out with the backward surge. When the *James Caird* came in again, three of the men got ashore, and they held the painter while I climbed some rocks with another line. A slip on the wet rocks twenty feet up nearly closed my part of the story just at the moment when we were achieving safety. A jagged piece of rock held me and at the same time bruised me sorely. However, I made fast the line, and in a few minutes we were all safe on the beach with the boat floating in the surging water just off the shore. We heard a gurgling sound that was sweet music in our ears, and, peering around, found a stream of fresh water almost at our feet. A moment later we were down on our knees drinking the pure ice-cold water in long draughts that put new life into us.

THE GHOST SHIP[1]

Richard Middleton
(1882-1911)

FAIRFIELD is a little village lying near the Portsmouth Road about half-way between London and the sea. Strangers who find it by accident now and then, call it a pretty, old-fashioned place; we, who live in it and call it home, don't find anything very pretty about it, but we should be sorry to live anywhere else. Our minds have taken the shape of the inn and the church and the green, I suppose. At all events we never feel comfortable out of Fairfield.

Of course the Cockneys, with their vasty houses and their noiseridden streets, can call us rustics if they choose, but for all that Fairfield is a better place to live in than London. Doctor says that when he goes to London his mind is bruised with the weight of the houses, and he was a Cockney born. He had to live there himself

[1] From *The Ghost Ship and Other Tales.*

when he was a little chap, but he knows better now. You gentlemen may laugh—perhaps some of you come from London way—but it seems to me that a witness like that it worth a gallon of arguments.

Dull? Well, you might find it dull, but I assure you that I've listened to all the London yarns you have spun to-night, and they're absolutely nothing to the things that happen at Fairfield. It's because of our way of thinking and minding our own business. If one of your Londoners were set down on the green of a Saturday night when the ghosts of the lads who died in the war keep tryst with the lasses who lie in the churchyard, he couldn't help being curious and interfering, and then the ghosts would go somewhere where it was quieter. But we just let them come and go and don't make any fuss, and in consequence Fairfield is the ghostjest place in all England. Why, I've seen a headless man sitting on the edge of the well in broad daylight, and the children playing about his feet as if he were their father. Take my word for it, spirits know when they are well off as much as human beings.

Still, I must admit that the thing I'm going to tell you about was queer even for our part of the world, where three packs of ghost-hounds hunt regularly during the season, and blacksmith's great-grandfather is busy all night shoeing the dead gentlemen's horses. Now that's a thing that wouldn't happen in London, because of their interfering ways, but blacksmith he lies up aloft and sleeps as quiet as a lamb. Once when he had a bad head he shouted down to them not to make so much noise, and in the morning he found an old guinea left on the anvil as an apology. He wears it on his watch-chain now. But I must get on with my story; if I start telling you about the queer happenings at Fairfield I'll never stop.

It all came of the great storm in the spring of '97, the year that we had two great storms. This was the first one, and I remember it very well, because I found in the morning that it had lifted the thatch of my pigsty into the widow's garden as clean as a boy's kite. When I looked over the hedge, widow—Tom Lamport's widow that was—was prodding for her nasturtiums with a daisy-grubber. After I had watched her for a little I went down to the Fox and Grapes to tell landlord what she had said to me. Landlord he laughed, being a married man and at ease with the sex. "Come to that," he said, "the tempest has blowed something into my field. A kind of a ship I think it would be."

I was surprised at that until he explained that it was only a ghost-ship and would do no hurt to the turnips. We argued that it had been blown up from the sea at Portsmouth, and then we talked of something else. There were two slates down at the parsonage and a big tree in Lumley's meadow. It was a rare storm.

I reckon the wind had blown our ghosts all over England. They were coming back for days afterwards with foundered horses and as footsore as possible, and they were so glad to get back to Fairfield that some of them walked up the street crying like little children. Squire said that his great-grandfather's great-grandfather hadn't looked so dead-beat since the battle of Naseby, and he's an educated man.

What with one thing and another, I should think it was a week before we got straight again, and then one afternoon I met the landlord on the green and he had a worried face. "I wish you'd come and have a look at that ship in my field," he said to me; "it seems to me it's leaning real hard on the turnips. I can't bear thinking what the missus will say when she sees it."

I walked down the lane with him, and sure enough there was a ship in the middle of his field, but such a ship as no man had seen on the water for three hundred years, let alone in the middle of a turnip-field. It was all painted black and covered with carvings, and there was a great bay window in the stern for all the world like the Squire's drawing room. There was a crowd of little black cannon on deck and looking out of her port-holes, and she was anchored at each end to the hard ground. I have seen the wonders of the world on picture-postcards, but I have never seen anything to equal that.

"She seems very solid for a ghost-ship," I said, seeing the landlord was bothered.

"I should say it's a betwixt and between," he answered, puzzling it over, "but it's going to spoil a matter of fifty turnips, and missus she'll want it moved." We went up to her and touched the side, and it was as hard as a real ship. "Now there's folks in England would call that very curious," he said.

Now I don't know much about ships, but I should think that that ghost-ship weighed a solid two hundred tons, and it seemed to me that she had come to stay, so that I felt sorry for landlord, who was a married man. "All the horses in Fairfield won't move her out of my turnips," he said, frowning at her.

Just then we heard a noise on her deck, and we looked up and saw that a man had come out of her front cabin and was looking down at us very peaceably. He was dressed in a black uniform set out with rusty gold lace, and he had a great cutlass by his side in a brass sheath. "I'm Captain Bartolomew Roberts," he said, in a gentleman's voice, "put in for recruits. I seem to have brought her rather far up the harbour."

"Harbour!" cried landlord; "why, you're fifty miles from the sea."

Captain Roberts didn't turn a hair. "So much as that, is it?" he said coolly. "Well, it's of no consequence."

Landlord was a bit upset at this. "I don't want to be unneighbourly," he said, "but I wish you hadn't brought your ship into my field. You see, my wife sets great store on these turnips."

The captain took a pinch of snuff out of a fine gold box that he pulled out of his pocket, and dusted his fingers with a silk handkerchief in a very genteel fashion. "I'm only here for a few months," he said; "but if a testimony of my esteem would pacify your good lady I should be content," and with the words he loosed a great gold brooch from the neck of his coat and tossed it down to landlord.

Landlord blushed as red as a strawberry. "I'm not denying she's fond of jewellery," he said, "but it's too much for half a sackful or turnips." And indeed it was a handsome brooch.

The captain laughed. "Tut, man," he said, "it's a forced sale, and you deserve a good price. Say no more about it"; and nodding good-day to us, he turned on his heel and went into the cabin. Landlord walked back up the lane like a man with a weight off his mind. "That tempest has blowed me a bit of luck," he said; "the missus will be main pleased with that brooch. It's better than the blacksmith's guinea any day."

Ninety-seven was Jubilee year, the year of the second Jubilee, you remember, and we had great doings at Fairfield, so that we hadn't much time to bother about the ghost-ship, though anyhow it isn't our way to meddle in things that don't concern us. Landlord, he saw his tenant once or twice when he was hoeing his turnips and passed the time of day, and landlord's wife wore her new brooch to church every Sunday. But we didn't mix much with the ghosts at any time, all except an idiot lad there was in the village, and he didn't know the difference between a man and a ghost, poor innocent! On Jubilee Day, however, somebody told Captain Roberts why the church bells were ringing, and he hoisted a flag and fired off his guns like a royal Englishman. 'Tis true the guns were shotted, and one of the round shot knocked a hole in Farmer Johnstone's barn, but nobody thought much of that in such a season of rejoicing.

It wasn't till our celebrations were over that we noticed that anything was wrong in Fairfield. 'Twas shoemaker who told me first about it one morning at the Fox and Grapes. "You know my great great-uncle?" he said to me.

"You mean Joshua, the quiet lad," I answered, knowing him well. "Quiet!" said shoemaker indignantly. "Quiet you call him, coming home at three o'clock every morning as drunk as a magistrate and waking up the whole house with his noise."

"Why, it can't be Joshua!" I said, for I knew him for one of the most respectable young ghosts in the village.

"Joshua it is," said shoemaker; "and one of these nights he'll find himself out in the street if he isn't careful."

This kind of talk shocked me, I can tell you, for I don't like to hear a man abusing his own family, and I could hardly believe that a steady youngster like Joshua had taken to drink. But just then in came butcher Aylwin in such a temper that he could hardly drink his beer. "The young puppy! the young puppy!" he kept on saying; and it was some time before shoemaker and I found out that he was talking about his ancestor that fell at Senlac.

"Drink?" said shoemaker hopefully, for we all like company in our misfortunes, and butcher nodded grimly.

"The young noodle," he said, emptying his tankard.

Well, after that I kept my ears open, and it was the same story all over the village. There was hardly a young man among all the ghosts of Fairfield who didn't roll home in the small hours of the morning the worse for liquor. I used to wake up in the night and hear them stumble past my house, singing outrageous songs. The worst of it was that we couldn't keep the scandal to ourselves, and the folk at Greenhill began to talk of "sodden Fairfield" and taught their children to sing a song about us:

> Sodden Fairfield, sodden Fairfield, has no use for bread-and-butter,
> Rum for breakfast, rum for dinner, rum for tea, and rum for supper!

We are easy-going in our village, but we didn't like that.

Of course we soon found out where the young fellows went to get the drink, and landlord was terribly cut up that his tenant should have turned out so badly, but his wife wouldn't hear of parting with the brooch, so that he couldn't give the Captain notice to quit. But as time went on, things grew from bad to worse, and at all hours of the day you would see those young reprobates sleeping it off on the village green. Nearly every afternoon a ghost-waggon used to jolt down to the ship with a lading of rum, and though the older ghosts seemed inclined to give the Captain's hospitality the go-by, the youngsters were neither to hold nor to bind.

So one afternoon when I was taking my nap I heard a knock at the door, and there was parson looking very serious, like a man with a job before him that he didn't altogether relish. "I'm going down to talk to the Captain about all this drunkenness in the village, and I want you to come with me," he said straight out.

I can't say that I fancied the visit much myself, and I tried to hint to parson that as, after all, they were only a lot of ghosts, it didn't very much matter.

"Dead or alive, I'm responsible for their good conduct," he said, "and I'm going to do my duty and put a stop to this continued disorder. And you are coming with me, John Simmons." So I went, parson being a persuasive kind of man.

We went down to the ship, and as we approached her I could see the Captain tasting the air on deck. When he saw parson he took off his hat very politely, and I can tell you that I was relieved to find that he had a proper respect for the cloth. Parson acknowledged his salute and spoke out stoutly enough. "Sir, I should be glad to have a word with you."

"Come on board, sir, come on board," said the Captain, and I could tell by his voice that he knew why we were there. Parson and I climbed up an uneasy kind of ladder, and the Captain took us into the great cabin at the back of the ship, where the bay-window was. It was the most wonderful place you ever saw in your life, all full of gold and silver plate, swords with jewelled scabbards, carved oak chairs, and great chests that looked as though they were bursting with guineas. Even parson was surprised, and he did not shake his head very hard when the Captain took down some silver cups and poured us out a drink of rum. I tasted mine, and I don't mind saying that it changed my view of things entirely. There was nothing betwixt and between about that rum, and I felt that it was ridiculous to blame the lads for drinking too much of stuff like that. It seemed to fill my veins with honey and fire.

Parson put the case squarely to the Captain, but I didn't listen much to what he said; I was busy sipping my drink and looking through the window at the fishes swimming to and fro over landlord's turnips. Just then it seemed the most natural thing in the world that they should be there, though afterwards, of course, I could see that that proved it was a ghost-ship.

But even then I thought it was queer when I saw a drowned sailor float by in the thin air with his hair and beard all full of bubbles. It was the first time I had seen anything quite like that at Fairfield.

All the time I was regarding the wonders of the deep, parson was telling Captain Roberts how there was no peace or rest in the village owing to the curse of drunkenness, and what a bad example the youngsters were setting to the older ghosts. The Captain listened very attentively, and only put in a word now and then about boys being boys and young men sowing their wild oats. But when parson had finished his speech he filled up our silver cups and said to parson, with a flourish, "I should be sorry to cause trouble anywhere where I have been made welcome, and you will be glad to hear that I put to sea to-morrow night. And now you must drink me a prosperous voyage." So we all stood up and drank the toast with honour, and that noble rum was like hot oil in my veins.

After that Captain showed us some of the curiosities he had brought back from foreign parts, and we were greatly amazed, though afterwards I couldn't clearly remember what they were. And then I found myself walking across the turnips with parson, and I was telling him of the glories of the deep that I had seen through the window of the ship. He turned on me severely. "If I were you, John Simmons," he said, "I should go straight home to bed." He has a way of putting things that wouldn't occur to an ordinary man, has parson, and I did as he told me.

Well, next day it came on to blow, and it blew harder and harder, till about eight o'clock at night I heard a noise and looked out into the garden. I dare say you won't believe me, it seems a bit tall even to me, but the wind had lifted the thatch of my pigsty into the widow's garden a second time. I thought I wouldn't wait to hear what widow had to say about it, so I went across the green to the Fox and Grapes, and the wind was so strong that I danced along on tip-toe like a girl at the fair. When

I got to the inn landlord had to help me shut the door; it seemed as though a dozen goats were pushing against it to come in out of the storm.

"It's a powerful tempest," he said, drawing the beer. "I hear there's a chimney down at Dickory End."

"It's a funny thing how these sailors know about the weather," I answered. "When Captain said he was going to-night, I was thinking it would take a capful of wind to carry the ship back to sea, but now here's more than a capful."

"Ah, yes," said landlord, "it's to-night he goes true enough, and, mind you, though he treated me handsome over the rent, I'm not sure it's a loss to the village. I don't hold with gentrice who fetch their drink from London instead of helping local traders to get their living."

"But you haven't got any rum like his," I said to draw him out.

His neck grew red above his collar, and I was afraid I'd gone too far; but after a while he got his breath with a grunt.

"John Simmons," he said, "if you've come down here this windy night to talk a lot of fool's talk, you've wasted a journey."

Well, of course, then I had to smooth him down with praising his rum and Heaven forgive me for swearing it was better than Captain's. For the like of that rum no living lips have tasted save mine and parson's. But somehow or other I brought landlord round, and presently we must have a glass of his best to prove its quality.

"Beat that if you can!" he cried, and we both raised our glasses to our mouths, only to stop half-way and look at each other in amaze. For the wind that had been howling outside like an outrageous dog had all of a sudden turned as melodious as the carol-boys of a Christmas Eve.

"Surely that's not my Martha," whispered landlord; Martha being his great-aunt that lived in the loft overhead.

We went to the door, and the wind burst it open so that the handle was driven clean into the plaster of the wall. But we didn't think about that at the time; for over our heads, sailing very comfortably through the windy stars, was the ship that had passed the summer in landlord's field. Her portholes and her bay-window were blazing with lights, and there was a noise of singing and fiddling on her decks. "He's gone," shouted landlord above the storm, "and he's taken half the village with him!" I could only nod in answer, not having lungs like bellows of leather.

In the morning we were able to measure the strength of the storm, and over and above my pigsty there was damage enough wrought in the village to keep us busy. True it is that the children had to break down no branches for the firing that autumn, since the wind had strewn the woods with more than they could carry away. Many of our ghosts were scattered abroad, but this time very few came back, all the young men having sailed with Captain; and not only ghosts, for a poor half-witted lad was missing, and we reckoned that he had stowed himself away or perhaps shipped as cabin-boy, not knowing any better.

What with the lamentations of the ghost-girls and the grumblings of families who had lost an ancestor, the village was upset for a while, and the funny thing was that it was the folk who had complained most of the carryings-on of the youngsters, who made most noise now that they were gone. I hadn't any sympathy with shoemaker or butcher, who ran about saying how much they missed their lads, but it made me grieve to hear the poor bereaved girls calling their lovers by name on the village green at nightfall. It didn't seem fair to me that they should have lost their men a second time, after giving up life in order to join them, as like as not. Still, not even a spirit can be sorry for ever, and after a few months we made up our mind that the folk who had sailed in the ship were never coming back, and we didn't talk about it any more.

And then one day, I dare say it would be a couple of years after, when the whole business was quite forgotten, who should come trapesing along the road from Portsmouth but the daft lad who had gone away with the ship, without waiting till he was dead to become a ghost. You never saw such a boy as that in all your life. He had a great rusty cutlass hanging to a string at his waist, and he was tattooed all over in fine colours, so that even his face looked like a girl's sampler. He had a handkerchief in his hand full of foreign shells and old-fashioned pieces of small money, very curious, and he walked up to the well outside his mother's house and drew himself a drink as if he had been nowhere in particular.

The worst of it was that he had come back as soft-headed as he went, and try as we might we couldn't get anything reasonable out of him. He talked a lot of gibberish about keel-hauling and walking the plank and crimson murders—things which a decent sailor should know nothing about, so that it seemed to me that for all his manners Captain had been more of a pirate than a gentleman mariner. But to draw sense out of that boy was as hard as picking cherries off a crab-tree. One silly tale he had that he kept on drifting back to, and to hear him you would have thought that it was the only thing that happened to him in his life. "We was at anchor," he would say, "off an island called the Basket of Flowers, and the sailors had caught a lot of parrots and we were teaching them to swear. Up and down the decks, up and down the decks, and the language they used was dreadful. Then we looked up and saw the masts of the Spanish ship outside the harbour. Outside the harbour they were, so we threw the parrots into the sea and sailed out to fight. And all the parrots were drowned in the sea and the language they used was dreadful." That's the sort of boy he was, nothing but silly talk of parrots when we asked him about the fighting. And we never had a chance of teaching him better, for two days after he ran away again, and hasn't been seen since.

That's my story, and I assure you that things like that are happening at Fairfield all the time. The ship has never come back, but somehow as people grow older they seem to think that one of these windy nights, she'll come sailing in over the hedges with all the lost ghosts on board. Well, when she comes, she'll be welcome. There's one ghost-lass that has never grown tired of waiting for her lad to return. Every night you'll see her out on the green, straining her poor eyes with looking for the mast-lights among the stars. A faithful lass you'd call her, and I'm thinking you'd be right.

Landlord's field wasn't a penny the worse for the visit, but they do say that since then the turnips that have been grown in it have tasted of rum.

UNITED STATES

THE VOYAGE OF *THE MAYFLOWER*[1]

William Bradford
(1590-1657)

ALL things being now ready, and every business dispatched, the company was caled togeather. Then they ordered and distributed their company for either shipe, as they conceived for the best. And chose a Governour and 2 or 3 assistants for each shipe, to order the people by the way, and see to the dispossing of there provissions, and shuch like affairs. All which was not only with the liking of the maisters of the ships, but according to their desires. Which being done, they sett sayle from thence aboute the 5 of August.

Being thus put to sea they had not gone farr, but Mr Reinolds the master of the leser ship complained that he found his ship so leak as he durst not put further to sea till she was mended. So the master of the biger ship (caled Mr Joans) being consulted with, they both resolved to put into Dartmouth and have her ther searched and mended, which accordingly was done, to their great charg and losse of time and a faire wind. She was hear thorowly searcht from steme to sterne, some leaks were found and mended, and now it was conceived by the workmen and all, that she was sufficiente, and they might proceede without either fear or danger. So with good hopes from hence, they put to sea againe, conceiving they should goe comfortably on, not looking for any more lets of this kind; but it fell out otherwise, for after they were gone to sea againe above 100 leagues without the Lands End, houlding company togeather all this while, the master of the small ship complained his ship was so leake as he must beare up or sinke at sea, for they could scarce free her with much pumping. So they came to consultation againe, and resolved both ships to bear up backe againe and put into Plimmoth, which accordingly was done. But no spetiall leake could be founde, but it was judged to be the generall weaknes of the shipe, and that shee would not prove sufficiente for the voiage. Upon which it was resolved to dismise her and parte of the companie, and proceede with the other shipe. The which (though it was greeveous, and caused great discouragemente) was put in execution. So after they had tooke out shuch provission as the other ship could well stow, and concluded both what number and what persons to send bak, they made another sad parting, the one ship going backe to London, and the other was to proceede on her viage. Those that went bak were for the most parte shuch as were willing so to doe, either out of some

[1] From *History of the Plymouth.*

discontente, or feare they conceived of the ill success of the vioage, seeing so many croses befale, and the year time so farr spente; but others, in regarde of their owne weaknes, and charge of many yonge children, were thought least usefull, and most unfite to bear the brunte of this hard adventure; unto which worke of God, and judgmente of their brethern, they were contented to submite. And thus, like Gedions armie, this small number was devided, as if the Lord by this worke of his providence thought these few to many for the great worke he had to doe. But here by the way let me show, how afterward it was found that the leaknes of this ship was partly by being overmasted, and too much pressed with sayles; for after she was sould and put into her old trime, she made many viages and performed her service very sufficiently, to the great profite of her owners. But more espetially, by the cuning and deceite of the master and his company, who were hired to stay a whole year in the cuntrie, and now fancying dislike and fearing wante of victeles, they ploted this strategem to free them selves; as afterwards was knowne, and by some of them confessed. For they apprehended that the greater ship, being of force, and in whom most of the provissions were stowed, she would retayne enough for her selfe, what soever became of them or the passengers; and indeed such speeches had been cast out by some of them; and yet, besides other incouragements, the cheefe of them that came from Leyden wente in this shipe to give the master contente. But so strong was self love and his fears, as he forgott all duty and former kindnesses, and delt thus falsly with them, though he pretended otherwise.

These troubles being blowne over, and now all being compacte togeather in one shipe, they put to sea againe with a prosperus winde, which continued diverce days togeather, which was some incouragemente unto them; yet according to the usuall maner many were afflicted with seasicknes. And I may not omite hear a spetiall worke of Gods providence. Ther was a proud and very profane yonge man, one of the sea-men, of a lustie, able body, which made him the more hauty; he would allway be contemning the poore people in their sicknes, and cursing them dayly with greevous execrations, and did not let to tell them, that he hoped to help to cast halfe of them over board before they came to their jurneys end, and to make mery with what they had; and if he were by any gently reproved, he would curse and swear most bitterly. But it pleased God before they came halfe seas over, to smite this yong man with a greeveous disease, of which he dyed in a desperate maner, and so was him selfe the first that was throwne overbord. Thus his curses light on his owne head; and it was an astonishmente to all his fellows, for they noted it to be the just hand of God upon him.

After they had injoyed faire winds and weather for a season, they were incountred many times with crosse winds, and mette with many feirce stormes, with which the shipe was shroudly shaken, and her upper works made very leakie;

and one of the maine beames in the midd ships was bowed and craked, which put them in some fear that the shipe could not be able to performe the voiage. So some of the cheefe of the company, perceiveing the mariners to feare the suffisiencie of the shipe, as appeared by their mutterings, they entred into serious consulltation with the master and other officers of the ship, to consider in time of the danger; and rather to returne then to cast them selves into a desperate and inevitable perill. And truly ther was great distraction and differance of oppinion amongst the mariners them selves; faine would they doe what could be done for their wages sake, (being now halfe the seas over) and on the other hand they were loath to hazard their lives too desperately. But in examening of all oppinions, the master and others affirmed they knew the ship to be stronge and firme underwater; and for the buckling of the maine beame, ther was a great iron scrue the passengers brought out of Holland, which would raise the beame into his place; the which being done, the carpenter and master affirmed that with a post put under it, set firme in the lower deck, and otherways bounde, he would make it sufficiente. And as for the decks and uper workes they would calke them as well as they could, and though with the workeing of the ship they would not longe keepe stanch, yet ther would otherwise be no great danger, if they did not overpress her with sails.

So they commited them selves to the will of God, and resolved to proceede. In sundrie of these stormes the winds were so feirce, and the seas so high, as they could not beare a knote of saile, but were forced to hull, for diverce days togither. And in one of them, as they thus lay at hull, in a mighty storme, a lustie yonge man (called John Howland) coming upon some occasion above the grattings, was, with a seele[1] of the shipe throwne into the sea; but it pleased God that he caught hould of the top-saile halliards, which hunge over board, and rane out at length; yet he held his hould (though he was sundrie fadomes under water) till he was hald up by the same rope to the brime of the water, and then with a boathooke and other means got into the shipe againe, and his life saved; and though he was something ill with it, yet he lived many years after, and became a profitable member both in church and coremone wealthe. In all this viage ther died but one of the passengers, which was William Butten, a youth, servant to Samuell Fuller, when they drew near the coast. But to omite other things, (that I may be breefe,) after longe beating at sea they fell with that land which is called Cape Cod; the which being made and certainly knowne to be it, they were not a little joyfull. After some deliberation had amongst them selves, and with the master of the ship, they tacked aboute and resolved to stande for the southward (the wind and weather being faire) to finde some place aboute Hudsons river for their habitation.

But after they had sailed that course aboute halfe the day, they fell amongst

[1] Roll.

deangerous shoulds and roring breakers, and they were so farr intangled ther with as they conceived them selves in great danger; and the wind shrinking upon them withall, they resolved to bear up againe for the Cape, and thought them selves hapy to gett out of those dangers before night overtooke them, as by Gods good providence they did. And the next day they gott into the Cape-harbor wher they ridd in saftie. A word or too by the way of this cape; it was thus first named by Capten Gosnole and his company, Anno: 1602, and after by Capten Smith was caled Cape James; but it retains the former name amongst sea-men. Also that pointe which first shewed those dangerous shoulds unto them, they called Pointe Care, and Tuckers Terrour; but the French and Dutch to this day call it Malabarr, by reason of those perilous shoulds, and the losses they have suffered their.

Being thus arived in a good harbor and brought safe to land, they fell upon their knees and blessed the God of heaven, who had brought them over the vast and furious ocean, and delivered them from all the periles and miseries therof, againe to set their feete on the firme and stable earth, their proper elemente.

THE PHANTOM ISLAND

Washington Irving
(1783-1859)

"THERE are more things in heaven and earth than are dreamed of in our philosophy," and among these may be placed that marvel and mystery of the seas, the Island of St Brandan. Those who have read the history of the Canaries—the Fortunate Islands of the ancients—may remember the wonders told of this enigmatical island. Occasionally it would be visible from their shores, stretching away in the clear bright west, to all appearance substantial like themselves, and still more beautiful. Expeditions would launch forth from the Canaries to explore this land of promise. For a time its sun-gilt peaks and long shadowy promontories would remain distinctly visible, but in proportion as the voyagers approached, peak and promontory would gradually fade away, until nothing would remain but blue sky above, and deep blue water below. Hence this mysterious isle was stigmatized by ancient cosmographers with the name of Aprositus or the Inaccessible. The failure of numerous expeditions sent in quest of it, both in ancient and modern days, have at length caused its very existence to be called in question, and it has been rashly pronounced a mere optical illusion, like the Fata Morgana of the Straits of Messina, or has been classed with those unsubstantial regions known to mariners as Cape Fly-away, and the coast of Cloud Land.

Let us not permit, however, the doubts of worldly-wise sceptics to rob us of all the glorious realms owned by happy credulity in days of yore. Be assured, O reader of easy faith!—thou for whom it is my delight to labour—be assured that such an island actually exists, and has from time to time been revealed to the gaze, and trodden by the feet of favoured mortals. Historians and philosophers may have their doubts, but its existence has been fully attested by that inspired race, the poets; who, being gifted with a kind of second-sight, are enabled to discern those mysteries of nature hidden from the eyes of ordinary men. To this gifted race it has ever been a kind of wonder-land. Here once bloomed, and perhaps still blooms, the famous garden of the Hesperides, with its golden fruit. Here, too, the sorceress Armida had her enchanted garden, in which she held the Christian paladin, Rinaldo, in delicious but inglorious thraldom, as set forth in the immortal lay of Tasso. It was in this island that Sycorax the witch held sway, when the good Prospero and his infant daughter Miranda, were wafted to its shores. Who does not know the tale as told in the magic page of Shakespere? The isle was then

> . . . full of noises,
> Sounds, and sweet airs, that give delight, and hurt not.

The island, in fact, at different times, has been under the sway of different powers—genii of earth, and air, and ocean, who have made it their shadowy abode. Hither have retired many classic but broken-down deities, shorn of almost all their attributes, but who once ruled the poetic world. Here Neptune and Amphitrite hold a diminished court—sovereigns in exile. Their ocean chariot, almost a wreck, lies bottom upward in some sea-beaten cavern; their pursy Tritons and haggard Nereids bask listlessly like seals about the rocks. Sometimes those deities assume, it is said, a shadow of their ancient pomp, and glide in state about a summer sea; and then, as some tall Indiaman lies becalmed with idly-flapping sail, her drowsy crew may hear the mellow note of the Triton's shell swelling upon the ear as the invisible pageant sweeps by.

On the shores of this wondrous isle the kraken heaves its unwieldy bulk, and wallows many a rood. Here the sea-serpent, that mighty but much-contested reptile, lies coiled up during the intervals of its revelations to the eyes of true believers. Here even the Flying Dutchman finds a port, and casts his anchor, and furls his shadowy sail, and takes a brief repose from his eternal cruisings.

In the deep bays and harbours of the island lies many a spell-bound ship, long since given up as lost by the ruined merchant. Here too its crew, long, long bewailed in vain, lie sleeping from age to age, in mossy grottoes, or wander about in pleasing oblivion of all things. Here, in caverns, are garnered up the priceless treasures lost in the ocean. Here sparkles in vain the diamond, and flames the carbuncle. Here are piled up rich bales of Oriental silks, boxes of pearls, and piles of golden ingots.

Such are some of the marvels related of this island, which may serve to throw light upon the following legend, of unquestionable truth, which I recommend to the implicit belief of the reader.

THE ADALANTADO OF THE SEVEN CITIES

Legend of St Brandan

In the early part of the fifteenth century, when Prince Henry of Portugal, of worthy memory, was pushing the career of discovery along the western coast of Africa, and the world was resounding with reports of golden regions on the mainland, and new-found islands in the ocean, there arrived at Lisbon an old bewildered pilot of the seas, who had been driven by tempests, he knew not whither, and raved about an island far in the deep, upon which he had landed, and which he had found peopled with Christians, and adorned with noble cities.

The inhabitants, he said, having never before been visited by a ship, gathered round, and regarded him with surprise. They told him they were descendants of a band of Christians who fled from Spain when that country was conquered by the Moslems. They were curious about the state of their fatherland, and grieved to hear that the Moslems still held possession of the kingdom of Granada. They would have taken the old navigator to church, to convince him of their orthodoxy; but, either through lack of devotion, or lack of faith in their words, he declined their invitation, and preferred to return on board his ship. He was properly punished. A furious storm arose, drove him from his anchorage, hurried him out to sea, and he saw no more of the unknown island.

This strange story caused great marvel in Lisbon and elsewhere. Those versed in history, remembered to have read, in an ancient chronicle, that, at the time of the conquest of Spain, in the eighth century, when the blessed cross was cast down, and the crescent erected in its place, and when Christian churches were turned into Moslem mosques, seven bishops at the head of seven bands of pious exiles, had fled from the peninsula, and embarked in quest of some ocean island or distant land, where they might found seven Christian cities, and enjoy their faith unmolested.

The fate of these saints-errant had hitherto remained a mystery, and their story had faded from memory; the report of the old tempest-tossed pilot, however, revived this long-forgotten theme; and it was determined by the pious and enthusiastic, that the island thus accidentally discovered, was the identical place of refuge, whither the wandering bishops had been guided by a protecting Providence, and where they had folded their flocks.

This most excitable of worlds has always some darling object of chimerical enterprise; the "Island of the Seven Cities" now awakened as much interest and longing among zealous Christians, as has the renowned city of Timbuctoo among adventurous travellers, or the north-west passage among hardy navigators; and it was a frequent prayer of the devout, that these scattered and lost portions of the Christian family might be discovered, and reunited to the great body of Christendom.

No one, however, entered into the matter with half the zeal of Don Fernando de Ulmo, a young cavalier of high standing in the Portuguese court, and of most sanguine and romantic temperament. He had recently come to his estate, and had run the round of all kinds of pleasures and excitements, when this new theme of popular talk and wonder presented itself. The island of the Seven Cities became now the constant subject of his thoughts by day, and his dreams by night: it even rivalled his passion for a beautiful girl, one of the greatest belles of Lisbon, to whom he was betrothed. At length, his imagination became so inflamed on the subject, that he determined to fit out an expedition at his own expense, and set sail in quest of this sainted island. It could not be a cruise of any great extent; for, according to the calculations of the tempest-tossed pilot, it must be somewhere in the latitude of the Canaries; which at that time, when the New World was as yet undiscovered, formed the frontier of ocean enterprise. Don Fernando applied to the crown for countenance and protection. As he was a favourite at court, the usual patronage was readily extended to him; that is to say, he received a commission from the king, Dom loam II., constituting him Adalantado, or military governor, of any country he might discover, with the single proviso, that he should bear all the expenses of the discovery, and pay a tenth of the profits to the crown.

Don Fernando now set to work in the true spirit of a projector. He sold acre after acre of solid land, and invested the proceeds in ships, guns, ammunition, and sea-stores. Even his old family mansion in Lisbon was mortgaged without scruple, for he looked forward to a palace in one of the Seven Cities of which he was to be Adalantado. This was the age of nautical romance, when the thoughts of all speculative dreamers were turned to the ocean. The scheme of Don Fernando, therefore, drew adventurers of every kind. The merchant promised himself new marts of opulent traffic; the soldier hoped to sack and plunder some one or other of those Seven Cities—even the fat monk shook off the sleep and sloth of the cloister, to join in a crusade which promised such increase to the possessions of the Church.

One person alone regarded the whole project with sovereign contempt and growling hostility. This was Don Ramiro Alvarez, the father of the beautiful Serafina, to whom Don Fernando was betrothed. He was one of those perverse, matter-of-fact old men, who are prone to oppose everything speculative and romantic. He had no faith in the Island of the Seven Cities; regarded the projected cruise as a crackbrained freak; looked with angry eye and internal heartburning on the conduct of his intended son-in-law, chaffering away solid lands for lands in the moon; and scoffingly dubbed him Adalantado of Cloud Land. In fact, he had never really relished the intended match, to which his consent had been slowly extorted, by the tears and entreaties of his daughter. It is true he could have no reasonable objections to the youth, for Don Fernando was the very flower of Portuguese chivalry. No one could excel him at the tilting-match or the riding at the ring; none was more bold and dexterous in the bull-fight; none composed more gallant madrigals in praise of his lady's charms, or sang them with sweeter tones to the accompaniment of her guitar; nor could any one handle the castanets and dance the bolero with more captivating grace. All these admirable qualities and endowments, however, though they had been sufficient to win the heart of Serafina, were nothing in the eyes of her unreasonable father. O Cupid, god of Love! why will fathers always be so unreasonable?

The engagement to Serafina had threatened at first to throw an obstacle in the way of the expedition of Don Fernando, and for a time perplexed him in the extreme. He was passionately attached to the young lady; but he was also passionately bent on this romantic enterprise. How should he reconcile the two passionate inclinations? A simple and obvious arrangement at length presented itself: marry Serafina, enjoy a portion of the honeymoon at once, and defer the rest until his return from the discovery of the Seven Cities!

He hastened to make known this most excellent arrangement to Don Ramiro, when the long-smothered wrath of the old cavalier burst forth. He reproached him with being the dupe of wandering vagabonds and wild schemers, and with squandering all his real possessions in pursuit of empty bubbles. Don Fernando was too sanguine a projector, and too young a man, to listen tamely to such language. He acted with what is technically called "becoming spirit." A high quarrel ensued; Don Ramiro pronounced him a madman, and forbade all farther intercourse with his daughter, until he should give proof of returning sanity, by abandoning this madcap enterprise; while Don Fernando flung out of the house, more bent than ever on the expedition, from the idea of triumphing over the incredulity of the grey-beard when he should return successful. Don Ramiro's heart misgave him. Who knows, thought he, but this crackbrained visionary may persuade my daughter to elope with him, and share his throne in this unknown paradise of fools? If I could only keep her safe until his ships are fairly out at sea!

He repaired to her apartment, represented to her the sanguine, unsteady character of her lover and the chimerical value of his schemes, and urged the propriety of suspending all intercourse with him until he should recover from his present hallucination. She bowed her head as if in filial acquiescence, whereupon he folded her to his bosom with parental fondness, and kissed away a tear that was stealing over her cheek, but as he left the chamber quietly turned the key in the lock; for though he was a fond father, and had a high opinion of the submissive temper of his child, he had a still higher opinion of the conservative virtues of lock and key, and determined to trust to them until the caravels should sail. Whether the damsel had been in any wise shaken in her faith as to the schemes of her lover by her father's eloquence, tradition does not say; but certain it is, that, the moment she heard the key turn in the lock, she became a firm believer in the Island of the Seven Cities.

The door was locked; but her will was unconfined. A window of the chamber opened into one of those stone balconies, secured by iron bars, which project like huge cages from Portuguese and Spanish houses. Within this balcony the beautiful Serafina had her birds and flowers, and here she was accustomed to sit on moonlight nights as in a bower, and touch her guitar and sing like a wakeful nightingale. From this balcony an intercourse was now maintained between the lovers, against which the lock and key of Don Ramiro were of no avail. All day would Fernando be occupied hurrying the equipments of his ships, but evenings found him in sweet discourse beneath his lady's window.

At length the preparations were completed. Two gallant caravels lay at anchor in the Tagus ready to sail at sunrise. Late at night, by the pale light of a waning moon, the lover had his last interview. The beautiful Serafina was sad at heart and full of dark forebodings; her lover full of hope and confidence. "A few short months," said he, "and I shall return in triumph. Thy father will then blush at his incredulity, and hasten to welcome to his house the Adalantado of the Seven Cities."

The gentle lady shook her head. It was not on this point she felt distrust. She was a thorough believer in the Island of the Seven Cities, and so sure of the success of the enterprise that she might have been tempted to join it had not the balcony been high and the grating strong. Other considerations induced that dubious shaking of the head. She had heard of the inconstancy of the seas, and the inconstancy of those who roam them. Might not Fernando meet with other loves in foreign ports ? Might not some peerless beauty in one or other of those Seven Cities efface the image of Serafina from his mind? Now let the truth be spoken—the beautiful Serafina had reason for her disquiet. If Don Fernando had any fault in the world, it was that of being rather inflammable and apt to take fire from every sparkling eye. He had been somewhat of a rover among the sex on shore—what might he be on sea?

She ventured to express her doubt, but he spurned at the very idea. "What! he false to Serafina! He bow at the shrine of another beauty? Never! never!" Repeatedly did he bend his knee, and smite his breast, and call upon the silver moon to witness his sincerity and truth.

He retorted the doubt, "Might not Serafina herself forget her plighted faith? Might not some wealthier rival present himself while he was tossing on the sea, and, backed by her father's wishes, win the treasure of her hand?"

The beautiful Serafina raised her white arms between the iron bars of the balcony, and, like her lover, invoked the moon to testify her vows. Alas!how little did Fernando know her heart. The more her father should oppose, the more would she be fixed in faith. Though years should intervene, Fernando on his return would find her true. Even should the salt sea swallow him up (and her eyes shed salt tears at the very thought), never would she be the wife of another!—Never, *never*, NEVER! She drew from her finger a ring gemmed with a ruby heart, and dropped it from the balcony, a parting pledge of constancy.

Thus the lovers parted, with many a tender word and plighted vow. But will they keep those vows? Perish the doubt! Have they not called the constant moon to witness?

With the morning dawn the caravels dropped down the Tagus, and put to sea. They steered for the Canaries, in those days the regions of nautical discovery and romance, and the outposts of the known world—for as yet Columbus had not steered his daring barks across the ocean. Scarce had they reached those latitudes, when they were separated by a violent tempest. For many days was the caravel of Don Fernando driven about at the mercy of the elements; all seamanship was baffled, destruction seemed inevitable, and the crew were in despair. All at once the storm subsided; the ocean sank into a calm; the clouds which had veiled the face of heaven were suddenly withdrawn, and the tempest-tossed mariners beheld a fair and mountainous island, emerging as if by enchantment from the murky gloom. They rubbed their eyes, and gazed for a time almost incredulously; yet there lay the island spread out in lovely landscapes, with the late stormy sea laving its shores with peaceful billows.

The pilot of the caravel consulted his maps and charts; no island like the one before him was laid down as existing in those parts. It is true, he had lost his reckoning in the late storm; but, according to his calculations, he could not be far from the Canaries, and this was not one of that group of islands. The caravel now lay perfectly becalmed off the mouth of a river, on the banks of which, about a league from the sea,was descried a noble city, with lofty walls and towers and a protecting castle.

After a timc, a stately barge with sixteen oars was seen emergmg from the river and approaching the caravel. It was quaintly carved and gilt; the oarsmen were clad in antique garb, their oars painted of a bright crimson; and they came slowly and solemnly, keeping time as they rowed to the cadence of an old Spanish ditty. Under a silken canopy in the stern sat a cavalier richly clad, and over his head was a banner bearing the sacred emblem of the cross.

When the barge reached the caravel, the cavalier stepped on board. He was tall and gaunt; with a long Spanish visage, moustaches that curled up to his eyes, and a forked beard. He wore gauntlets reaching to his elbows, a Toledo blade strutting out behind, with a basket-hilt, in which he carried his handkerchief. His air was lofty and precise, and bespoke indisputably the hidalgo. Thrusting out a long, spindle leg, he took off a huge sombrero, and swaying it until the feather swept the ground, accosted Don Fernando in the old Castilian language, and with the old Castilian courtesy welcomed him to the Island of the Seven Cities.

Don Fernando was overwhelmed with astonishment. Could this be true? Had he really been tempest-driven to the very land of which he was in quest?

It was even so. That very day the inhabitants were holding high festival in commemoration of the escape of their ancestors from the Moors. The arrival of the caravel at such a juncture was considered a good omen—the accomplishment of an ancient prophecy, through which the island was to be restored to the great community of Christendom. The cavalier before him was grand-chamberlain, sent by the alcayde to invite him to the festivities of the capital.

Don Fernando could scarce believe that this was not all a dream. He made known his name, and the object of his voyage. The grand-chamberlain declared that all was in perfect accordance with the ancient prophecy, and that the moment his credentials were presented, he would be acknowledged as the Adalantado of the Seven Cities. In the meantime, the day was waning; the barge was ready to convey him to the land, and would as assuredly bring him back.

Don Fernando's pilot, a veteran of the seas, drew him aside and expostulated against his venturing, on the mere word of a stranger, to land in a strange barge on an unknown shore. "Who knows, Señor, what land this is, or what people inhabit it?"

Don Fernando was not to be dissuaded. Had he not believed in this island when all the world doubted ? Had he not sought it in defiance of storm and tempest, and was he now to shrink from its shores when they lay before him in calm weather? In a word, was not faith the very cornerstone of his enterprise?

Having arrayed himself, therefore, in gala dress befitting the occasion, he took his seat in the barge. The grand-chamberlain seated himself opposite. The rowers plied their oars, and renewed the mournful old ditty, and the gorgeous but unwieldy barge moved slowly through the water.

The night closed in before they entered the river, and swept along past rock and promontory, each guarded by its tower. At every post they were challenged by the sentinel.

"Who goes there ?"

"The Adalantado of the Seven Cities."

"Welcome, Señor Adalantado. Pass on."

Entering the harbour they rowed close by an armed galley of ancient form. Soldiers with crossbows patrolled the deck.

Who goes there ?" "The Adalantado of the Seven Cities."

"Welcome, Señor Adalantado. Pass on."

They landed at a broad flight of stone steps, leading up between two massive towers, and knocked at the water-gate. A sentinel, in ancient steel casque, looked from the barbican.

"Who is there ?"

"The Adalantado of the Seven Cities."

"Welcome, Señor Adalantado."

The gate swung open, grating upon rusty hinges. They entered between two more rows of warriors in Gothic armour, with crossbows, maces, battle-axes, and faces old-fashioned as their armour. There were processions through the streets, in commemoration of the landing of the seven Bishops and their followers, and bonfires at which effigies of losel Moors expiated their invasion of Christendom by a kind of *auto-da-fé*. The groups round the fires, uncouth in their attire, looked like the fantastic figures that roam the streets in Carnival time. Even the dames who gazed down from Gothic balconies hung with antique tapestry resembled effigies dressed up in Christmas mummeries. Everything, in short, bore the stamp of former ages, as if the world had suddenly rolled back for several centuries. Nor was this to be wondered at. Had not the Island of the Seven Cities been cut off from the rest of the world for several hundred years; and were not these the modes and customs of Gothic Spain before it was conquered by the Moors?

Arrived at the palace of the alcayde, the grand-chamberlain knocked at the portal. The porter looked through a wicket, and demanded who was there.

"The Adalantado of the Seven Cities."

The portal was thrown wide open. The grand-chamberlain led the way up a vast, heavily-moulded marble staircase, and into a hall of ceremony where was the alcayde with several of the principal dignitaries of the city, who had a marvellous resemblance, in form and feature, to the quaint figures in old illuminated manuscripts.

The grand-chamberlain stepped forward and announced the name and title of the stranger guest, and the extraordinary nature of his mission. The announcement appeared to create no extraordinary emotion or surprise, but to be received as the anticipated fulfilment of a prophecy.

The reception of Don Fernando, however, was profoundly gracious, though in the same style of stately courtesy which everywhere prevailed. He would have produced his credentials, but this was courteously declined. The evening was devoted to high festivity; the following day, when he should enter the port with his caravel, would be devoted to business, when the credentials would be received in due form, and he inducted into office as Adalantado of the Seven Cities.

Don Fernando was now conducted through one of those interminable suites of apartments, the pride of Spanish palaces, all furnished in a style of obsolete magnificence. In a vast saloon blazing with tapers was assembled all the aristocracy and fashion of the city; stately dames and cavaliers, the very counterpart of the figures in the tapestry which decorated the walls. Fernando gazed in silent marvel. It was a reflex of the proud aristocracy of Spain in the time of Roderick the Goth.

The festivities of the evening were all in the style of solemn and antiquated ceremonial. There was a dance, but it was as if the old tapestry were put in motion, and all the figures moving in stately measure about the floor. There was one exception, and one that told powerfully upon the susceptible Adalantado. The alcayde's daughter—such a ripe, melting beauty!Her dress, it is true, like the dresses of her neighbours, might have been worn before the flood, but she had the black Andalusian eye, a glance of which, through its long dark lashes, is irresistible. Her voice, too, her manner, her undulating movements, all smacked of Andalusia, and showed how female charms may be transmitted from age to age, and clime to clime, without ever going out of fashion. Those who know the witchery of the sex, in that most amorous part of amorous old Spain, may judge of the fascination to which Don Fernando was exposed, as he joined in the dance with one of its most captivating descendants.

He sat beside her at the banquet—such an old-world feast! such obsolete dainties! At the head of the table the peacock, that bird of state and ceremony, was served up in full plumage on a golden dish. As Don Fernando cast his eyes down the glittering board, what a vista presented itself of odd heads and head-dresses—of formal bearded dignitaries and stately dames, with castellated locks and towering plumes! Is it to be wondered at that he should turn with delight from these antiquated figures to the alcayde's daughter, all smiles and dimples, and melting looks and melting accents ? Besides—for I wish to give him every excuse in my power—he was in a particularly excitable mood from the novelty of the scene before him, from this realization of all his hopes and fancies, and from frequent draughts of the wine-cup presented to him at every moment by officious pages during the banquet.

In a word—there is no concealing the matter—before the evening was over, Don Fernando was making love outright to the alcayde's daughter. They had wandered together to a moonlit balcony of the palace, and he was charming her ear with one of those love-ditties with which, in a like balcony, he had serenaded the beautiful Serafina.

The damsel hung her head coyly. "Ah! Señor, these are flattering words; but you cavaliers who roam the seas are unsteady as its waves. Tomorrow you will be throned in state, Adalantado of the Seven Cities; and will think no more of the alcayde's daughter."

Don Fernando, in the intoxication of the moment, called the moon to witness his sincerity. As he raised his hand in adjuration, the chaste moon cast a ray upon the ring that sparkled on his finger. It caught the damsel's eye. "Señor Adalantado," said she archly, "I have no faith in the moon, but give me that ring upon your finger in pledge of the truth of what you profess."

The gallant Adalantado was taken by surprise; there was no parrying this sudden appeal; before he had time to reflect, the ring of the beautiful Serafina glittered on the finger of the alcayde's daughter.

At this eventful moment the chamberlain approached with lofty demeanour, and announced that the barge was waiting to bear him back to the caravel. I forbear to relate the ceremonious partings with the alcayde and his dignitaries, and the tender farewell of the alcayde's daughter. He took his seat in the barge opposite the grand-chamberlain. The rowers plied their crimson oars in the same slow and stately manner to the cadence of the same mournful old ditty. His brain was in a whirl with all that he had seen, and his heart now and then gave him a twinge as he thought of his temporary infidelity to the beautiful Serafina. The barge sallied out into the sea, but no caravel was to be seen; doubtless she had been carried to a distance by the current of the river. The oarsmen rowed on; their monotonous chant had a lulling effect. A drowsy influence crept over Don Fernando. Objects swam before his eyes. The oarsmen assumed odd shapes as in a dream. The grand-chamberlain grew larger and larger, and taller and taller. He took off his huge sombrero, and held it over the head of Don Fernando, like an extinguisher over a candle. The latter cowered beneath it; he felt himself sinking in the socket.

"Good-night, Señor Adalantado of the Seven Cities!" said the grand-chamberlain.

The sombrero slowly descended—Don Fernando was extinguished!

How long he remained extinct no mortal man can tell. When he returned to consciousness, he found himself in a strange cabin, surrounded by strangers. He rubbed his eyes, and looked round him wildly. Where was he? On board a Portuguese ship, bound to Lisbon. How came he there? He had been taken senseless from a wreck drifting about the ocean.

Don Fernando was more and more confounded and perplexed. He recalled, one by one, everything that had happened to him in the Island of the Seven Cities, until he had been extinguished by the sombrero of the grand-chamberlain.

But what had happened to him since? What had become of his caravel? Was it the wreck of her on which he had been found floating?

The people about him could give no information on the subject. He entreated them to take him to the Island of the Seven Cities, which could not be far off. Told them all that had befallen him there. That he had but to land to be received as Adalantado; when he would reward them magnificently for their services.

They regarded his words as the ravings of delirium, and in their honest solicitude for the restoration of his reason, administered such rough remedies, that he was fain to drop the subject and observe a cautious taciturnity.

At length they arrived in the Tagus, and anchored before the famous city of Lisbon. Don Fernando sprang joyfully on shore, and hastened to his ancestral mansion. A strange porter opened the door, who knew nothing of him or of his family; no people of the name had inhabited the house for many a year.

He sought the mansion of Don Ramiro. He approached the balcony beneath which he had bidden farewell to Serafina. Did his eyes deceive him? No! There was Serafina herself among the flowers in the balcony. He raised his arms toward her with an exclamation of rapture. She cast upon him a look of indignation, and, hastily retiring, closed the casement with a slam that testified her displeasure.

Could she have heard of his flirtation with the alcayde's daughter? But that was mere transient gallantry. A moment's interview would dispel every doubt of his constancy.

He rang at the door; as it was opened by the porter he rushed up stairs; sought the well-known chamber, and threw himself at the feet of Serafina. She started back with affright, and took refuge in the arms of a youthful cavalier.

"What mean you, Señor," cried the latter, "by this intrusion?"

"What right have you to ask the question?" demanded Don Fernando fiercely.

"The right of an affianced suitor!"

Don Fernando started and turned pale. "O Serafina! Serafina!" cried he in a tone of agony, "is this thy plighted constancy ?"

"Serafina? What mean you by Serafina, Señor? If this be the lady you intend, her name is Maria."

"May I not believe my senses? May I not believe my heart?" cried Don Fernando. "Is not this Serafina Alvarez, the original of yon portrait, which, less fickle than herself, still smiles on me from the wall?"

"Holy Virgin!" cried the young lady, casting her eyes upon the portrait. "He is talking of my great-grand mother!"

An explanation ensued, if that could be called an explanation, which plunged the unfortunate Fernando into tenfold perplexity. If he might believe his eyes, he saw before him his beloved Serafina; if he might believe his ears, it was merely her hereditary form and features, perpetuated in the person of her great-granddaughter.

His brain began to spin. He sought the office of the Minister of Marine, and made a report of his expedition, and of the Island of the Seven Cities, which he had so fortunately discovered. Nobody knew anything of such an expedition or such an island. He declared that he had undertaken the enterprise under a formal contract with the crown, and had received a regular commission, constituting him Adalantado. This must be a matter of record, and he insisted loudly that the books of the department should be consulted. The wordy strife at length attracted the attention of an old gray-headed clerk, who sat perched on a high stool, at a high desk, with iron-rimmed spectacles on the top of a thin, pinched nose, copying records into an enormous folio. He had wintered and summered in the department for a great part of a century, until he had almost grown to be a piece of the desk at which he sat; his memory was a mere index of official facts and documents, and his brain was little better than red tape and parchment. After peering down for a time from his lofty perch, and ascertaining the matter in controversy, he put his pen behind his ear, and descended. He remembered to have heard something from his predecessor about an expedition of the kind in question, but then it had sailed during the reign of Dom Ioam II., and he had been dead at least a hundred years. To put the matter beyond dispute, however, the archives of the Torre do Tombo, that sepulchre of old Portuguese documents, were diligently searched, and a record was found of a contract between the crown and one Fernando de Ulmo, for the discovery of the Island of the Seven Cities, and of a commission secured to him as Adalantado of the country he might discover.

"There!" cried Don Fernando triumphantly, "there you have proof before your own eyes of what I have said. I am the Fernando de Ulmo specified in that record. I have discovered the Island of the Seven Cities, and am entitled to be Adalantado, according to contract."

The story of Don Fernando had certainly, what is pronounced the best of historical foundation, documentary evidence; but when a man, in the bloom of youth, talked of events that had taken place above a century previously, as having happened to himself, it is no wonder that he was set down for a madman.

The old clerk looked at him from above and below his spectacles, shrugged his shoulders, stroked his chin, reascended his lofty stool, took the pen from behind his ears, and resumed his daily and eternal task, copying records into the fiftieth volume of a series of gigantic folios. The other clerks winked at each other shrewdly, and dispersed to their several places, and poor Don Fernando, thus left to himself, flung out of the office, almost driven wild by these repeated perplexities.

In the confusion of his mind, he instinctively repaired to the mansion of Alvarez, but it was barred against him. To break the delusion under which the youth apparently laboured, and to convince him that the Serafina about whom he raved was really dead, he was conducted to her tomb. There she lay, a stately matron, cut out in alabaster; and there lay her husband beside her—a portly cavalier in armour; and there knelt, on each side, the effigies of a numerous progeny, proving that she had been a fruitful vine. Even the very monument gave evidence of the lapse of time; the hands of her husband, folded as if in prayer, had lost their fingers, and the face of the once lovely Serafina was without a nose.

Don Fernando felt a transient glow of indignation at beholding this monumental proof of the inconstancy of his mistress; but who could expect a mistress to remain constant during a whole century of absence? And what right had he to rail about constancy, after what had passed between himself and the alcayde's daughter? The unfortunate cavalier performed one pious act of tender devotion; he had the alabaster nose of Serafina restored by a skilful statuary, and then tore himself from the tomb.

He could now no longer doubt the fact, that, somehow or other, he had skipped over a whole century, during the night he had spent at the Island of the Seven Cities; and he was now as complete a stranger in his native city as if he had never been there. A thousand times did he wish himself back to that wonderful island, with its antiquated banquet halls, where he had been so courteously received; and now that the once young and beautiful Serafina was nothing but a great-grandmother in marble, with generations of descendants, a thousand times would he recall the melting black eyes of the alcayde's daughter, who doubtless, like himself, was still flourishing in fresh juvenility, and breathe a sweet wish that he were seated by her side.

He would at once have set on foot another expedition, at his own expense, to cruise in search of the sainted island, but his means were exhausted. He endeavoured to rouse others to the enterprise, setting forth the certainty of profitable results, of which his own experience furnished such unquestionable proof. Alas! no one would give faith to his tale; but looked upon it as the feverish dream of a shipwrecked man. He persisted in his efforts; holding forth in all places and all companies, until he became an object of jest and jeer to the light-minded, who mistook his earnest enthusiasm for a proof of insanity; and the very children in the streets bantered him with the title of "The Adalantado of the Seven Cities."

Finding all efforts in vain, in his native city of Lisbon, he took shipping for the Canaries, as being nearer the latitude of his former cruise, and inhabited by people given to nautical adventure. Here he found ready listeners to his story; for the old pilots and mariners of those parts were notorious island-hunters, and devout believers in all the wonders of the seas. Indeed, one and all treated his adventure as a common occurrence, and turning to each other, with a sagacious nod of the head, observed, "He has been at the Island of St Brandan."

They then went on to inform him of that great marvel and enigma of the ocean; of its repeated appearance to the inhabitants of their islands; and of the many but ineffectual expeditions that had been made in search of it. They took him to a promontory of the island of Palma, whence the shadowy St Brandan had oftenest been descried, and they pointed out the very tract in the west where its mountains had been seen.

Don Fernando listened with rapt attention. He had no longer a doubt that this mysterious and fugacious island must be the same with that of the Seven Cities; and that some supernatural influence connected with it had operated upon himself, and made the events of a night Occupy the space of a century.

He endeavoured, but in vain, to rouse the islanders to another attempt at discovery; they had given up the Phantom Island as indeed inaccessible. Fernando, however, was not to be discouraged. The idea wore itself deeper .and deeper in his mind, until it became the engrossing subject of his thoughts and object of his being. Every morning he would repair to the promontory of Palma, and sit there throughout the livelong day, in hopes of seeing the fairy mountains of St Brandon peering above the horizon; every evening he returned to his home a disappointed man, but ready to resume his post on the following morning.

His assiduity was all in vain. He grew grey in his ineffectual attempt; and was at length found dead at his post. His grave is still shown in the island of Palma, and a cross is erected on the spot where he used to sit and look out upon the sea, in hopes of the reappearance of the Phantom Island.

A DESCENT INTO THE MAELSTROM[1]

Edgar Allan Poe
(1809-1849)

WE HAD now reached the summit of the loftiest crag. For some minutes the old man seemed too much exhausted to speak.

"Not long ago," said he at length, "and I could have guided you on this route as well as the youngest of my sons; but, about three years past, there happened to me an event such as never before happened to mortal man—or at least such as no man ever survived to tell of—and the six hours of deadly terror which I then endured have broken me up body and soul. You suppose me a *very* old man—but I am not. It took less than a single day to change these hairs from a jetty black to white, to weaken my limbs, and to unstring my nerves, so that I tremble at thc lcast exertion, and am frightened at a shadow. Do you know that I can scarcely look over this little cliff without getting giddy ?"

The "little cliff" upon whose edge he had so carelessly thrown himself down to rest that the weightier portion of his body hung over it, while he was only kept

---

[1] From *Tales of Mystery and Imagination.*

from falling by the tenure of his elbow on its extreme and slippery edge—this "little cliff" arose, a sheer unobstructed precipice of black shining rock, some fifteen or sixteen hundred feet from the world of crags beneath us. Nothing would have tempted me within half a dozen yards of its brink. In truth so deeply was I excited by the perilous position of my companion, that I fell at full length upon the ground, clung to the shrubs around me, and dared not even glance upward at the sky—while I struggled in vain to divest myself of the idea that the very foundations of the mountain were in danger from the fury of the winds. It was long before I could reason myself into sufficient courage to sit up and look out into the distance.

"You must get over these fancies," said the guide,"for I have brought you here that you might have the best possible view of the scene of that event I mentioned—and to tell you the whole story with the spot just under your eye.

"We are now" he continued in that particularizing manner which distinguished him—"we are now close upon the Norwegian coast—in the sixty-eighth degree of latitude—in the great province of Nordland—and in the dreary district of Lofoden. The mountain upon whose top we sit is Helseggen, the Cloudy. Now raise yourself up a little higher—hold, on to the grass if you feel giddy—so—and look out, beyond the belt of vapour beneath us, into the sea."

I looked dizzily, and beheld a wide expanse of ocean, whose waters were so inky a hue as to bring at once to my mind the Nubian geographer's account of the *Mare Tenebrarum.* A panorama more deplorably desolate no human imagination can conceive. To the right and left, as far as the eye could reach, there lay outstretched, like ramparts of the world, lines of horridly black and beetling cliff, whose character of gloom was but the more forcibly illustrated by the surf which reared high up against it, its white and ghastly crest, howling and shrieking for ever. Just opposite the promontory upon whose apex we were placed, and at a distance of some five or six miles out at sea, there was visible a small, bleak-looking island; or, more properly, its position was discernible through the wilderness of surge in which it was enveloped. About two miles nearer the land, arose another of smaller size, hideously craggy and barren, and encompassed at various intervals by a cluster of dark rocks.

The appearance of the ocean, in the space between the more distant island and the shore, had something very unusual about it. Although, at the time, so strong a gale was blowing landward that a brigg in the remote offing lay to under a double-reefed trysail, and constantly plunged her whole hull out of sight, still there was here nothing like a regular swell, but only a short, quick, angry cross dashing of water in every direction—as well in the teeth of the wind as otherwise. Of foam there was little except in the immediate vicinity of the rocks.

"The island in the distance," resumed the old man, "is Moskoe. That a mile to the northward is Ambaaren. Yonder are Islesen, Hotholm, Keildhelm, Suarven, and Buckholm. Farther off—between Moskoe and Vurrgh—are Otterholm, Flimen, Sandflesen, and Stockholm. These are the true names of the places—but why it has been thought necessary to name them at all, is more than either you or I can understand. Do you hear anything? Do you see any change in the water?"

We had now been about ten minutes upon the top of Helseggen, to which we had ascended from the interior of Lofoden, so that we had caught no glimpse of the sea until it had burst upon us from the summit. As the old man spoke I became aware of a loud and gradually increasing sound, like the moaning of a vast herd of buffaloes upon an American prairie; and at the same moment I perceived that what seamen term the 'chopping' character of the ocean beneath us, was rapidly changing into a current which set to the eastward. Even while I gazed, this current acquired a monstrous velocity. Each moment added to its speed—to its headlong impetuosity. In five minutes the whole sea, as far as Vurrgh, was lashed into ungovernable fury; but it was between Moskoe and the coast that the main uproar held its sway. Here the vast bed of the waters, seamed and scarred into a thousand conflicting channels, burst suddenly into frenzied convulsion—heaving, boiling, hissing—gyrating in gigantic and innumerable vortices, and all whirling and plunging on to the eastward with a rapidity which water never elsewhere assumes, except in precipitous descents.

In a few minutes more, there came over the scene another radical alteration. The general surface grew somewhat more smooth, and the whirlpools, one by one, disappeared, while prodigious streaks of foam became apparent where none had been seen before. These streaks, at length, spreading out to a great distance, and entering into combination, took unto themselves the gyratory motion of the subsided vortices, and seemed to form the germ of another more vast. Suddenly—very suddenly—this assumed a distinct and definite existence, in a circle of more than a mile in diameter. The edge of the whirl was represented by a broad belt of gleaming spray; but no particle of this slipped into the mouth of the terrific funnel, whose interior, as far as the eye could fathom it, was a smooth, shining, and jet-black wall of water, inclined to the horizon at an angle of some forty-five degrees, speeding dizzily round and round with a swaying and sweltering motion, and sending forth to the winds an appalling voice, half shriek, half roar, such as not even the mighty cataract of Niagara ever lifts up in its agony to Heaven.

The mountain trembled to its very base, and the rock rocked. I threw myself upon my face, and clung to the scant herbage in an excess of nervous agitation.

"This," said I at length, to the old man—"this *can* be nothing else but the great whirlpool of the Maelstrom."

"So it is sometimes termed," said he. "We Norwegians call it the Moskoe-strom, from the island of Moskoe in the midway."

The ordinary account of this vortex had by no means prepared me for what I saw. That of Jonas Ramus, which is perhaps the most circumstantial of any, cannot impart the faintest conception either of the magnificence or of the horror of the scene—or of the wild bewildering sense of *the novel* which confounds the beholder. I am not sure from what point of view the writer in question surveyed it, nor at what time, but it could neither have been from the summit of Helseggen, nor during a storm. There are some passages of his description nevertheless, which may be quoted for their details, although their effect is exceedingly feeble in conveying an impression of the spectacle.

"Between Lofoden and Moskoe," he says, "the depth of the water is between thirty-six and forty fathoms; but on the other side, toward Ver (Vurrgh) this depth decreases so as not to afford a convenient passage for a vessel, without the risk of splitting on the rocks, which happens even in the calmest weather. When it is flood, the stream runs up the country between Lofoden and Moskoe with a boisterous rapidity; but the roar of its impetuous ebb to the sea is scarce equalled by the loudest and most dreadful cataracts; the noise being heard several leagues off, and the vortices or pits are of such an extent and depth, that if a ship comes within its attraction, it is inevitably absorbed and carried down to the bottom, and there beat to pieces against the rocks; and when the water relaxes, the fragments thereof are thrown up again. But these intervals of tranquillity are only at the turn of the ebb and flood, and in calm weather, and last but a quarter of an hour, its violence gradually returning. When the stream is most boisterous, and its fury heightened by a storm, it is dangerous to come within a Norway mile of it. Boats, yachts, and ships have been carried away by not guarding against it before they were carried within its reach. It likewise happens frequently, that whales come too near the stream, and are overpowered by its violence; and then it is impossible to describe their howlings and bellowings in their fruitless struggles to disengage themselves. A bear once, in attempting to swim from Lofoden to Moskoe, was caught by the stream and borne down, while he roared terribly, so as to be heard on shore. Large stocks of firs and pine-trees, after being absorbed by the current, rise again broken and torn to such a degree as if bristles grew upon them. This plainly shows the bottom to consist of craggy rocks, among which they are whirled to and fro. This stream is regulated by the flux and reflux of the sea—it being constantly high and low water every six hours. In the year 1645, early in the morning of Sexagesima Sunday, it raged with such a noise and impetuosity that the very stones of the houses on the coast fell to the ground."

In regard to the depth of the water, I could not see how this could have been ascertained at all in the immediate vicinity of the vortex. The "forty fathoms" must have reference only to portions of the channel close upon the shore of either Moskoe or Lofoden. The depth in the middle of the Moskoe-strom must be immeasurably greater; and no better proof of this fact is necessary than can be obtained from even the sidelong glance into the abyss of the whirl which may be had from the highest crag of Helseggen. Looking down from this pinnacle upon the howling Phlegethon below, I could not help smiling at the simplicity with which the honest Jonas Ramus records, as a matter difficult of belief, the anecdotes of the whales and the bears, for it appeared to me, in fact, a self evident thing, that the largest ships of the line in existence, coming within the influence of that deadly attraction, could resist it as little as a feather the hurricane, and must disappear bodily at once.

The attempts to account for the phenomenon—some of which I remember, seemed to me sufficiently plausible in perusal—now wore a very different and unsatisfactory aspect. The idea generally received is that this, as well as three smaller vortices among the Ferroe Islands, "have no other cause than the collision of waves rising and failing, at flux and reflux, against a ridge of rocks and shelves, which confines the water so that it precipitates itself like a cataract; and thus the higher the flood rises, the deeper the fall must be, and the natural result of all is a whirlpool or vortex, the prodigious suction of which is sufficiently known by lesser experiments.—" These are the words of the *Encyclopadia Britannica.* Kircher and others imagine that in the centre of the channel of the Maelstrom is an abyss penetrating the globe, and issuing in some very remote part—the Gulf of Bothnia being somewhat decidedly named in one instance. This opinion, idle in itself, was the one to which, as I gazed, my imagination most readily assented; and, mentioning it to the guide, I was rather surprised to hear him say that, although it was the view almost universally entertained of the subject by the Norwegians, it nevertheless was not his own. As to the former notion, he confessed his inability to comprehend it; and here I agreed with him—for, however conclusive on paper, it becomes altogether unintelligible, and even absurd, amid the thunder of the abyss.

"You have had a good look at the whirl now," said the old man, "and if you will creep round this crag, so as to get in its lee, and deaden the roar of the water, I will tell you a story that will convince you I ought to know something of the Moskoe-strom."

I placed myself as desired, and he proceeded.

"Myself and my two brothers once owned a schooner-rigged smack of about seventy tons burthen, with which we were in the habit of fishing among the islands beyond Moskoe, nearly to Vurrgh. In all violent eddies at sea there is good fishing at proper opportunities, if one has only the courage to attempt it; but among the whole of the Lofoden coastmen, we three were the only ones who made a regular business of going out to the islands, as I tell you. The usual grounds are a great way down to the southward. There fish can be got at all hours, without much risk, and therefore these places were preferred. The choice spots over here among the rocks, however, not only yield the finest variety, but in far greater abundance; so that we often got in a single day, what the more timid of the craft could not scrape together in a week. In fact, we made it a matter of desperate speculation—the risk of life standing instead of labour, and courage answering for capital.

"We kept the smack in a cove about five miles higher up the coast than this; and it was our practice, in fine weather, to take advantage of the fifteen minutes' slack to push across the main channel of the Moskoestrom, far above the pool, and then drop down upon anchorage somewhere near Otterholm, or Sandflesen, where the eddies are not so violent as elsewhere. Here we used to remain until nearly time for slack-water again, when we weighed and made for home. We never set out upon this expedition without a steady side wind for coming and going,—one that we felt sure would not fail us before our return—and we seldom made a miscalculation upon this point. Twice, during six years, we were forced to stay all night at anchor on account of a dead calm, which is a rare thing indeed just about here; and once we had to remain on the grounds nearly a week, starving to death, owing to a gale which blew up shortly after our arrival, and made the channel too boisterous to be thought of. Upon this occasion we should have been driven out to sea in spite of everything, (for the whirlpools threw us round and round so violently, that, at length, we fouled our anchor and dragged it,) if it had not been that we drifted into one of the innumerable cross-currents—here to-day and gone to-morrow,—which drove us under the lee of Flimen, where, by good luck, we brought up.

"I could not tell you the twentieth part of the difficulties we encountered 'on the ground'—it is a bad spot to be in even in good weather—but we made shift always to run the gauntlet of the Moskoe-strom itself without accident; although at times my heart has been in my mouth when we happened to be a minute or so behind or before the slack. The wind sometimes was not as strong as we thought it at starting, and then we made rather less way than we could wish, while the current rendered the smack unmanageable. My eldest brother had a son eighteen years old, and I had two stout boys of my own. These would have been of great assistance at such times, in using the sweeps as well as afterward in fishing—but, somehow, although we ran the risk ourselves, we had not the heart to let the young ones get into danger—for, after all said and done, it *was* a horrible danger, and that is the truth.

"It is now within a few days of three years since what I am going to tell you occurred. It was on the 10th of July, 18—, a day which the people of this part of the world will never forget—for it was one in which blew the most terrible hurricane that ever came out of the heavens. And yet all the moîning, and indeed until late in the afternoon, there was a gentle and steady breeze from the south-west, while the sun shone brightly, so that the oldest seaman among us could not have foreseen what was to follow.

"The three of us—my two brothers and myself—had crossed over to the islands about two o'clock P.M., and soon nearly loaded the smack with fine fish, which we all remarked were more plenty that day than we had ever known them. It was just seven, *by my watch,* when we weighed and started for home, so as to make the worst of the Strom at slack water, which we knew would be at eight.

"We set out with a fresh wind on our starboard quarter, and for some time spanked along at a great rate, never dreaming of danger, for indeed we saw not the slightest reason to apprehend it. All at once we were taken aback by a breeze from over Helseggen. This was most unusual—something that had never happened to us before—and I began to feel a little uneasy, without exactly knowing why. We put the boat on the wind, but could make no headway at all for the eddies, and I was upon the point of proposing to return to the anchorage, when, looking astern, we saw the whole horizon covered with a singular copper-coloured cloud that rose with the most amazing velocity.

"In the meantime the breeze that had headed us off fell away and we were dead becalmed, drifting about in every direction. This state of things, however, did not last long enough to give us time to think about it. In less than a minute the storm was upon us—in less than two the sky was entirely overcast—and what with this and the driving spray, it become suddenly so dark that we could not see each other in the smack.

"Such a hurricane as then blew it is folly to attempt describing. The oldest seaman in Norway never experienced anything like it. We had to let our sails go by the run before it cleverly took us; but, at the first puff, both our masts went by the board as if they had been sawed off—the mainmast taking with it my youngest brother who had lashed himself to it for safety.

"Our boat was the lightest feather of a thing that ever sat upon water. It had a complete flush deck, with only a small hatch near the bow, and this hatch it had always been our custom to batten down when about to cross the Strom, by way of precaution against the chopping seas. But for this circumstance we should have foundered at once—for we lay entirely buried for some moments. How my eldest brother escaped destruction I cannot say, for I never had an opportunity of ascertaining. For my part, as soon as I had let the foresail run, I threw myself flat on deck, with my feet against the narrow gunwale of the bow, and with my hands grasping a ring-bolt near the foot of the foremast. It was mere instinct that prompted me to do this—which was undoubtedly the best thing I could have done—for I was much too flurried to think.

"For some moments we were completely deluged, as I say, and all this time I held my breath, and clung to the bolt. When I could stand it no longer, I raised myself upon my knees, still keeping hold with my hands and thus got my head clear. Presently our little boat gave herself a shake just as a dog does in coming out of the water, and thus rid herself, in some measure, of the seas. I was now trying to get the better of the stupor that had come over me, and to collect my senses so as to see what was to be done, when I felt somebody grasp my arm. It was my eldest brother, and my heart leaped for joy, for I had made sure that he was overboard—but the next moment all this joy was turned to horror—for he put his mouth close to my ear, and screamed out the word *'Moskoestrom!'*

"No one will ever know what my feelings were at that moment. I shook from head to foot as if I had had the most violent fit of ague. I knew what he meant by that one word well enough—I knew what he wished to make me understand. With the wind that now drove us on, we were bound for the whirl of the Strom, and nothing could save us.

"You perceive that in crossing the Strom *channel,* we always went a long way up above the whirl, even in the calmest weather, and then had to wait and watch carefully for the slack—but now we were driving right upon the pool itself, and in such a hurricane as this! 'To be sure,' I thought, 'we shall get there just about the slack—there is some little hope in that'—but in the next moment I cursed myself for being so great a fool as to dream of hope at all. I knew very well that we were doomed, had we been ten times a ninety-gun ship.

"By this time the first fury of the tempest had spent itself, or perhaps we did not feel it so much, as we scudded before it, but at all events the seas, which at first had been kept down by the wind, and lay flat and frothing, now got up into absolute mountains. A singular change, too, had come over the heavens. Around in every direction it was still as black as pitch, but nearly overhead there burst out, all at once, a circular rift of clear sky—as clear as I ever saw—and of a deep bright blue—and through it there blazed forth the full moon with a lustre that I never before knew her to wear. She lit up everything about us with the greatest distinctness—but, oh God, what a scene it was to light up!

"I now made one or two attempts to speak to my brother—but in some manner which I could not understand, the din had so increased that I could not make him hear a single word, although I screamed at the top of my voice in his ear. Presently he shook his head, looking as pale as death, and held up one of his fingers, as if to say *'listen!'*

"At first I could not make out what he meant—but soon a hideous thought flashed upon me. I dragged my watch from its fob. It was not going. I glanced at its face in the moonlight and then burst into tears as I flung it far away into the ocean. *It had run down at seven o'clock! We were behind the time of the slack and the whirl of the Strom was in full fury!*

"When a boat is well built, properly trimmed, and not deep laden, the waves in a strong gale, when she is going large, seem always to slip from beneath her—which appears strange to a landsman, and this is what is called *'riding,'* in sea phrase.

"Well, so far we had ridden the waves very cleverly; but presently a gigantic sea happened to take us right under the counter, and bore us with it as it rose—up—up—as if into the sky. I would not have believed that any wave could rise so high. And then down we came with a sweep, a slide, and a plunge that made me feel sick and dizzy, as if I was falling from some lofty mountain-top in a dream. But while we were up I had thrown a quick glance around—and that one glance was all-sufficient. I saw our exact position in an instant. The Moskoe-strom whirlpool was about a quarter of a mile dead ahead—but no more like the every-day Moskoe-strom than the whirl, as you now see it, is like a mill race. If I had not known where we were, and what we had to expect, I should not have recognized the place at all. As it was, I involuntarily closed my eyes in horror. The lids clenched themselves together as if in a spasm.

"It could not have been more than two minutes afterwards until we suddenly felt the waves subside, and were enveloped in foam. The boat made a sharp half-turn to larboard, and then shot off in its new direction like a thunderbolt. At the same moment the roaring noise of the water was completely drowned in a kind of shrill shriek—such a sound as you might imagine given out by the water-pipes of many thousand steam vessels letting off their steam all together. We were now in the belt of surf that always surrounds the whirl; and I thought, of course, that another moment would plunge us into the abyss, down which we could only see indistinctly on account of the amazing velocity with which we were borne along. The boat did not seem to sink into the water at all, but to skim like an air-bubble upon the surface of the surge. Her starboard side was next the whirl, and on the larboard arose the world of ocean we had left. It stood like a huge writhing wall between us and the horizon.

"It may appear strange, but now, when we were in the very jaws of the gulf, I felt more composed than when we were only approaching it. Having made up my mind to hope no more, I got rid of a great deal of that terror which unmanned me at first. I suppose it was despair that strung my nerves.

"It may look like boasting—but what I tell you is the truth—I began to reflect how magnificent a thing it was to die in such a manner, and how foolish it was in me to think of so paltry a consideration as my own individual life, in view of so wonderful a manifestation of God's power. I do believe that I blushed with shame when this idea crossed my mind. After a little while I became possessed with the keenest curiosity about the whirl itself. I positively felt a *wish* to explore its depths, even at the sacrifice I was going to make; and my principal grief was that I should never be able to tell my old companions on shore about the mysteries I should see.

These, no doubt, were singular fancies to occupy a man's mind in such extremity—and I have often thought since, that the revolutions of the boat around the pool might have rendered me a little lightheaded.

"There was another circumstance which tended to restore my self possession; and this was the cessation of the wind, which could not reach us in our present position—for, as you saw for yourself, the belt of the surf is considerably lower than the general bed of the ocean, and this latter now towered above us, a high, black, mountainous ridge. If you have never been at sea in a heavy gale, you can form no idea of the confusion of mind occasioned by the wind and spray together. They blind, deafen, and strangle you, and take away all power of action or reflection. But we were now, in a great measure, rid of these annoyances—just as death-condemned felons in prison are allowed petty indulgences, forbidden them while their doom is yet uncertain.

"How often we made the circuit of the belt it is impossible to say. We careered round and round for perhaps an hour, flying rather than floating, getting gradually more and more into the middle of the surge, and then nearer and nearer to its horrible inner edge. All this time I had never let go of the ring-bolt. My brother was at the stern, holding on to a small empty water-cask which had been securely lashed under the coop of the counter, and was the only thing on deck that had not been swept overboard when the gale first took us. As we approached the brink of the pit he let go his hold upon this, and made for the ring, from which, in the agony of his terror, he endeavoured to force my hands, as it was not large enough to afford us both a secure grasp. I never felt deeper grief than when I saw him attempt this act—although I knew he was a madman when he did it—a raving maniac through sheer fright. I did not care, however, to contest the point with him. I knew it could make no difference whether either of us held on at all; so I let him have the bolt, and went astern to the cask. This there was no great difficulty in doing; for the smack flew round steadily enough, and upon an even keel—only swaying to and fro with the immense sweeps and swelters of the whirl. Scarcely had I secured myself in my new position, when we gave a wild lurch to starboard, and rushed headlong into the abyss. I muttered a hurried prayer to God and thought all was over.

"As I felt the sickening sweep of the descent, I had instinctively tightened my hold upon the barrel, and closed my eyes. For some seconds I dared not open them—while I expected instant destruction, and wondered that I was not already in my death-struggles with the water. But moment after moment elapsed. I still lived. The sense of falling had ceased; and the motion of the vessel seemed much as it had been before, while in the belt of foam, with the exception that she now lay more along. I took courage and looked once again upon the scene.

"Never shall I forget the sensation of awe, horror, and admiration with which

I gazed about me. The boat appeared to be hanging, as if by magic, midway down, upon the interior surface of a funnel vast in circumference, prodigious in depth, and whose perfectly smooth sides might have been mistaken for ebony, but for the bewildering rapidity with which they spun round, and for the gleaming and ghastly radiance they shot forth, as the rays of the full moon, from that circular rift amid the clouds which I have already described, streamed in a flood of golden glory along the black walls, and far away down into the inmost recesses of the abyss.

"At first I was too much confused to observe anything accurately. The general burst of terrific grandeur was all that I beheld. When I recovered myself a little, however, my gaze fell instinctively downward. In this direction I was able to obtain an unobstructed view, from the manner in which the smack hung on the inclined surface of the pool. She was quite upon an even keel—that is to say, her deck lay in a plane parallel with that of the water—but this latter sloped at an angle of more than forty-five degrees, so that we seemed to be lying upon our beam-ends. I could not help observing, nevertheless, that I had scarcely more difficulty in maintaining my hold and footing in this situation, than if we had been upon a dead level; and this I suppose was owing to the speed at which we revolved.

"The rays of the moon seemed to search to the very bottom of the profound gulf; but still I could make out nothing distinctly on account of a thick mist in which everything there was enveloped, and over which there hung a magnificent rainbow, like that narrow and tottering bridge which Mussulmans say is the only pathway between Time and Eternity. This mist, or spray, was no doubt occasioned by the clashing of the great walls of the funnel, as they all met together at the bottom—but the yell that went up to the Heavens from out of that mist I dare not attempt to describe.

"Our first slide into the abyss itself, from the belt of foam above, had carried us a great distance down the slope; but our further descent was by no means proportionate. Round and round we swept—not with any uniform movement—but in dizzying swings and jerks, that sent us sometimes only a few hundred yards—sometimes nearly the complete circuit of the whirl. Our progress downward, at each revolution, was slow, but very perceptible!

"Looking about me upon the wide waste of liquid ebony on which we were thus borne, I perceived that our boat was not the only object in the embrace of the whirl. Both above and below us were visible fragments of vessels, large masses of building-timber and trunks of trees, with many smaller articles, such as pieces of house furniture, broken boxes, barrels and staves. I have already described the unnatural curiosity which had taken the place of my original terrors. It appeared to grow upon me as I drew nearer and nearer to my dreadful doom. I now began to watch, with a strange interest, the numerous things that floated in our company.

I *must* have been delirious, for I even sought *amusement* in speculating upon the relative velocities of their several descents toward the foam below. 'This fir-tree,' I found myself at one time saying, 'will certainly be the next thing that takes the awful plunge and disappears,'—and then I was disappointed to find that the wreck of a Dutch merchant ship overtook it and went down before. At length, after making several guesses of this nature, and being deceived in all—this fact—the fact of my invariable miscalculation, set me upon a train of reflection that made my limbs again tremble, and my heart beat heavily once more.

"It was not a new terror that thus affected me, but the dawn of a more exciting *hope.* This hope arose partly from memory, and partly from present observation. I called to mind the great variety of buoyant matter that strewed the coast of Lofoden, having been absorbed and then thrown forth by the Moskoe-strom. By far the greater number of the articles were shattered in the most extraordinary way—so chafed and roughened as to have the appearance of being stuck full of splinters —but then I distinctly recollected that there were *some* of them which were not disfigured at all. Now I could not account for this difference except by supposing that the roughened fragments were the only ones which had been *completely absorbed—that* the others had entered into the whirl at so late a period of the tide, or, from some reason, had descended so slowly after entering, that they did not reach the bottom before the turn of the flood came, or of the ebb, as the case might be. I conceived it possible, in either instance, that they might thus be whirled up again to the level of the ocean, without undergoing the fate of those which had been drawn in more early or absorbed more rapidly. I made, also, three important observations. The first was, that as a general rule, the larger the bodies were, the more rapid their descent—the second, that, between two masses of equal extent, the one spherical, and the other *of any other shape* the superiority in speed of descent was with the sphere—the third, that, between two masses of equal size, the one cylindrical, and the other of any other shape, the cylinder was absorbed more slowly. Since my escape, I have had several conversations on this subject with an old schoolmaster in the district; and it was from him that I learned the use of the words 'cylinder' and 'sphere.' He explained to me—although I have forgotten the explanation—how what I observed was, in fact, the natural consequence of the forms of the floating fragments—and showed me how it happened that a cylinder, swimming in a vortex, offered more resistance to its suction, and was drawn in with greater difficulty than an equally bulky body, of any form whatever.

"There was one startling circumstance which went a great way in enforcing these observations, and rendering me anxious to turn them to account, and this was that, at every revolution we passed something like a barrel, or else the yard or the mast of a vessel, while many of these things, which had been on

a coming gale—seas washing over the whole forward part of the vessel, and her bows beating against them with a force and sound like the driving of piles. The watch, too, seemed very busy trampling about decks, and singing out at the ropes. A sailor can tell, by the sound, what sail is coming in; and, in a short time, we heard the top-gallant sails come in, one after another, and then the flying jib. This seemed to ease her a good deal, and we were fast going off to the land of Nod, when — bang, bang, bang—on the scuttle, and "All hands, reef topsails, ahoy!" started us out of our berths; and, it not being very cold weather, we had nothing extra to put on, and were soon on deck. I shall never forget the fineness of the sight. It was a clear, and rather a chilly night; the stars were twinkling with an intense brightness, and as far as the eye could reach there was not a cloud to be seen. The horizon met the sea in a defined line. A painter could not have painted so clear a sky. There was not a speck upon it. Yet it was blowing great guns from the northwest. When you can see a cloud to windward, you feel that there is a place for the wind to come from; but here it seemed to come from nowhere. No person could have told from the heavens, by their eyesight alone, that it was not a still summer's night. One reef after another we took in the topsails, and before we could get them hoisted up we heard a sound like a short, quick rattling of thunder, and the jib was blown to atoms out of the bolt-rope. We got the topsails set, and the fragments of the jib stowed away, and the fore topmast staysail set in its place, when the great mainsail gaped open, and the sail ripped from head to foot. "Lay up on that main yard and furl the sail, before it blows to tatters!" shouted the captain; and in a moment we were up, gathering the remains of it upon the yard. We got it wrapped round the yard, and passed gaskets over it as snugly as possible, and were just on deck again, when with another loud rent, which was heard throughout the ship, the fore topsail, which had been double-reefed, split in two athwartships, just below the reef-band, from earing to earing. Here again it was—down yard, haul out reef-tackles, and lay out upon the yard for reefing. By hauling the reef-tackles chock-a-block we took the strain from the other earings, and passing the close-reef earing, and knotting the points carefully, we succeeded in setting the sail, close reefed.

We had but just got the rigging coiled up, and were waiting to hear "Go below the watch!" when the main royal worked loose from the gaskets, and blew directly out to leeward, flapping, and shaking the mast like a wand. Here was a job for somebody. The royal must come in or be cut adrift, or the mast would be snapped short off. All the light hands in the starboard watch were sent up one after another, but they could do nothing with it. At length, John, the tall Frenchman, the head of the starboard watch (and a better sailor never stepped upon a deck), sprang aloft, and, by the help of his long arms and legs, succeeded, after a hard struggle—the sail blowing over the yard-arm to leeward, and the skysail adrift directly over his head—in smothering it and frapping it with long pieces of sinnet. He came very near being blown or shaken from the yard several times, but he was a true sailor, every finger a fish-hook. Having made the sail snug, he prepared to send the yard down, which was a long and difficult job, for, frequently, he was obliged to stop, and hold on with all his might for several minutes, the ship pitching so as to make it impossible to do anything else at that height. The yard at length came down safe, and, after it, the fore and mizzen royal yards were sent down. All hands were then sent aloft, and for an hour or two we were hard at work, making the booms well fast, unreeving the studding-sail and royal and skysail gear, getting rolling-ropes on the yard, setting up the weather breast-backstays, and making other preparations for a storm. It was a fine night for a gale; just cool and bracing enough for quick work, without being cold, and as bright as day. It was sport to have a gale in such weather as this. Yet it blew like a hurricane. The wind seemed to come with a spite, an edge to it, which threatened to scrape us off the yards. The force of the wind was greater than I had ever felt it before; but darkness, cold, and wet are the worst parts of a storm, to a sailor.

Having got on deck again, we looked round to see what time of night it was, and whose watch. In a few minutes the man at the wheel struck four bells, and we found that the other watch was out, and our own half out. Accordingly, the starboard watch went below, and left the ship to us for a couple of hours, yet with orders to stand by for a call.

Hardly had they got below, before away went the fore topmast staysail, blown to ribands. This was a small sail, which we could manage in the watch, so that we were not obliged to call up the other watch. We laid out upon the bowsprit, where we were under water half the time, and took in the fragments of the sail, and, as she must have some head sail on her, prepared to bend another staysail. We got the new one out into the nettings; seized on the tack, sheets, and halyards, and the hanks; manned the halyards, cut adrift the frapping-lines, and hoisted away; but before it was half-way up the stay it was blown all to pieces. When we belayed the halyards, there was nothing left but the bolt-rope. Now large eyes began to show themselves in the foresail, and, knowing that it must soon go, the mate ordered us upon the yard to furl it. Being unwilling to call up the watch who had been on deck all night, he roused out the carpenter, sailmaker, cook, and steward, and with their help we manned the fore yard, and, after nearly half an hour's struggle, mastered the sail, and got it well furled round the yard. The force of the wind had never been greater than at this moment. In going up the rigging, it seemed absolutely to pin us down to the shrouds; and, on the yard, there was no such thing as a face to windward. Yet here was no driving sleet, and darkness, and wet, and cold, as off Cape Horn; and instead of stiff oil-cloth suits, southwester caps, and thick boots, we had on hats, round jackets, duck trousers, light shoes, and everything light and easy. These things make a great difference to a sailor. When we got on deck, the man at the wheel struck eight bells (four o'clock in the morning), and "All Star-bowlines, ahoy!" brought the other watch up, but there was no going below for us. The gale was now at its height, "blowing like scissors and thumb-screws"; the captain was on deck; the ship, which was light, rolling and pitching as though she would shake the long sticks out of her, and the sails were gaping open and splitting in every direction. The mizzen topsail, which was a comparatively new sail, and close reefed, split from head to foot, in the bunt; the fore topsail went, in one rent, from clew to earing, and was blowing to tatters; one of the chain bowstays parted; the spritsail yard sprung in the slings; the martingale had slued away off to leeward; and owing to the long dry weather, the lee rigging hung in large bights at every lurch. One of the main topgallant shrouds had parted; and, to crown all, the galley had got adrift, and gone over to leeward, and the anchor on the lee bow had worked loose, and was thumping the side. Here was work enough for all hands for half a day. Our gang laid out on the mizzen topsail yard, and after more than half an hour's hard work, furled the sail, though it bellied out over our heads, and again, by a slat of the wind, blew in under the yard with a fearful jerk, and almost threw us off from the foot-ropes.

Double gaskets were passed round the yards, rolling tackles and other gear bowsed taut, and everything made as secure as it could be. Coming down, we found the rest of the crew Just laying down the fore rigging, having furled the tattered topsail, or, rather, swathed it round the yard, which looked like a broken limb, bandaged. There was no sail now on the ship, but the spanker and the close-reefed main topsail, which still held good. But this was too much after sail, and order was given to furl the spanker. The braiIs were hauled up, and all the light hands in the starboard watch sent out on the gaff to pass the gaskets; but they could do nothing with it. The second mate swore at them for a parcel of "sogers," and sent up a couple of the best men; but they could do no better, and the gaff was lowered down. All hands were now employed in setting up the lee rigging, fishing the spritsail yard, lashing the galley, and getting tackles upon the martingale, to bowse it to windward. Being in the larboard watch, my duty was forward, to assist in setting up the martingale. Three of us were out on the martingale guys and back-ropes for more than an half an hour, carrying out, hooking and unhooking the tackles, several times buried in the seas, until the mate ordered us in, from fear of our being washed off. The anchors were then to be taken up on the rail, which kept all hands on the forecastle for an hour, though every now and then the seas broke over it, washing the rigging off to leeward, filling the lee scuppers breast-high, and washing chock aft to the taffrail.

Having got everything secure again, we were promising ourselves some breakfast, for it was now nearly nine o'clock in the forenoon, when the main topsail showed evident signs of giving way. Some sail must be kept on the ship, and the captain ordered the fore and main spencer gaffs to be lowered down, and the two spencers (which were storm sails, bran-new, small, and made of the strongest canvas) to be got up and bent; leaving the topsail to blow away, with a blessing on it, if it would only last until we could get the spencers. These we bent on very carefully, with strong robands and seizings, and, making tackles fast to the clews, bowsed them down to the water-ways. By this time the main topsail was among the things that have been, and we went aloft to stow away the: remnant of the last sail of all those which were on the ship twenty-four hours before. The spencers were now the only whole sails on the ship, and, being strong and small, and near the deck, presenting but little surface to the wind above the rail, promised to hold out well. Hove-to under these, and eased by having no sail above the tops, the ship rose and fell, and drifted off to leeward like a line-of-battle ship.

It was now eleven o'clock, and the watch was sent below to get breakfast, and at eight bells (noon), as everything was snug, although the gale had not in the least abated, the watch was set, and the other watch and idlers sent below. For three days and three nights the gale continued with unabated fury, and with singular regularity. There were no lulls, and very little variation in its fierceness. Our ship, being light, rolled so as almost to send the fore-yard-arm under water, and drifted off bodily to leeward. All this time there was not a cloud to be seen in the sky, day or night; no, not so large as a man's hand. Every morning the sun rose cloudless from the sea, and set again at night in the sea, in a flood of light. The stars, too, came out of the blue one after another, night after night, unobscured, and twinkled as clear as on a still, frosty night at home, until the day came upon them. All this time the sea was rolling in immense surges, white with foam, as far as the eye could reach, on every side, for we were now leagues and leagues from shore.

The between-decks being empty, several of us slept there in hammocks, which are the best things in the world to sleep in during a storm; it not being true of them, as it is of another kind of bed, "when the wind blows the cradle will rock;" for it is the ship that rocks, while they hang vertically from the beams. During these seventy-two hours we had nothing to do but to turn in and out, four hours on deck, and four below, eat, sleep, and keep watch. The watches were only varied by taking the helm in turn, and now and then by one of the sails, which were furled, blowing out of the gaskets, and getting adrift, which sent us up on the yards, and by getting tackles on different parts of the rigging, which were slack. Once the wheel-rope parted, which might have been fatal to us, had not the chief mate sprung instantly with a relieving tackle to windward, and kept the tiller up, till a new rope could be rove. On the morning of the twentieth, at daybreak, the gale had evidently done its worst, and had somewhat abated; so much so that all hands were called to bend new sails, although it was still blowing as hard as two common gales. One at a time, and with great difficulty and labour, the old sails were unbent and sent down by the buntlines, and three new topsails, made for the homeward passage round Cape Horn, which had never been bent, were got up from the sail-room, and, under the care of the sailmaker, were fitted for bending, and sent up by the halyards into the tops, and, with stops and frapping-lines, were bent to the yards, close-reefed, sheeted home, and hoisted. These were bent one at a time, and with the greatest care and difficulty. Two spare courses were then got up and bent in the same manner and furled, and a storm-jib, with the bonnet off, bent and furled to the boom. It was twelve o'clock before we got through, and five hours of more exhausting labour I never experienced; and no one of that ship's crew, I will venture to say, will ever desire again to unbend and bend five large sails in the teeth of a tremendous northwester. Towards night a few clouds appeared in the horizon, and, as the gale moderated, the usual appearance of driving clouds relieved the face of the sky. The fifth day after the commencement of the storm, we shook a reef out of each topsail, and set the reefed foresail jib, and spanker, but it was not until after eight days of reefed topsails that we had a whole sail on the ship, and then it was quite soon enough, for the captain was anxious to make up for leeway, the gale having blown us half the distance to the Sandwich Islands.

Inch by inch, as fast as the gale would permit, we made sail on the ship, for the wind still continued ahead, and we had many days' sailing to get back to the longitude we were in when the storm took us. For eight days more we beat to windward under a stiff top-gallant breeze, when the wind shifted and became variable. A light southeaster, to which we could carry a reefed topmast studding sail, did wonders for our dead reckoning.

Friday, December 4th. After a passage of twenty days, we arrived at the mouth of the Bay of San Francisco.

MOBY DICK[1]

Herman Melville
(1819-1891)

I

Sing Out for the Whale

ONE morning shortly after breakfast, Ahab, as was his wont, ascended the cabin gangway to the deck. There most sea-captains usually walk at that hour, as country gentlemen, after the same meal, take a few turns in the garden.

Soon his steady, ivory stride was heard, as to and fro he paced his old rounds, upon planks so familiar to his tread, that they were all over dented, like geological stones, with the peculiar mark of his walk. Did you fixedly gaze, too, upon that ribbed and dented brow; there also, you would see still stranger footprints—the footprints of his one unsleeping, ever pacing thought.

But on the occasion in question, these dents looked deeper, even as his nervous step that morning left a deeper mark. And, so full of his thought was Ahab, that at every uniform turn that he made, now at the mainmast and now at the binnacle, you could almost see that thought turn in him as he turned, and pace in him as he paced; so completely possessing him, indeed, that it all but seemed the inward mould of every outer movement.

"D'ye mark him, Flask?" whispered Stubb; "the chick that's in him pecks the shell. 'Twill soon be out."

The hours wore on;—Ahab now shut up within his cabin; anon, pacing the deck, with the same intense bigotry of purpose in his aspect.

It drew near the close of day. Suddenly he came to a halt by the bulwarks, and inserting his bone leg into the auger-hole there, and with one hand grasping a shroud, he ordered Starbuck to send everybody aft.

"Sir!" said the mate, astonished at an order seldom or never given on shipboard except in some extraordinary case.

"Send everybody aft," repeated Ahab. "Mastheads, there! come down!"

When the entire ship's company were assembled, and with curious and not wholly unapprehensive faces, were eyeing him, for he looked not unlike the weather horizon when a storm is coming up, Ahab, after rapidly glancing over the bulwarks, and then darting his eyes among the crew, started from his standpoint; and as though not a soul were nigh him resumed his heavy turns upon the deck. With bent head and half-slouched hat he continued to pace, unmindful of the

[1] From *Moby Dick, or the White Whale.*

wondering whispering among the men; till Stubb cautiously whispered to Flask, that Ahab must have summoned them there for the purpose of witnessing a pedestrian feat. But this did not last long. Vehemently pausing he cried:-

"What do ye do when ye see a whale, men?"

"Sing out for him!" was the impulsive rejoinder from a score of clubbed voices.

"Good!" cried Ahab, with a wild approval in his tones; observing the hearty animation into which his unexpected question had so magnetically thrown them.

"And what do ye next, men?"

"Lower away, and after him!"

"And what tune is it ye pull to, men?"

"A dead whale or a stove boat!"

More and more strangely and fiercely glad and approving grew the countenance of the old man at every shout; while the mariners began to gaze curiously at each other, as if marvelling how it was that they themselves became so excited at such seemingly purposeless questions.

But, they were all eagerness again, as Ahab, now half revolving in his pivot-hole, with one hand reaching high up a shroud, and tightly, almost convulsively grasping it, addressed them thus—

"All ye mastheaders have before now heard me give orders about a white whale. Look ye! d'ye see this Spanish ounce of gold?"—holding up a broad bright coin to the sun—" it is a sixteen dollar piece, men. D'ye see it? Mr Starbuck, hand me yon top-maul."

While the mate was getting the hammer, Ahab, without speaking, was slowly rubbing the gold piece against the skirts of his jacket, as if to heighten its lustre, and without using any words was meanwhile lowly humming to himself, producing a sound so strangely muffled and inarticulate that it seemed the mechanical humming of the wheels of his vitality in him.

Receiving the top-maul from Starbuck, he advanced towards the mainmast with the hammer uplifted in one hand, exhibiting the gold with the other, and with a high raised voice exclaiming: "Whosoever of ye raises me a white-headed whale with a wrinkled brow and a crooked jaw; whosoever of ye raises me that white-headed whale, with three holes punctured in his starboard fluke—look ye, whosoever of ye raises me that same white whale, he shall have this gold ounce, my boys!"

"Huzza!huzza !" cried the seamen, as with swinging tarpaulins they hailed the act of nailing the gold to the mast.

"It's a white whale, I say," resumed Ahab, as he threw down the top-maul; "a white whale. Skin your eyes for him men; look sharp for white water; if ye see but a bubble, sing out."

All this while Tashtego, Daggoo, and Queequeg had looked on with even more intense interest and surprise than the rest, and at the mention of the wrinkled brow and crooked jaw, they had started as if each was separately touched by some specific recollection.

"Captain Ahab," said Tashtego, "that white whale must be the same that some call Moby Dick."

"Moby Dick?" shouted Ahab. "Do ye know the white whale then, Tash?"

"Does he fan-tail a little curious, sir, before he goes down ?" said the Gay-Header deliberately.

"And he has a curious spout too," said Daggoo, "very bushy, even for a parmacetty, and mighty quick, Captain Ahab?"

"And he have one, two, tree oh!good many iron in him hide, too, Captain," cried Queequeg disjointedly. "All twisketee be-twisk, like him—him" faltering hard for a word, and screwing his hand round and round as though uncorking a bottle—"like him—him."

"Corkscrew!" cried Ahab; "ay, Queequeg, the harpoons lie all twisted and wrenched in him; ay, Daggoo, his spout is a big one, like a whole shock of wheat, and white as a pile of our Nantucket wool after the great annual sheep-shearing; aye, Tashtego, and he fan-tails like a split jib in a squall. Death and devils! Men, it is Moby Dick ye have seen—Moby Dick—Moby Dick!"

"Captain Ahab," said Starbuck, who with Stubb and Flask, had thus far been eyeing his superior with increasing surprise, but at last seemed struck with a thought which somewhat explained all the wonder. "Captain Ahab, I have heard of Moby Dick—but it was not Moby Dick that took off thy leg?"

"Who told thee that?" cried Ahab; then pausing. "Aye, Starbuck; aye, my hearties all round; it was Moby Dick that dismasted me; Moby Dick that brought me to this dead stump I stand on now. Aye, Aye," he shouted with a terrific, loud, animal sob, like that of a heart-stricken moose; "aye, aye! it was that accursed white whale that razed me; made a poor pegging lubber of me for ever and a day!. Then tossing both arms, with measureless imprecations, he shouted out: "Aye, Aye! and I'll chase him round Good Hope, and round the Horn, and round the Norway Maelstrom, and round perdition's flames before I give him up. And this is what ye have shipped for, men! to chase that white whale on both sides of land, and over all sides of earth, till he spouts black blood and rolls fin out. What say ye, men, will ye splice hands on it, now? I think ye do look brave."

"Aye, aye!" shouted the harpooners and seamen, running closer to the excited old man: "a sharp eye for the White Whale: a sharp lance for Moby Dick!"

"God bless ye," he seemed to half sob and half shout, "God bless ye, men. Steward!go draw the great measure of grog. Death to Moby Dick! God hunt us all, if we do not hunt Moby Dick to his death!"

II
The White Whale

I, Ishmael, was one of that crew; my shouts had gone up with the rest; my oath had been welded with theirs; and stronger I shouted, and more did I hammer and clinch my oath, because of the dread in my soul. A wild, mystical sympathetical feeling was in me; Ahab's quenchless feud seemed mine. With greedy ear I learned the history of that murderous monster against whom I and all the others had taken our oaths of violence and revenge.

For some time past, though at intervals only, the unaccompanied, secluded White Whale had haunted those uncivilized seas mostly frequented by the Sperm Whale fishermen. But not all of them knew of his existence; only a few of them, comparatively, had knowingly seen him; while the number who as yet had actually and knowingly given battle to him, was small indeed. For, owing to the large number of whale cruisers; the disorderly way they were sprinkled over the entire watery circumference, many of them adventurously pushing their quest along solitary latitudes, so as seldom or never for a whole twelvemonth or more on a stretch, to encounter a single news-telling sail of any sort; the inordinate length of each separate voyage; the irregularity of the times of sailing from home; all these, with other circumstances, direct and indirect, long obstructed the spread through the whole world-wide whaling-fleet of the special individualizing tidings concerning Moby Dick. It was hardly to be doubted, that several vessels reported to have encountered, at such or such a time, or on such or such a meridian, a sperm whale of uncommon magnitude and malignity, which whale, after doing great mischief to his assailants, had completely escaped them; to some minds it was not an unfair presumption, I say, that the whale in question must have been no other than Moby Dick. Yet as of late the sperm whale fishery had been marked by various and not unfrequent instances of great ferocity, cunning, and malice in the monster attacked; therefore it was, that those who by accident ignorantly gave battle to Moby Dick; such hunters, perhaps, for the most part, were content to ascribe the peculiar terror he bred, more, as it were, to the perils of the Sperm Whale fishery at large, than to the individual cause. In that way, mostly, the disastrous encounter between Ahab and the whale had hitherto been popularly regarded.

As for those who, previously hearing of the White Whale, by chance caught sight of him; in the beginning of the thing they had every one of them, almost, as boldly and fearlessly lowered for him, as for any other whale of that species. But at length, such calamities did ensue in these assaults—not restricted to sprained wrists and ankles, broken limbs, or devouring amputations—but fatal to the last degree of fatality; those repeated disastrous repulses, all accumulating and piling their terrors upon Moby Dick; those things had gone far to shake the fortitude of many brave hunters, to whom the story of the White Whale had eventually come.

Nor did wild rumours of all sorts fail to exaggerate, and still the more horrify the true histories of these deadly encounters. For not only do fabulous rumours naturally grow out of the very body of all surprising terrible events—as the smitten tree gives birth to its fungi; but, in maritime life, far more than in that of *terra firma*, wild rumours abound, wherever there is any adequate reality for them to cling to. And as the sea surpasses the land in this matter, so the whale fishery surpasses every other sort of maritime life, in the wonderfulness and. fearfulness of the rumours which sometimes circulate there.

No wonder, then, that ever gathering volume from the mere transit over the widest watery spaces, the outblown rumours of the White Whale did in the end incorporate with themselves all manner of morbid hints, the half-formed fœtal suggestions of supernatural agencies, which eventually invested Moby Dick with new terrors unborrowed from anything that visibly appears. So that in many cases such a panic did he finally strike, that few who by those rumours, at least, had heard of the White Whale, few of those hunters were willing to encounter the perils of his jaw.

One of the wild suggestions referred to, as at last coming to be linked with the White Whale in the minds of the superstitiously inclined, was the unearthly conceit that Moby Dick was ubiquitous; that he had actually been encountered in opposite latitudes at one and the same instant of time.

Nor, credulous as such minds must have been, was this conceit altogether without some faint show of superstitious probability. For as the secrets of the currents in the seas have never yet been divulged even to the most erudite research, so the hidden ways of the Sperm Whale when beneath the surface remain, in great part, unaccountable to his pursuers; and from time to time have originated the most curious and contradictory speculations regarding them, especially concerning the mystic modes whereby, after sounding to a great depth, he transports himself with such vast swiftness to the most widely distant points.

It is a thing well known to both American and English whaleships, and as well a thing placed upon authoritative record years ago by Scoresby, that some whales have been captured far north in the Pacific, in whose bodies have been found the barbs of harpoons darted in the Greenland seas. Nor is it to be gainsaid, that in some of these instances it has been declared that the interval of time between the two assaults could not have exceeded very many days. Hence, by inference, it has been believed by some whalemen, that the Nor'-West Passage, so long a problem to man, was never a problem to the whale. So that here, in the real living experience of living men, the prodigies related in old times of the inland Strello mountain in Portugal (near whose top there was said to be a lake in which the wrecks of ships floated up to the surface); and that still more wonderful story of the Arethusa fountain near Syracuse (whose waters were believed to have come from the Holy Land by an underground passage); these fabulous narrations are almost fully equalled by the realities of the whaleman.

Forced into familiarity, then, with such prodigies as these, and knowing that after repeated, intrepid assaults, the White Whale had escaped alive, it cannot be much matter of surprise that some whalemen should go still further in their superstitions; declaring Moby Dick not only ubiquitous, but immortal. (For immortality is but ubiquity in time); and though groves of spears should be planted in his flanks, he would still swim away unharmed; or if indeed he should ever be made to spout thick blood, such a sight would be but a ghastly deception; for again in unensanguined billows hundred of leagues away, his unsullied jet would once more be seen.

But even stripped of these supernatural surmisings, there was enough in the earthly make and incontestable character of the monster to strike the imagination with unwonted power. For, it was not so much his uncommon bulk that so much distinguished him from other sperm whales, but, as was elsewhere thrown out— a peculiar snow-white wrinkled forehead, and a high, pyramidal white hump. These were his prominent features; the tokens whereby, even in the limitless, uncharted seas, he revealed his identity, at a long distance, to those who knew him.

The rest of his body was so streaked, and spotted, and marbled with the same shrouded hue, that, in the end, he had gained his distinctive appellation of the White Whale; a name indeed, literally justified by his vivid aspect, when seen gliding *at* high noon through a dark blue sea, leaving a milky-way wake of creamy foam, all spangled with golden gleamings. Nor was it his unwonted magnitude, nor his remarkable hue, nor yet his deformed lower jaw, that so much invested the whale with natural terror, as that unexampled, intelligent malignity which, according to specific accounts, he had over and over again evinced in his assaults. More than all, his treacherous retreats struck more of dismay than perhaps else. For, when swimming before his exulting pursuers, with every apparent symptom of alarm, he had several times been known to turn round suddenly, and, bearing down upon them, either stave their boats to splinters, or drive them back in consternation to their ship.

Already several fatalities had attended his chase. But though similar disasters, however little bruited ashore, were by no means unusual in the fishery; yet, in most instances, such seemed the White Whale's infernal forethought of ferocity, that every dismembering or death that he caused, was not wholly regarded as having been inflicted by an unintelligent agent.

Judge, then, to what pitches of inflamed, distracted fury the minds of his more desperate hunters were impelled, when amid the chips of chewed boats, and the sinking limbs of torn comrades, they swam out of the white curds of the whale's direful wrath into the serene, exasperating sunlight, that smiled on, as if at a birth or a bridal.

His three boats stove around him, and oars and men both, whirling in the eddies; one captain, seizing the line-knife from his broken prow, had dashed at the whale, as an Arkansas duellist at his foe, blindly seeking with a six-inch blade, to reach the fathom-deep life of the whale. That captain was Ahab. And then it was, that suddenly sweeping his sickle-shaped lower jaw beneath him, Moby Dick had reaped away Ahab's leg, as a mower a blade of grass in the field. No turbaned Turk, no hired Venetian or Malay, could have smote him with more seeming malice. Small reason was there to doubt, then, that ever since that almost fatal encounter, Ahab had cherished a wild vindictiveness against the whale, all the more fell, for that in his frantic morbidness he at last came to identify with him, not only all his bodily woes, but all his intellectual and spiritual exasperations. The White Whale swam before him as the monomaniac incarnation of all those malicious agencies which some deep men feel eating in them, till they are left living on with half a heart and half a lung. That intangible malignity which has been found from the beginning; which the ancient Ophites of the east reverenced in their statue devil;—Ahab did not fall down and worship it like them; but deliriously transferring its idea to the abhorred white whale, he pitted himself, all mutilated, against it. All that most maddens and torments; all that stirs up the lees of things; all truth with malice in it; all that cracks the sinews and cakes the brain; the subtle demonisms of life and thought; all evil, to crazy Ahab, were visibly personified, and made practically assailable in Moby Dick. He piled upon the whale's white hump the sum of all the general rage and hate felt by his whole race from Adam down.

III

Moby Dick's Last Fight

That night, in the mid-watch, when the old man—as his wont at intervals—stepped forth from the scuttle in which he leaned, and went to his pivot-hole, he suddenly thrust out his face fiercely, snuffing up the sea air as a sagacious ship's dog will, in drawing nigh to some barbarous isle. He declared that a whale must be near. Soon that peculiar odour, sometimes to a great distance given forth by the living Sperm Whale, was palpable to all the watch; nor was any mariner surprised when, after inspecting the compass, and then the dog-vane, and then ascertaining the precise bearing of the odour as nearly as possible, Ahab rapidly ordered the ship's course to be slightly altered, and the sail to be shortened.

The acute policy dictating these movements was sufficiently vindicated at daybreak by the sight of a long sleek on the sea directly and lengthwise ahead, smooth as oil, and resembling in the pleated watery wrinkles bordering it, the polished metallic-like marks of some swift tide-rip, at the mouth of a deep, rapid stream.

"Man the mastheads!Call all hands!"

Thundering with the butts of three clubbed handspikes on the forecastle deck, Daggoo roused the sleepers with such judgement claps that they seemed to exhale from the scuttle, so instantaneously did they appear with their clothes in their hands.

"What d'ye see?" cried Ahab, flattening his face to the sky.

"Nothing, nothing, sir!" was the sound hailing down in reply.

"T'gallant-sails! stunsails alow and aloft, and on both sides!"

All sail being set, he now cast loose the life-line, reserved for swaying him to the mainroyal masthead; and in a few moments they were hoisting him thither, when, while but two-thirds of the way aloft, and while peering ahead through the horizontal vacancy between the maintopsail and top-gallant-sail, he raised a gull-like cry in the air, "There she blows! —there she blows! A hump like a snow-hill! It is Moby Dick!"

Fired by the cry which seemed simultaneously taken up by the three look-outs, the men on deck rushed to the rigging to behold the famous whale they had so long been pursuing. Ahab had now gained his final perch, some feet above the other look-outs, Tashtego standing just beneath him on the cap of the top-gallant-mast, so that the Indian's head was almost on a level with Ahab's heel. From this height the whale was now seen some mile or so ahead, at every roll of the sea revealing his high sparkling hump, and regularly jetting his silent spout into the air. To the credulous mariners it seemed the same silent spout they had so long ago beheld in the moonlit Atlantic and Indian Oceans.

"And did none of ye see it before?" cried Ahab, hailing the perched men all around him.

"I saw him almost the same instant, sir, that Captain Ahab did, and I cried out," said Tashtego.

"Not the same instant; not the same—no, the doubloon is mine, Fate reserved the doubloon for me. I only; none of ye could have raised the White Whale first. There she blows! there she blows! There she blows! There again!—there again!" he cried, in long-drawn, lingering, methodic tones, attuned to the gradual prolongings of the whale's visible jets. "He's going to sound! In stunsails! Down top-gallant-sails! Stand by three boats. Mr Starbuck, remember, stay on board, and keep the ship. Helm there! Luff, luff a point! So; steady, man, steady! There go flukes. No, no; only black water! All ready the boats there? Stand by, stand by!

Lower me, Mr Starbuck; lower, lower—quick, quicker!" and he slid through the air to the deck.

"He is heading straight to leeward, sir," cried Stubb; "right away from us; cannot have seen the ship yet."

"Be dumb, man! Stand by the braces! Hard down the helm !—brace up! Shiver her!—shiver her! So; well that! Boats, boats!"

Soon all the boats but Starbuck's were dropped; the boat-sails set; all the paddles plying; with rippling swiftness, shooting to leeward; and Ahab heading the onset. A pale, death-glimmer lit up Fedallah's sunken eyes; a hideous motion gnawed his mouth.

Like noiseless nautilus shells, their light prows sped through the sea; but only slowly they neared the foe. As they neared him, the ocean grew still more smooth; seemed drawing a carpet over its waves; seemed a noon-meadow, so serenely it spread. At length the breathless hunter came so nigh his seemingly unsuspecting prey, that his entire dazzling hump was distinctly visible, sliding along the sea as if an isolated thing, and continually set in a revolving ring of finest, fleecy, greenish foam. He saw the vast involved wrinkles of the slightly projecting head beyond. Before it, far out on the soft Turkish-rugged waters, went the glistening white shadows from his broad, milky forehead, a musical rippling play fully accompanying the shade; and behind, the blue waters interchangeably flowed over into the moving valley of his steady wake; and on either hand bright bubbles arose and danced by his side. But these were broken again by the light toes of hundreds of gay fowl softly feathering the sea, alternate with their fitful flight; and like to some flagstaff rising from the painted hull of an argosy, the tall but shattered pole of a recent lance projected from the white whale's back; and at intervals one of the cloud of soft-toed fowls hovering, and to and fro skimming like a canopy over the fish, silently perched and rocked on this pole, the long tail feathers streaming like pennons.

A gentle joyousness—a mighty mildness of repose in swiftness, invested the gliding whale. Not the white bull Jupiter swimming away with ravished Europa clinging to his graceful horns; his lovely, leering eyes sideways intent upon the maid; with smooth bewitching fleetness, rippling straight for the nuptial bower in Crete; not Jove did surpass the glorified White Whale as he so divinely swam.

On each soft side—coincident with the parted swell, that but once leaving him, then flowed so wide away—on each bright side, the whale shed off enticings. No wonder there had been some among the hunters who namelessly transported and allured by all this serenity had ventured to assail it; but had fatally found that quietude but the vesture of tornadoes. Yet, calm, enticing calm, oh, whale!thou glidest on, to all who for the first time eye thee, no matter how many in that same way thou may'st have bejuggled and destroyed before.

And thus, through the serene tranquillities of the tropical sea, among waves whose hand-clappings were suspended by exceeding rapture, Moby Dick moved on, still withholding from sight the full terrors of his submerged trunk, entirely hiding the wretched hideousness of his jaw. But soon the fore part of him slowly rose from the water; for an instant his whole marbleised body formed a high arch, like Virginia's Natural Bridge, and warningly waving his bannered flukes in the air. The grand god revealed himself, sounded, and went out of sight. Hoveringly halting, and dipping on the wing, the white sea-fowls longingly lingered over the agitated pool that he left.

With oars speak, and paddles down, the sheets of their sails adrift, the three boats now stilly floated, awaiting Moby Dick's appearance.

"An hour," said Ahab, standing rooted in his boat's stern, and he gazed beyond the whale's place, towards the dim blue spaces and wide wooing vacancies to leeward. It was only an instant, for again his eyes seemed whirling round in his head as he swept the watery circle. The breeze now freshened; the sea began to swell.

"The birds!—the birds!" cried Tashtego.

In long Indian file, as when herons take wing, the white birds were now all flying towards Ahab's boat; and when within a few yards began fluttering over the water there, wheeling round and round, with Joyous, expectant cries. Their vision was keener than man's; Ahab could discover no sign in the sea. But suddenly as he peered down and into its depths, he profoundly saw a white living spot no bigger than a white weasel, with a wonderful celerity uprising, and magnifying as it rose, till it turned, and then there were plainly revealed two long crooked rows of white, glistening teeth, floating up from the undiscoverable bottom. It was Moby Dick's open mouth and scrolled jaw; his vast, shadowed bulk still half blending with the blue of the sea. The glittering mouth yawned beneath the boat like an open-doored marble tomb; and giving one sidelong sweep with his steering oar, Ahab whirled the craft aside from this tremendous apparition. Then, calling upon Fedallah to change places with him, went forward to the bows, and seizing Perth's harpoon, commanded his crew to grasp their oars and stand by to stern.

Now, by reason of this timely spinning round the boat upon its axis, its bow, by anticipation, was made to face the whale's head while yet under water. But as if perceiving this stratagem, Moby Dick, with that malicious intelligence ascribed to him, sidelingly transplanted himself, as it were, in an instant, shooting his plaited head lengthwise beneath the boat.

Through and through; through every plank and each rib, it thrilled for an instant, the whale obliquely lying on his back, in the manner of a biting shark, slowly and feelingly taking its bows full within his mouth, so that the long, narrow, scrolled lower-jaw curled high up into the open air, and one of the teeth caught in a rowlock. The bluish pearl-white of the inside of the jaw was within six inches of Ahab's head, and reached higher than that. In this altitude the White Whale now shook the slight cedar as a mildly cruel cat her mouse. With unastonished eyes Fedallah gazed, and crossed his arms; but the tiger-yellow crew were tumbling over each other's heads to gain the uttermost stern.

And now, while both elastic gunwales were springing in and out, as the whale dallied with the doomed craft in this devilish way; and from his body being submerged beneath the boat, he could not be darted at from the bows, for the bows were almost inside of him, as it were; and while the other boats involuntarily paused, as before a quick crisis impossible to withstand, then it was that monomaniac Ahab, furious with this tantalizing vicinity of his foe, which placed him all alive and helpless in the very jaws he hated; frenzied with all this, he seized the long bone with his naked hands, and wildly strove to wrench it from its grip. As he now thus vainly strove, the jaw slipped from him; the frail gunwales bent in, collapsed and snapped, as both jaws, like an enormous shears, sliding further aft, bit the craft completely in twain, and locked themselves fast again in the sea, midway between the two floating wrecks. These floated aside, the broken ends drooping, the crew at the sternwreck clinging to the gunwales, and striving to hold fast to the oars to lash them across.

At that preluding moment, ere the boat was yet snapped, Ahab, the first to perceive the whale's intent, by the crafty upraising of his head, a movement that loosed his hold for the time; at that moment his hand had made one final effort to push the boat out of the bite. But only slipping further into the whale's mouth, and tilting over sideways as it slipped, the boat had shaken off his hold on the jaw; spilled him out of it, as he leaned to the push; and so he fell flat-faced upon the sea.

Ripplingly withdrawing from his prey, Moby Dick now lay at a little distance, vertically thrusting his oblong white head up and down in the billows; and at the same time slowly revolving his whole splendid body; so that when his vast wrinkled forehead rose—some twenty or more feet out of the water—the now rising swells, with all their confluent waves, dazzling broke against it; vindictively tossing their shivered spray still higher into the air. So, in a gale, the but half baffled Channel billows only recoil from the base of the Eddystone, triumphantly to overlap its summit with their scud.

But soon resuming his horizontal attitude, Moby Dick swam swiftly round and round the wrecked crew; sideways churning the water in his vengeful wake, as if lashing himself up to still another and more deadly assault. The sight of the splintered boat seemed to madden him, as the blood of grapes and mulberries cast before Antiochus's elephants in the book of Maccabees. Meanwhile Ahab half smothered in the foam of the whale's insolent tail, and too much of a cripple to swim,—though he could still keep afloat, even in the heart of such a whirlpool as that; helpless Ahab's head was seen, like a tossed bubble which the least chance shock might burst. From the boat's fragmentary stern, Fedallah incuriously and mildly eyed him; the clinging crew, at the other drifting end, could not succour him; more than enough was it for them to look to themselves. For so revolvingly appalling was the White Whale's aspect, and so planetarily swift the ever-contracting circles he made, that he seemed horizontally swooping upon them. And though the other boats, unharmed, still hovered hard by, still they dared not pull into the eddy to strike, lest that should be the signal for the instant destruction of the jeopardized castaways, Ahab and all; nor in that case could they themselves hope to escape. With straining eyes, then, they remained on the outer edge of the direful zone, whose centre had now become the old man's head.

Meantime, from the beginning all this had been descried from the ship's mastheads; and squaring her yards, she had borne down upon the scene; and was now so nigh, that Ahab in the water hailed her;—"Sail on the"— but that moment a breaking sea dashed on him from Moby Dick, and whelmed him for the time. But struggling out of it again, and chancing to rise on a towering crest, he shouted,—"Sail on the whale !Drive him off!"

The *Pequod's* prows were pointed; and breaking up the charmed circle, she effectually parted the White Whale from his victim. As he sullenly swam off, the boats flew to the rescue.

Dragged into Stubb's boat with bloodshot blinded eyes, the white brine caking in his wrinkles; the long tension of Ahab's bodily strength did crack, and helplessly he yielded to his body's doom: for a time, lying all crushed in the bottom of Stubb's boat, like one trodden under foot of herds of elephants. Far inland, nameless wails came from him, as desolate sounds from our ravines.

But the intensity of his physical prostration did but so much the more abbreviate it. In an instant's compass, great hearts sometimes condense to one deep pang, the sum-total of those shallow pains kindly diffused through feebler men's whole lives. And so, such hearts, though summary in each one suffering; still, if the gods decree it, in their lifetime aggregate a whole age of woe, wholly made up of instantaneous intensities; for even in their pointless centres those noble natures contain the entire circumferences of inferior souls.

"The harpoon," said Ahab, half-way rising, and draggingly leaning on one bended arm—"is it safe?"

"Aye, sir, for it was not darted; this is it," said Stubb, showing it. "Say it before me;—any missing men?"

"One, two, three, four, five;—there were five oars, sir, and here are five men."

"That's good.—Help me, man; I wish to stand. So, so, I see him! there! there!

going to leeward still; what a leaping spout!Hands off from me! The eternal sap runs in Ahab's bones again! Set the sail; out oars; the helm!"

It is often the case that when a boat is stove, its crew, being picked up by another boat, help to work that second boat; and the chase is thus continued with what is called double-banked oars. It was thus now. But the added power of the boat did not equal the added power of the whale, for he seemed to have treble-banked his every fin; swimming with a velocity which plainly showed, that if now, under these circumstances, pushed on, the chase would prove an indefinitely prolonged, if not a hopeless one; nor could any crew endure for so long a period, such an unintermitted, intense straining at the oar; a thing barely tolerable only *in* some one brief vicissitude. The ship itself, then, as it sometimes happens, offered the most promising intermediate means of overtaking the chase. Accordingly, the boats now made for her, and were soon swayed up to their cranes—the two parts of the wrecked boat having been previously secured by her—and then hoisting everything to her side, and stacking the canvas high up, and sideways outstretching it with stunsails, like the double-jointed wings of an albatross; the *Pequod* bore down in the leeward wake of Moby Dick. At the well-known, methodical intervals, the whale's glittering spout was regularly announced from the manned mastheads; and when he would be reported as just gone down, Ahab would take the time, and then pacing the deck, binnacle-watch in hand, so soon as the last sound of the allotted hour expired, his voice was heard—"Whose is the doubloon now? D'ye see him?" and if the reply was "No, sir!" straightway he commanded them to lift him to his perch. In this way the day wore on; Ahab, now aloft and motionless; anon, unrestingly pacing the planks.

As he was thus walking, uttering no sound, except to hail the men aloft, or to bid them hoist a sail still higher, or to spread one to a still greater breadth—thus to and fro pacing, beneath his slouched hat, at every turn he passed his own wrecked boat, which had been dropped upon the quarter-deck, and lay there reversed, broken bow to shattered stern. At last he paused before it; and as in an already over-clouded sky fresh troops of clouds will sometimes sail across, so over the old man's face there now stole some such added gloom as this.

Stubb saw him pause; and perhaps intending, not vainly, though, to evince his own unabated fortitude, and thus keep up a valiant place in his Captain's mind, he advanced, and eyeing the wreck exclaimed— "The thistle the ass refused it pricked his mouth too keenly, sir; ha! ha!"

"What soulless thing is this that laughs before a wreck? Man, man! did I not know thee brave as fearless fire (and as mechanical) I could swear thou wert a poltroon. Groan nor laugh should be heard before a wreck."

"Aye, sir," said Starbuck, drawing near, "'tis a solemn sight; an omen, and an ill one."

"Omen? omen?—the dictionary! If the gods think to speak outright to man, they will honourably speak outright; not shake their heads, and give an old wife's darkling hint.—Begone! Ye two are the opposite poles of one thing; Starbuck is Stubb reversed, and Stubb is Starbuck; and ye two are all mankind; and Ahab stands alone among the millions of the peopled earth, nor gods nor men his neighbours! Cold, cold—I shiver!—How now? Aloft there? D'ye see him? Sing out for every spout, though he spout ten times a second!"

The day was nearly done; only the hem of his golden robe was rustling. Soon, it was almost dark, but the look-out men still remained unset.

"Can't see the spout now, sir;—too dark"—cried a voice from the air.

"How heading when last seen?"

"As before, sir—straight to leeward."

"Good! he will travel slower now 'tis night. Down royals and top-gallant stunsails, Mr Starbuck. We must not run over him before morning; he's making a passage now, and may heave-to a while. Helm there! keep her full before the wind!— Aloft! come down!—Mr Stubb, send a fresh hand to the foremast head, and see it manned till morning."—Then advancing towards the doubloon in the mainmast— "Men, this gold is mine, for I earned it; but I shall let it abide here till the White Whale is dead; and then, whosoever of ye first raises him, upon the day he shall be killed, this gold is that man's; and if on that day I shall again raise him, then, ten times its sum shall be divided among all of ye! Away now!—the deck is thine, Sir."

And so saying, he placed himself half-way within the scuttle, and slouching his hat, stood there till dawn, except when at intervals rousing himself to see how the night wore on.

At daybreak the three mastheads were punctually manned afresh.

"D'ye see him?" cried Ahab after allowing a little space for the light to spread.

"See nothing, sir."

"Turn up all hands and make sail! he travels faster than I thought for;—the top-gallant sails!—aye, they should have been kept on her all night. But no matter—'tis but resting for the rush."

The ship tore on, leaving such a furrow in the sea as when a cannonball, missent, becomes a ploughshare and turns up the level field.

"By salt and hemp!" cried Stubb, "but this swift motion of the deck creeps up one's legs and tingles at the heart. This ship and I are two grave fellows! Ha! ha! Some one take me up, and launch me, spine-wise, on the sea, for by live-oaks!my spine's a keel. Ha, ha!we go the gait that leaves no dust behind!"

"There she blows—she blows!—she blows!—right ahead!" was now the masthead cry.

"Aye, aye!" cried Stubb, "I knew it—ye can't escape—blow on and split your spout, O Whale!the mad fiend himself is after ye! Blow your trump—blister your lungs! Ahab will dam off your blood, as a miller shuts his water-gate upon the stream."

And Stubb did but speak out for well-nigh all that crew. The frenzies of the chase had by this time worked them bubblingly up, like old wine worked anew. Whatever pale fears and forebodings some of them might have felt before; these were not only now kept out of sight through the growing awe of Ahab, but they were broken up, and on all sides routed, as timid prairie hares that scatter before the bounding bison. The hand of Fate had snatched all their souls; and by the stirring perils of the previous day; the rack of the past night's suspense; the fixed unfearing, blind, reckless way in which their wild craft went plunging towards its flying mark; by all these things, their hearts were bowled along. The wind that made great bellies of their sails, and rushed the vessel on by arms invisible as irresistible; this seemed the symbol of that unseen agency which so enslaved them to the race.

They were one man, not thirty. For as the one ship that held them all, though it was put together of all contrasting things—oak, and maple, and pine wood; iron, and pitch, and hemp—yet all these ran into each other in the one concrete hull, which shot on its way, both balanced and directed by the long central keel; even so, all the individualities of the crew. This man's valour, that man's fear; guilt and guiltiness, all varieties were welded into oneness, and were all directed to that fatal goal which Ahab their one lord and keel did point to.

The rigging lived. The mastheads, like the tops of tail palms, were outspreadingly tufted with arms and legs. Clinging to a spar with one hand, some reached forth the other with impatient wavings; others, shading their eyes from the vivid sunlight, sat far out on the rocking yards; all the spars in full bearing of mortals, ready and ripe for their fate. Ah! how they still strove through that infinite blueness to seek out the thing that might destroy them!

"Why sing ye not out for him, if ye see him?" cried Ahab, when, after the lapse of some minutes since the first cry, no more had been heard. "Sway me up, men; ye have been deceived; not Moby Dick casts one odd jet that way, and then disappears."

It was even so; in their headlong eagerness, the men had mistaken some other thing for the whale-spout, as the event itself soon proved; for hardly had Ahab reached his perch; hardly was the rope belayed to its pin on deck, when he struck the key-note to an orchestra, that made the air vibrate as with the combined discharges of rifles. The triumphant halloo of thirty buckskin lungs was heard, as—much nearer to the ship than the place of the imaginary jet, less than a mile ahead—Moby Dick bodily burst into view. For not by any calm and indolent spoutings; not by the peaceable gush of that mystic fountain in his head, did the

White Whale now reveal his vicinity; but by the far more wondrous phenomenon of breaching. Rising with his utmost velocity from the furthest depths, the Sperm Whale thus booms his entire bulk into the pure element of air, and piling up a mountain of dazzling foam, shows his place to the distance of seven miles and more. In those moments, the torn, enraged waves he shakes off seem his mane; in some cases this breaching is his act of defiance.

"There she breaches! there she breaches!" was the cry, as in his immeasurable bravadoes the White Whale tossed himself salmon-like to Heaven. So suddenly seen in the blue plain of the sea, and relieved against the still bluer margin of the sky, the spray that he raised, for the moment, intolerably glittered and glared like a glacier; and stood there gradually fading away from its first sparkling intensity, to the dim and fading mistiness of an advancing shower in a vale.

"Aye, breach your last to the sun, Moby Dick!" cried Ahab, "thy hour and thy harpoon are at hand! Down! down all of ye, but one man at the fore. The boats!—stand by!

Unmindful of the tedious rope-ladders of the shrouds, the men, like shooting stars, slid to the deck, by the isolated backstays and halyards; while Ahab, less dartingly, but still rapidly, was dropped from his perch.

"Lower away," he cried, so soon as he had reached his boat—a spare one, rigged the afternoon previous. "Mr Starbuck, the ship is thine—keep away from the boats, but keep near them. Lower all!"

As if to strike a quick terror into them, by this time being the first assailant himself, Moby Dick had turned, and was now coming for the three crews. Ahab's boat was central; and cheering his men, he told them he would take the whale head-and-head,—that is, pull straight up to his forehead,—a not uncommon thing; for when within a certain limit, such a course excludes the coming onset from the whale's sidelong vision. But ere that close limit was gained, and while yet all three boats were plain as the ship's three masts to his eye; the White Whale, churning himself into furious speed, almost in an instant as it were, rushing among the boats with open jaws, and lashing tail, offered appalling battle on every side; and heedless of the irons darted at him from every boat, seemed only intent on annihilating each separate plank of which those boats were made. But skilfully manoeuvred, incessantly wheeling like trained chargers in the field; the boats for a while eluded him; though, at times, but by a plank's breadth; while all the time, Ahab's unearthly slogan tore every other cry but his to shreds.

But at last in his untraceable evolutions, the White Whale so crossed and recrossed, and in a thousand ways entangled the slack of the three lines now fast to him, that they foreshortened, and, of themselves, warped the devoted boats towards the planted irons in him; though now for a moment the whale drew aside a little, as if to rally for a more tremendous charge. Seizing that opportunity, Ahab first paid out more line; and then was rapidly hauling and jerking in upon it again—hoping that way to disencumber it of some snarls—when lo!—a sight more savage than the embattled teeth of sharks!

Caught and twisted—corkscrewed in the mazes of the line—loose harpoons and lances, with all their bristling barbs and points, came flashing and dripping up to the chocks in the bows of Ahab's boat. Only one thing could be done. Seizing the boat-knife, he critically reached within—through—and then, without—the rays of steel; dragged in the line beyond, passed it, inboard, to the bowsman, and then, twice sundering the rope near the chocks—dropped the intercepted fagot of steel into the sea; and was all fast again. That instant, the White Whale made a sudden rush among the remaining tangles of the other lines; by so doing, irresistibly dragged the more involved boats of Stubb and Flask towards his flukes; dashed them together like two rolling husks on a surf-beaten beach, and then, diving down into the sea, disappeared in a coiling maelstrom, in which, for a space, the odorous cedar chips of the wrecks danced round and round, like the grated nutmeg in a swiftly stirred bowl of punch.

While the two crews were yet circling in the waters, reaching out after the revolving line-tubs, oars, and other floating furniture, while aslope little Flask bobbed up and down like an empty vial, twitching his legs upwards to escape the dreaded jaws of sharks; and Stubb was lustily singing out for some one to ladle him up; and while the old man's line-now parting—admitted of his pulling into the creamy pool to rescue whom he could;—in that wild simultaneousness of a thousand concreted perils,—Ahab's yet unstricken boat seemed drawn up towards Heaven by invisible wires,—as, arrow-like, shooting perpendicularly from the sea, the White Whale dashed his broad forehead against its bottom, and sent it, turning over and over, into the air; till it fell again—gunwale downwards—and Ahab and his men struggled out from under it, like seals from a seaside cave.

The first uprising momentum of the whale—modifying its direction as he struck the surface—involuntarily launched him along it, to a little distance from the centre of the destruction he had made; and with his back to it, he now lay for a moment slowly feeling with his flukes from side to side; and whenever a stray oar, bit of plank, the least chip or crumb of the boats touched his skin, his tail swiftly drew back, and came sideways, smiting the sea. But soon, as if satisfied that his work for that time was done, he pushed his plaited forehead through the ocean, and trailing after him the intertangled lines, continued his leeward way at a traveller's methodic pace.

As before, the attentive ship having descried the whole fight, again came bearing down to the rescue, and dropping a boat, picked up the floating mariners, tubs, oars, and whatever else could be caught at, and safely landed them upon her decks. Some sprained shoulders, wrists, and ankles; livid contusions; wrenched harpoons and lances; inextricable intricacies of rope; shattered oars and planks; all these were there; but no fatal or even serious ill seemed to have befallen anyone. As with Fedallah the day before, so Ahab was now found grimly clinging to his boat's broken half, which offered a comparatively easy float; nor did it exhaust him as the previous day's mishap.

But when he was helped to the deck, all eyes were fastened upon him; as instead of standing by himself he still half-hung upon the shoulder of Starbuck, who had thus far been the foremost to assist him. His ivory leg had been snapped off, leaving but one short sharp splinter.

"Aye, aye, Starbuck, 'tis sweet to lean sometimes, be the leaner who he will; and would old Ahab had leaned oftener than he has."

"The ferrule has not stood, sir," said the carpenter, now coming up; "I put good work into that leg."

"But no bones broken, sir, I hope," said Stubb with true concern.

"Aye! and all splintered to pieces, Stubb! d'ye see it? But even with a broken bone, old Ahab is untouched; and I account no living bone of mine one jot more me than this dead one that's lost. Nor white whale, nor man, nor fiend, can so much as graze old Ahab in his own proper and inaccessible being. Can any lead touch yonder floor, any mast scrape yonder roof? Aloft there! which way?"

"Dead to leeward, sir."

"Up helm, then; pile on the sail again, shipkeepers; down the rest of the spare boats and rig them—Mr Starbuck, away, and muster the boats' crews."

"Let me first help thee towards the bulwarks, sir."

"Oh, oh, oh! how this splinter gores me now! Accursed fate! that the unconquerable captain in the soul should have such a craven mate !"

"Sir?"

"My body, man, not thee. Give me something for a cane—there, that shivered lance will do. Muster the men. Surely I have not seen him yet. By heaven, it cannot be !—missing ?—quick! call them all."

The old man's hinted thought was true. Upon mustering the company, the Parsee was not there.

"The Parsee!" cried Stubb, "he must have been caught in."

"The black vomit wrench thee! Run all of ye above, alow, cabin, forecastle—find him—not gone—not gone!"

But quickly they returned to him with the tidings that the Parsee was nowhere to be found.

"Aye, sir," said Stubb—"caught among the tangles of your line. I thought I saw him dragged under."

"*My* line? *My* line? Gone? Gone? What means that little word? What death-knell rings in it, that old Ahab shakes as if he were the belfry. The harpoon, too!

Toss over the litter there, d'ye see it?—the forged iron, men, the White Whale's—no, no, no, blistered fool!this hand did dart it! 'Tis in the fish! Aloft there! Keep him nailed. Quick! all hands to the rigging of the boats—collect the oars—harpooners! the irons, the irons! Hoist the royals higher—a pull on all the sheets! Helm there! steady, steady, for your life! I'll ten times girdle the unmeasured globe; yea and dive straight through it, but I'll slay him yet!"

"Great God! but for one single instant show thyself," cried Starbuck. "Never, never wilt thou capture him, old man. In Jesus' name, no more of this, that's worse than devil's madness. Two days chased; twice stove to splinters; thy very leg once more snatched from under thee; thy evil shadow gone—all good angels mobbing thee with warnings; what more wouldst thou have? Shall we keep chasing this murderous fish till he swamps the last man ? Shall we be dragged by him to the bottom of the sea? Shall we be towed by him to the infernal world? Oh, oh! Impiety and blasphemy to hunt him more!"

"Starbuck, of late I've felt strangely moved to thee; ever since that hour we both saw—thou know'st what, in one another's eyes. But in this matter of the whale, be the front of thy face to me as the palm of this hand—a lipless, unfeatured blank. Ahab is for ever Ahab, man. This whole act's immutably decreed. 'Twas rehearsed by thee and me a billion years before this ocean rolled. Fool! I am the Fates' lieutenant; I act under orders. Look thou, underling! that thou obeyest mine. Stand round me, men. Ye see an old man cut down to the stump; leaning on a shivered lance; propped up on a lonely foot. 'Tis Ahab—his body's part; but Ahab's soul's a centipede, that moves upon a hundred legs. I feel strained, half stranded, as ropes that tow dismasted frigates in a gale; and I may look so. But ere I break, ye'll hear me crack; and till ye hear *that,* know that Ahab's hawser tows his purpose yet. Believe ye, men, in the things called omens? Then laugh aloud, and cry encore! For ere they drown, drowning things will twice rise to the surface; then rise again, to sink for evermore. So with Moby Dick—two days he's floated—to-morrow will be the third. Aye, men, he'll rise once more—but only to spout his last."

The morning of the third day dawned fair and fresh, and once more the solitary night-man at the fore-masthead was relieved by crowds of the daylight look-outs, who dotted every mast and almost every spar.

"D'ye see him?" cried Ahab. "Aloft there. What d'ye see?"

"Nothing, sir."

"Nothing! The doubloon goes a-begging! See the sun! Aye, aye, it must be so. I've over-sailed him. How, got the start? Aye, he's chasing *me,* now; not I, *him*—that's bad. I might have known it, too. Fool! the lines—the harpoons he's towing. Aye, aye, I have run him by last night. About! About! Come down, all of ye, but the regular look-outs! Man the braces!"

Steering as she had done, the wind had been somewhat on the *Pequod's* quarter, so that now being pointed in the reverse direction, the braced ship sailed hard upon the breeze as she rechurned the cream in her own white wake.

"Against the wind he now steers for the open jaw," murmured Starbuck to himself, as he coiled the new-hauled main-brace upon the rail. "God keep us, but already my bones feel damp within me, and from the inside wet my flesh. I misdoubt me that I disobeyed my God in obeying him!"

"Stand by to sway me up!" cried Ahab, advancing to the hempen basket. "We should meet him soon."

"Aye, aye, sir," and straightway Starbuck did Ahab's bidding, and once more Ahab swung on high.

A whole hour now passed; gold-beaten out to ages. Time itself now held long breaths with keen suspense. But at last, some three points off the weather-bow, Ahab descried the spout again, and instantly from the three mastheads three shrieks went up as if the tongues of fire had voiced it.

"Forehead to forehead I meet thee, this third time, Moby Dick! On deck there! Brace sharper up; crowd her into the wind's eye. He's too far off to lower yet, Mr Starbuck. The sails shake! Stand over that helmsman with a topmaul!So, so he travels fast, and I must down."

He gave the word, and still gazing round him, was steadily lowered through the cloven blue air to the deck.

In due time the boats were lowered; but as standing in his shallop's stern, Ahab just hovered upon the point of the descent, he waved to the mate, who held one of the tackle-ropes on deck, and bade him pause.

"Starbuck!"

"Sir?"

"For the third time my soul's ship starts upon this voyage, Starbuck."

"Aye, sir, thou wilt have it so."

"Some ships sail from their ports, and ever afterwards are missing, Starbuck! Some men die at ebb tide; some at low water; some at the full of the flood; and I feel now like a billow that's all one crested comb, Starbuck. Lower away! Stand by the crew!"

In an instant the boat was pulling round close under the stern.

"The sharks! the sharks!" cried a voice from the low cabin-window there. "O master, my master, come back!"

But Ahab heard nothing; for his own voice was high-lifted then; and the boat leaped on.

Yet the voice spake true; for scarce had he pushed from the ship, when numbers of sharks, seemingly rising from out the dark waters beneath the hull, maliciously snapped at the blades of the oars, every time they dipped in the water; and in this way accompanied the boat with their bites. It is a thing not uncommonly happening to the whaleboats in those swarming seas; the sharks at times apparently following them in the same prescient way that vultures hover over the banners of marching regiments in the east. But these were the first sharks that had been observed by the *Pequod* since the White Whale had been first descried; and whether it was that Ahab's crew were all such tiger-yellow barbarians, and therefore their flesh more musky to the senses of sharks —a matter sometimes well known to affect them—however it was, they seemed to follow that one boat without molesting the others.

"Heart of wrought steel," murmured Starbuck, gazing over the side, and following with his eyes the receding boat, "canst thou yet ring boldly to that sight? lowering thy keel among ravening sharks, and followed by them, open-mouthed, to the chase; and this the critical third day ? For when three days flow together in one continuous intense pursuit, be sure the first in the morning, the second the noon, and the third the evening and the end of that thing—be that end what it may."

The boats had not gone very far, when by a signal from the mastheads—a downward pointed arm, Ahab knew that the whale had sounded; but intending to be near him at the next rising, be held on his way a little sideways from the vessel; the becharmed crew maintaining the profoundest silence, as the head-beat waves hammered and hammered against the opposing bow.

Suddenly the waters around them slowly swelled in broad circles, then quickly upheaved, as if sideways sliding from a submerged berg of ice, swiftly rising to the surface. A low rumbling sound was heard; a subterraneous hum; and then all held their breaths; as bedraggled with trailing ropes, and harpoons, and lances, a vast form shot lengthwise, but obliquely from the sea. Shrouded in a thin drooping veil of mist, it hovered for a moment in the rainbowed air; and then fell swamping back into the deep. Crushed thirty feet upwards, the waters flashed for an instant like heaps of fountains, then brokenly sank in a shower of flakes, leaving the circling surface creamed like new milk round the marble trunk of the whale.

"Give way!" cried Ahab to the oarsmen and the boats darted forward to the attack; but maddened by yesterday's fresh irons that corroded in him, Moby Dick seemed combinedly possessed by all the angels that fell from heaven. The wide tiers of welded tendons overspreading his broad white forehead, beneath the transparent skin, looked knitted together; as head on, he came churning his tail among the boats; and once more flailed them apart; spilling out the irons and lances from the two mates' boats, and dashing in one side of the upper part of their bows, but leaving Ahab's almost without a scar.

While Daggoo and Queequeg were stopping the strained planks; and as the whale swimming out from them, turned, and showed one entire flank as he shot by them again; at that moment a quick cry went up. Lashed round and round to the fish's back; pinioned in the turns upon turns in which, during the past night, the whale had reeled the involutions of the lines around him, the half-torn body of the Parsee was seen; his sable raiment frayed to shreds; his distended eyes turned full upon old Ahab.

The harpoon dropped from his hand.

"Befooled, befooled!"—drawing in a long lean breath—"Aye, Parsee! I see thee again. Aye, and thou goest before; and this, *this* then is the hearse that thou didst promise. But I hold thee to the last letter of thy word. Where is the second hearse? Away, mates, to the ship! Those boats are useless now; repair them if ye can in time, and return to me; if not, Ahab is enough to die. Down, men! the first thing that but offers to jump from this boat I stand in, that thing I harpoon. Ye are not other men, but my arms and legs; and so obey me. Where's the whale? gone down again?"

But he looked too nigh the boat; for as if bent upon escaping with the corpse he bore, and as if the particular place of the last encounter had been but a stage in his leeward voyage, Moby Dick was now again steadily swimming forward; and had almost passed the ship, which thus far had been sailing in the contrary direction to him, though for the present her headway had been stopped. He seemed swimming with his utmost velocity, and now only intent upon pursuing his own straight path in the sea.

"Oh! Ahab," cried Starbuck, "not too late is it, even now, the third day, to desist. See! Moby Dick seeks thee not. It is thou, thou, that madly seekest him!"

Setting sail to the rising wind, the lonely boat was swiftly impelled to leeward by both oars and canvas. And at last when Ahab was sliding by the vessel, so near as plainly to distinguish Starbuck's face as he leaned over the rail, he hailed him to turn the vessel about, and follow him, not too swiftly, at a judicious interval. Glancing upwards, he saw Tashtego, Queequeg, and Daggoo, eagerly mounting to the three mastheads; while the oarsmen were rocking in the two staved boats which had just been hoisted to the side, and were busily at work in repairing them. One after the other, through the port-holes, as he sped, he also caught flying glimpses of Stubb and Flask, busying themselves on deck among bundles of new irons and lances. As he saw all this; as he heard the hammers in the broken boats; far other hammers seemed driving a nail into his heart. But he rallied. And now marking that the vane of flag was gone from the main masthead, he shouted to Tashtego, who had just gained that perch, to descend again for another flag, and a hammer and nails, and so nail it to the mast.

Whether ragged by the three days' running chase, and the resistance to his swimming in the knotted hamper he bore; or whether it was some latent deceitfulness and malice in him; whichever was true, the White Whale's way now began to abate, as it seemed, from the boat so rapidly nearing him once more;

though indeed the whale's last start had not been so long a one as before. And still as Ahab glided over the waves the unpitying sharks accompanied him; and so pertinaciously stuck to the boat; and so continually bit at the plying oars, that the blades became jagged and crunched, and left small splinters in the sea, at almost every dip.

"Heed them not! those teeth but give new rowlocks to your oars. Pull on! 'tis the better rest, the shark's jaw than the yielding water."

"But at every bite, sir, the thin blades grow smaller and smaller!"

"They will last long enough! Pull on! But who can tell"—he muttered—"whether these sharks swim to feast on a whale or on Ahab? But pull on! Aye, all alive now—we near him. The helm! take the helm; let me pass,"—and so saying, two of the oarsmen helped him forward to the bows of the still flying boat.

At length as the craft was cast to one side, and ran ranging along with the White Whale's flank, he seemed strangely oblivious of its advance—as the whale sometimes will—and Ahab was fairly within the smoky mountain mist, which, thrown off from the whale's spout, curled round his great Monadnock hump. He was even thus close to him; when, with body arched back, and both arms lengthwise high-lifted to the poise, he darted his fierce iron, and his far fiercer curse into the hated whale. As both steel and curse sank to the socket, as if sucked into a morass, Moby Dick sideways writhed; spasmodically rolled his nigh flank against the bow, and, without staving a hole in it, so suddenly canted the boat over, that had it not been for the elevated part of the gunwale to which he then clung, Ahab would have once more been tossed into the sea. As it was, three of the oarsmen—who foreknew not the precise instant of the dart, and were therefore unprepared for its effects—these were flung out; but so fell, that, in an instant two of them clutched the gunwale again, and rising to its level on a combing wave, hurled themselves bodily inboard again; the third man helplessly drooping astern, but still afloat and swimming.

Almost simultaneously, with a mighty volition of ungraduated instantaneous swiftness, the White Whale darted through the weltering sea. But when Ahab cried out to the steersman to take new turns with the line, and hold it so; and commanded the crew to turn round on their seats, and tow the boat up to the mark; the moment the treacherous line felt that double strain and tug, it snapped in the empty air!

"What breaks in me? Some sinew cracks!—'tis whole again; oars! oars! Burst in upon him!"

Hearing the tremendous rush of the sea-crashing boat, the whale wheeled round to present his blank forehead at bay; but in that evolution, catching sight of the nearing black hull of the ship; seemingly seeing in it the source of all his persecutions; bethinking it—it may be—a larger and nobler foe; of a sudden he bore down upon its advancing prow, smiting his jaws amid fiery showers of foam.

Ahab staggered; his hand smote his forehead. "I grow blind; hands! stretch out before me that I may yet grope my way. Is't night?"

"The whale!The ship!" cried the clinging oarsmen.

"Oars! oars! Slope downwards to thy depths, O sea, that ere it be for ever too late, Ahab may slide this last, last time upon his mark! I see: the ship!the ship! Dash on, my men! Will ye not save my ship?"

But as the oarsmen violently forced their boat through the sledgehammering seas, the before whale-smitten bow-ends of two planks burst through, and in an instant almost, the temporarily disabled boat lay nearly level with the waves; its half-wading, splashing crew, trying hard to stop the gap and bale out the pouring water.

Meantime, for that one holding instant, Tashtego's mast-head hammer remained suspended in his hand; and the red flag, half-wrapping him as with a plaid, then streamed itself straight out from him, as his own forward-flowing heart; while Starbuck and Stubb, standing upon the bowsprit beneath, caught sight of the down-coming monster just as soon as he.

"The whale! the whale! Up helm, up helm! Oh, all ye sweet powers of air, now hug me close! Let not Starbuck die, if die he must, in a woman's fainting fit. Up helm, I say—ye fools, the jaw! the jaw! Is this the end of all my bursting prayers? all my life-long fidelities? Oh, Ahab, Ahab, lo, thy work. Steady! helmsman, steady! Nay, nay! Up helm again! He turns to meet us! Oh, his unappeasable brow drives on towards one, whose duty tells him he cannot depart. My God, stand by me now!"

"Stand not by me, but stand under me, whoever you are that will now help Stubb; for Stubb, too, sticks here. I grin at thee, thou grinning whale! Whoever helped Stubb, or kept Stubb awake, but Stubb's own unwinking eye? And now poor Stubb goes to bed upon a mattress that is all too soft; would it were stuffed with brushwood. I grin at thee, thou grinning whale! Look ye, moon and stars! I call ye assassins of as good a fellow as ever spouted up his ghost. For all that, I would yet ring glasses with ye, would ye but hand the cup! Oh, oh, oh, oh! thou grinning whale, but there'll be plenty of gulping soon! Why fly ye not, O Ahab? For me, off shoes and jacket to it; let Stubb die in his drawers! A most mouldy and over-salted death, though;—cherries! cherries! cherries! Oh, Flask, for one red cherry ere we die!"

"Cherries? I only wish that we were where they grow. Oh, Stubb, I hope my poor mother's drawn my part-pay ere this; if not, few coppers will come to her now, for the voyage is up."

From the ship's bows, nearly all the seamen now hung inactive; hammers, bits of plank, lances, and harpoons, mechanically retained in their hands, just as they had darted from their various employments; all their enchanted eyes intent upon the whale, which from side to side strangely vibrating his predestinating head, sent a broad band of over-spreading semi-circular foam before him as he rushed. Retribution, swift vengeance, eternal malice were in his whole aspect, and spite of all that mortal man could do, the solid white buttress of his forehead smote the ship's starboard bow, till men and timbers reeled. Some fell flat upon their faces. Like dislodged trucks, the heads of the harpooners aloft shook on their hull-like necks. Through the breach, they heard the waters pour, as mountain torrents down a flume.

"The ship! The hearse!—the second hearse!" cried Ahab from the boat; "its wood could only be American!"

Diving beneath the settling ship, the Whale ran quivering along its keel, but turning under water, swiftly shot to the surface again, far off the other bow, but within a few yards of Ahab's boat, where, for a time, he lay quiescent.

"I turn my body from the sun. What ho, Tashtego! let me hear thy hammer. Oh! ye three unsurrendered spires of mine; thou uncracked keel; and only god-bullied hull; thou firm deck, and haughty helm, and Pole-pointed prow—death-glorious ship! must ye then perish, and without me? Am I cut off from the last fond pride of meanest shipwrecked captains? Oh, lonely death on lonely life! Oh, now I feel my topmost greatness lies in my topmost grief. Ho, ho! from all your furthest bounds, pour ye now in, ye bold billows of my whole foregone life, and top this one piled comber of my death!Towards thee I roll, thou all-destroying but unconquering whale; to the last I grapple with thee; from hell's heart I stab at thee; for hate's sake I spit my last breath at thee. Sink all coffins and all hearses to one common pool! and since neither can be mine let me then tow to pieces, while still chasing thee, though tied to thee, thou damned whale! *Thus,* I give up the spear."

The harpoon was darted; the stricken whale flew forward; with igniting velocity the line ran through the groove; ran foul. Ahab stooped to clear it; he did clear it; but the flying turn caught him round the neck, and voicelessly as Turkish mutes bow-string their victims, he was shot out of the boat, ere the crew knew he was gone. Next instant, the heavy eyesplice in the rope's final end flew out of the stark-empty tub, knocked down an oarsman, and smiting the sea, disappeared in its depth.

For an instant, the tranced boat's crew stood still; then turned.

"The ship! Great God, where is the ship?"

Soon they through dim, bewlldering mediums saw her sidelong fading phantom, as in the gaseous Fata Morgana; only the uppermost masts out of water; while fixed by infatuation or fidelity, or fate, to their once lofty perches, the pagan harpooners still maintained their sinking lookouts on the sea. And now, concentric circles seized the lone boat itself, and all its crew, and each floating oar, and every lance-pole and spinning, animate and inanimate, all round and round in one vortex, carried the smallest chip of the *Pequod* out of sight.

But as the last whelmings intermixingly poured themselves over the sunken head of the Indian at the mainmast, leaving a few inches of the erect spar yet visible, together with long streaming yards of the flag, which calmly undulated, with ironical coincidings, over the destroying billows they almost touched;—at that instant, a red arm and a hammer hovered backwardly uplifted in the open air, in the act of nailing the flag faster and yet faster to the subsiding spar. A sky-hawk that tauntingly had followed the main-truck downwards from its natural home among the stars, pecking at the flag, and incommoding Tashtego there; this bird now chanced to intercept its broad fluttering wing between the hammer and the wood; and simultaneously feeling that ethereal thrill, the submerged savage beneath, in his death-grasp, kept his hammer frozen there; and so the bird of heaven, with unearthly shrieks, and his imperial beak thrust upwards, and his whole captive form folded in the flag of Ahab, went down with his ship, which, like Satan, would not sink to hell till she had dragged a living part of heaven along with her, and helmeted herself with it.

Now small fowls flew screaming over the yet yawning gulf; a sullen white surf beat against its steep sides; then all collapsed, and the great shroud of the sea rolled on as it rolled five thousand years ago.

HIGH-WATER MARK[1]

Francis Bret Harte
(1839-1902)

WHEN the tide was out on the Dedlow Marsh its extended dreariness was patent. Its spongy, low-lying surface, sluggish, inky pools, and tortuous sloughs, twisting their slimy way, eel-like, toward the open bay, were all hard facts. So were the few green tussocks, with their scant blades, their amphibious flavour, and unpleasant dampness. And if you choose to indulge your fancy,—although the flat monotony of the Dedlow Marsh was not inspiring,—the wavy line of scattered drift gave an unpleasant consciousness of the spent waters, and made the dead certainty of the returning tide a gloomy reflection, which no present sunshine could dissipate. The greener meadow-land seemed oppressed with this

[1] From *The Luck of Roaring Camp and Other Stories*.

idea, and made no positive attempt at vegetation until the work of reclamation should be complete. In the bitter fruit of the low cranberrybushes one might fancy he detected a naturally sweet disposition curdled and soured by an injudicious course of too much regular cold water.

The vocal expression of the Dedlow Marsh was also melancholy and depressing. The sepulchral boom of the bittern, the shriek of the curlew, the scream of passing brent, the wrangling of quarrelsome teal, the sharp, querulous protest of the startled crane, and syllabled complaint of the "killdeer" plover, were beyond the power of written expression. Nor was the aspect of these mournful fowls at all cheerful and inspiring. Certainly not the blue heron standing mid-leg deep in the water, obviously catching cold in a reckless disregard of wet feet and consequences; nor the mournful curlew, the dejected plover, or the lowspirited snipe, who saw fit to join him in his suicidal contemplation; nor the impassive kingfisher—an ornithological Marius—reviewing the desolate expanse; nor the black raven that went to and fro over the face of the marsh continually, but evidently couldn't make up his mind whether the waters had subsided, and felt low-spirited in the reflection that, after all this trouble, he wouldn't be able to give a definite answer. On the contrary, it was evident at a glance that the dreary expanse of Dedlow Marsh told unpleasantly on the birds, and that the season of migration was looked forward to with a feeling of relief and satisfaction by the full-grown, and of extravagant anticipation by the callow, brood. But if Dedlow Marsh was cheerless at the slack of the low tide, you should have seen it when the tide was strong and full; when the damp air blew chilly over the cold, glittering expanse, and came to the faces of those who looked seaward like another tide; when a steel-like glint marked the low hollows and the sinuous line of slough; when the great shell-incrusted trunks of fallen trees arose again, and went forth on their dreary, purposeless wanderings, drifting hither and thither, but getting no farther toward any goal at the falling tide or the day's decline than the cursed Hebrew in the legend; when the glossy ducks swung silently, making neither ripple nor furrow on the shimmering surface; when the fog came in with the tide and shut out the blue above, even as the green below had been obliterated; when boatmen, lost in that fog, paddling about in a hopeless way, started at what seemed the brushing of mermen's fingers on the boat's keel, or shrank from the tufts of grass spreading around like the floating hair of a corpse, and knew by these signs that they were lost upon Dedlow Marsh, and must make a night of it, and a gloomy one at that,—then you might know something of Dedlow Marsh at high water.

Let me recall a story connected with this latter view which never failed to recur to my mind in my long gunning excursions upon Dedlow Marsh. Although the event was briefly recorded in the county paper, I had the story, in all its eloquent detail, from the lips of the principal actor. I cannot hope to catch the varying emphasis and peculiar colouring of feminine delineation, for my narrator was a woman; but I'll try to give at least its substance.

She lived midway of the great slough of Dedlow Marsh and a goodsized river, which debouched four miles beyond into an estuary formed by the Pacific Ocean, on the long sandy peninsula which constituted the south-western boundary of a noble bay. The house in which she lived was a small frame cabin raised from the marsh a few feet by stout piles, and was three miles distant from the settlements upon the river. Her husband was a logger,—a profitable business in a county where the principal occupation was the manufacture of lumber.

It was the season of early spring, when her husband left on the ebb of a high tide, with a raft of logs for the usual transportation to the lower end of the bay. As she stood by the door of the little cabin when the voyagers departed she noticed a cold look in the south-eastern sky, and she remembered hearing her husband say to his companions that they must endeavour to complete their voyage before the coming of the southwesterly gale which he saw brewing. And that night it began to storm and blow harder than she had ever before experienced, and some great trees fell in the forest by the river, and the house rocked like her baby's cradle.

But, however the storm might roar about the little cabin, she knew that one she trusted had driven bolt and bar with his own strong hand, and that had he feared for her he would not have left her. This, and her domestic duties, and the care of her little sickly baby, helped to keep her mind from dwelling on the weather, except, of course, to hope that he was safely harboured with the logs at Utopia in the dreary distance. But she noticed that day, when she went out to feed the chickens and look after the cow, that the tide was up to the little fence of their gardenpatch, and the roar of the surf on the south beach, though miles away, she could hear distinctly. And she began to think that she would like to have some one to talk with about matters, and she believed that if it had not been so far and so stormy, and the trail so impassable, she would have taken the baby and have gone over to Ryckman's, her nearest neighbour. But then, you see, he might have returned in the storm, all wet, with no one to see to him; and it was a long exposure for baby, who was croupy and ailing.

But that night, she never could tell why, she didn't feel like sleeping or even lying down. The storm had somewhat abated, but she still "sat and sat," and even tried to read. I don't know whether it was a Bible or some profane magazine that this poor woman read, but most probably the latter, for the words all ran together and made such sad nonsense that she was forced at last to put the book down and turn to that dearer volume which lay before her in the cradle, with its white initial leaf yet unsoiled, and try to look forward to its mysterious future. And, rocking the cradle, she thought of everything and everybody, but still was wide awake as ever.

It was nearly twelve o'clock when she at last laid down in her clothes. How long she slept she could not remember, but she awoke with a dreadful choking in her throat, and found herself standing, trembling all over, in the middle of the room, with her baby clasped to her breast, and she was "saying something." The baby cried and sobbed, and she walked up and down trying to hush it, when she heard a scratching at the door. She opened it fearfully, and was glad to see it was only old Pete, their dog, who crawled, dripping with water, into the room. She would like to have looked out, not in the faint hope of her husband's coming, but to see how things looked; but the wind shook the door so savagely that she could hardly hold it. Then she sat down a little while, and then she lay down again a little while. Lying close by the wall of the little cabin, she thought she heard once or twice something scrape slowly against the clapboards, like the scraping of branches. Then there was a little gurgling sound, "like the baby made when it was swallowing"; then something went "click-click" and "cluck-cluck," so that she sat up in bed. When she did so she was attracted by something else that seemed creeping from the back door towards the centre of the room. It wasn't much wider than her little finger, but soon it swelled to the width of her hand, and began spreading all over the floor. It was water.

She ran to the front door and threw it wide open, and saw nothing but water. She ran to the back door and threw it open, and saw nothing but water. She ran to the side window, and, throwing that open, she saw nothing but water. Then she remembered hearing her husband once say that there was no danger in the tide, for that fell regularly, and people could calculate on it, and that he would rather live near the bay than the river, whose banks might overflow at any time. But was it the tide? So she ran again to the back door, and threw out a stick of wood. It drifted away towards the bay. She scooped up some of the water and put it eagerly to her lips. It was fresh and sweet. It was the river, and not the tide !

It was then—oh, God be praised for His goodness! she did neither faint nor fail; it was then—blessed be the Saviour, for it was His merciful hand that touched and strengthened her in this awful moment—that fear dropped from her like a garment, and her trembling ceased. It was then and thereafter that she never lost her self-command, through all the trials of that gloomy night.

She drew the bedstead towards the middle of the room, and placed a table upon it, and on that she put the cradle. The water on the floor was already over her ankles, and the house once or twice moved so perceptibly, and seemed to be racked so, that the closet doors all flew open. Then she heard the same rasping and thumping against the wall, and looking out, saw that a large up-rooted tree, which had lain near the road at the upper end of the pasture, had floated down to the house. Luckily its long roots dragged in the soil and kept it from moving as rapidly as the current, for had it struck the house in its full career, even the strong nails and bolts in the piles could not have withstood the shock. The hound had leaped upon its knotty surface, and crouched near the roots shivering and whining. A ray of hope flashed across her mind. She drew a heavy blanket from the bed, and, wrapping it about the babe, waded in the deepening waters to the door. As the tree swung again, broadside on, making the little cabin creak and tremble, she leaped on to its trunk. By God's mercy she succeeded in obtaining a footing on its slippery surface, and, twining an arm about its roots, she held in the other her moaning child. Then something cracked near the front porch, and the whole front of the house she had just quitted fell forward,—just as cattle fail on their knees before they lie down,—and at the same moment the great redwood-tree swung round and drifted away with its living cargo into the black night.

For all the excitement and danger, for all her soothing of her crying babe, for all the whistling of the wind, for all the uncertainty of her situation, she still turned to look at the deserted and water-swept cabin. She remembered even then, and she wonders how foolish she was to think of it at that time, that she wished she had put on another dress and the, baby's best clothes; and she kept praying that the house would be spared so that he, when he returned, would have something to come to, and it wouldn't be quite so desolate, and—how could he ever know what had become of her and baby? And at the thought she grew sick and faint. But she had something else to do besides worrying, for whenever the long roots of her ark struck an obstacle, the whole trunk made half a revolution, and twice dipped her in the black water. The hound, who kept distracting her by running up and down the tree and howling, at last fell off at one of these collisions. He swam for some time beside her, and she tried to get the poor beast upon the tree, but he "acted silly" and wild, and at last she lost sight of him for ever. Then she and her baby were left alone. The light which had burned for a few minutes in the deserted cabin was quenched suddenly. She could not then tell whether she was drifting. The outline of the white dunes on the peninsula showed dimly ahead, and she judged the tree was moving in a line with the river. It must be about slack water, and she had probably reached the eddy formed by the confluence of the tide and the overflowing waters of the river. Unless the tide fell soon, there was present danger of her drifting to its channel, and being carried out to sea or crushed in the floating drift. That peril averted, if she were carried out on the ebb toward the bay, she might hope to strike one of the wooded promontories of the peninsula, and rest till daylight. Sometimes she thought she heard voices and shouts from the river, and the bellowing of cattle and bleating of sheep. Then again it was only the ringing in her ears and throbbing of her heart. She found at about this time that she was so chilled and stiflened in her cramped position that she could scarcely move, and the baby cried so when she put it to her breast that she noticed the milk refused to flow; and she was so frightened at that, that she put her head under her shawl, and for the first time cried bitterly.

When she raised her head again, the boom of the surf was behind her, and she knew that her ark had again swung round. She dipped up the water to cool her parched throat, and found that it was salt as her tears. There was a relief, though, for by this sign she knew that she was drifting with the tide. It was then the wind went down, and the great and awful silence oppressed her. There was scarcely a ripple against the furrowed sides of the great trunk on which she rested, and around her all was black gloom and quiet. She spoke to the baby just to hear herself speak, and to know that she had not lost her voice. She thought then,—it was queer, but she could not help thinking it,—how awful must have been the night when the great ship swung over the Asiatic peak, and the sounds of creation were blotted out from the world. She thought, too, of mariners clinging to spars, and of poor women who were lashed to rafts, and beaten to death by the cruel sea. She tried to thank God that she was thus spared, and lifted her eyes from the baby, who had fallen into a fretful sleep. Suddenly, away to the southward, a great light lifted itself out of the gloom, and flashed and flickered, and flickered and flashed again. Her heart fluttered quickly against the baby's cold cheek. It was the lighthouse at the entrance of the hay. As she was yet wondering, the tree suddenly rolled a little, dragged a little, and then seemed to lie quiet and still. She put out her hand and the current gurgled against it. The tree was aground, and, by the position of the light and the noise of the surf, aground upon the Dedlow Marsh.

Had it not been for her baby, who was ailing and croupy, had it not been for the sudden drying up of that sensitive fountain, she would have felt safe and relieved. Perhaps it was this which tended to make all her impressions mournful and gloomy. As the tide rapidly fell, a great flock of black brent fluttered by her, screaming and crying. Then the plover flew up and piped mournfully, as they wheeled around the trunk, and at last fearlessly lit upon it like a grey cloud. Then the heron flew over and around her, shrieking and protesting, and at last dropped its gaunt legs only a few yards from her. But, strangest of all, a pretty white bird, larger than a dove,—like a pelican, but not a pelican—circled around and around her. At last it lit upon a rootlet of the tree, quite over her shoulder. She put out her hand and stroked its beautiful white neck, and it never appeared to move. It stayed there so long that she thought she would lift up the baby to see it, and try to attract her attention. But when she did so, the child was so chilled and cold, and had such a blue look under the little lashes which it didn't raise at all, that she screamed aloud and the bird flew away, and she fainted.

Well, that was the worst of it, and perhaps it was not so much, after all, to any but herself. For when she recovered her senses it was bright sunlight, and dead low water. There was a confused noise of guttural voices about her, and an old squaw, singing an Indian "hushaby," and rocking herself from side to side before a fire built on the Marsh, before which she, the recovered wife and mother, lay weak and weary. Her first thought was for her baby, and she was about to speak, when a young squaw, who must have been a mother herself, fathomed her thought and brought her the "mowitch," pale but living, in such a queer little willow cradle all bound up, just like the squaw's own young one, that she laughed and cried together, and the young squaw and the old squaw showed their big white teeth and glinted their black eyes and said,

"Plenty get well, skeena mowitch," "wagee man come plenty soon," and she could have kissed their brown faces in her joy. And then she found that they had been gathering berries on the marsh in their queer, comical baskets, and saw the skirt of her gown fluttering on the tree from afar, and the old squaw couldn't resist the temptation of procuring a new garment, and came down and discovered the "wagee" woman and child. And of course she gave the garment to the old squaw, as you may imagine, and when *he* came at last and rushed up to her, looking about ten years older in his anxiety, she felt so faint again that they had to carry her to the canoe. For, you see, he knew nothing about the flood until he met the Indians at Utopia, and knew by the signs that the poor woman was his wife. And at the next high-tide he towed the tree away back home, although it wasn't worth the trouble, and built another house, using the old tree for the foundation and props, and called it after her, "Mary's Ark!" But you may guess the next house was built above High-water Mark. And that's all.

Not much, perhaps, considering the malevolent capacity of the Dedlow Marsh. But you must tramp over it at low water, or paddle over it at high tide, or get lost upon it once or twice in the fog, as I have, to understand properly Mary's adventure, or to appreciate duly the blessing of living beyond High-water Mark.

THE DEVIL AT SEA[1]

Henry van Dyke

(1852-)

THIS is a true tale of Holland in war-time. But it is not a military story. It is a story of the sea—

> The opaline, the plentiful and strong—

likewise the perilous.

I

In the quaint Dutch village of Oudwyk, on the shore of the North Sea, lived the widow Anny Minderop with her sons. In her girlhood she had been a school-

[1] From *The Golden Key*.

teacher, and had married Karl Minderop, the handsome skipper of a fishing smack. Her husband was lost in a storm on the Dogger Bank; but he left her two boys, a little brick cottage, and a small sum of money invested in Dutch East India bonds. The income from these she doubled by turning her cottage into a modest tea-andcoffee house for the service of travellers by "fiets" or automobile, who "biked" or motored from The Hague, or Leyden, or Haarlem, to see the picturesque village with its ancient, high-shouldered church and its *koepeltje,* commanding a wide view over the ragged dunes and the long smooth beach.

The tea-house, with its gaily painted door and window-shutters, was set in a tiny, exuberant garden on the edge of the sand-hills, looking out across the tulip-flooded flatlands towards Haarlem, whose huge church of St Bavo dominated the level landscape like a mountain.

The drinkables provided by Mevrouw Minderop for her transient guests were cheering, and she had secret recipes for honey-cake and jam roly-poly of an incredible excellence. The fame of her neatness, her amiability, and her superior cookery spread abroad quietly among the *intelligentsia* in such matters. There was no publicity, no advertising except a little placard over the garden-gate, with WELTEVREDEN in gilt letters on a bright blue ground. But there was a steady trickle of patrons, and business was good enough to keep the house going.

I fell into the afternoon habit of riding out from my office in The Hague when work was slack, to have a cup of tea, a roly-poly, and perhaps a tiny glass of anisette with my pipe. These creature comforts were mildly spiced by talks with the plump widow in my stumbling Dutch, or her careful creaking English.

She always reminded me of the epitaph—in an Irish church I think—which recorded of a certain lady that "she was bland, passionate, and deeply religious, and worked beautifully in crewels." Anny Minderop was a Calvinist of the straitest sect, but distinctly of the Martha-type. She did not allow her faith in the absolute foreordination of all events to interfere with her anxious care in the baking of honey-cake and the brewing of tea and coffee.

The passionate element of her nature was centred on her two boys, who were rapidly growing to be equal to one man. He was a two-sided man. Karel, the older, was a brown-haired fleshy youth, with slow movements and a deep-rooted love of gardening. He had already found a good place with a tulip-grower in Oudwyk-Binnen. Klaas was a towheaded, blue-eyed lad about thirteen years old, sturdy in figure, rather stolid in manner, but full of adventure. He dreamed of more exciting things than the growing of bulbs. He had the blood of old Tasman and Heemskerck in his veins. The sea had cast her spell upon him. He was determined to be a sailor, a fisherman, an explorer, a captain; and ultimately, of course, in his dreams he saw himself an admiral, or at least a rear-admiral—a *schout-bij-nacht,* as the Dutch picturesquely call it.

"Little Mother," he would say, "didn't Holland win her glory from the sea?"

"Yes, sonny," she would answer, "but it cost her dear. Many brave Dutch bones sleep under the waters."

"What difference? It's as good sleeping under the waters as in the wormy dust of the graveyard. A man must die some time."

"But you're not a man yet. You're only a boy. It is foolish to risk losing your life before you've got it."

"I've got it already, mother. Look how big and strong I am for my age. None of the boys can throw me; and Skipper Houthof says I can tie all the sailor's knots. You don't want me to waste all that sticking bulbs in the ground and waiting for 'em to grow."

"Gardening is a good business, sonny; it was the first that God gave to man. It is safe and quiet. It is just reaping the fruit of His bounty."

"Yes, but the Bible says that they that go down to the sea in ships behold His wonders in the deep. I'd rather see one wonder than raise a million tulips. Och, mammy dear, let me be a sailor."

"But how are you going to do it? Nobody wants a boy."

"Mother dear, I'll tell you. Skipper Houthof is going to sail in his new lugger *Zeehond,* June fifth, for the herring-fishing. He's got a great crew—those big Diepen brothers, very strong men, elders in the kirk, and the two brothers Wynkoop, and little Pier Vos, and old Steenis, and Beekman, Groen, and Bruin who always go together, and Brouwer—those are all good Christians, you know, always go to the meeting and sing hymns. The skipper is taking young Arie Bok—you know that nice boy in our school—just my age—as cabin boy—says he'll take me too. Won't you please let me go?"

"That would make just thirteen on the ship," said the widow, who had been counting her crochet-stitches.

"Yes, but what difference? You always told me not to have these bybeliefs."

"That is right. Yet old customs sometimes have good reasons. You must let me weigh it over in my mind, Klaas; to-morrow I will tell you."

The boy went out of the room, and the widow Minderop turned to me as I sat smoking and thinking.

"It is hard to decide," she said. "Skipper Houthof is a good man, though he's young for his place. Those big Diepen brothers are fine seamen, none better; they're God-fearing men, too, though they shout too loud in meeting, and sometimes they drink too much old *Jenever* and make trouble in the village. But it isn't the captain and the crew I'm afraid of. It's the sea—the hungry sea that took my lad's father."

"Well" I answered, "it surely is hard to decide for others; not easy even to decide for ourselves. Perhaps it is just as well that in the long run a Wiser Person decides what will happen to us. Your Klaas is a good boy, and this seems to be a good crew. When a lad is in love with the sea, you may hold him back for a while, but the only possible way to cure him is to let him try it—and even that doesn't always work. Perhaps it ought not to. It is in God's hand—the sea also is His."

"I believe it," she answered, "but it is a strain on my faith, when I remember—"

II

The fifth of June came around in due season. The sturdy *Zeehond,* spick and span with her new rigging, fresh paint, brown sails, nets neatly stowed under tarpaulin, rowboats on deck, lay with the rest of the herring fleet in the small stone-walled haven, easily the queen of the fleet. Flags and streamers fluttered in the light breeze; the stone walls were lined with people, chattering, singing, and shouting huzzah. As the little ships began to stir some one struck up a hymn. The loudest singers were the big Diepen brothers, tall, heavily built, masterful men. Their light grey eyes shone under heavy brows in their tanned faces, like lustrous shells in a tangle of brown seaweed. They shouted the familiar tune an octave below the key.

Some of the crowd were weeping. There is something like a wedding in the sailing of a ship; it draws tears from the sentimental.

But Anny Minderop was not crying. She wanted her eyes clear to see the last of her boy Klaas. She wanted her silk handkerchief dry to wave to him as he leaned over the *hakkebord,* looking back.

Nothing could have been more fair and promising than the departure of the herring fleet that year. It is true that the green-grey expanse of water which is called in Germany the German Ocean, and elsewhere the North Sea, is always harsh and treacherous, often covered with danger-hiding fog, and sometimes swept by insane tempests. It is true also that in the gruesome war-time the perils of the deep were increased by German submarines and floating mines. For these the cautious Captain Houthof kept a sharp look-out. But the big Diepen brothers, and under their influence the rest of the crew, recked little of these uncharted dangers. Their mind was on the fishing and the profits to follow. A typical Dutchman faces a risk calmly if there is a chance of good gain behind it.

The reports from the fishing banks were all encouraging. The fish were already there, and coming in abundantly. They could be seen on the surface, milling around in vast circles, as if baby whirlwinds were lightly passing over the water. It was going to be a great catch for the *Zeehond,* predicted the Diepens. God was on their side, this time. He was going to make them rich if they obeyed Him.

"Even you," said the giant Simon, clapping the boy Klaas on the shoulder with a hand like a baked ham, "even you, my young one, shall carry home a pocketful of gulden to your mother, if you are good and say your prayers every day."

The boy stood as stiff as he could under the heavy caress and thanked the big man, who seemed to be really fond of him.

So far as I was able to learn afterwards, the voyage went splendidly for about three weeks. Weather fair; fishing fine; eighty tons of herring; everybody working hard and cheerful. Klaas and Arie wore their fingers sore hauling and mending the nets. The salt stung them fiercely. But it was great fun. They ate like pigs and slept like logs. Simon Diepen never would let them go to sleep without saying their prayers. The tone of the lugger was a compound of fervent piety, tense work, and high good humour. Even if the other men had wanted to slacken on the piety, the Diepens would not allow it. By their bigness, their strength, and their masterful ways they bossed the ship, including the young captain. Little Pict Vos followed them like a dog. He looked on them as Apostles. The rest of the crew stood in awe, and if they sinned at all, were careful to do it out of sight and hearing of the devout giants.

With the fourth week of the voyage came a strange alteration in the luck. Weather grew cold, rough, foggy, dangerous. Fish became scarce and hard to catch. Worst of all, the gin, of which a liberal supply had been provided for daily use, gave out entirely. The Diepens, who were heavy drinkers but always steady on their legs, felt the lack more than they knew. They grew nervous, moody, quick-tempered, overbearing. They brooded over the Bible, and said there was something wrong with the *Zeehond;* God's judgment followed her for sin.

One evening in a billowing fog the lugger ran close to a mass of wreckage from some lost ship. Entangled in it were two wooden cases. The Diepens pulled them aboard, and took them down below to open them. No one dared dispute their right. They found the cases full of bottles, one of which they uncorked. It was a strange liquor, but it looked, and smelled, and tasted like dark gin. It made them feel at home. The second bottle added to this effect. The third and fourth bottles they took up to the skipper.

"Look, captain," they said very solemnly, "here is a proof that we are not yet castaways. God has warned us. Now if we repent and put away our sins, He will spare us. But we must pray hard and do His will."

Then they went below and opened another bottle. But before it was finished they fell asleep, with the Bible open between them at the Book of Revelation.

In the morning grey they came on deck and Pier Vos followed them. The skipper was taking a turn at the wheel. All three of the men seemed steady on their legs, but their eyes were wild. Simon lifted up his face and began to talk with God. The skipper said he could not hear the words, but he heard the trombone voice in which God answered. Then Simon came up close, and said:

"I am Christ. God has just told me that I must clean the Devil out of this ship. He is here, in the things, in the men, especially in that damned old helmsman, Steenis. You can see the Devil looking out of his eyes."

"But what will you do?" asked the skipper. "Have a care! We must answer for everything."

"I have no care," said Simon, "but to do what God tells me. You must follow. Men will judge us, but our conscience will be clean. My brother Jan and Pier Vos heard God speak to me. The ship must be cleaned. Do not interfere, or the Devil will get you too."

Simon went on his heel and went below. From that moment on the lugger a fatal insanity reigned and a superstitious cowardice trembled before it.

Just what happened on the doomed vessel will never be fully known. A week later a Norwegian steamship picked up the *Zeehond,* drifting helpless on the water. Three men were missing; mast and rigging, gear and boats, all gone; deck and forecastle smeared with blood; she was a gruesome floating ruin. The Norwegian towed her into Hull.

The big Diepens, Pier Vos, and two others were sent to Holland in a fast steamer. The skipper and four others were brought on a slower boat, not yet in.

The general outline of the tragedy had been printed promptly in the newspapers. But I wanted to know the particulars. What happened to the two boys? Was my blue-eyed friend Klaas safe? How had he been affected by his first adventure at sea?

III

The summer day brightened and gloomed in the sky as I wheeled along the beach toward Oudwyk and the cottage Weltevreden.

"Well contented" the name means. It is much used for houses great and small in Holland, and represents one aspect of the Dutch character. Would Mevrouw Minderop be so well contented now, after this tragedy? Or would her calm be broken, as the July afternoon threatened to break under the heavy thunder-clouds looming in the west?

After I had passed the populous bathing-station of Scheveningen the coast stretched before me in long monotony. On the right rose the dunes; steep banks and hillocks, yellowish grey on their face, crested above with rusty shrubs and tufts of wire-grass, like the wisps of hair on an old man's head. Under my wheel crunched the ashen sand of the desolate beach; bare of life, empty even of beautiful shells; tossed and tormented by the fitful wind in the dry places; corroded and wrinkled in the damp places by the waves, which advanced menacing and roaring, spread out, and then withdrew whispering, as if they conspired some day to conquer and overwhelm this low-lying, rich, obstinate land of dikes and dunes. On the left the North Sea brooded; pallid, *verdâtre,* like the rust on copper; a curious, envious, discontented sea, darkened by black cloud shadows, lit suddenly and strangely by vivid streaks of light like signals of danger, fading on the horizon into the grey mist and leaden clouds.

What wonder that the Hollanders, facing ever this menace and mystery of seeping tides and swelling billows that threaten to rob them of their hard-won land, have developed the stubborn courage, the dour pertinacity that mark their race? What wonder that on the other side, having thus far won the victory of resistance to wild waters and foreign tyrants, they are at times extravagantly merry, full of loud laughter and song, the best fighters and feasters in the world ? Look at the brave gaiety of Franz Hals' *Arquebusiers* or Van der Helst's *Banquet of the Target Company.*

When I pushed my bicycle up one of the sandy tracks that lead inland, I found myself in another, and to my eyes pleasanter, world. The sea was hidden, for the most part, by the crest of the dunes. The hills and hollows lay around me in green confusion. Mosses and trailing vines covered the ground. Clumps of pine-trees, clusters of oaks, thickets of birch and alder, were scattered here and there. Larks warbled from the sky; wrens and finches sang in the copse; rabbits scuttled into the thick bushes. It was a little wilderness, but no desert.

Presently the outlying houses of Oudwyk appeared, and at last the red gable and blue gate of Weltevreden, sitting quiet in its gay little garden. Roses and lilies, geraniums and fuchsias portioned the light into many colours by the secret alchemy of flowers. The reseda sweetened the air with its clean scent. The place was a monument of the skill and care with which man makes the best of Nature's gifts.

Within, the widow Minderop sat at her crochet-work in the tea-room. The uncertain weather had hindered other guests. She rose from her chair, dropping her work, and came to meet me with unusual eagerness.

"Yes, mynheer," she cried as if there were only one subject worthy of speech, "my Klaas is safe. God has delivered him from the sea and from those wicked men. I have a telegram from him. He is coming home to-day. Och, how I hanker to see him, to know really how he is."

A moment later the door opened and the boy came in; tanned, weather-beaten, a bit the worse for wear, but stark and sound as ever. Only his face was older, as if he had lived through years. He embraced his mother with boyish affection, saluted me with grave friendliness, and then sat down at the table to partake of coffee with unlimited honeycakes and rolls.

At our request he began to unfold the story of his weird adventure. Reluctantly at first, and with some interruptions, (which I leave out,) he told what had happened on the lugger, and how it had struck him.

"In the beginning," he said, "it was splendid. The weather was good. The *Zeehond* is a great ship. She rides over the waves like a water-fowl. None of them could smash her. The fishing was lucky. Everybody was in a good humour. Och, mother, the sea is just wonderful, I just love it.

"I don't know how long it was before the change came. The fishing petered out; the gin—you know how much those big Diepens drink—was all gone. They got cross and grumpy and angry at nothing. They sang and prayed more than ever; but it sounded to me as if they were not praying *to* God so much as *at* some one that they hated on the ship.

"Mother, that's an awful thing—to hear men pray *at* people instead of *to* God! It scared me. What if God should overhear them?

"Then, after four or five days, those Diepens fished up two boxes out of the sea, and took them below. They were full of strange liquor, and Simon and Jan began to drink again, more than ever. But the drink did not make them cheerful and friendly. It made them black and sour and full of wickedness.

"Something happened on deck in the morning, before I was up. Simon told how God had spoken to him, and said that 'he was Christ our Saviour, and that there were devils in the ship, and that Simon must clean them out, by book or by crook, no matter what it cost, no matter who got hurt. That was what our Saviour did on earth.'

"But, mother, when Christ was here many people who had devils came to Him and He *never* hurt one of them. He was kind to them. He delivered them. He made them well. That is why I was sure that it could not be the spirit of Jesus who entered into Simon. It was the big Devil himself who came in with pride and anger and strong drink.

"But Jan believed what Simon said because he was like him. And Piet Vos believed because he was Simon's little hound. And the skipper thought he had heard God's voice speaking to Simon; but he was really just plain scared because the Diepens were so big and strong and fierce. The rest of the crew were scared too, except three men. These were the ones that Simon said had devils because he hated them.

"The first was old Steenis the helmsman. He wouldn't give in to the Diepens at all. He said they were just crazy. So Jan and Simon fell on him at the wheel; cracked his head open with a belaying pin so that the blood and brains spilled on the deck; and threw him into the sea.

"Och, mother, it was frightful. Arie Bok and I were scared sick. But inside I was not afraid. I remembered what you told me about God taking care of us if we try to do right, and I thought that a real Hollander ought never to *show* that he's afraid anyhow.

"Why didn't we do something to stop the butchery? But what could we do? If we had stood up against those big, beastly men, they would have laughed, and snapped us in two like a pipe-stem. All we could do was to cry, and beg them to stop, and say our prayers, and keep as far as we could from the bloody work.

"The next two that were killed were Beekman and Brouwer. They were quiet men, kind of dull and stupid. But Simon said they had devils —dumb devils, he called them. So he made them dance on the deck for about an hour to shake the devils out.

"But Simon and Jan and little Piet said the dancing was bad—Devil dancing, they called it; no good at all. So they drove poor old Beekman and Brouwer down below, and bashed their heads in with iron bars, and cut their breasts open with knives to let the devils loose. Then they dragged the bodies on deck, all bloody, and threw them into the sea. While they were doing this all of them sang a hymn.

"Mother, it made me so sick, I thought I was going to die.

"The next day they set to work on the ship. They said it was poisoned by the devils and must be cleansed all over. So they cut down the mast and the rigging and threw them overboard. The rowboats, the nets, the empty barrels that stood on deck, everything was chucked into the water. Even the woodwork was hacked and broken. It made my heart bleed to see the lovely *Zeehond* abused and spoiled that way. She was so good and strong. What harm had she done?

"Then we drifted around three or four days—I don't know how long—like a log in the sea. We had no food except salt herrings and a few crusts of bread. But at every meal those black Diepens prayed and sang hymns and drank gin. It was filthy.

"Then a ship from Norway picked us up, and I got home somehow, I don't know just how. Och, mother, mother, I've been through hell."

The lad lost control of himself; fell on his knees beside his mother and put his head on her lap, shaken by the dry sobs of a boy ashamed to cry.

She stroked his yellow hair gently and dropped a kiss on it.

"Cry, darling," she murmured, "cry! It will do you good. You've come *through.* God has delivered you. And now you know what the sea can do to men, you'll give it up."

The boy lifted his head. His blue eyes sparkled through tears. His lips were firm again.

"Mother dear," he cried, "it was *not* the sea. It was the beastly *men.* The sea is *clean.* The sea was *kind* to us. It was vanity and hatred and drink that made the trouble. Rum and religion don't mix well. They let the big Devil into proud men. I'm going to sea again, some day. But I'll stay with you, dearest, till I grow up."

BOUND FOR RIO GRANDE

A.E. Dingle
(1874-   )

I

THE old man's broken teeth gleamed through tight, thin lips whenever his rheumy eyes glimpsed the lofty spars of the clipper in the bay. She was the only deepwaterman in port.

"Blood boat!" he chattered. "A blood boat. But you don't git no more o' my blood, not by a damn sight!"

Hastily turning away, the old man shambled along the wharf, at the end of which stood an office. Opposite the office, bright and cheery against the grey and dirt of the waterside, a tiny store kept its door open, revealing an interior to set the pulses of an ancient mariner leaping. Never a yellow oilskin, nor a bit of rope; nor one block or shackle offended the eye grown weary through half a century of salty servitude.

Glossy plugs of black tobacco; clay pipes of virgin whiteness and lissome shape; woolly comforters and stout shore-going winter socks; old, tasty cheese and soft, white bread; fat sausage and luscious, boneless ham; all these things, mere fancies of the dreaming sailor-man at sea, were clear to the view of old Pegwell through the open door of the little store as he paced up and down before the office, waiting for the man to whom he was to make application for the job of watchman of the wharf.

There was a sharp hint of frost in the air; a sharper threat of wind. There was just enough of brine and breeze, just a trace. It smelt of salt water and of boats, with never an obtrusive reminder of hardcase deepwater ships.

Ah! There was a snug harbour indeed for a battered old seadog. If a chap could expect to come at last into such a fair haven as that little store now he wouldn't mind a few decades of bitter travail at sea.

"Hell's delight! Fat chance I got o' savin' money now!" he growled.

He sought for a match, found none. It was just his luck. But he had a few pennies. He would buy matches in that store. He waited until the stream of lunch customers thinned out, and entered.

"Box o' lucifers," he demanded, slapping down the coin. His eyes wandered around the homey little place. There were things he had not noticed before from outside. Red candy; bright painted toys; rubber bails. Children came there evidently. What sort of children would come to that neighbourhood for toys?

"Your matches, sir," said a rippling, laughing voice; and old Pegwell turned around sharply and discovered why children might well come to that store. Men, too. A twenty-year-old girl was offering him matches. Her big brown eyes danced mischievously. She was as trim as a brand-new China clipper.

"Thank 'e, ma'am," said Pegwell, as he grabbed the matches and shuffled out, dazzled and confused by the vision. He was still dazzled, his box of matches unopened, when he stumbled against the man he had waited to see.

"Heard you wanted a watchman, sir," said old Pegwell respectfully. He proffered a bundle of ship's discharges as evidence of character. The man glanced through them, glanced keenly at the old man, and nodded.

"Night work," he said. "Six to six. If you suit, in a month I'll give you a day shift, turn and turn about. Nothing much to do here, but you'll have to watch out for strangers. Lot of crooks on the water nowadays. Rum, dope, all sorts. Start to-night."

Old Pegwell had landed his first shore job. For the first time since starting out to earn his own living he could afford to gaze curiously at a sailorman, going large, staggering along to the next' blind pig.

"Sailors is a lot o' lummoxes," he decided. "Like kids."

> "If yuh save up yer money, an' don't git on th' rocks,
> Yuh'll have plenty o' tobacker in yer old tobacker box,"

he sang quaveringly.

He pulled up sharply, ceasing his song, and drifted over toward the little store again. He would have to find some place to live, to sleep at least. That girl looked different from others he had known. Perhaps she would tell him where to seek. He walked in, more confidently than before. He had a shore job now.

"Plug o' tobacker, miss," he asked for. The girl appeared from behind a provision case, putting on a smile as she emerged. A man thrust back deeper into the shadow. Pegwell saw nothing of the forced smile or the man. His eyes were roving, taking in the wealth of the stock. When he turned to take his tobacco the girl's smile was sunny enough. He felt encouraged.

"Beg y' pardon, miss, I just got a job on th' wharf, and thought likely you could direc' me where to git a bed, cheap. I ain't a pertickler chap. Just es long's there ain't too many bugs, or—"

"You got a job on the wharf?" interrupted a man's voice. A youth, who might have been good-looking if he could have changed his eyes, came from behind the provision case and scowled surlily. "What job ?"

"Watchman," said Pegwell importantly. "Night watchman. Know any place I kin get a doss?"

"How did you get to hear about this job ? I'm livin' here right along, lookin' for a job, and a stranger comes along and lands it over my head. You're a sailor, ain't you?"

"No; watchman," retorted old Pegwell. "Was a sailorman. Had good discharges. I'm a watchman now. D'you know of a place I kin sleep, miss?"

The youth dragged the girl aside, and they muttered together, ignoring Pegwell. Presently the girl spoke sharply, angrily.

"It's best for you to go away, Larry. It's a good thing you never heard of the wharf job. Too many old friends hanging around there! You've signed on in the *Stella.* Now you go. You know what the judge said. Go to work, like a decent fellow, and you won't be watched like a—"

"Go to work ? Hell!I'm willing to go to work, Mary, but what d'you want to shove me off into a damned old square rigger for? Ain't there work to be got—"

"It's best that you go away for a while," insisted the girl. "You were lucky to escape jail when that gang of smugglers got caught. I'm not sure now that the judge was satisfied about you. If you stay around here they're sure to watch you".

"Beg pardon, miss, but if you know of a place" interrupted Pegwell impatiently. Larry swung around and grinned crookedly.

"All right, sister," he told her. "I'll do it to please you." He took Pegwell's arm. "I'll find you a bed, old timer. What time d'you go to work?"

"Six. Want to get a sleepin' place afore that."

"Meet me here at five-thirty. I'll have a bunk for you by then."

Pegwell started off for a walk, but streets were a barren wilderness to him. He gravitated toward the harbour. He found himself somehow in front of the little store. It was a long time from five-thirty. Methodically he noted the contents of the window, grew amazed at the number and variety.

"Larry hasn't come back yet," the girl called out from the store. "Won't you wait inside?"

Pegwell looked sheepish. Sailors of the deep waters were always easily abashed in the presence of a decent woman. Pegwell scarcely dared to look up from the floor as he entered. But the girl began to chatter to him, and he felt at ease when she handed him a match for his cold pipe. In ten minutes he was spinning her fearsome yarns. In half an hour they were friends. She confided little scraps of her own affairs.

"Larry's a good fellow," she said, a bit sadly. "Too good. He's easy to lead. There has been a lot of smuggling along the front lately, and he ought to have kept away. But he always seems to have money, never goes to work, and when a big capture was made he was under suspicion. The judge told him he had better go to work, then folks would be apt to believe that he was innocent. Of course he is innocent! My brother Larry couldn't be a crook, Mr. Pegwell. But he has been under suspicion, and I made him join that big sailing ship, the *Stella,* for a voyage. When he comes back everything will be forgotten, and he can—Oh, here's Jack! Excuse me, Mr. Pegwell."

A tall, brown-faced man of thirty limped in. Pegwell was no keen-eyed Solon concerning women of Mary Bland's sort; but when he saw her pretty face light up and her big brown eyes flash at the appearance of this good-looking fellow who limped on a shortened leg, he knew he was intruding. Puffing furiously at his pipe, he stumped out upon the front.

At five-thirty Larry found Pegwell sitting on the cap log of the wharf.

"Come on, old timer. I got a fine bunk for you," said Larry. Pegwell followed him.

"I heared you be goin' in th' *Stella,*" remarked Pegwell.

"I ain't proud of it," retorted Larry.

"I just come home in her. A hell ship, she is! Can sail, though. You ain't old an' stiff. Do yer work an' don't give th' mates no slack, an' you'll be all kiff, me son."

Larry glanced curiously at the queer old man who thought fit to preach duty to him.

They turned down by a disused and evil-smelling fish dock, out of sight of a growing district.

"Have to cross the creek in a boat," grinned Larry. "Save time, see. You have to be on the job, now, but other times you can walk around. Here y' are."

At the foot of a perpendicular ladder of boards nailed on a slimy pile a boat lay. Three husky boatmen grinned up knowingly at Larry. A blue canvas sea bag lay in the bottom of the boat, doubled up, like a dead man.

"Take good care of my old friend," Larry ordered. He gently drew Pegwell to the ladder. "Hurry up, old timer. Soon's they see you snug they have to come back for me."

Pegwell stepped on the ladder.

"Ho!" he said. "That's your sea bag, hey? Well, me son, do yer work an' give the mates no slack, an'—"

Something heavy fell upon his grey old head. He tumbled into the boat. As he pitched forward Pegwell heard the laugh of his friend Larry, and he realized the treatment awaiting him.

The tail clipper put to sea. On her forecastlehead men tramped drearily around the capstan. Hard-bitted officers cursed them; an exasperated tugboat skipper bawled; the anchor clung tenaciously to the mud.

> "An' awa-ay, Rio! Awa-ay, Rio!
> Sing fare yew well, my bonny young gal,
> We are boun' fer Rio Grande!"

A quavery, broken old pipe raised that chantey. The mate left the knighthead, plunging in among the desolate crew, thumping, thumping, cursing venomously.

"You sojers!" he yelped. "You double-left-legged sojers! Here's old Noah come to life again, and you let him show you your work!Heave, blind you! Heave! Sing out, old Noah! Why, damn my eyes, if it ain't old Pegwell come with us again!"

The mate stood off a pace, staring at Pegwell. Sailormen rarely made two voyages in the *Stella.*

"I didn't join, sir," protested Pegwell, ceasing his song. All the men stopped. Pegwell had tried to persuade the captain he was not one of his crew as soon as he recovered his wits. The result had been painful. "I got to be on the job at six, sir. I'll lose my new job. I wuz shanghaied—"

A fist thumped him hard between the shoulders, driving him back to his capstan bar with coughing lungs.

"Sing out! Start something! Heave, damn you!" retorted the mate, and fell upon the miserable gang tooth and nail. The tug hooted owlishly.

A jolly good ship, an' a jolly good crew:
Awa-ay, Rio!
A jolly good mate, an' a good skipper, too,
An' we're boun' for Rio Grande!

Pegwell tramped around the capstan. A donkey yoked to the bar of a mill. A sailor bound by a lifetime of hard usage to a habit of obedience.

Pegwell's bunk had bugs. All the bunks had bugs. Pegwell's bunk was beneath a sweat leak where a bit of dry rot had crumbled a corner of a deck beam. But Larry's sea bag, a blue canvas bag made by a sailorman, revealed itself full of amazing comforts. The old fellow had never owned such a bag. There were blankets. Woollen, not woolly. Warm underwear, stockings, shirts. Good oil-skins, leakproof boots. There was a real steel razor; a real steel sheath-knife. A great bundle of soap and matches; white enamelware dish and pannikin; and a dainty thing that puzzled Pegwell until he opened it. It was a folder of blue cloth, tied about with a silken cord. On the flat side was worked in silk, beautifully, "Larry; from Mary."

Inside, cunning pockets were full of needles, thread, buttons, scissors. And tucked into the innermost fold was a note, in a slender hand bearing signs of stress, bidding Larry act the man, wishing him luck, praying for his safe return. The feel of it gave old Pegwell a warm thrill.

"Hey, me son, I want that bunk!" he announced grimly, shaking the shoulder of a sleeping ordinary seaman whose bunk was leakless. "C'm on. Out of it! Able seamen comes lust, me lad."

Pegwell carefully placed his needle case in a dry place, then hauled the youth out onto the filthy floor, cotton blanket and all. Even youth must yield to experience when youth is seasick, and experience runs along lines of deep water pully-haul.

Pegwell now had the cleanest, driest bunk in the forecastle. He stole lemons from the steward, which he hid cunningly. From time to time he cut one in slices, fastened it to ship's side or bunk board, thereby driving puzzled bugs to other, less exclusive quarters. He stole nails from Chips; made shelves for his little comforts, pegs for his fine new clothes. He stole a bit of white line from the bosun and made a pair of flat sennit bands by which his spare blankets swung from the bunk above.

By the time the clipper crossed the line Pegwell only dimly remembered Larry's treachery. He only mistily recalled the job he had got but had never worked at. It was easy for the old man to slip back into the habits of a lifetime; even though the ship was a hard place. The great outstanding point was that for the first time in his dreary life old Pegwell sailed deep water possessed of everything necessary for comfort, and some luxuries to boot. And this he owed to Mary Bland.

Old Pegwell usually fell asleep with a flash-back of memory to a snug little store on a dingy waterside, overladen with a stock of wonders, presided over by a laughing girl whose big, brown, friendly eyes sometimes held just a trace of trouble. Then he would think darkly of Larry, only to sink into sound slumber in the warmth of Larry's woollies under Larry's blankets.

II

Pegwell's bunk was no longer dry. No man's bunk was. The forecastle was a reeling, freezing, weeping dungeon peopled with miserable devils to whom hell would have been heaven. For thirty days the clipper had been battered by a northwesterly gale off Cape Horn.

When a man came from the wheel after a two hours' trick he was blue, and tottery, and grinning, and more than a little insane.

Pegwell stood his wheel warm and dry. He felt the bitterness of the weather and the ship's stress, but for once his old bones were not racked with extreme cold. The ship steered badly. They sent the young ordinary seamen to hold the lee spokes.

"You just put yet weight to it when I shoves the helm up or down, me son," said Pegwell. The lad's teeth chattered; his lanky body, undernourished, 'twixt boy and man, shook like a royal mast under a thrashing sail.

"Y—yessir!" he chattered, fearfully.

Pegwell glanced sharply at the lad once or twice. Since their first encounter over the change of bunks, the lad had not been remarkable for politeness toward the old man. But there was no hint of impudence in that "Yessir!" The boy looked blue.

Grumbling, taking a hand from the wheel when he could, gripping a spoke desperately to check it, the old man peeled off his heavy monkey jacket.

"Slip into this yer jacket, me son!" he roared, and put his shoulder to the spokes, bringing the ship to her course before the mate arrived. The lad thawed. When the watch was up, he was glowing. Old Pegwell was warm, but wet through with driving snow. He watched his chance to shuffle along the main deck between seas. The lad, less cautious, started first.

When they were in the deep waist, the new helmsman let the ship go off and a mile long hissing sea reared up and fell aboard the length of her. Pegwell grabbed a lifeline. When the decks cleared themselves through the ports, he clawed his way choking and blinded to the forecastle, soaked to the skin, his broken teeth chattering with the icy chill.

"Where's th' young feller?" he chattered.

"I see him bashed up against th' galley," growled the man nearest. "He'll git here. Can't lose them kind."

He didn't "git here." The young ordinary seaman never rounded the Horn. He went overboard to death wearing old Pegwell's monkey jacket.

Making northing and westing with dry decks, though the wind was bitterly cold, men with all the sailorman's improvidence discarded tattered oilskins and soggy socks. And with all the fiendish frailty of Cape Horn weather, the fair wind blew itself out, a rolling calm followed, and then another, fiercer northwesterly gale shrieked down and drove the ship back into the murderous gray seas to the southward.

Pegwell clambered stiffly out of the rigging after re-tying the points of the reefed main topsail. The maindeck was a seething chaos of ropesnarled water. In the roaring torrent men were being hurled along the deck. Only a frantically waving arm or leg indicated that a man was not dead. Then a greater sea thundered aboard. It smashed the boat gallows. The boats hung over the side, precariously held by the ropes.

A spare topmast was torn loose from chain lashings and chocks: a massive stick of Oregon pine, roughly squared, it hurtled aft on the torrent, broke a sailor's half drowned body cruelly, and crashed end on against the poop bulkhead.

Pegwell and the watch fought with the spar. The seas endued the timber with devilish spite. Twice all hands were torn from their hold, rolled about the flooded decks in the icy water, battered near to death by the murderous stick.

In a lull they secured the spar. The boats were gone. They picked up tangled gear, and took two mangled men from the meshes.

The wind struck afresh. It staggered the ship. And while she staggered and hung poised another chuckling sea climbed over the six foot bulwarks and filled her decks.

"Bill's hurted bad, now, sir," screamed Pegwell, shivering in the grip of cold and numb agony. Bill was the bosun. He hung twisted and pallid between the two men who lifted him. They bore him forward. Chips stood across the sill of the smashed door of the tiny cabin they shared.

"This ain't no place for a hutred man!" Chips grumbled. "Tell th' Old Man he ought t' be took care of aft."

They told the skipper.

"No room aft," the skipper howled at them. "Put him in the forecastle if it's any drier."

They bore the man below. Instinctively they laid him in old Pegwell's bunk, for it was driest. All were wet. Pegwell's at least boasted woollen coverings.

Pegwell himself covered the silent form with a blanket. He needed no hint to cover the pallid face too. He made no protest when a sailor gently pulled another blanket from under the bosun.

"Jack's cruel cold, mate," said the sailor. He wrapped Jack, another storm victim, in the blanket with roughened hands that trembled.

Overhead the seas thundered on deck. The *Stella* fought her stubborn way against the gale under three lower topsails, reefed upper main topsail, and treble reefed foresail with a ribbon of fore topmast staysail.

The gale died out. A fair wind came. The ship sped north again, scarred but sound, clothed in new canvas, triumphant. They buried Bill and Jack in Pegwell's bedding.

By this time Pegwell had little left of his grand outfit. As the rags of his mates gave out, he grumblingly gave of his store. Grumbled and gave. That was Pegwell. But he never let go of that little blue cloth needle case inscribed, "Larry; from Mary." Slyly he had picked at the stitches until the word "Larry" was becoming indistinguishable. When a few more threads fell out he could show his treasure to incredulous sailormen, and they would never know that the obliterated name was not his own.

The crew scuttled from the *Stella* like rats when she docked. Only Pegwell hung on. Alone of the outward bound crew before the mast, he stubbornly resisted all the efforts of the mates to get him out. They could ship a new crew homeward at half the wages paid outward. None of the deserters waited for their wages. Their forfeited pay was so much profit to the ship. But Pegwell refused to be driven out. Cheerless and bare his bunk might be. It was. There was always the little blue folded housewife to remind him that he had a shore job once over against a snug little store. And the ambition that had flamed then still burned.

As for quitting the ship, Pegwell had wages due. Not a lot, but wages still. If he completed the voyage, drawing no advance whatever, buying nothing from the slop chest, he would have coming to him a nice little nest egg which might hatch into a home at last. That nest egg loomed big to the captain.

"Set him to chipping cable," said the skipper. "Work him up!"

The mates worked him up, cruelly, but they could not work him out.

Homeward bound round the Horn, Pegwell showed his little blue housewife to the new hands. They were a hard lot. They made ribald fun about it. They stole his poor bedding, and dared him to identify it. He endured. They stole his sea boots. Pegwell endured that, too. But somebody stole his little blue housewife, worked in silk, "—; from Mary," and there was a fight.

It was a young weasel of a wastrel who tried to prevent Pegwell from taking back his treasure. A weasel bred in the muck of the water front; cunning and full of devious fighting tricks. But the old seaman fought on sure feet on a reeling deck; fought with righteous fury swelling his breast; fought without feeling the brutal knee or the gouging thumb. And he beat his man, recovered his treasure, and earned much freedom from molestation.

In the bleak, soul-searching gales off Cape Stiff, Pegwell suffered intensely. He shivered and froze in silence.

The old sailor had always his little blue cloth treasure. He whispered his troubles to it as he shivered in his wet bed—it was the one comfort nobody could take from him. He might shake with cold and wet all through a watch below, but there was ever before him the vision of that snug little store, the pretty, laughing girl whose big brown eyes yet held a trace of trouble. Somehow he grew to fasten the responsibility for that trouble on Larry. And, once established, his own grievance against the man smouldered fiercer.

When the tall clipper furled her sails in her home port again, Pegwell's bitterness against Larry Bland had intensified to such a degree as to surprise the old chap himself. Bitterness formed no part of his real nature. But it was winter again; the snow fell; the streets, from the ship, looked dreary and inhospitable. And old Pegwell had nothing but rags to cover his aching bones.

The rest of the fo'mast hands had drawn something on account of wages and gone ashore to spend that and mortgage the balance due. But not old Pegwell. He would carry ashore every dollar coming to him from the voyage he ought never to have made. He would buy a suit of clothes and stout shoes that would last, put the rest of his money in safe hands, then look for Larry.

"It'll be him and me fer it!" he muttered.

III

The ship paid off. Soulless wretches who had whined and cringed under the punishment of the sea rolled up bold and blusterous, full of hot courage at twenty-five cents a hot shot, cursing captain and mates and ship as they took their pitiful pay.

In an hour Pegwell entered the little store, and in ten seconds more a Cape Horn Voyage in a cardcase packet was a vanished horror. The big brown eyes of Mary Bland glistened with welcome, even though at first they had been cloudy with uncertainty.

"I am so glad to see you again, Pegwell," she cried. "It was so good of you to change places with Larry. I hope you had a good voyage. Won't you come inside?"

Pegwell grinned sourly as he followed her into the snug little room behind the shop. He had meant to say something about that change of jobs. Instead, with a warmth seeping through his bones clear to his heart, mellowing it again, he forgot Larry and smoked himself into rosy visions under the musical spell of her voice.

In an hour they were as intimate as before the *Stella* went out. Mary had told him, shyly, that Jack wanted a speedy wedding; she had barely hinted that brother Larry was a stumbling block, immediately suppressing the hint. She had offered to work Pegwell's name into the little blue housewife where the word "Larry" had been picked out; and when she took it from him her eyes were suspiciously moist. Pegwell noticed it, though the girl tried hard to hide her feelings.

Then Jack came in and old Pegwell went out. The gladness in Mary's eyes, the pride in those of the stalwart cripple, gave the old mariner a thrill. It made him boil, too. There was a couple just aching for each other, hindered by a waster of a brother not worth a crocodile's tear.

"Hullo, old Pegwell," smiled Jack as he passed. He stuck out a strong brown hand in a hearty grip. "Mighty glad to see you again. Ought to stay this time. Going to buy Mary's shop, she tells me. Hurry up, old fellow. She's keeping me waiting all on your account."

Jack laughed, and went to Mary's side, leaving Pegwell wondering. He waited out in the cold street until Jack came out, then joined him in his walk and put the question bluntly:

"What's Larry up to?"

Jack was serious. His smile fled at the blunt demand. Anger was in his eyes, but he dismissed it. Pegwell, shrewder perhaps than he was given credit for being, noticed these little things. He put two and two together handily enough, and found the amount was four—no more or less.

"I wish Larry would either get bumped off or caught with the goods, Pegwell,"

Jack said. "He's breaking Mary's heart. She won't believe any wrong about him, yet she knows he's bound hellbent for ruin. If he was dead she would be better off. The rat has taken all her little savings and is about eating up her profits now. She won't marry, though God knows Larry's way of living don't influence me a bit where she's concerned. If Larry got sent up for a long stretch it would be better for Mary, though she would mourn him as if he was dead. I wish she would get rid of the store, quit this neighbourhood, and let me make her happy. But she won't, as long as that rat is loose."

"Didn't 'e go to work on the dock?" asked Pegwell, raging. "'E bunged me off in th' *Stella* and took my job, didn't he?"

"He held the job for one week and quit," Jack replied. "He said he'd made a killing at the races. Two watchmen since have either fallen off the dock at night or been thrown off." Jack was silent for a moment.

"Pegwell," said Jack at length, "I'm glad you're home. You can do a lot for Mary. I ought not to mention this to a soul; but I believe you are her friend."

"Friend?" rasped Pegwell. "Mister, you're bloody foolish! That little gal kin use me fer a door mat an' I'll show you what sort of a friend I am fust time I set eyes on that Larry!"

"Not so loud," Jack whispered. They passed a policeman, who nodded to Jack. "Pegwell, they're out to get Larry now! I have done all I can. I can't shield him any longer. He's out of town for a while, but when he comes back he's going to be jumped on, and he'll get ten years."

"Wot d'you think I can do?" demanded Pegwell. "Can I save him when you can't? Want me to go up for him, same as I made a Cape voyage in a hell ship for him ?" The old man was furious.

"You can only be a friend and comfort to Mary," said Jack quietly. Pegwell's wrinkled face was screwed up grotesquely with the intensity of his thought.

"Seems to me," he said, "if you was to sort of hurry her into a weddin', maybe you could do a bit o' comfortin' yourself. If I had money enough to offer to buy her shop off her I c'd take care o' the Larry rat."

"Oh, you have money enough," retorted Jack quietly. "Mary said long ago you could pay out of the profits. You only need about a hundred to pay down. I guess you have that much."

Pegwell was apparently not listening; yet in fact he was: He seemed to be looking sheer through the cold, grey drizzle into the future, and if his worn, lined old face was any guide, what he saw in the dim perspective of imagination held more light than shadow.

"What's th' wust this yer Larry's done?" he suddenly asked. "Killed anybody?"

"Oh, no," replied Jack swiftly. "Nothing like that."

"Been wreckin' some young gal—"

"No more than he has wrecked Mary's youth," Jackinterrupted. "He's just a plain crook. Dope smuggling; peddling, too. The worst he's done is to sell dope to school kids. Bad enough I'd say."

"Not quite es bad es murder, I s'pose," Pegwell growled, "though be damned ef I know why it ain't. Anyhow, Jack, me lad, you take the advice of a old lummox, marry Mary whether she wants to or not, and i'll promise to take care o' Larry. I'll see he don't git sent up. You tell her. I be going round to-night again and see how fur you're right about that hunderd down and hunderd when you ketch me shop purchase proppisition. S'long, Jack. Set them weddin' bells to ringin'."

Late that night Mary Bland bade Pegwell good night at the door of the little shop. She was rosy and smiling. Her brown eyes were wide and bright. Pegwell had never seen her so completely alive and gladsome. She shook his hand twice, and just for a tiny instant a speck of cloud flickered in her eyes.

"If you believe you can help Larry, I know you can," she said. "I know he will be safe in your care, old Pegwell."

"He'll git a man's chance, you kin make sartin," stated Pegwell. "Good night, Missy, an' Gawd keep you smilin'. I'll be around to meet Jack in the mornin' and settle about the shop. Forgit yer troubles. Th' cops don't want Larry. If they did they couldn't git him."

At the end of the week Old Pegwell took undivided charge of the little shop, while Jack and Mary went about on some mysterious business connected with a license. Old Pegwell stood in the door watching them, and his old pipe emitted clouds of smoke in sympathy with the depth of his breathing. He felt queerly tight about the heart.

"Gawd bless 'em, goddammit!" he barked chokily.

A man came to buy tobacco. The two men stared at each other.

"Damn my eyes if 't ain't old Pegwell!" roared the mate of the *Stella*. "Come to moorings at last, hey, you old fox?"

"Aye, mister, you won't bullydam old Pegwell no more. When d'ye sail?"

The mate laughed, picking up his change.

"Next Saturday. I'll put yer name on yer old bunk. Or p'raps you'd tike to sail bosun, hey ?"

Pegwell laughed comfortably. He spread his feet wide as he stood again in the doorway, gazing after the rolling figure of the mate. At last, at last he was man enough to tell a first mate to go scratch his ear. He turned to go inside, for the air was cold in spite of the sun, and the shop must be kept warm, when a scurrying figure doubled the corner, burst in after him, and slammed the door.

Larry Bland stood there before him, panting, wild-eyed.

"Where's Mary?" he rasped.

"Gone out, me son," said Pegwell grimly. "Just calm down. I own this here shop now. What kin I do for you?"

Larry glanced around the place furtively. He had a hunted look. Pegwell remembered Jack's words. A dark shape appeared against the glass of the door outside and Larry made for the inside room. Pegwell hastened him in as the door opened and a policeman entered.

"Larry Bland just came in here. Where is he?" he demanded.

"Orf'cer, Larry Bland shanghaied me a v'yage round Cape Stiff," grinned Pegwell. "D'you 'magine he'd come where I be?"

"I saw him open the door."

"Aye, an' he dam' soon shut it again!"

The policeman stepped to the door of the inner room and peered inside. Old Pegwell heaved a tremendous sigh of relief when he quickly turned and bolted from the shop. Larry had taken care of his own concealment. He crawled in through a rear window when Pegwell called his name.

"Where's Mary gone?" he asked hoarsely. Larry looked scared. "I got to get to her."

"You can't get to her," returned Pegwell. "If it's the coppers you're scared of, lay low and keep your head. I won't let no cops git you, 'less you cuts up rough. You git upstairs to yer own room, while I thinks out what to do."

"You ain't gettin' even are you?" snarled Larry suspiciously.

"In my own way, yes, me son. My way don't mean lettin' no cops git Mary Bland's brother. You duck into cover."

When Mary and Jack returned she ran up to old Pegwell and kissed him warmly. She blushed at his gaze and shyly showed him a brand-new wedding ring. Jack laughed.

"I took your advice, Pegwell," he said. "No time like the present. So now you're sole proprietor here. We'll come back to-morrow to get Mary's few belongings. Just now I want her to myself. So long. Come, Mary!"

They left quickly, leaving old Pegwell hot with unspoken felicitations. Larry crept down. He had heard Mary's voice.

"Get outa sight!" snapped Pegwell. "Dammit! The street's full o' coppers !"

Larry ducked. He was frankly terrified.

When Mary appeared in the morning to pack her things Larry was securely out of sight. Old Pegwell had been busy all night. He had made a stout, roomy chest, iron cleated and hinged. He had made Larry help him, keeping him in mind of the police. Now Larry crouched in the big chest in the cellar, while Mary sang happily and packed her small trifles in the bright little rooms above.

"I do hope you will enjoy every hour here, Pegwell," Mary said when ready to leave. "Jack rather rushed me off my feet; but I'm glad, because he said you promised to see that Larry comes to no harm."'

"Missy" replied Pegwell gravely, "I won't let Larry get into no trouble with the police. I'm goin' to try to make a man outa him. So good luck to you, and God bless you. May all yer troubles be little 'uns, and if so be you wants a rattle, why—"

The old fellow glanced around the little shop, seeking for the bundle of rattles that hung somewhere; but he felt a warm, moist kiss on his cheek, the door opened, and she was gone.

On Thursday the police visited the shop again. Larry was known to be in the district.

"He wuz here, but I ain't seen him to-day," said Pegwell. The old chap was in a sweating fret. Larry was getting impatient. He had demanded to see his sister and threatened to take his chance on the street. Pegwell had to lock the chest on him.

"He's likely to come back then," decided the officer in charge. "One o' you camp here," he told one of his men.

"I don't think he'll bother me much," Pegwell volunteered. "He done me dirt and knows I'll git even."

Pegwell was outwardly cool; inwardly, when that policeman took up his station in the inner room, he was all a-quiver. The noon stream of customers came in and kept him busy; but he dreaded the quiet of the afternoon. Another policeman came to take a turn of duty over night, and slept in a chair in the back room. Pegwell, upstairs, remained awake all night, listening lest the officer go exploring, dreading every moment to hear some betraying sound from the cramped Larry in the cellar.

All day Friday he had no chance to give Larry either food or water. All he could do was to pass hurriedly by and murmur through the lid of the chest a few harsh words of reassurance that relief was at hand. In the evening he closed the shop, left the policeman in sole charge, and went out for an hour. When he came back again he began to make up several small parcels of tobacco.

"Got a bit o' trade from the *Stella*" he told the policeman. "Nothin' like slops and tobacker for profits, mister. Ever think o' startin' a shop?"

"Shop, hell!" growled the policeman. "I deal in men, old salt." "Men is queer, that's true," said Pegwell.

At eleven o'clock a cart rattled up to the door, loaded up with sea chests and bags, with two husky toughs beside the driver and a heap of brutish bodies snoring in the back.

"Come for th' slops an' tobacker," they said.

"Here's th' tobacker," said Pegwell. "Slop chest is in th' basement. Pretty heavy. I'll give y' a hand."

"We can handle it," returned the huskies, and one of them winked at Pegwell.

Pegwell chatted to the policeman as he handed out the tobacco parcels. He talked loudly, calling the policeman "officer" as the chest was carried past. That was for Larry's benefit. Otherwise Larry might wonder what was being done to him and make some unfortunate noise.

"All right?" asked Pegwell.

"O. K.," the leader said, and paid over the money he had been counting out to Pegwell. Pegwell carefully set it aside, to buy a wedding present for somebody he knew; then he joined the policeman for a good-night smoke, chatting quite brilliantly, surprising himself.

Before daylight the next morning, old Pegwell was busy with broom and scraper on his sidewalk, for snow had fallen in the night. The water of the harbour was grey and cruel. Old Pegwell glanced out, shivered, and plied his broom. He was glad he had not to be out there, perhaps stamping around a capstan. It felt good to know that. It made him sing.

> And awa-ay, Rio! Awa-ay, Rio!
> Then fare you well, my bonny young gal,
> For we're bound for Rio Grande!

From down the bay came the hoot of a tug. And, clear and sharp, metallically shattering the morning heaviness, came also the clack, clack, clack of capstan paws, the "fare you well" of an outward bounder.

ROUNDING CAPE HORN[1]

Felix Riesenberg

(1879-)

ON A clear Monday morning, the 7th of February, 1898, to be exact, the captain, after working up his A.M. sight, came on deck and announced a good observation. It was the first time the sun had been visible in some days, and by working a Sumner, he found we were on a line cutting close past Cape St John, on Staten Land, having sailed the ship down between the Falkland Islands and Cape Virgins by dead reckoning. We were coiling down the gear after the morning washdown, and I was busy at the monkey rail, when he came on deck with his results, and imparted the above information to the mate in my hearing.

[1] From *Under Sail*.

"Better send a hand to the main skys'l yard, Mr Zerk," said the captain, in conclusion.

I was handy, and at a nod from the mate sprang up the Jacob's ladder and on to the ratlines, going up like a monkey, out over the futtock shrouds, up the topmast rigging, narrowing to the topmast crosstrees, in through the horns of the crosstrees, and on farther up the t'gallant and royal rigging, on the slight rope ladders abaft the mast. Coming to the skysail mast, hardly larger round than the stick of a fair catboat, I shinned up with the help of the halyards, and swung myself astride of the yard, my arm about the aerie pinnacle of the main truck. From my vantage point, the sea was truly an inspiring sight; clear as crystal, the limpid air stretched free to the distant horizon without a mist or cloud to mar the panorama of vast blue ocean. I felt as though I had suddenly been elevated to a heaven far above the strife and trouble of the decks below.

For the moment I forgot the object of my climb, in the contemplation of the sparkling scene stretching as far as eye could reach. I glanced down to the narrow deck far beneath, white in the sun, the black top of the bulwarks outlining the plan of the ship against the deep blue waters; my eye followed the easy curves of the square canvas on the main, the great breadth of the yards extending to port and starboard, and I wondered that so small a ship could support such an avalanche of sail as bowled along under my feet. Aft, a foamy wake stretched for a mile or two, for we were sailing at a fairish speed with the wind from the north, a point on the port quarter.

I saw the men flaking down the fore tops'l halyards, clear for running, on the top of the forward house, and I saw the mate watching me from the weather fore pinrail, his head thrown back as he gazed aloft; something told me to get busy, and I looked far ahead to the south.

A faint blue streak on the horizon held my eyes. Accustomed to the sight of land from out at sea, through my voyages in the schoolship, still I hesitated to name it land. We were sixty-two days out, and land looked strange. Again I brought my sight to bear upon the distant sky-line ahead; there was no mistaking the dim outline of land rising from the sea at a point immediately to the south of us and reaching westward.

"Land ho!" I hailed the deck.

"Where away ?" came the voice of Captain Nichols.

"A point on the lee bow sir!"

"All right! lay down!" shouted the mate, evidently not intending that I should further enjoy my lofty perch on the skysail yard.

We raised the land rapidly, the breeze increasing slightly as the day advanced. At noon Staten Land was visible from the deck, and by eight bells in the afternoon watch we were sailing past the bold shores, some ten miles distant, and drawing the land well abeam. Running south for a good offing, and taking in our light sails with the coming of darkness, we hauled our wind to the starboard quarter at the end of the last dog watch and headed bravely for old "Cape Stiff."

Captain Nichols might have ventured through the Strait of Le Maire, with the weather we were having, though at the best it is taking chances to keep the land too close aboard when in the troubled latitudes of Terra Del Fuego. Countless ships, with the fine *Duchesse de Berry* among the last of them, have ground their ribs against the pitiless rocks that gird those coasts. However, we were enjoying the rarest of Cape Horn weather—sunshine, fair wind, and a moderate sea.

For the first time in many weary days, we livened things up with a chantey as we swigged away on the braces and tautened every stitch of canvas with well stretched sheets and halyards.

Jimmy Marshall had just started "Whiskey for my Johnnie," and the captain came forward on the break of the poop and joined in the chorus in a funny, squeaky voice—but none of us dared laugh at him. He was so delighted with the progress we were making, and the chance that we might slip by the "corner" in record time, that nothing was too good for us. The mate came down from his high-horse, and with Mr Stoddard and Chips, who had just finished their supper and were stepping out on deck, to join them, the full after guard took up the refrain—and the words rose in a great volume of deep sea song.

"Oh, whiskey—my Johnnie;
Yes, whiskey made me sell my coat,
Whiskey, my Johnnie.
Oh, whiskey's what keeps me afloat,
Oh, whiskey for my Johnnie."

When we pumped her out that night at the main pump, for the ship was almost on an even keel, we noted the skipper had begun to stump the quarter deck in a very excited way, constantly ducking up and down the companion, and scanning the horizon with an anxious eye. Cape pigeons were circling close to the ship with an endless chatter, and far above us swung a huge, dun-coloured fulmar gull, its white belly clean against the grey sky.

"There is something doing with the glass," remarked Frenchy, eyeing the skipper. "We'll have some weather to look out for before long,'' and all of us watched the gull with fascinated eyes. Jimmy and Brenden agreed with Frenchy that we were in for heavy weather.

But in spite of these dire predictions, and in spite of a "red dawn," the day broke and continued fair, and we were again regaled with a glimpse of land, jagged sombre peaks, jutting into the sky to the north like the cruel teeth of a ragged saw, grey-blue above the far horizon.

I was aft flaking down the mizzen tops'l halyards on the morning following the landfall, when Captain Nichols stumped past me from the break of the poop to the companion. He had been up all night, and the continuation of fine weather evidently pleased and surprised him. He had a pair of binoculars in his hand, and, in passing, he stopped and offered the glasses to me, pointing to the southernmost promontory, a cold blue knob rising from the sea:

"That's Cape Horn over there, Felix. Take a good look at it. You may never see it again, if you were born lucky."

Almost staggered by this sudden good fortune, I brought the captain's glasses in focus on the dreaded cape, my whole being thrilled with the pleasure of looking through those excellent binoculars at that distant point of rock, the outpost of the New World, jutting far into the southern ocean. I doubt if the gallant old Dutchman, Schouten, who first 'doubled' it, experienced half the exhilaration that I did on first beholding that storied headland. At four bells in the morning watch I went to the wheel, and while the watch swabbed down the decks after the morning washdown, I was privileged to look at the Cape out of the corner of my eye, between times keeping the "lubber's line" of the compass bowl on sou'west by sou', for the skipper had shaped a course a point or so further off shore, as the currents had evidently set us in toward the land during the night and he wished to keep his safe offing.

The wind in the meantime had veered round to west-nor'-west, blowing directly off the land and with increasing force. The light sails were taken in again, and by eight bells we were under t'gans'ls, upper and lower tops'ls, reefed fores'l, reefed mains'l, spanker, jib, and topmast stays'ls.

As I left the wheel and went forward, I determined to attempt a pencil sketch of Cape Horn, the weather being too dull for a photograph, even if the land were not too distant. The result, after some trials, and the loss of my breakfast, which was nothing, resulted in a fair representation of what we saw of the Cape, and I turned into my bunk with a feeling of satisfaction. After all, it was worth a good deal to have actually set eyes upon the Horn.

When we turned out at one bell, for dinner, we found the wind had veered farther to the west, we were sailing by the wind with the starboard tacks aboard, the cold spray from a rising sea breaking over the fo'c'sle head and spattering against the fo'c'sle door.

Jimmy sat up and rubbed his eyes as the watch was called, and swore gently under his breath. Brenden went out on deck to take a look at the weather. "Hell, we got it now. I have seen this before. D'you feel the ice?" he asked.

Indeed we all felt the drop in the temperature, and the short snappy jerk of the ship, as she met the new direction of the sea, was anything but pleasant.

Coffee was served out to us that noon instead of lime juice, and the warmth was welcome; it helped wash down the last cooked meal that Chow was able to prepare for ten days.

Mustering on deck at eight bells, we found we were driving south under a leaden sky. Cape Horn, still dimly visible, was soon shut off, vanishing in a cloud cap over the land astern. We were sailing due south, the wind having headed us, and at four bells, the wind rapidly increasing in violence, the starboard watch turned out to help in shortening down. We at once took in the t'gans'ls, mains'l, and jib, and these were followed in quick succession by other canvas, until at eight bells we had the *Fuller* stripped to her lower tops'ls, close reefed main upper tops'l, and storm stays'ls. The sea rose to mammoth proportions, fetching as it did from the very edge of the Antarctic ice barrier.

The canvas aloft soon became stiff with ice, and all gear on the ship was coated with frozen rain, as we were swept by a succession of rain and hail storms. At nightfall we were hove to, on the starboard tack under goose-winged main lower tops'l, reefed main trys'l, and storm stays'l. The oil tank forward was dripping its contents on the sea, and two oil bags were slung from the fore and main weather channels.

The storm, for the wind had now increased to fully sixty miles an hour, held steady from the west until midnight. Then it suddenly went to nor'west, and in the squalls, when the wind rose to hurricane force, the *Fuller* lay over on her beam ends. A vicious cross sea added its danger to the situation. All hands were then on deck, remaining aft near the mizzen rigging. The fo'c'sle, galley, and forward cabin were awash. Four men braced themselves at the spokes of the wheel, under the eye of the second mate, and relieving tackles were hooked to ease the "kick" of the tiller. Preventer braces and rolling tackles, got up earlier in the day, were hove taut to steady the heavy spars aloft. All loose gear was streaming to leeward, washing in the sea, through the open scuppers and freeing ports. A fierce boiling of white phosphorescent wave caps lit the sea as it broke over the ship, intensifying the black pandemonium overhead. The sleetladen spume shot over the prostrate vessel m a continuous roar, drowning all attempts at shouting of orders.

It was during the wild but fascinating hours of this night that I realized the high quality of seamanship that had prepared us for an ordeal such as we are going through. The consummate skill with which the great wooden craft was being handled came home to me with a force that could not be denied. How easily a bungling lubber might have omitted some precaution, or carried sail improperly, or have done, or not done, the thousand things that would have spelled disaster!

The captain and mate stood at the lee of the mizzen mast, each with a turn of the tops'l sheets about him, and hitched over the monkey rail. The rest of us, crouching at the lee of the cabin trunk, knee deep in the water when she went over in the heavier squalls, held our places wondering what turn things would take next. Looking through one of the after cabin ports, on my way to the wheel, I saw Chow and Komoto, the cabin boy, packing a box by the light of the small lamp swinging in-its gimbals. They were evidently getting ready to leave—where to—themselves and their gods alone knew.

All things have an end, and the Stygian blackness of the night gave way to grey streaks of dawn that broke upon us, revealing a scene of utmost desolation. A note of order was given to the wild confusion of the gale-wracked fabric, when Chips, his lanky figure skimming along the life line, and his sounding rod sheltered under his long oil coat, ventured to the main fife rail to sound the well. As for the crew, we were soaked with salt water and frozen to the marrow. The main lower tops'l had blown from the bolt ropes during the night; we never missed it until morning. Twenty feet of the lee bulwark—the port side was gone, and a flapping rag of canvas at the main hatch told us that the tarpaulin was torn. Looking forward through the whistle of wind and spume that cut across the sharply tilted rigging, the scene was one of terrific strife, as though some demon ruler of the sea had massed his forces, and was making a desperate drive for the destruction of the wooden handiwork of man upon which he dared to venture over those forbidden wastes.

No matter how miserable one may be, action of some kind always comes as a relief. Our hard lot on the *Fuller* was positively made more bearable by the added hardships of the storm, and when the night was past we were glad to force our chilled limbs and hungry bellies to some sort of effort. Anything was better than to hang to the mizzen rigging and slowly freeze to death. The torn hatch tarpaulin was a serious matter. The merchant service holds no higher duty, where passengers are not carried, than the duty towards cargo. This is often forgotten by men who lack the true traditions of the sea. But our officers were well alive to the importance, not only of bringing our ship around the Horn, but of bringing her cargo through in good condition.

The mate, followed by Axel, Brenden, Frenchy, and Mike, a husky, well-set-up sailor of the starboard watch, went into the waist and worked their way along the deck at great peril. After much trouble they managed to wedge down the flapping canvas, which was under a constant deluge of blue water, whole seas coming aboard in quick succession.

By noon the weather abated somewhat, and we got the ship under fore and mizzen lower tops'ls, and close reefed main upper tops'l. Before nightfall we had sent down what remained of the main lower tops'l, and bent a new sail. That afternoon we experienced an adventure fraught with much excitement to us of the port watch. The jib having worked loose from the gaskets, by constant dipping into the sea, as the ragged crests of blue water buried the bowsprit and jibboom, six of us were ordered out to secure the sail by passing a three-inch manila line around the sail and boom.

Brenden, Scouse, Frenchy, and I were on the weather side, and Joe and Martin went out on the boom to leeward. The job was almost finished, two seas had already drenched us, and we were chilled with the dip in the cold water, when the ship rose to a heavy roller, her bow lifted high into the eye of the wind, and then plunged down into the deep trough between two seas. The momentum was so great that she failed to rise quickly enough, and her jibboom stabbed right into the heart of the onrushing wall of cold blue water, regardless of the half dozen luckless wretches clinging to the furled canvas with all their might. The great sea went on over us, thundering down on the fo'c'sle head, and rushing aft along the deck in a noisy white cataract of foam. When she shook free we were left clinging to the jibboom like drowned rats, that is, all of us but Joe.

Aft on the poop, the mate heard our cries, and, springing to the lee rail, he yanked a bight of line from a pin and hove it overboard, catching Joe just in time as he rose close along side. When she heeled to leeward, ready hands hauled the half-drowned Joe on board. Captain Nichols had come up on the first cry, and taking Joe into the cabin, he poured out a liberal hooker of whiskey from the medicine chest. The funny part of the whole thing was that Joe was more thankful for the drink than for his escape from certain death, for we never could have lowered a boat in that sea.

We got a watch below that night, and the cook managed to heat some coffee, but cold salt beef and hard tack were all that the kids contained when we went below for supper. Wrapped in our damp clothes we managed to peg in a few hours of necessary sleep. Life, for a week afterward, was not worth living, unless one held some latent strain of the old berserker flowing through his veins. It was a fight, and the elements charged us and flanked us in midnight fury, increasingly cold as we edged farther to the south in our attempt to round the meridian of Cape Horn.

In latitude 56^0 29' S. and longitude 68^0 42' W. From Greenwich, about sixty sea miles S.W. by W. from Cape Horn, lies the island of Diego Ramirez, a weather-worn rock jutting from the black waters of the subAntarctic. Ten days after fetching away from the Cape, we beat south and sighted this grim sentinel, the outpost of the tempest and the gale-ten days of such seagoing as seldom falls to the men who nowadays go down to the sea in steamers.

Under conditions of the kind we experienced, every man was put to the test, and his worth as a member of the crew clearly established. Fortunately for us, and for the races representative in our small company—of which we boasted quite a few—no strain of yellow fear developed during the days and nights when the work aloft called for the performance of duty dangerous in the extreme. Not one of us but had been shipmates with men lost overboard, or maimed for life in accidents to sail or spars. Never was there a moment's hesitation to lay aloft, or out on a swaying buckling yard in the black cover of night, to grapple with canvas hard and unruly. No work was too trying, and no hours of labour too long. We thought nothing of the eternal injustice of a fate that sent us out to sea to fight for our very lives on a ship far too big for so small a crew to handle safely, if indeed any crew of mere men could ever *safely* handle so large a ship.

Never was there a suspicion of holding back, and through it all, the discipline of the disgruntled warmer latitudes was dropped and orders were quickly obeyed as a matter of course; yes, as a matter of self preservation. The disgusting profanity of warmer climes was laid in the discard for a while, and we were men doing men's work.

Wet and hunger were the rule; to be chilled with the cold was normal, and our salvation was the constant struggle with the working of the ship. Accidents occurred, and old Jimmy lay in his bunk with his right arm in a bandage from a dislocation due to a fall on the slippery deck. This was roughly set by the captain with the help of the mate and the carpenter. The galley fire had hardly been lighted an hour at a time, as the seas flooded everything forward. Cold salt junk—from the harness casks to the kids—comprised the mainstay of our ration, not to mention the daily whack of mouldy, weevily hard tack. Had it not been for an occasional steaming hot can of slops, called tea and coffee, we should have surely perished.

Our oilskins were in shreds, boots leaked, and every stitch of clothing in the ship was damp, except when dried by the heat of our bodies. Had I been told of this before starting out—well, I suppose I would not have believed it—and when I say that during it all we had a fairly good time, and managed to crack jokes and act like a lot of irresponsible asses, it goes to prove that man was born to be kicked; be he on a sailing ship around the Horn, on the hard edge of the Arctic littoral, or in the bloody trenches; fate is always there to step in and deliver the necessary bumping.

FRANCE

HOW PANTAGRUEL MET WITH A GREAT STORM AT SEA AND OF WHAT COUNTENANCES PANURGE AND FRIAR JOHN KEPT THEREIN[1]

François Rabelais
(1495-1553)

THE next Day we espied nine Sail that came spooming before the Wind; they were full of Dominicans, Jesuits, Capuchins, Hermits, Austins, Bernardins, Celestins, Theatins, Egnatins, Amadeans, Cordeliers, Carmelites, Minims, and the Devil and all of other holy Monks and Fryars, who were going to the Council of Chesil, to sift and garble some Articles of Faith against the new Hereticks. Panurge was overjoy'd to see them, being most certain of good Luck for that Day and a long Train of others. So, having courteously saluted the goodly Fathers, and recommended the Salvation of his precious Soul to their Devout Prayers and private Ejaculations, he caus'd seventy eight dozen of Westphalia Hams, Unites of Pots of Caviar, Tens of Bolonia Sawsages, Hundreds of Botargoes, and Thousands of fine Angels, for the Souls of the Dead, to be thrown on board their Ships.

Pantagruel seem'd metagroboliz'd, dozing, out of sorts, and as melancholick as a Cat; Friar John, who soon perceiv'd it, was enquiring of him whence should come this unusual Sadness? when the Master, whose Watch it was, observing the fluttering of the Ancient above the Poop, and seeing that it began to overcast, judg'd that we should have Wind; therefore he bid the Boatswain call Hands upon Deck, Officers, Sailors, Foremast Men, Swabbers and Cabin-boys, and even the Passengers; made 'era first settle their Top-sails, take in their Spreet-sail; then he cry'd:

"In with your Top-sails. Lower the Fore-sail. Tallow under the Parrels. Brace up close all them Sails. Strike your Top-masts to the Cap. Make all sure with your Sheeps-feet. Lash your guns fast."

All this was nimbly done. Immediately it blow'd a Storm; the Sea began to roar, and swell Mountain high: the Rut of the Sea was great, the Waves breaking upon our Ships Quarter, the North-West Wind bluster'd and overblow'd: boisterous Gusts; dreadful Clashings and deadly Scuds of Wind whistled through our Yards, and made our Shrouds rattle again. The Thunder grumbled so horridly that you would have thought Heaven had been tumbling about our Ears; at the same time

[1] From *Pantagruel's Voyage to the Oracle of the Bottle.* From the translation by Peter Motteux (1694).

it Lighten'd, Rain'd, Hail'd; the Sky lost its transparent hue, grew dusky, thick, and gloomy, so that we had no other Light than that of the Flashes of Lightning and rending of the Clouds. The Hurrucans, Flaws, and sudden Whirlwinds began to make a Flame about us by the Lightnings, Fiery Vapours, and other Aerial Ejaculations. Oh! how our Looks were full of Amazement and Trouble, while the sawcy Winds did rudely lift up above us the Mountainous Waves of the Main. Believe me, it seem'd to us a lively Image of the Chaos, where Fire, Air, Sea, Land, and all the Elements were in a refractory Confusion.

Poor Panurge, having, with the full Contents of the inside of his Doublet, plentifully fed the Fish, greedy enough of such odious Fare, sat on the Deck all in a heap, most sadly cast down, moping and half dead; invok'd and call'd to his Assistance all the blessed he and she Saints he could muster up, swore and vow'd to confess in Time and Place convenient, and then bawl'd out frightfully:

"Steward, Maistre d'Hostel, see hoe, my Friend, my Father, my Uncle, pr'ythee let's have a Piece of Powder'd Beef or Pork. We shall drink but too much anon, for ought I see; eat little and drink the more shall hereafter be my Motto, I fear. Would to our dear Lord, and to our blessed, worthy and sacred Lady, I were now, I say, this very Minute of an Hour, well on shore on *Terra firma,* hale and easie. O Twice and thrice happy those that plant Cabbages! O Destinies, why did you not spin me for a Cabbage Planter? O how few are they to whom Jupiter hath been so favourable as to predestinate them to plant Cabbage! They have always one Foot on the Ground, and the other not far from it. Dispute who will of Felicity, and *summum bonum;* for my part, whosoever plants Cabbages, is now by my Decree proclaim'd most happy; for as good a reason as the Philosopher Pyrho, being in the same Danger, and seeing a Hog near the Shore eating some scatter'd Oats, declar'd it happy in two respects, first, because it had plenty of Oats, and besides that was on Shore. Hah, for a Divine and Princely Habitation, commend me to the Cows Floor.

"Murther! This Wave will sweep us away, blessed Saviour! O, my Friends! a little Vinegar. I sweat again with meer Agony. Alas, the Misen-Sail's split, the Gallery's wash'd away, the Masts are sprung, the Main-Top-Mast Head dives into the Sea; the Keel is up to the Sun; our Shrouds are almost all broke, and blown away. Alas! Alas! Where is our Main Course? *Ael is verlooren by Godt.* Our Top-Mast is run adrift. Alas! Who shall have this Wreck? Friends, lend me here behind you one of these Wales. Your Lanthorn is fallen, my Lads. Alas!don't let go the Main-tack nor the Bowlin. I hear the Block crack, is it broke? For the Lord's sake, let us save the Hull, and let all the Rigging be damn'd. Be be be bous, bous, bous. Look to the Needle of your Compass, I beseech you, good Sir Astrophel, and tell us, if you can, whence comes this storm. My Heart's sunk down below my Midriff. By my troth I am in a sad fright. Bou, bou, bou, bous, bous, I am lost for ever. Bou,

bou, bou, bou, Otto to to to to ti. Bou, bou, bou, ou, ou, ou, bou, bou, bous. I sink, I'm drowned, I'm gone, good People, I'm drowned."

Pantagruel, having first implor'd the help of the Great and Almighty Deliverer, and pray'd publickly with fervent Devotion, by the Pilot's Advice held tightly the Mast of the Ship. Friar John had stript himself to his Waistcoat, to help the Seamen. Epistemon, Ponocrates, and the rest did as much. Panurge alone sat upon Deck, weeping and howling. Friar John espy'd him, going on the Quarter-Deck, and said to him:

"Odzoons, Panurge the Calf, Panurge the Whiner, Panurge the Brayer, would it not become thee much better to lend us here a helping Hand than to lie lowing like a Cow."

"Be, be, be, bous, bous, bous," return'd Panurge. "Friar John, my Friend, my good Father, I am drowning. The Water is got into my Shoes by the Collar. Alas!Alas!Now am I like your Tumblers, my Feet stand higher than my Head."

"Come hither, and be damn'd, thou pitiful Devil, and help us," (said Friar John) who fell a-swearing and cursing like a Tinker. "In the name of thirty Legions of black Devils, come, Will you come ?"

"Don't let us swear at this time," said Panurge, "Holy Father, my Friend, don't swear, I beseech you. To-morrow as much as you please. Holos, holos, alas, our Ship leaks. Good People, I drown, I die. *Consummaturn est.* I am sped."

"By the Virtue," (said Friar John) "of the Blood, if I hear thee again howling, I'll maul thee worse than any Sea-Wolf. Ods fish, why don't we take him up by the Lugs, and throw him overboard to the bottom of the Sea? Here, Sailor, how honest Fellow! Thus, thus, my Friend, hold fast above. In truth here is a sad Lightning and Thundering. I think that all the Devils are got loose. Here, Mate, my Lad, hold fast till I have made a double Knot. O brave Boy! Would to Heaven thou wert Abbot of Talemouze, and that he that is, were Guardian of Croullay. Hold Brother Ponocrates, you will hurt yourself, Man. Epistemon, pr'y thee stand off out of the Hatchway. Methinks I saw the Thunder fall there but just now. Con the Ship, so ho!"

"Be, be, be, bous, bous, bous," cry'd Panurge. "I am lost. I see neither Heaven nor Earth. Would I were at this present Hour in the Close at Seville, or at Innocent's the Pastry-Cook, over against the painted Wine-Vault at Chinon, though I were to strip to my Doublet, and bake the petty Pasties myself. Hark'ee, my Friends, since we cannot get safe into Port, let us come to an Anchor into some Road, no matter whither. Drop all your Anchors, let us be out of Danger, I beseech you. Here honest Tar, get you into the Chains and heave the Lead, an't please you. Let us know how many Fathom Water we are in. Sound, Friend, in the Lord Harry's Name!"

"Helm a lee, hoh," cry'd the Pilot. "Helm a lee. A Hand or two at the Helm.

About Ships with her. Helm a lee. Helm a lee. Stand off from the Leech of the Sail. Hoh, Belay, here make fast below. Hoh, Helm a lee. Lash sure the Helm a lee, and let her drive."

"The Lord and the Blessed Virgin be with us," said Panurge. "Holas, alas. I drown, be be be bous, be bous bous. *In manus.* Good Heaven, send me some Dolphin to carry me safe on shore, like a pretty little Arion. I shall make shift to sound the Harp if' it be not unstrung."

"Shore, shore!" cry'd Pantagruel. "Land to, my Friends. I see Land. Pluck up a good Spirit, Boys, 'tis within a kenning, so we are not far from a Port. I see the Sky clearing up to the Northwards. Look to the South-east."

"Courage, my Hearts," said the Pilot, "now she'll bear the hullock of a Sail. The sea is much smoother. Some Hands aloft, to the Main Top. Put the Helm a weather. Steady, steady. Haul your aftermisen Bowlins. Haul, haul, haul. Thus, thus, and no nearer. Mind your Steerage. Bring your main Tack aboard. Clear your Sheets. Clear your Bowlins. Port, port, helm a lee."

"Loft, loft," cry'd the Quartermaster, that con'd the Ship. "Keep her full. Loft the Helm."

"Loft it is," answer'd the Steersman.

"Keep her thus. Get the Bonnets fix'd. Steady, steady."

"That's well said," said Friar John, "Good. Loft, loft. Helm a weather. That's well said and thought on. Methinks the Storm is almost over. It was high time, faith. However, the Lord be thanked. Our Devils begin to scamper. Out with all your Sails. Hoist your Sails. Hoist. That's spoke like a Man. Hoist. Hoist."

"Cheer up, my merry Mates all," cry'd out Epistemon. "I see already Castor on the right. Ho, ho. I see Land too. Let her bear it with the Hatbout. I see a good many People on the Beach. I see a Light on an Obeliscolychny."

"Shorten your Sails," said the Pilot. "Fetch the Sounding Line. We must double that point of Land and mind the Sands."

"We are clear of them," said the Sailors.

Soon after "Away she goes," quoth the Pilot, "and so doth the rest of our Fleet. Help came in good season."

"By St John," said Panurge, "this is spoke somewhat like. Oh the sweet Word! There's the Soul of Musick in it. What cheer ho? fore and aft? Oh ho! All is well. The Storm is over. I beseech ye, be so kind as to let me be the first that is set on shore. Shall I help you still? Here, let me see, I'll coyle this Rope. I have plenty of Courage, and of Fear as little as may be. Give it me yonder, honest Tar. No, no, I have not a bit of Fear. Indeed that same Decumane Wave that took us fore and aft somewhat alter'd my Pulse. Down with your Sails, well said. How now, Friar John, you do nothing? Is it time for us to drink now? Shall I come and help you again? Pork and Pease choke me, if I do not heartily repent, tho' too late, not having followed the doctrine of the good Philosopher, who tells us, That to walk by the Sea, and to navigate by the Shore, are very safe and pleasant Things; just as 'tis to go on foot when we hold our Horse by the Bridle. Hah, hah, hah, by G— all goes well. —Hark you me, dear Soul, a word with you—but pray be not angry. How thick do you judge the Planks of our Ship to be?"

"Some two good Inches and upwards," return'd the Pilot. "Don't fear."

"Odskilderkins," said Panurge, "it seems then we are within two Fingers breadth of Damnation. Is this one of the nine Comforts of Matrimony? Ah, dear Soul, you do well to measure the Danger by the Yard of Fear. For my part I have none on't. My Name is William Dreadnought. As for Heart, I have more than enough on't. I mean none of your Sheeps Heart; but of Wolfs Heart, the Courage of a Bravoe. By the Pavilion of Mars, I fear nothing but Danger."

SHIPWRECK OF A MODEST YOUNG LADY[1]

Bernardin de Saint-Pierre
(1737-1814)

AT ABOUT seven in the morning we heard the sound of drums in the woods; it announced the approach of the governor, Monsieur de la Bourdonnais, who soon after arrived on horseback, at the head of a detachment of soldiers armed with muskets, and a crowd of islanders and negroes. He drew up his soldiers upon the beach, and ordered them to make a general discharge. This was no sooner done, than we perceived a glimmering light upon the water, which was instantly followed by the report of a cannon. We judged that the ship was at no great distance, and all ran towards that part whence the light and sound proceeded. We now discerned through the fog the hull and yards of a large vessel. We were so near to her that, notwithstanding the tumult of the waves, we could distinctly hear the whistle of the boatswain and the shouts of the sailors, who cried out three times, *VIVE LE ROI!* this being the cry of the French in extreme danger, as well as in exuberant joy;—as though they wished to call their prince to their aid, or to testify to him that they are prepared to lay down their lives in his service.

As soon as the *Saint-Géran* perceived that we were near enough to render her assistance, she continued to fire guns regularly at intervals of three minutes. Monsieur de la Bourdonnais caused great fires to be lighted at certain distances upon the strand, and sent to all the inhabitants of the neighbourhood in search of

[1] From *Paul and Virginia.*

provisions, planks, cables, and empty barrels. A number of people soon arrived, accompanied by their negroes loaded with provisions and cordage, which they had brought from the plantations of Golden Dust, from the district of La Flaque, and from the river of the Rampart. One of the most aged of these planters, approaching the governor, said to him:

"We have heard all night hollow noises in the mountains; in the woods, the leaves of the trees are shaken, although there is no wind; the seabirds seek refuge upon the land; it is certain that all these signs announce a hurricane."

"Well, my friends," answered the governor, "we are prepared for it, and no doubt the vessel is also."

Everything, indeed, presaged the near approach of the hurricane. The centre of the clouds in the zenith was of a dismal black, while their skirts were tinged with a copper-coloured hue. The air resounded with the cries of tropic-birds, petrels, frigate-birds, and innumerable other seafowl which, notwithstanding the obscurity of the atmosphere, were seen coming from every point of the horizon to seek for shelter in the island.

Towards nine in the morning we heard in the direction of the ocean the most terrific noise, like the sound of thunder mingled with that of torrents rushing down the steeps of lofty mountains. A general cry was heard of "There is the hurricane!" and the next moment a frightful gust of wind dispelled the fog which covered the Isle of Amber and its channel. The *Saint-Géran* then presented herself to our view, her deck crowded with people, her yards and topmasts lowered, and her flag half-mast high, moored by four cables at her bow and one at her stern. She had anchored between the Isle of Amber and the mainland, inside the chain of reefs which encircles the island, and which she had passed through in a place where no vessel had ever passed before. She presented her head to the waves that rolled in from the open sea, and as each billow rushed into the narrow strait where she lay, her bow lifted to such a degree as to show her keel; and at the same moment her stern, plunging into the water, disappeared altogether from our sight, as if it were swallowed up by the surges. In this position, driven by the winds and waves towards the shore, it was equally impossible for her to return by the passage through which she had made her way; or, by cutting her cables, to strand herself upon the beach, from which she was separated by sandbanks and reefs of rocks. Every billow which broke upon the coast advanced roaring to the bottom of the bay, throwing up heaps of shingle to the distance of fifty feet upon the land; then, rushing back, laid bare its sandy bed, from which it rolled immense stones, with a hoarse and dismal noise. The sea, swelled by the violence of the wind, rose higher every moment; and the whole channel between this island and the Isle of Amber was soon one vast sheet of white foam, full of yawning pits of black and deep billows. Heaps of this foam, more than six feet high, were piled up at the bottom of the bay; and the winds which swept its surface carried masses of it over the steep sea-bank, scattering it upon the land to the distance of half a league. These innumerable white flakes, driven horizontally even to the very foot of the mountains, looked like snow issuing from the bosom of the ocean. The appearance of the horizon portended a lasting tempest; the sky and the water seemed blended together. Thick masses of cloud, of a frightful form, swept across the zenith with the swiftness of birds, while others appeared motionless as rocks. Not a single spot of blue sky could be discerned in the whole firmament; and a pale yellow gleam only lightened up all the objects of the earth, the sea, and the skies.

From the violent rolling of the ship, what we all dreaded happened at last. The cables which held her bow were torn away; she then swung to a single hawser, and was instantly dashed upon the rocks, at the distance of half a cable's length from the shore. A general cry of horror issued from the spectators. Paul rushed forward to throw himself into the sea, when, seizing him by the arm,

"My son," I exclaimed, "would you perish ?"

"Let me go to save her," he cried, "or let me die!"

Seeing that despair had deprived him of reason, Domingo and I, in order to preserve him, fastened a long cord round his waist, and held it fast by the end. Paul then precipitated himself towards the *Saint-Géran*, now swimming, and now walking upon the rocks. Sometimes he had hopes of reaching the vessel, which the sea, by the reflux of its waves, had left almost dry, so that you could have walked round it on foot; but suddenly the billows, returning with fresh fury, shrouded it beneath mountains of water, which then lifted it upright upon its keel. The breakers at the same moment threw the unfortunate Paul far upon the beach, his legs bathed in blood, his bosom wounded, and himself half dead. The moment he had recovered the use of his senses, he arose, and returned with new ardour towards the vessel, the parts of which now yawned asunder from the violent strokes of the billows. The crew then, despairing of their safety, threw themselves in crowds into the sea upon yards, planks, hencoops, tables, and barrels.

At this moment we beheld an object which wrung our hearts with grief and pity: a young lady appeared in the stern-gallery of the *Saint-Géran*, stretching out her arms towards him who was making so many efforts to join her. It was Virginia. She had discovered her lover by his intrepidity. The sight of this amiable girl, exposed to such horrible danger, filled us with unutterable despair. As for Virginia, with a firm and dignified mien, she waved her hand, as if bidding us an eternal farewell. All the sailors had flung themselves into the sea, except one, who still remained upon the deck, and who was naked, and strong as Hercules. This man approached Virginia with respect, and kneeling at her feet, attempted to force her to throw off her clothes; but she repulsed him with modesty, and turned away her head. Then were heard redoubled cries from the spectators,

"Save her!Save her!Do not leave her!"

But at that moment a mountain billow, of enormous magnitude, engulfed itself between the Isle of Amber and the coast, and menaced the shattered vessel, towards which it rolled bellowing, with its black sides and foaming head. At this terrible sight the sailor flung himself into the sea, and Virginia, seeing death inevitable, crossed her hands upon her breast, and, raising upwards her serene and beauteous eyes, seemed an angel prepared to take her flight to heaven.

Oh, day of horror! Alas! everything was swallowed up by the relentless billows. The surge threw some of the spectators, whom an impulse of humanity had prompted to advance towardsVirginia, far upon the beach, and also the sailor who had endeavoured to save her life. This man, who had escaped from almost certain death, kneeling upon the sand, exclaimed:

"Oh my God! Thou hast saved my life, but I would have given it willingly for that excellent young lady, who persevered in not undressing herself as I had done."

HOW MALICIOUS GILLIATT FOUGHT THE TEMPEST[1]

Victor Hugo (1802-1885)

IN THE middle of the night he awoke suddenly and with a jerk like the recoil of a spring.

He opened his eyes.

The Douvres, rising high over his head, were lighted up as by the white glow of burning embers. Over all the dark escarpment of the rock there was a light like the reflection of a fire.

The aspect of the sea was extraordinary.

The water seemed a-fire. As far as the eye could reach, among the reefs and beyond them, the sea ran with flame. The flame was not red; it had nothing in common with the grand living fires of volcanic craters or of great furnaces. There was no sparkling, no glare, no purple edges, no noise. Long trails of a pale tint simulated upon the water the folds of a winding sheet. A trembling glow was spread over the waves. It was the spectre of a great fire rather than the fire itself. It was in some degree like the glow of unearthly flames lighting the inside of a sepulchre. A burning darkness.

The night itself, dim, vast and wide-diffused, was the fuel of that cold flame.

---

[1] From *The Toilers of the Sea.* From the translation by W. Moy Thomas.

It was a strange illumination issuing out of blindness. The shadows even formed part of that phantom-fire.

The sailors of the Channel are familiar with those indescribable phosphorescences, full of warning for the navigator. By this light surrounding objects lose their reality. A spectral glimmer renders them, as it were, transparent. Rocks become no more than outlines. Cables of anchors look like iron bars heated to a white heat. The nets of the fishermen beneath the water seem webs of fire. The half of the oar above the waves is dark as ebony, the rest in the sea like silver. Every boat leaves a furrow behind it like a comet's tail. The fish are tongues of fire, or fragments of the forked lightning, moving in the depths.

The reflection of this brightness had passed over the closed eyelids of Gilliatt in the sloop. It was this that had awakened him.

The ebb tide had run out, and the waters were beginning to rise again. The funnel, which had become disengaged during his sleep, was about to enter again into the yawning hollow above it.

It was rising slowly.

A rise of another foot would have entangled it in the wreck again. A rise of one foot is equivalent to half-an-hour's tide. If he intended, therefore, to take advantage of that temporary deliverance once more within his reach, he had just half-an-hour before him.

He leaped to his feet.

Gilliatt knew the sea in all its phases. Notwithstanding all her tricks, and often as he had suffered from her terrors, he had long been her companion. That mysterious entity which we call the ocean had nothing in its secret thoughts which he could not divine. Observation, meditation, and solitude had given him a quick perception of coming changes, of wind, or cloud, or wave.

Gilliatt hastened to the top ropes and payed out some cable; then being no longer held fast by the anchors, he seized the boat-hook of the sloop, and pushed her towards the entrance to the gorge some fathoms from the *Durande,* and quite near to the breakwater. Here, as the Guernsey sailors say, it had *du rang.* In less than ten minutes the sloop was withdrawn from beneath the carcase of the wreck. There was no further danger of the funnel being caught in a trap. The tide might rise now.

And yet Gilliatt's manner was not that of one about to take his departure.

He stood considering the light upon the sea once more; but his thoughts were not of starting. He was thinking of how to fix the sloop again, and how to fix it more firmly than ever, though near to the exit from the defile.

Up to this time he had only used the two anchors of the sloop, and. had not yet employed the little anchor of the *Durande,* which he had found among the breakers. He now let go this third anchor, taking care to fasten the cable to a rope, one end of which was slung through the anchor ring, while the other was attached to the windlass of the sloop. In this manner he made a kind of triangular, triple anchorage, much stronger than the moorings with two anchors. All this indicated keen anxiety, and a redoubling of precautions. The sloop being fixed in its new position, he went in quest of the strongest chain which he had in his store-cavern, and attaching it to the nails driven into the two Douvres, he fortified from within with this chain the rampart of planks and beams, already protected from without by the cross chain.

Suddenly he paused to listen.

A feeble, indistinct sound seemed to reach his ear from somewhere in the far distance.

He listened a second time. The distant noise recommenced. Gilliatt shook his head like one who recognizes at last something familiar to him.

A few minutes later he was at the other extremity of the alley between the rocks, at the entrance facing the east, which had remained open until then, and by heavy blows of his hammer was driving large nails into the sides of the gullet near "The Man" rock, as he had done at the gullet of the Douvres.

The nails being driven, Gilliatt dragged beams and cords and then chains to the spot; and without taking his eyes off his work, or permitting his mind to be diverted for a moment, he began to construct across the gorge of "The Man," with beams fixed horizontally, and made fast by cables, one of those open barriers which science has now adopted under the name of breakwaters.

Meanwhile the sun had risen, and was shining brightly. The sky was clear, the sea calm.

Gilliatt pressed on with his work. He, too, was calm; but there was anxiety in his haste. He passed with long strides from rock to rock, and returned dragging wildly sometimes a rider, sometimes a binding stake. The work was executed so fast that it was rather a rapid growth than a construction.

The first cross pieces of the breakwater being fixed, Gilliatt mounted upon them and listened once more.

The murmurs had become significant.

He continued his construction. He supported it with the two catheads of the *Durande,* bound to the frame of beams by cords passing through the three pulley-sheaves. The construction was little more than a colossal hurdle, having beams for rods and chains in the place of wattles.

He climbed again upon the barrier and listened.

The noises from the horizon had ceased; all was still.

The sea was smooth and quiet; the deep blue of the sky responded to the deep green tint of the ocean. Not a cloud on high; not a line of foam below. It was impossible to imagine a lovelier day.

On the verge of the horizon a flight of birds of passage formed a long dark line against the sky. They were flying fast as if alarmed.

Gilliatt set to work again to raise the breakwater. He raised it as high as he could; as high, indeed, as the curving of the rocks would permit.

Towards noon the sun appeared to him to give more than its usual warmth. Standing upon the powerful frame which he had built up, he paused again to survey the wide expanse.

The sea was more than tranquil. It was a dull dead calm. No sail was visible. The sky was everywhere clear; but from blue it had become white. The whiteness was singular. To the west, and upon the horizon, was a little spot of a sickly hue. The spot remained in the same place, but by degrees grew larger. Near the breakers the waves shuddered; but very gently.

Gilliatt had done well to build his breakwater.

A tempest was approaching.

The elements had determined to give battle.

Gilliatt ascended to the summit of the Great Douvre. From hence he could see around the horizon. The western side was appalling. A wall of cloud spread across it, barring the wide expanse from side to side, and ascending slowly from the horizon towards the zenith. This wall, straight lined, vertical, without a crevice in its height, without a rent in its structure, seemed built by the square and measured by the plumb-line. It was cloud in the likeness of granite. Its escarpment, completely perpendicular at the southern extremity, curved a little towards the north, like a bent sheet of iron, presenting the steep, slippery face of an inclined plane. The dark wall enlarged and grew; but its entablature never ceased for a moment to be parallel with the horizon line, which was almost indistinguishable in the gathering darkness. Silently, and altogether, the airy battlements ascended. No undulation, no wrinkle, no projection changed its shape or moved its place. The aspect of this immobility in movement was impressive. The sun, pale in the midst of a strange sickly transparence, lighted up this outline of the Apocalypse. Already the cloudy bank had blotted out one half the space of the sky; shelving like the fearful talus of the abyss. It was the uprising of a dark mountain between earth and heaven.

It was night falling suddenly upon midday.

There was a heat in the air as from an oven door, coming from that mysterious mass on mass. The sky, which from blue had become white, was now turning from white to a slatey grey. The sea beneath was leaden-hued and dull. There was no breath, no wave, no noise. Far as eye could reach, the desert ocean. No sail was visible on any side. The birds had disappeared. Some monstrous treason seemed abroad.

Gilliatt stood there motionless a few moments, his eye fixed upon the cloud bank, as if mentally taking a sounding of the tempest. His *galerienne* was in the pocket of his jacket; he took it out and placed it on his head. He put on his overalls, and his waterproof overcoat, like a knight who puts on his armour at the moment of battle. He had no shoes; but his naked feet had become hardened to the rocks.

This preparation for the storm being completed, he looked down upon his breakwater, grasped the knotted cord hurriedly, descended from the plateau of the Douvres, stepped on to the rocks below and hastened to his store cavern. A few moments later he was at work. The vast silent cloud might have heard the strokes of his hammer. With the nails, ropes, and beams which still remained, he constructed for the eastern gullet, a second frame, which he succeeded in fixing at ten or twelve feet from the other.

Suddenly an immense peal of thunder burst upon the air. Gilliatt himself felt the shock. No electric flash accompanied the report. It was a blind peal. The silence was profound again. There was an interval, as when combatants take up their position. Then appeared slowly, one after the other, great shapeless flashes; these flashes were silent. The wall of cloud was now a vast cavern, with roofs and arches. Outlines of forms were traceable among them; monstrous heads were vaguely shadowed forth; rocks seemed to stretch out; elephants bearing turrets, seen for a moment, vanished. Sheets of clouds undulated like folds of giant flags.

Suddenly GIlliatt felt a breath moving his hair. Two or three large spots of rain fell heavily around him on the rock. Then there was a second thunder clap. The wind was rising.

The terror of darkness was at its highest point. The first peal of thunder had shaken the sea; the second rent the wall of cloud from top to base; a breach was visible; the pent up deluge rushed towards it; the rent became like a gulf filled with rain. The outpouring of the tempest had begun.

Rain, wind, lightnings, thunder, waves swirling upwards to the clouds, foam, hoarse noises, whistlings, mingled together like monsters suddenly unloosened.

For a solitary man, imprisoned with an over-loaded vessel, between two dangerous rocks in mid-ocean, no crisis could have been more menacing. The danger of the tide, over which he had triumphed, was nothing compared with the danger of the tempest.

Surrounded on all sides by dangers, Gilliatt, at the last moment, and before the crowning peril, had developed an ingenious strategy. He had secured his basis of operations in the enemies' territory; had pressed the rock into his service. The Douvres, originally his enemy, had become his second in that immense duel. Out of that sepulchre he had constructed a fortress. He was built up among those formidable sea ruins. He was blockaded, but well defended. He had, so to speak, set his back against the wail, and stood face to face with the hurricane. He had barricaded the narrow strait, that highway of the waves. The sloop might be considered secure on three sides. Closely wedged between the two interior walls of the rock, made fast by three anchorings, she was sheltered from the north by the Little Douvre, on the south by the Great one; terrible escarpments more accustomed to wreck vessels than to save them. On the western side she was protected by the frame of timbers made fast and nailed to the rocks—a third barrier which had withstood the rude floodtide of the sea; a veritable citadel gate, having for its sides the columns of the rock—the two Douvres themselves. Nothing was to be feared from that side. It was on the eastern side only that there was danger.

On that side there was no protection but the breakwater. A breakwater requires at least two frames. Gilliatt had only had time to construct one. He was compelled to build the second in the very presence of the tempest.

The wildness of the storm went on increasing. All the tumult of the wide expanse rushed towards the Douvres. Voices were heard in the darkness. What could they be? The ancient terror of the sea was there. At times they seemed to speak as if some one was uttering words of command. There were clamours, strange trepidations, and then that majestic roar which the mariners call the "Ocean cry." The indefinite and flying eddies of the wind whistled, while curling the waves and flinging them like giant quoits, cast by invisible athletes, against the breakers. The enormous surf streamed over all the rocks; torrents above; foam below. Then the roaring was redoubled. No uproar of men or beasts could yield an idea of that din which mingled with the incessant breaking of the sea. The clouds cannonaded, the hailstones poured their volleys, the surf mounted to the assault. As far as eye could reach, the sea was white; ten leagues of yeasty water filled the horizon.

Meanwhile Gilliatt seemed to pay no attention to the storm. His head was bent over his work. The second framework began to approach completion. To every clap of thunder he replied with a blow of his hammer, making a cadence which was audible even amidst that tumult. He was bare-headed, for a gust had carried away his *galérienne*. He suffered from a burning thirst. Little pools of rain had formed in the rocks around him. From time to time he took some water in the hollow of his hand and drank. Then, without even looking upward to observe the storm, he applied himself anew to his task.

All might depend upon a moment. He knew the fate that awaited him if his breakwater should not be completed in time. Of what avail could it be to lose a moment in looking for the approach of death?

The storm had now rotated to the west, and was expending its fury upon the barricades of the two Douvres. But Gilliatt had faith in his breakwaters, and with good reason. These barricades, made of a great portion of the fore-part of the

Durande, took the shock of the waves easily. To demolish them it would have been necessary to overthrow the Douvres themselves.

The second frame of the eastern barrier was nearly completed. A few more knots of rope and ends of chains and this new rampart would be ready to play its part in barring out the storm.

Suddenly there was a great brightness; the rain ceased; the clouds rolled asunder; the wind had just shifted; a sort of high, dark window opened in the zenith, and the lightnings were extinguished. The end seemed to have come.

It was but the commencement. The change of wind was from the northwest to the north-east. The storm was preparing to burst forth again with a new legion of hurricanes. The north was about to mount to the assault. Sailors call this dreaded moment of transition the "Return storm." The southern wind brings most rain, the north wind most lightning.

The attack, coming now from the east, was directed against the weak point of the position.

This time Gilliatt interrupted his work and looked around him. He stood erect upon a curved projection of the rock behind the second barrier, which was nearly finished. If the first frame had been carried away, it would have broken down the second, which was not yet consolidated, and must have crushed him. Gilliatt, in the place that he had chosen, must in that case have been destroyed before seeing the sloop, the machinery, and all his work shattered and swallowed up in the gulf. Such was the possibility which awaited him. He accepted it, and contemplated it sternly.

In that wreck of all his hopes, to die at once would have been his desire; to die first, as he would have regarded it—for the machinery produced in his mind the effect of a living being. He moved aside his hair, which was beaten over his eyes by the wind, grasped his trusty mallet, drew himself up in a menacing attitude, and awaited the event.

He was not kept long in suspense.

A flash of lightning gave the signal; the livid opening in the zenith closed; a driving torrent of rain fell; then all became dark, save where the lightning broke forth once more. The attack had recommenced in earnest.

A heavy swell, visible from time to time ln the blaze of the lightning, was rolling in the east beyond "The Man" rock. It resembled a huge wall of glass. It was green and without foam, and it stretched across the wide expanse. It was advancing towards the breakwater, increasing as it approached.

The great wave struck "The Man" rock, broke in twain, and passed beyond. The broken wave, rejoined, formed a mountain of water, and instead of advancing in parallel line as before, came down perpendicularly upon the breakwater. The shock was terrific: the whole wave became a roaring surf.

For some moments the sea drowned everything. Nothing was visible except the furious waters, an enormous breadth of foam, the whiteness of a winding sheet blowing in the draught of a sepulchre; nothing was heard but the roaring storm working devastation around.

When the foam subsided, Gilliatt was still standing at his post. The barrier had stood firm.

Suddenly a crash was heard, resounding and prolonging itself through the defile at some distance behind him: a crash more terrible than any he had yet heard.

It came from the direction of the sloop.

Something disastrous was happening there.

Gilliatt hastened toward it.

From the eastern gullet where he was, he could not see the sloop on account of the sharp turns of the pass. At the last turn he stopped and waited for the lightning.

The first flash revealed to him the position of affairs.

The rush of the sea through the eastern entrance had been met by a blast of wind from the other end. A disaster was near at hand.

The sloop had received no visible damage; anchored as she was, the storm had little power over her, but the carcase of the *Durande* was distressed. It was entirely out of the sea in the air, exposed. The breach which Gilliatt had made, and which he had passed the engine through, had rendered the hull still weaker. The keelson was snapped, the vertebral column of the skeleton was broken.

The hurricane had passed over it. Scarcely more than this was needed to complete its destruction. The planking of the deck had bent like an open book. The square opening which he had cut in the keel had become a gaping wound. The wind had converted the smooth cut hole into a ragged fracture. This transverse breach separated the wreck in two. The after-part, nearest to the sloop, had remained firm in its bed of rocks. The forward portion which faced him was hanging. The whole mass oscillated, as the wind moved it, with a doleful noise. Fortunately the sloop was no longer beneath it. But this swinging movement shook the other portion of the hull, still wedged and immovable as it was between the two Douvres. Under the obstinate assaults of the gale, the dislocated part might suddenly carry away the other portion, which almost touched the sloop. In this case, the whole wreck, together with the sloop and the engine, must be swept into the sea and swallowed up.

Gilliatt was one of those who are accustomed to snatch the means of safety out of danger itself. He collected his ideas for a moment. Then he hastened to his arsenal and brought his hatchet. He mounted upon the wreck, got a footing on that part of the planking which had not given way, and leaning over the precipice of the pass between the Douvres, he began to cut away the broken joists and the planking which supported the hanging portion of the hull.

His object was to effect the separation of the two parts of the wreck, to disencumber the half which remained firm, to throw overboard what the waves had seized, and thus share the prey with the storm. Five or six pieces of the planking only, bent and started but not broken, still held. Their fractures creaked and enlarged at every gust, and the axe, so to speak, had but to help the labour of the wind.

The tempest had reached its highest point. Hitherto the storm had seemed to work its own imperious will, to give the impulse, to drive the waves to frenzy. Below was fury—above anger. But the intoxication of its own horrors had confused it. It had become a mere whirlwind; it was a blindness leading to night. There are times when tempests become frenzied, when the heavens are attacked with a sort of delirium; when the firmament raves and hurls its lightnings blindly. It is at that instant that in the blackest spot of the clouds, a circle of blue light appears, which the Spanish sailors of ancient times called the eye of the tempest, *el ojo de la tempestad.* That terrible eye looked down upon Gilliatt.

Gilliatt raised his head. After every stroke of his hatchet he stood erect and gazed upwards, almost haughtily. He was watchful as well as bold. He planted his feet only where the wreck was firm. He ventured his life, and yet was careful; for his determined spirit, too, had reached its highest point. The strokes of his hatchet were like blows of defiance. It was a contest with the elements for the prize at his feet.

He passed to and fro upon the tottering wreck, making the deck tremble under his steps, striking, cutting, hacking with the hatchet in his hand, pallid in the gleam of the lightning, his long hair streaming, his feet naked, in rags, his face covered with the foam of the sea, but grand still amid that maelstrom of the thunderstorm.

Against these furious powers man has no weapon but his invention. Invention was Gilliatt's triumph. His object was to allow all the dislocated portions of the wreck to fall together. For this reason he cut away the broken portions without entirely separating them, leaving some parts on which they still swung.

Suddenly he stopped, holding his axe in the air. The operation was complete. The entire portion went with a crash. The mass rolled down between the two Douvres, just below Gilliatt. It fell perpendicularly into the water, struck the rocks, and stopped in the defile before touching the bottom. Enough remained out of the water to rise more than twelve feet above the waves. The vertical mass of planking formed a wall between the two Douvres; like the rock overturned crosswise higher up the defile, it allowed only a slight stream of foam to pass through at its two extremities, and thus was a fifth barricade improvised by Gilliatt against the tempest in that passage of the seas. The hurricane itself, in its blind fury, had assisted in the construction of this last barrier. Henceforth, let the storm do what it might, there was nothing to fear for the sloop or the machinery. Between the barrier of the Douvres, which covered them on the west, and the barricade which protected them from the east, no heavy sea or wind could reach them.

Gilliatt had plucked safety out of the catastrophe itself. The storm had been his fellow-labourer in the work. This done, he took a little water in the palm of his hand from one of the rain-pools, and drank: and then, looking upward at the storm said with a smile,

"Bungler."

HOW DANTÈS ESCAPED FROM THE CHÂTEAU D'IF[1]

Alexandre Dumas (1806-1870)

ON THE bed, at full length, and faintly lighted by the pale ray that penetrated the window, was visible a sack of coarse cloth, under the large folds of which were stretched a long and stiflened form; it was Faria's last winding-sheet—a winding-sheet which, as the turnkey said, cost so little. All, then, was completed. A material separation had taken place between Dantès and his old friend; he could no longer see those eyes which had remained open as if to look even beyond death; he could no longer clasp that hand of industry which had lifted for him the veil that had concealed hidden and obscure things. Faria, the usual and the good companion, with whom he was accustomed to live so intimately, no longer breathed. He seated himself on the edge of that terrible bed, and fell into a melancholy and gloomy reverie.

Alone!—he was alone again!—again relapsed into silence! he found himself once again in the presence of nothingness! Alone!—no longer to see, no longer to hear the voice of the only human being who attached him to life! Was it not better, like Faria, to seek the presence of his Maker, and learn the enigma of life at the risk of passing through the mournful gate of intense suffering? The idea of suicide, driven away by his friend, and forgotten in his presence whilst living, arose like a phantom before him in presence of his dead body.

"If I could die," he said, "I should go where he goes, and should assuredly find him again. But how to die? It is very easy," he continued, with a smile of bitterness; "I will remain here, rush on the first person that opens the door, will strangle him, and then they will guillotine me."

But as it happens that in excessive griefs, as in great tempests, the abyss is found

[1] From *The Count of Monte Cristo*.

between the tops of the loftiest waves, Dantès recoiled from the idea of this infamous death, and passed suddenly from despair to an ardent desire for life and liberty.

"Die! Oh no!" he exclaimed, "not die now, after having lived and suffered so long and so much! Die! yes, had I died years since; but now it would be, indeed, to give way to my bitter destiny. No, I desire to live; I desire to struggle to the very last; I wish to reconquer the happiness of which I have been deprived. Before I die I must not forget that I have my executioners to punish, and perhaps, too, who knows, some friends to reward. Yet they will forget me here, and I shall die in my dungeon like Faria."

As he said this, he remained motionless, his eyes fixed like a man struck with a sudden idea, but whom this idea fills with amazement. Suddenly he rose, lifted his hand to his brow as if his brain were giddy, paced twice or thrice round his chamber, and then paused abruptly at the bed.

"Ah! ah!" he muttered, "who inspires me with this thought? Is it thou, gracious God ? Since none but the dead pass freely from this dungeon, let me assume the place of the dead.''

Without giving himself time to reconsider his decision, and, indeed, that he might now allow his thoughts to be distracted from his desperate resolution, he bent over the appalling sack, opened it with the knife which Faria had made, drew the corpse from the sack, and transported it along the gallery to his own chamber, laid it on his couch, passed round its head the rag he wore at night round his own, covered it with his counterpane, once again kissed the ice-cold brow, and tried vainly to close the resisting eyes, which glared horribly; turned the head towards the wall, so that the gaoler might, when he brought his evening meal, believe that he was asleep, as was his frequent custom; returned along the gallery, threw the bed against the wall, returned to the other cell, took from the hiding-place the needle and thread, flung off his rags, that they might feel naked flesh only beneath the coarse sackcloth, and getting inside the sack, placed himself in the posture in which the dead body had been laid, and sewed up the mouth of the sack withinside.

The beating of his heart might have been heard, if by any mischance the gaolers had entered at that moment. Dantès might have waited until the evening visit was over, but he was afraid the governor might change his resolution, and order the dead body to be removed earlier. In that case his last hope would have been destroyed. Now his project was settled under any circumstances, and he hoped thus to carry it into effect. If during the time he was being conveyed the grave-diggers should discover that they were conveying a live instead of a dead body, Dantès did not intend to give them time to recognize him, but with a sudden cut of the knife, he meant to open the sack from top to bottom, and, profiting by their alarm, escape; if they tried to catch him, he would use his knife.

If they conducted him to the cemetery and laid him in the grave, he would allow himself to be covered with earth, and then, as it was night, the grave-diggers could scarcely have turned their backs, ere he would have worked his way through the soft soil and escape, hoping that the weight would not be too heavy for him to support. If he was deceived in this, and the earth proved too heavy he would be stifled, and then, so much the better, all would be over. Dantès had not eaten since the previous evening, but he had not thought of hunger or thirst, nor did he now think of it. His position was too precarious to allow him even time to reflect on any thought but one.

The first risk that Dantès ran was that the gaoler, when he brought him his supper at seven o'clock, might perceive the substitution he had effected; fortunately, twenty times at least, from misanthropy or fatigue, Dantès had received his gaoler in bed, and then the man placed his bread and soup on the table, and went away without saying a word. This time the gaoler might not be silent as usual, but speak to Dantès, and seeing that he received no reply, go to the bed, and thus discover all.

When seven o'clock came, Dantès' agony really commenced. His hand placed upon his heart was unable. to repress .its throbbings, whilst, with the other, he wiped the perspiration from his temples. From time to time shudderings ran through his whole frame, and collapsed his heart as if it were frozen. Then he thought he was going to die. Yet the hours passed on without any stir in the *Château,* and Dantès felt he had escaped this first danger: it was a good augury. At length, at about the hour the governor had appointed, footsteps were heard on the stairs. Edmond felt that the moment had arrived, and summoning up all his courage, held his breath, happy if at the same time he could have repressed in like manner the hasty pulsation of his arteries.

They stopped at the door—there were two steps, and Dantès guessed it was the two grave-diggers who came to seek him—this idea was soon converted into certainty, when he heard the noise they made in putting down the hand-bier. The door opened, and a dim light reached Dantès' eyes through the coarse sack that covered him; he saw two shadows approach his bed, a third remaining at the door with a torch in his hand. Each of these two men, approaching the ends of the bed, took the sack by its extremities.

"He's heavy though for an old and thin man," said one, as he raised the head.

"They say every year adds half a pound to the weight of the bones," said another, lifting the feet.

"Have you tied the knot?" inquired the first speaker.

"What would be the use of carrying so much more weight?" was the reply; "I can do that when we get there."

"Yes, you're right," replied the companion.

"What's the knot for?" thought Dantès.

They deposited the supposed corpse on the bier. Edmond stiffened himself in order to play his part of a dead man, and then the party, lighted by the man with the torch, who went first, ascended the stairs. Suddenly he felt the fresh and sharp night air, and Dantès recognized the *Mistral.* It was a sudden sensation, at the same time replete with delight and agony. The bearers advanced twenty paces, then stopped, putting their bier down on the ground. One of them went away, and Dantès heard his shoes on the pavement.

"Where am I then?" he asked himself.

"Really, he is by no means a light load!" said the other bearer, sitting on the edge of the hand-barrow. Dantès' first impulse was to escape, but fortunately he did not attempt it.

"Light me, you!" said the other bearer, "or I shall not find what I am looking for."

The man with the torch complied, although not asked in the most polite terms.

"What can he be looking for?" thought Edmond. "The spade perhaps."

An exclamation of satisfaction indicated that the grave-digger had found the object of his search.

"At last," said the other, "not without some trouble though."

"Yes," was the answer, "but it has lost nothing by waiting."

As he said this, the man came towards Edmond, who heard a heavy and sounding substance laid down beside him, and at the same moment a cord was fastened round his feet with sudden and painful violence.

"Well, have you tied the knot?" inquired the grave-digger who was looking on.

"Yes, and pretty tight too, I can tell you," was the answer.

"Move on, then." And the bier was lifted once more, and they proceeded.

They advanced fifty paces farther, and then stopped to open a door, then went forward again. The noise of the waves dashing against the rocks on which the *château* is built, reached Dantès' ears distinctly as they progressed.

"Bad weather!" observed one of the bearers; "not a pleasant night for a dip in the sea."

"Why, yes, the abbé runs a chance of being wet," said the other; and then there was a burst of brutal laughter.

Dantès did not comprehend the jest, but his hair stood erect on his head.

"Well, here we are at last," said one of them.

"A little farther—a little farther," said the other. "You know very well that the last was stopped on his way, dashed on the rocks, and the governor told us next day that we were careless fellows."

They ascended five or six more steps, and then Dantès felt that they took him one by the head and the other by the heels, and swung him to and fro.

"One!" said the grave-diggers. "Two! Three !"

And at the same instant Dantès felt himself flung into the air like a wounded bird falling, falling with a rapidity that made his blood curdle. Although drawn downwards by the same heavy weight which hastened his rapid descent, it seemed to him as if the time were a century. At last, with a terrific dash, he entered the ice-cold water, and as he did so he uttered a shrill cry, stifled in a moment by his immersion beneath the waves.

Dantès had been flung into the sea, into whose depths he was dragged by a thirty-six pound shot tied to his feet.

The sea is the cemetery of Château d'If.

Dantès, although giddy and almost suffocated, had yet sufficient presence of mind to hold his breath; and as his right hand (prepared as he was for every chance) held his knife open, he rapidly ripped up the sack, extricated his arm, then his head; but in spite of all his efforts to free himself from the shot, he felt it dragging him down still lower. He then bent his body, and by a desperate effort severed the cord that bound his legs, at the moment he was suffocating. With a vigorous spring he rose to the surface of the sea, whilst the shot bore to its depths the sack that had so nearly become his shroud.

Dantès merely paused to breathe, and then dived again, in order to avoid being seen. When he arose a second time, he was fifty paces from where he had first sunk. He saw overhead a black and tempestuous sky, over which the wind was driving the fleeting vapours that occasionally suffered a twinkling star to appear; before him was the vast expanse of waters, sombre and terrible, whose waves foamed and roared as if before the approach of a storm. Behind him, blacker than the sea, blacker than the sky, rose like a phantom the giant of granite, whose projecting crags seemed like arms extended to seize their prey; and on the highest rock was a torch that lighted two figures. He fancied these two forms were looking at the sea; doubtless these strange grave-diggers had heard his cry. Dantès dived again, and remained a long time beneath the water. This manoeuvre was already familiar to him, and usually attracted a crowd of spectators in the bay before the lighthouse at Marseilles when he swam there, and who, with one accord, pronounced him the best swimmer in the port. When he reappeared the light had disappeared.

It was necessary to strike out to sea. Ratonneau and Pomègue are the nearest isles of all those that surround the Château d'If; but Ratonneau and Pomègue are inhabited, together with the islet of Daume; Tiboulen or Lemaire were the most secure. The isles of Tiboulen and Lemaire are a league from the Château d'If. Dantès, nevertheless, determined to make for them. But how could he find his way in the darkness of the night? At this moment he saw before him, like a brilliant star, the lighthouse of Planier. By leaving this light on the right, he kept the isle of Tiboulen a little on the left; by turning to the left, therefore, he would find it. But, as we have said, it was at least a league from the Château d'If to this island. Often in prison Faria had said to him, when he saw him idle and inactive, "Dantès, you must not give way to this listlessness; you will be drowned if you seek to escape, and your strength has not been properly exercised and prepared for exertion." These words rang in Dantès' ears, even beneath the waves; he hastened to cleave his way through them to see if he had not lost his strength. He found with pleasure that his captivity had taken away nothing of his power, and that he was still master of that element on whose bosom he had so often sported as a boy.

Fear, that relentless pursuer, clogged Dantès' efforts. He listened if any noise was audible; each time that he rose over the waves his looks scanned the horizon, and strove to penetrate the darkness. Every wave seemed a boat in his pursuit, and he redoubled exertions that increased his distance from the *Château*, but the repetition of which weakened his strength. He swam on still, and already the terrible *Château* had disappeared in the darkness. He could not see it, but he *felt* its presence. An hour passed, during which Dantès, excited by the feeling of freedom, continued to cleave the waves.

"Let us see," said he, "I have swum above an hour, but as the wind is against me, that has retarded my speed; however, if I am not mistaken, I must be close to the isle of Tiboulen. But what if I were mistaken."

A shudder passed over him. He sought to tread water, in order to rest himself; but the sea was too violent, and he felt that he could not make use of this means of repose.

"Well," said he, "I will swim on until I am worn out, or the cramp seizes me, and then I shall sink."

And he struck out with the energy of despair.

Suddenly the sky seemed to him to become still darker and more dense, and compact clouds lowered towards him; at the same time he felt a violent pain in his knee. His imagination told him a ball had struck him, and that in a moment he would hear the report; but he heard nothing. Dantès put out his hand, and felt resistance; he then extended his leg, and felt the land, and in an instant guessed the nature of the object he had taken for a cloud.

Before him rose a mass of strangely formed rocks, that resembled nothing so much as a vast fire petrified at the moment of its most fervent combustion. It was the isle of Tiboulen.

Dantès rose, advanced a few steps, and, with a fervent prayer of gratitude, stretched himself on the granite, which seemed to him softer than down. Then, in spite of the wind and rain, he fell into the deep sweet sleep of those worn out by fatigue.

At the expiration of an hour Edmond was awakened by the roar of the thunder. The tempest was unchained and let loose in all its fury; from time to time a flash of lightning stretched across the heavens like a fiery serpent, lighting up the clouds that rolled on like the waves of an immense chaos.

Dantès had not been deceived—he had reached the first of the two isles, which was, in reality, Tiboulen. He knew that it was barren and without shelter; but when the sea became more calm, he resolved to plunge into its waves again, and swim to Lemaire, equally arid, but larger, and consequently better adapted for concealment.

An overhanging rock offered him a temporary shelter, and scarcely had he availed himself of it when the tempest burst forth in all its fury.

Edmond felt the rock beneath which he lay tremble, the waves, dashing themselves against the granite rock, wetted him with their spray. In safety, as he was, he felt himself become giddy in the midst of this war of the elements and the dazzling brightness of the lightning. It seemed to him that the island trembled to its base, and that it would, like a vessel at anchor, break her moorings and bear him off into the centre of the storm.

He remembered then that he had not eaten or drunk for four and twenty hours. He extended his hands, and drank greedily of the rainwater that had lodged in a hollow of the rock.

As he rose, a flash of lightning that seemed as if the whole of the heavens were opened, illumined the darkness. By its light, between the isle of Lemaire and Cape Croiselle, a quarter of a league distant, Dantès saw, like a spectre, a fishing-boat driven rapidly on by the force of the winds and waves. A second after, he saw it again, approaching nearer. Dantès cried at the top of his voice to warn them of their danger, but they saw it themselves. Another flash showed him four men clinging to the shattered mast and the rigging, while a fifth clung to the broken rudder. The men he beheld saw him doubtless, for their cries were carried to his ears by the wind. Above the splintered mast a sail rent to tatters was waving; suddenly the ropes that still held it gave way, and it disappeared in the darkness of the night like a vast sea-bird.

At the same moment a violent crash was heard, and cries of distress. Perched on the summit of the rock, Dantès saw, by the lightning, the vessel in pieces; and amongst the fragments were visible the agonized features of the unhappy sailors. Then all became dark again.

Dantès ran down the rocks at the risk of being himself dashed to pieces; he listened, he strove to examine, but he heard and saw nothing—all human cries had ceased, and the tempest alone continued to rage.

By degrees the wind abated, vast grey clouds rolled towards the west, and the blue firmament appeared studded with bright stars. Soon a red streak became visible in the horizon, the waves whitened, a light played over them, and gilded their foaming crests with gold.

It was day.

Dantès stood silent and motionless before this vast spectacle, for since his captivity he had forgotten it. He turned towards the fortress, and looked both at the sea and the land. The gloomy building rose from the bosom of the ocean with that imposing majesty of inanimate objects that seems at once to watch and to command.

It was about five o'clock. The sea continued to grow calmer.

"In two or three hours," thought Dantès, "the turnkey will enter my chamber, find the body of my poor friend, recognize it, seek for me in vain, and give the alarm. Then the passage will be discovered; the men who cast me into the sea, and who must have heard the cry I uttered, will be questioned. Then boats filled with armed soldiers will pursue the wretched fugitive. The cannon will warn every one to refuse shelter to a man wandering about naked and famished. The police of Marseilles will be on the alert by land, whilst the government pursues me by sea. I am cold, I am hungry. I have lost even the knife that saved me. Oh, my God! I have suffered enough surely. Have pity on me, and do for me what I am unable to do for myself."

As Dantès (his eyes turned in the direction of the Château d'If) uttered this prayer, he saw appear, at the extremity of the isle of Pomègue, like a bird skimming over the sea, a small bark, that the eye of a sailor alone could recognize as a Genoese tartane. She was coming out of Marseilles barbour, and was standing out to sea rapidly, her sharp prow cleaving through the waves.

"Oh!" cried Edmond, "to think that in half an hour I could join her, did I not fear being questioned, detected, and conveyed back to Marseilles! What can I do? What story can I invent? Under pretext of trading along the coast, these men, who are in reality smugglers, will prefer selling me to doing a good action. I must wait. But I cannot—I am starving.

In a few hours my strength will be utterly exhausted; besides, perhaps I have not been missed at the fortress. I can pass as one of the sailors wrecked last night. This story will pass current, for there is no one left to contradict me."

As he spoke, Dantès looked towards the spot where the fishing-vessel had been wrecked, and started. The red cap of one of the sailors hung to a point of the rock, and some beams that had formed part of the vessel's keel, floated at the foot of the crags.

In an instant Dantès' plan was formed. He swam to the cap, placed it on his head, seized one of the beams, and struck out so as to cross the line the vessel was taking.

"I am saved !" murmured he.

And this conviction restored his strength.

He soon perceived the vessel, which, having the wind right ahead, was tacking between the Château d'If and the tower of Planier. For an instant he feared lest the bark, instead of keeping inshore, should stand out to sea; but he soon saw by her manœuvres that she wished to pass, like most vessels bound for Italy, between the islands of Jaros and Calaseraigne. However, the vessel and the swimmer insensibly neared one another, and in one of its tacks the bark approached within a quarter of a mile of him. He rose on the waves, making signs of distress; but no one on board perceived him, and the vessel stood on another tack. Dantès would have cried out, but he reflected that the wind would drown his voice.

It was then he rejoiced at his precaution in taking the beam, for without it he would have been unable, perhaps, to reach the vessel—certainly to return to shore, should he be unsuccessful in attracting attention.

Dantès, although almost sure as to what course the bark would take, had yet watched it anxiously until it tacked and stood towards him. Then he advanced; but before they had met, the vessel again changed her direction.

By a violent effort he rose half out of the water, waving his cap, and uttering a loud shout peculiar to sailors.

This time he was both seen and heard, and the tartane instantly steered towards him. At the same time he saw they were about to lower a boat.

An instant after, the boat, rowed by two men, advanced rapidly towards him. Dantès abandoned the beam, which he thought now useless, and swam vigorously to meet them. But he had reckoned too much upon his strength, and then he felt how serviceable the beam had been to him. His arms grew stiff, his legs had lost their flexibility, and he was almost breathless.

He uttered a second cry. The two sailors redoubled their efforts, and one of them cried in Italian, "Courage!"

The word reached his ear as a wave which he no longer had the strength to surmount passed over his head. He rose again to the surface, supporting himself by one of those desperate efforts a drowning man makes, uttered a third cry, and felt himself sink again, as if the fatal shot were again tied to his feet. The water passed over his head, and the sky seemed livid. A violent effort again brought him to the surface. He felt as if something seized him by the hair, but he saw and heard nothing. He had fainted.

When he opened his eyes, Danres found himself on the deck of the tartane. His first care was to see what direction they were pursuing. They were rapidly leaving the Château d'If behind.

Dantès was so exhausted that the exclamation of joy he uttered was mistaken for a sigh.

As we have said, he was lying on the deck. A sailor was rubbing his limbs with a woollen cloth; another, whom he recognized as the one who had cried out "Courage!" held a gourd full of rum to his mouth; whilst the third, an old sailor, at once the pilot and captain, looked on with that egotistical pity men feel for a misfortune that they have escaped yesterday and which may overtake them to-morrow.

"Who are you ?" said the pilot, in bad French.

"I am," replied Dantès in bad Italian, "a Maltese sailor. We were coming from Syracuse laden with grain. The storm of last night overtook us at Cape Morgiou, and we were wrecked on these rocks. You have saved my life, and I thank you."

"Now what are we to do with you ?" said the captain.

"Alas! anything you please. My captain is dead; I have barely escaped; but I am a good sailor. Leave me at the first port you make; I shall be sure to find employment."

"Do you know the Mediterranean?"

"I have sailed over it since my childhood."

"You know the best harbours?"

"There are few ports that I could not enter or leave with my eyes shut."

"I say, captain," said the sailor who had cried "Courage!" to Dantès, "if what he says is true, what hinders his staying with us?"

"If he says true," said the captain doubtingly. "But in his present condition he will promise anything, and take his chance of keeping it afterwards."

"I will do more than I promise," said Dantès.

"We shall see," returned the other, smiling.

"As you will!" said Dantès, getting up. "Where are you going?" "To Leghorn."

"Then why, instead of tacking so frequently, do you not sail nearer the wind?"

"Because we should run straight on to the island of Rion."

"You shall pass it by twenty fathoms."

"Take the helm then, and let us see what you know."

The young man took the helm, ascertaining by a slight pressure if the vessel answered the rudder, and seeing that, without being a first rate sailer, she yet was tolerably obedient: "To the braces!" said he.

The four seamen who composed the crew, obeyed, whilst the pilot looked on.

"Haul taut!" They obeyed.

"Belay !"

This order was also executed, and the vessel passed, as Dantès had predicted, twenty fathoms to the right.

"Bravo!" cried the captain.

"Bravo!" repeated the sailors.

And they all regarded with astonishment this man whose eye had recovered an intelligence and his body a vigour they were far from suspecting.

"You see," said Dantès, quitting the helm, "I shall be of some use to you at least during the voyage. If you do not want me at Leghorn, you can leave me there, and

I will pay you out of the first wages I get, for my food and the clothes you lend me."

"Ah," said the captain," we can agree very well, if you are reasonable." "Give me what you give the others," returned Dantès.

"That's not fair," said the seaman who had saved Dantès, "for you know more than we do."

"What's that to you, Jacopo?" returned the captain. "Every one is free to ask what he pleases."

"That's true," replied Jacopo, "I only made a remark."

"Well, you would do much better to lend him a jacket and a pair of trousers, if you have them."

"No," said Jacopo, "but I have a shirt and a pair of trousers." "That is all I want," interrupted Dantès. "Thank you, my friend."

Jacopo dived into the hold and soon returned with what Edmond wanted.

"Now, then, do you wish for anything else?" said the captain.

"A piece of bread and another glass of the capital rum I tasted, for I have not eaten or drunk for a long time."

He had not, in truth, tasted food for forty hours. They brought him a piece of bread, and Jacopo offered him the gourd.

"Larboard your helm !" cried the captain to the helmsman.

Dantès glanced to the same side as he lifted the gourd to his mouth. "Halloa! what's the matter at the Château d'If?" said the captain. A small white cloud, which had attracted Dantès' attention, crowned the summit of the bastion of the Château d'If. A moment later the faroff report of a gun was heard. The sailors looked at one another. "What does it mean?" asked the captain.

"A prisoner has escaped from Château d'If, and they are firing the alarm gun," replied Dantès.

The captain glanced at him, but he had lifted the rum to his lips, and was drinking it with so much composure that his suspicions, if he had any, died away.

"At any rate," murmured he, "if it be, so much the better, for I have made a rare acquisition."

Under pretence of being fatigued, Dantès asked to take the helm. The helmsman, enchanted to be relieved, looked at the captain who, by a nod, indicated that he might abandon it to his new comrade. Dantès could thus keep his eye on Marseilles.

"What is the day of the month ?" asked he of Jacopo, who sat down beside him.

"The 28th of February."

"In what year?" asked Dantès.

"In what year! You ask me in what year!"

"Yes," replied the young man, "I ask you in what year."

"You have forgotten?"

"I was so frightened last night," said Dantès, laughing, "that I have almost lost my memory. I ask you what year is it?"

"1829," said Jacopo.

It was fourteen years, day for day, since Dantès' arrest.

He was nineteen when he entered the Château d'If; he was thirtythree when he escaped. A sorrowful smile passed over his face; he asked himself what had become of Mercédès, who must believe him dead. Then his eyes lighted up with hatred as he thought of the three men who had caused him so long and wretched a captivity. He renewed against Danglars, Fernand, and Villefort the oath of implacable vengeance he had made in his dungeon. This oath was no longer a vain menace; for the fastest sailer in the Mediterranean would have been unable to overtake the little tartane, that with every stitch of canvas set, was flying before the wind to Leghorn.

A WHALE OF UNKNOWN SPECIES[1]

Jules Verne
(1828-1905)

WE WERE at last on the scene of the last frolics of the monster; and the truth was, no one lived really on board. The entire crew were under the influence of such nervous excitement as I could not give the idea of. They neither ate nor slept. Twenty times a day some error of estimation, or the optical delusion of a sailor perched on the yards, caused intolerable frights; and these emotions, twenty times repeated, kept us in a state too violent not to cause an early reaction.

And, in fact, the reaction was not slow in coming. For three months—three months, each day of which lasted a century—the *Abraham Lincoln* ploughed all the waters of the North Pacific, running down all the whales signalled, making sharp deviations from her route, veering suddenly from one tack to another, and not leaving one point of the Chinese or Japanese coast unexplored. And yet nothing was seen but the immense waste of waters—nothing that resembled a gigantic narwhal, nor a submarine islet, nor a wreck, nor a floating reef, nor anything at all supernatural.

The reaction, therefore, began. Discouragement at first took possession of all minds, and opened a breach for incredulity. A new sentiment was experienced on

[1] From *Twenty Thousand Leagues Under the Sea.*

board, composed of three-tenths of shame and seventenths of rage. They called themselves fools for being taken in by a chimera, and were still more furious at it. The mountains of arguments piled up for a year fell down all at once, and all every one thought of was to make up the hours of meals and sleep which they had so foolishly sacrificed.

With the mobility natural to the human mind, they threw themselves from one excess into another. The warmest partisans of the enterprise became finally its most ardent detractors. The reaction ascended from the depths of the vessel, from the coal-hole, to the officers' ward-room, and certainly, had it not been for very strong determination on the part of Captain Farragut, the head of the frigate would have been definitely turned southward,

However, this useless search could be no further prolonged. No crew of the American navy had ever shown more patience or zeal; its want of success could not be imputed to it. There was nothing left to do but to return.

A representation in this sense was made to the commander. The commander kept his ground. The sailors did not hide their dissatisfaction, and the service suffered from it. I do not mean that there was revolt on board, but after a reasonable period of obstinacy the commander, like Columbus before him, asked for three days' patience. If in three days the monster had not reappeared, the man at the helm should give three turns of the wheel, and the *Abraham Lincoln* should make for the European seas.

Two days passed. The frigate kept up steam at half-pressure. Large quantities of bacon were trailed in the wake of the ship, to the great satisfaction of the sharks. The frigate lay to, and her boats were sent in all directions, but the night of the 4th of November passed without unveiling the submarine mystery.

Japan lay less than 200 miles to leeward. Eight bells had just struck as I was leaning over the starboard side. Conseil, standing near me, was looking straight in front of him. The crew, perched in the ratlins, were keeping a sharp look-out in the approaching darkness. Officers with their night-glasses swept the horizon.

Looking at Conseil, I saw that the brave fellow was feeling slightly the general influence—at least it seemed to me so. Perhaps for the first time, his nerves were vibrating under the action of a sentiment of curiosity.

"Well, Conseil," said I, "this is your last chance of pocketing 2000 dollars."

"Will monsieur allow me to tell him that I never counted upon the reward, and if the Union had promised 100,000 dollars it would never be any the poorer."

"You are right, Conseil. It has been a stupid affair, after all. We have lost time and patience, and might just as well have been in France six months ago."

"Yes, in monsieur's little apartments, classifying monsieur's fossils, and monsieur's babiroussa would be in its cage in the Jardin des Plantes, attracting all the curious people in Paris."

"Yes, Conseil, and besides that we shall get well laughed at."

"Certainly," said Conseil tranquilly. "I think they will laugh at monsieur. And I must say—"

"What, Conseil?"

"That it will serve monsieur right! When one has the honour to be a *savant* like monsieur, one does not expose—"

Conseil did not finish his compliment. In the midst of general silence Ned Land's voice was heard calling out,—

"Look out, there! The thing we are looking for is on our weather beam!"

At this cry the entire crew rushed towards the harpooner. Captain, officers, masters, sailors, and cabin-boys, even the engineers left their engines, and the stokers their fires. The order to stop her had been given, and the frigate was only moving by her own momentum. The darkness was then profound, and although I knew the Canadian's eyes were very good, I asked myself what he could have seen, and how he could have seen it. My heart beat violently.

At two cables' length from the *Abraham Lincoln* on her starboard quarter, the sea seemed to be illuminated below the surface. The monster lay some fathoms below the sea, and threw out the very intense but inexplicable light mentioned in the reports of several captains. This light described an immense and much-elongated oval, in the centre of which was condensed a focus the over-powering brilliancy of which died out by successive gradations.

"It is only an agglomeration of phosphoric particles," cried one of the officers.

"No, sir," I replied with conviction. "Never did pholas or salpæ produce such a light as that. That light is essentially electric. Besides—see! look out! It moves—forward—on to us!"

A general cry rose from the frigate.

"Silence!" called out the captain. "Up with the helm! Reverse the engines!"

The frigate thus tried to escape, but the supernatural animal approached her with a speed double her own.

Stupefaction, more than fear, kept us mute and motionless. The animal gained upon us. It made the round of the frigate, which was then going at the rate of fourteen knots, and enveloped her with its electric ring like luminous dust. Then it went two or three miles off, leaving a phosphoric trail like the steam of an express locomotive. All at once, from the dark limits of the horizon, where it went to gain its momentum, the monster rushed towards the frigate with frightful rapidity, stopped suddenly at a distance of twenty feet, and then went out, not diving, for its brilliancy did not die out by degrees, but all at once, as if turned off. Then it reappeared on the other side of the ship, either going round her or gliding under her hull. A collision might have occurred at any moment, which might have been fatal to us.

I was astonished at the way the ship was worked. She was being attacked instead of attacking; and I asked Captain Farragut the reason.

On the captain's generally impassive face was an expression of profound astonishment.

"M. Aronnax," he said, "I do not know with how formidable a being I have to deal, and I will not imprudently risk my frigate in the darkness. We must wait for daylight, and then we shall change parts."

"You have no longer any doubt, captain, of the nature of the animal?"

"No sir. It is evidently a gigantic narwhal, and an electric one too."

"Perhaps," I added, "we can no more approach it than we could a gymnotus or a torpedo."

"It may possess as great blasting properties, and if it does it is the most terrible animal that ever was created. That is why I must keep on my guard."

All the crew remained up that night. No one thought of going to sleep. The *Abraham Lincoln* not being able to compete in speed, was kept under half-steam. On its side the narwhal imitated the frigate, let the waves rock it at will, and seemed determined not to leave the scene of combat.

Towards midnight, however, it disappeared, dying out like a large glowworm. At seven minutes to one in the morning a deafening whistle was heard, like that produced by a column of water driven out with extreme violence.

The captain, Ned Land, and I were then on the poop, peering with eagerness through the profound darkness.

"Ned Land," asked the commander, "have you often heard whales roar?"

"Yes, captain, often; but never such a whale as I earned 2000 dollars by sighting."

"True, you have a right to the prize; but tell me, is it the same noise they make?"

"Yes, sir; but this one is incomparably louder. It is not to be mistaken. It is certainly a cetacean there in our seas. With your permission, sir, we will have a few words with him at daybreak."

"If he is in a humour to hear them, Mr Land," said I, in an unconvinced tone.

"Let me get within a length of four harpoons," answered the Canadian, "and he will be obliged to listen to me."

"But in order to approach him," continued the captain, "I shall have to put a whaler at your disposition."

"Certainly sir."

"But that will be risking the lives of my men."

"And mine too," answered the harpooner simply.

About 2 A.M. the luminous focus reappeared, no less intense, about five miles to the windward of the frigate. Notwithstanding the distance and the noise of the wind and sea, the loud strokes of the animal's tail were distinctly heard, and even its panting breathing. When the enormous narwhal came up to the surface to breathe, it seemed as if the air rushed into its lungs like steam in the vast cylinders of a 2000 horse-power engine.

"Hum!" thought I, "a whale with the strength of a cavalry regiment would be a pretty whale!"

Until daylight we were all on the *qui vive,* and then the fishing tackle was prepared. The first mate loaded the blunderbusses, which throw harpoons the distance of a mile, and long duck-guns with explosive bullets, which inflict mortal wounds even upon the most powerful animals. Ned Land contented himself with sharpening his harpoon—a terrible weapon in his hands.

Day began to break, and with the first glimmer of dawn the electric light of the narwhal disappeared. At 7 A.M. a very thick sea-fog obscured the atmosphere, and the best glasses could not pierce it.

I climbed the mizenmast and found some officers already perched on the mastheads.

At 8 A.M. the mist began to clear away. Suddenly, like the night before, Ned Land's voice was heard calling,—

" The thing in question on the port quarter!"

All eyes were turned towards the point indicated. There, a mile and a half from the frigate, a large black body emerged more than a yard above the waves. Its tail, violently agitated, produced a considerable eddy. Never did caudal appendage beat the sea with such force. An immense track, dazzlingly white, marked the passage of the animal, and described a long curve.

The frigate approached the cetacean, and I could see it well. The accounts of it given by the *Shannon* and *Helvetia* had rather exaggerated its dimensions, and I estimated its length at 150 feet only. As to its other dimensions, I could only conceive them to be in proportion.

Whilst I was observing it, two jets of vapour and water sprang from its ventholes and ascended to a height of fifty yards, thus fixing my opinion as to its way of breathing. I concluded definitely that it belonged to the vertebrate branch of mammalia, order of cetaceans, family . . . .

Here I could not decide. The order of cetaceans comprehends three families—whales, cachalots, and dolphins—and it is in the last that narwhals are placed.

The crew were waiting impatiently for their captain's orders. Farragut, after attentively examining the animal, had the chief engineer called. "Is your steam up?" asked the captain.

"Yes, captain," answered the engineer.

"Then make up your fires and put on all steam."

Three cheers greeted this order. The hour of combat had struck. Some minutes afterwards the funnels of the frigate were giving out torrents of black smoke, and the deck shook under the trembling of the boilers.

The *Abraham Lincoln,* propelled by her powerful screw, went straight at the animal, who let her approach to within half a cable's length, and then, as if disdaining to dive, made a little attempt at flight, and contented itself with keeping its distance.

This pursuit lasted about three-quarters of an hour, without the frigate gaining four yards on the cetacean. It was quite evident she would never reach it at that rate.

The captain twisted his beard impatiently.

"Ned Land!" called the captain, "do you think I had better have the boats lowered?"

"No, sir," answered Ned Land, "for that animal won't be caught unless it chooses."

"What must be done, then?"

"Force steam if you can, captain, and I, with your permission, will post myself under the bowsprit, and if we get within a harpoon length I shall hurl one."

"Very well," said the captain. "Engineer, put on more pressure."

Ned Land went to his post, the fires were increased, the screw revolved forty-three times a minute, and the steam poured out of the valves. The log was heaved, and it was found that the frigate was going eighteen miles and five-tenths an hour. But the animal went eighteen and fivetenths an hour too.

During another hour the frigate kept up that speed without gaining a yard. It was humiliating for one of the quickest vessels in the American navy. The crew began to get very angry. The sailors swore at the animal, who did not deign to answer them. The captain not only twisted his beard, he began to gnaw it too. The engineer was called once more.

"Have you reached your maximum of pressure?" asked the captain.

"Yes sir."

The captain ordered him to do all he could without absolutely blowing up the vessel, and coal was at once piled up on the fires. The speed of the frigate increased. Her masts shook again. The log was again heaved, and this time she was making nineteen miles and three-tenths.

"All steam on!" called out the captain.

The engineer obeyed. The manometer marked ten degrees. But the cetacean did the nineteen miles and three-tenths as easily as the eighteen and five-tenths.

What a chase! I cannot describe the emotion that made my whole being vibrate again. Ned Land kept at his post, harpoon in hand. The animal allowed itself to be approached several times. Sometimes it was so near that the Canadian raised his hand to hurl the harpoon, when the animal rushed away at a speed of at least thirty miles an hour, and even during our maximum of speed it bullied the frigate, going round and round it.

A cry of fury burst from all lips. We were not further advanced at twelve o'clock than we had been at eight. Captain Farragut then made up his mind to employ more direct means.

"Ah!" said he, "so that animal goes faster than my ship! Well, we'll see if he'll go faster than a conical bullet. Master, send your men to the forecastle."

The forecastle gun was immediately loaded and pointed. It was fired, but the ball passed some feet above the cetacean, which kept about half a mile off.

"Let some one else try!" called out the captain. "Five hundred dollars to whomsoever will hit the beast!"

An old gunner with a grey beard—I think I see now his calm face as he approached the gun—put it into position and took a long aim. A loud report followed and mingled with the cheers of the crew.

The bullet reached its destination; it struck the animal, but, gliding off the rounded surface, fell into the sea two miles off.

"Malediction!" cried the captain; "that animal must be clad in six-inch iron plates. But I'll catch it, if I have to blow up my frigate!"

It was to be hoped that the animal would be exhausted, and that it would not be indifferent to fatigue like a steam-engine. But the hours went on, and it showed no signs of exhaustion.

It must be said, in praise of the *Abraham Lincoln,* that she struggled on indefatigably. I cannot reckon the distance we made during this unfortunate day at less than 300 miles. But night came on and closed round the heaving ocean.

At that minute, I believed our expedition to be at an end, and that we should see the fantastic animal no more.

I was mistaken, for at 10.50 P.M. the electric light reappeared, three miles windward to the frigate, clear and intense as on the night before.

The narwhal seemed motionless. Perhaps, fatigued with its day's work, it was sleeping in its billowy cradle. That was a chance by which the captain resolved to profit.

He gave his orders. The *Abraham Lincoln* was kept up at half-steam, and advanced cautiously so as not to awaken her adversary. It is not rare to meet in open sea with whales fast asleep, and Ned Land had harpooned many a one in that condition. The Canadian went back to his post under the bowsprit.

The frigate noiselessly approached, and stopped at two cables' length from the animal. No one breathed. A profound silence reigned on deck. We were not 1000 feet from the burning focus, the light of which increased and dazzled our eyes.

At that minute, leaning on the forecastle bulwark, I saw Ned Land below me, holding the martingale with one hand and with the other brandishing his terrible harpoon, scarcely twenty feet from the motionless animal.

All at once he threw the harpoon, and I heard the sonorous stroke of the weapon, which seemed to have struck a hard body.

The electric light suddenly went out, and two enormous waterspouts fell on the deck of the frigate, running like a torrent from fore to aft, upsetting men, and breaking the lashing of the spars.

A frightful shock followed. I was thrown over the rail before I had time to stop myself, and fell into the sea.

Although I was surprised by my unexpected fall, I still kept a very distinct impression of my sensations. I was at first dragged down to a depth of about twenty feet. I was a good swimmer, and this plunge did not make me lose my presence of mind. Two vigorous kicks brought me back to the surface.

My first care was to look for the frigate. Had the crew seen me disappear? Had the *Abraham Lincoln* veered round? Would the captain have a boat lowered? Might I hope to be saved?

The darkness was profound. I perceived a black mass disappearing in the east, the beacon lights of which were dying out in the distance. It was the frigate. I gave myself up.

"Help! help!" cried I, swimming towards the frigate with desperate strokes.

My clothes embarrassed me. The water glued them to my body. They paralysed my movements. I was sinking.

"Help!" rang out again in the darkness.

This was the last cry I uttered. My mouth filled with water. I struggled not to be sucked into the abyss.

Suddenly my clothes were seized by a vigorous hand, and I felt myself brought back violently to the surface of the water, and I heard—yes, I heard these words uttered in my ear,—

" If monsieur will have the goodness to lean on my shoulder, monsieur will swim much better."

I seized the arm of my faithful Conseil.

"You !" I cried—" you!"

"Myself," answered Conseil, "at monsieur's service."

"Did the shock throw you into the sea too?"

"No; but being in the service of monsieur, I followed him."

The worthy fellow thought that quite natural.

"What about the frigate?" I asked.

"The frigate!" answered Conseil, turning on his back; "I think monsieur will do well not to count upon the frigate."

"Why?"

"Because, as I jumped into the sea, I heard the man at the helm call out, 'The screw and the rudder are broken.'"

"Broken ?"

"Yes, by the monster's tusk. It is the only damage she has sustained, I think, but without a helm she can't do anything for us."

"Then we are lost!"

"Perhaps," answered Conseil tranquilly. "In the meantime we have still several hours before us, and in several hours many things may happen."

The *sang-froid* of Conseil did me good. I swam more vigorously, but encumbered by my garments, which dragged me down like a leaden weight, I found it extremely difficult to keep up. Conseil perceived it.

"Will monsieur allow me to make a slit?" said he. And, slipping an open knife under my clothes, he slit them rapidly from top to bottom. Then he quickly helped me off with them whilst I swam for both. I rendered him the same service, and we went on swimming near each other.

In the meantime our situation was none the less terrible. Perhaps our disappearance had not been remarked, and even if it had, the frigate could not tack without her helm. Our only chance of safety was in the event of the boats being lowered.

The collision had happened about 11 P.M. About 1 A.M. I was taken with extreme fatigue, and all my limbs became stiff with cramp. Conseil was obliged to keep me up, and the care of our preservation depended upon him alone. I heard the poor fellow breathing hard, and knew he could not keep up much longer.

"Let me go! Leave me!" I cried.

"Leave monsieur? Never!" he answered. "I shall drown with him."

Just then the moon appeared through the fringe of a large cloud that the wind was driving eastward. The surface of the sea shone under her rays. I lifted my head and saw the frigate. She was five miles from us, and only looked like a dark mass, scarcely distinguishable. I saw no boats.

I tried to call out, but it was useless at that distance. My swollen lips would not utter a sound. Conseil could still speak, and I heard him call out "Help!" several times.

We suspended our movements for an instant and listened. It might be only a singing in our ears, but it seemed to me that a cry answered Conseil's.

"Did you hear?" I murmured.

"Yes, yes!"

And Conseil threw another despairing cry into space. This time there could be no mistake. A human voice answered ours. Was it the voice of some other victim of the shock, or a boat hailing us in the darkness? Conseil made a supreme effort, and, leaning on my shoulder whilst I made a last struggle for us both, he raised himself half out of the water, and I heard him shout. Then my strength was exhausted, my fingers slipped, my mouth filled with salt water, I went cold all over, raised my head for the last time, and began to sink.

At that moment I hit against something hard, and I clung to it in desperation. Then I felt myself lifted up out of the water, and I fainted. I soon came to, thanks to the vigorous friction that was being applied to my body, and I half opened my eyes. "Conseil!" I murmured.

"Did monsieur ring?" answered Conseil.

Just then, by the light of the moon that was getting lower on the horizon, I perceived a face that was not Conseil's, but which I immediately recognized.

"Ned!" I cried.

"The same, sir, looking after his prize," replied the Canadian.

"Were you thrown into the sea when the frigate was struck?"

"Yes, sir, but, luckier than you, I soon got upon a floating island."

"An island ?"

"Yes, or if you like better, on our giant narwhal."

"What do you mean, Ned?"

"I mean that I understand now why my harpoon did not stick into the skin, but was blunted."

"Why, Ned, why?"

"Because the beast is made of sheet-iron plates."

I wriggled myself quickly to the top of the half-submerged being or object on which we had found refuge. I struck my foot against it. It was evidently a hard and impenetrable body, and not the soft substance which forms the mass of great marine mammalia. But this hard body could not be a bony carapace like that of antediluvian animals. I could not even class it amongst amphibious reptiles, such as tortoises and alligators, for the blackish back that supported me was not scaly but smooth and polished.

The blow produced a metallic sound, and, strange as it may appear, seemed caused by being struck on riveted plates. Doubt was no longer possible. The animal, monster, natural phenomenon that had puzzled the entire scientific world, and misled the imagination of sailors in the two hemispheres, was, it must be acknowledged, a still more astonishing phenomenon, a phenomenon of man's making. The discovery of the existence of the most fabulous and mythological being would not have astonished me in the same degree. It seems quite simple that anything prodigious should come from the hand of the Creator, but to find the impossible realized by the hand of man was enough to confound the imagination.

We were lying upon the top of a sort of submarine boat, which looked to me like an immense steel fish. Ned Land's mind was made up on that point, and Conseil and I could only agree with him.

"But then," said I, "this apparatus must have a locomotive machine, and a crew inside of it to work it."

"Evidently," replied the harpooner, "and yet for the three hours that I have inhabited this floating island, it has not given sign of life."

"The vessel has not moved?"

"No M. Aronnax. It is cradled in the waves, but it does not move."

"We know, without the slightest doubt, however, that it is endowed with great speed, and as a machine is necessary to produce the speed, and a mechanician to guide it, I conclude from that that we are saved."

"Hum" said Ned Land in a reserved tone of voice.

At that moment, and as if to support my arguments, a boiling was heard at the back of the strange apparatus, the propeller of which was evidently a screw, and it began to move. We only had time to hold on to its upper part, which emerged about a yard out of the water. Happily its speed was not excessive.

"As long as it moves horizontally," murmured Ned Land, "I have nothing to say. But if it takes it into its head to plunge, I would not give two dollars for my skin!"

The Canadian might have said less still. It therefore became urgent to communicate with whatever beings were shut up in the machine. I looked on its surface for an opening, a panel, a "man hole," to use the technical expression; but the lines of bolts, solidly fastened down on the joints of the plates, were clear and uniform.

Besides, the moon then disappeared and left us in profound obscurity. We were obliged to wait till daybreak to decide upon the means of penetrating to the interior of this submarine boat.

Thus, then, our safety depended solely upon the caprice of the mysterious steersmen who directed this apparatus, and if they plunged we were lost!Unless that happened I did not doubt the possibility of entering into communication with them. And it was certain that unless they made their own air they must necessarily return from time to time to the surface of the ocean to renew their provision of breathable molecules. Therefore there must be an opening which put the interior of the boat into communication with the atmosphere.

As to the hope of being saved by Commander Farragut, that had to be completely renounced. We were dragged westward, and I estimated that our speed, relatively moderate, attained twelve miles an hour. The screw beat the waves with mathematical regularity, sometimes emerging and throwing the phosphorescent water to a great height.

About 4 A.M. the rapidity of the apparatus increased. We resisted with difficulty this vertiginous impulsion, when the waves beat upon us in all their fury. Happily Ned touched with his hand a wide balustrade fastened on to the upper part of the iron top, and we succeeded in holding on to it solidly.

At last this long night slipped away. My incomplete memory does not allow me to retrace all the impressions of it. A single detail returns to my mind. During certain lullings of the sea and wind, I thought several times I heard vague sounds, a sort of fugitive harmony produced by faroff chords. What, then, was the mystery of this submarine navigation, of which the entire world vainly sought the explanation? What beings lived in this strange boat? What mechanical agent allowed it to move with such prodigious speed?

When daylight appeared the morning mists enveloped us, but they soon rose, and I proceeded to make an attentive examination of the sort of horizontal platform we were on, when I felt myself gradually sinking.

"Mille diables!" cried Land, kicking against the sonorous metal, "open, inhospitable creatures!"

But it was difficult to make oneself heard amidst the deafening noise made by the screw. Happily the sinking ceased.

Suddenly a noise like iron bolts being violently withdrawn was heard from the interior of the boat. One of the iron plates was raised, a man appeared, uttered a strange cry, and disappeared immediately.

Some moments after, eight strong fellows, with veiled faces, silently appeared, and dragged us down into their formidable machine.

ATLANTIS[1]

Jules Verne
(1828-1905)

AS SOON as I was dressed I went into the saloon. The compass was not reassuring. The direction of the *Nautilus* was S.S.W. We were turning our backs on Europe.

I waited impatiently for our bearings to be taken. About 11.30 A.M. the reservoirs were emptied, and our apparatus went up to the surface of the ocean. I sprang upon the platform. Ned Land preceded me there.

There was no land in sight. Nothing but the immense sea. A few sails on the horizon, doubtless those that go as far as San Roque in search of favourable winds for doubling the Cape of Good Hope. The weather was cloudy. A gale was springing up.

Ned, in a rage, tried to pierce the misty horizon. He still hoped that behind the mist stretched the land so much desired.

---

[1] From *Twenty Thousand Leagues Under the Sea.*

At noon the sun appeared for an instant. The first officer took advantage of the gleam to take the altitude. Then, the sea becoming rougher, we went down again, and the panel was closed.

An hour afterwards, when I consulted the map, I saw that the position of the *Nautilus* was indicated upon it by 16° 17' long, and 33° 22' lat., at 150 leagues from the nearest coast. It was no use to dream of escaping now, and I leave Ned Land's anger to be imagined when I informed him of our situation.

On my own account I was not overwhelmed with grief. I felt relieved from a weight that was oppressing me, and I could calmly take up my habitual work again.

That evening, about 11 P.M., I received the very unexpected visit of Captain Nemo. He asked me very graciously if I felt fatigued from sitting up so late the night before. I answered in the negative.

"Then, M. Aronnax, I have a curious excursion to propose to you."

"What is it, captain?"

"You have as yet only been on the sea-bottom by daylight. Should you like to see it on a dark night?" "I should like it much."

"It will be a fatiguing walk, I warn you. You will have to go far, and climb a mountain. The roads are not very well kept in repair."

"What you tell me makes me doubly curious. I am ready to follow you."

"Come, then, professor. We will go and put on our diving dresses." When we reached the ward-room I saw that neither my companions nor any of the crew were to follow us in our excursion. Captain Nemo had not even asked me to take Ned or Conseil.

In a few minutes we had put on our apparatus. They placed on our backs the reservoirs full of air, but the electric lamps were not prepared. I said as much to the captain.

"They would be of no use to us," he answered.

I thought I had not heard aright, but I could not repeat my observation, for the captain's head had already disappeared under its metallic covering. I finished harnessing myself, felt that some one placed an iron spiked stick in my hand, and a few minutes later, after the usual manœuvre, we set foot on the bottom of the Atlantic, at a depth of 150 fathoms.

Midnight was approaching. The waters were in profound darkness, but Captain Nemo showed me a reddish point in the distance, a sort of large light shining about two miles from the *Nautilus*. What this fire was, with what fed, why and how it burnt in the liquid mass, I could not tell. Anyway it lighted us, dimly it is true, but I soon became accustomed to the peculiar darkness, and I understood, under the circumstances, the uselessness of the Ruhmkorff apparatus.

Captain Nemo and I walked side by side directly towards the light. The flat soil ascended gradually. We took long strides, helping ourselves with our sticks, but our progress was slow, for our feet often sank in a sort of mud covered with seaweed and flat stones.

As we went along I heard a sort of pattering above my head. The noise sometimes redoubled, and produced something like a continuous shower. I soon understood the cause. It was rain falling violently and crisping the surface of the waves. Instinctively I was seized with the idea that I should be wet through. By water, in water! I could not help laughing at the odd idea. But the truth is that under a thick diving dress the liquid element is no longer felt, and it only seems like an atmosphere rather denser than the terrestrial atmosphere, that is all.

After half an hour's walking the soil became rocky. The medusæ, the microscopic crustaceans, the pennatules slightly lighted us with their phosphorescent gleams. I caught a glimpse of heaps of stones covered by some millions of zoophytes and thickets of seaweed. My foot often slipped upon this viscous carpet of seaweed and without my stick I should have fallen several times. Turning, I still saw the white light of the *Nautilus* beginning to gleam in the distance.

The heaps of stones of which I have just spoken were heaped on the bottom of the ocean with a sort of regularity I could not explain to myself. I perceived gigantic furrows which lost themselves in the distant darkness, the length of which escaped all valuation. Other peculiarities presented themselves that I did not know how to account for. It seemed to me that my heavy leaden shoes were crushing a litter of bones that cracked with a dry noise. What then was this vast plain I was thus moving across. I should have liked to question the captain, but his language by signs, that allowed him to talk to his companions when they followed him in his submarine excursions, was still incomprehensible to me.

In the meantime the reddish light that guided us increased and inflamed the horizon. The presence of this fire under the seas excited my curiosity to the highest pitch. Was it some electric effluence? Was I going towards a natural phenomenon still unknown to the *savants* of the earth? Or—for this thought crossed my mind—had the hand of man any part in the conflagration? Had it lighted this fire? Was I going to meet in this deep sea companions and friends of Captain Nemo living the same strange life, and whom he was going to see? All these foolish and inadmissible ideas pursued me, and in that state of mind, ceaselessly excited by the series of marvels that passed before my eyes, I should not have been surprised to see at the bottom of the sea, one of the submarine towns Captain Nemo dreamed of.

Our road grew lighter and lighter. The white light shone from the top of a mountain about eight hundred feet high. But what I perceived was only a reflection made by the crystal of the water. The fire, the source of the inexplicable light, was on the opposite side of the mountain.

Amidst the stony paths that furrowed the bottom of the Atlantic Captain Nemo went on without hesitating. He knew the dark route, had doubtless often been along it, and could not lose himself in it. I followed him with unshaken confidence. He appeared, whilst walking before me, like one of the sea genii, and I admired his tall stature like a black shadow on the luminous background of the horizon.

It was one o'clock in the morning. We had reached the first slopes of the mountain. But the way up led through the difficult paths of a vast thicket.

Yes, a thicket of dead trees, leafless, sapless, mineralized under the action of the water, overtopped here and there by gigantic pines. It was like a coal-series, still standing, holding by its roots to the soil that had given way, and whose branches, like fine black paper-cuttings, stood out against the watery ceiling. My readers may imagine a forest on the side of the Hartz Mountains, but forest and mountain sunk to the bottom of the sea. The paths were encumbered with seaweed and fucus, amongst which swarmed a world of crustaceans. I went on climbing over the rocks, leaping over the fallen trunks, breaking the sea-creepers that balanced from one tree to another, startling the fish that flew from branch to branch. Pressed onwards I no longer felt any fatigue. I followed my guide, who was never fatigued.

What a spectacle! How can I depict it? How describe the aspect of the woods and rocks in this liquid element, their lower parts sombre and wild, the upper coloured with red tints in the light which the reverberating power of the water doubled? We were climbing rocks which fell in enormous fragments directly afterwards with the noise of an avalanche. Right and left were deep dark galleries where sight was lost. Here opened vast clearings that seemed made by the hand of man, and I asked myself sometimes if some inhabitant of these submarine regions was not about to appear suddenly.

But Captain Nemo still went on climbing. I would not be left behind. My stick lent me useful aid. A false step would have been dangerous in these narrow paths, hollowed out of the sides of precipices; but I walked along with a firm step without suffering from vertigo. Sometimes I jumped over a crevice the depth of which would have made me recoil on the glaciers of the earth;sometimes I ventured on the vacillating trunks of trees thrown from one abyss to another without looking under my feet, having only eyes to admire the savage sites of that region. There, monumental rocks perched on these irregularly-cut bases seemed to defy the laws of equilibrium. Between their stony knees grew trees like a jet of water under strong pressure, sustaining and sustained by the rocks. Then, natural towers, large scarps cut perpendicularly like a fortress curtain, inclining at an angle which the laws of gravitation would not have authorized on the surface of the terrestrial regions.

And did I not myself feel the difference due to the powerful density of the water, when, notwithstanding my heavy garments, my brass headpiece, my metal soles, I climbed slopes impracticably steep, clearing them, so to speak, with the lightness of an isard or a chamois?

I feel that this recital of an excursion under the sea cannot sound probable. I am the historian of things that seem impossible, and that yet are real and incontestable. I did not dream. I saw and felt.

Two hours after having quitted the *Nautilus* we had passed the trees, and a hundred feet above our heads rose the summit of the mountain, the projection of which made a shadow on the brilliant irradiation of the opposite slope. A few petrified bushes were scattered hither and thither in grimacing zigzags. The fish rose in shoals under our footsteps like birds surprised in the tall grass. The rocky mass was hollowed out into impenetrable confractuosities, deep grottoes, bottomless holes, in which I heard formidable noises. My blood froze in my veins when I perceived some enormous antennæ barricading my path, or some frightful claw shutting up with noise in the dark cavities. Thousands of luminous points shone amidst the darkness. They were the eyes of gigantic crustaceans, giant lobsters setting themselves up like halberdiers, and moving their claws with the clanking sound of metal; titanic crabs pointed like cannon on their carriages, and frightful poulps, intertwining their tentacles like a living nest of serpents.

What was this exorbitant world that I did not know yet? To what order belonged these articulates to which the rock formed a second carapace ? Where had Nature found the secret of their vegetating existence, and for how many centuries had they lived thus in the lowest depths of the ocean?

But I could not stop. Captain Nemo, familiar with these terrible animals, paid no attention to them. We had arrived at the first plateau, where other surprises awaited me. There rose picturesque ruins which betrayed the hand of man, and not that of the Creator. They were vast heaps of stones in the vague outlines of castles and temples, clothed with a world of zoophytes in flower, and, instead of ivy, seaweed and fucus clothed them with a vegetable mantle.

But what, then, was this portion of the globe swallowed up by cataclysms? Who had placed these rocks and stones like dolmens of antihistorical times? Where was I? Where had Captain Nemo's whim brought me to?

I should have liked to question him. As I could not do that, I stopped him. I seized his arm. But he, shaking his head, and pointing to the last summit, seemed to say to me,—

"Higher! Still higher!"

I followed him with a last effort, and in a few minutes I had climbed the peak that overtopped for about thirty feet all the rocky mass.

I looked at the side we had just climbed. The mountain only rose seven or eight hundred feet above the plain; but on the opposite side it commanded from twice that height the depths of this portion of the Atlantic. My eyes wandered over a large space lighted up by a violent fulguration. In fact, this mountain was a volcano. At fifty feet below the peak, amidst a rain of stones and scoriæ?, a wide crater was vomiting forth torrents of lava which fell in a cascade of fire into the bosom of the liquid mass. Thus placed, the volcano, like an immense torch, lighted up the lower plain to the last limits of the horizon.

I have said that the submarine crater threw out lava, but not flames. The oxygen of the air is necessary to make a flame, and it cannot exist in water; but the streams of red-hot lava struggled victoriously against the liquid element, and turned it to vapour by its contact. Rapid currents carried away all this gas in diffusion, and the lava torrent glided to the foot of the mountain like the eruption of Vesuvius on another Torre del Greco.

There, before my eyes, ruined, destroyed, overturned, appeared a town, its roofs crushed in, its temples thrown down, its arches dislocated, its columns lying on the ground, with the solid proportions of Tuscan architecture still discernible upon them; further on were the remains of a gigantic aqueduct; here, the encrusted base of an Acropolis, and the outlines of a Parthenon; there, some vestiges of a quay, as if some ancient port had formerly sheltered, on the shores of an extinct ocean, merchant vessels and war triremes; farther on still, long lines of ruined walls, wide deserted streets, a second Pompeii buried under the waters, raised up again for me by Captain Nerno.

Where was I? Where was I ? I wished to know at any price. I felt I must speak, and tried to take off the globe of brass that imprisoned my head.

But Captain Nemo came to me and stopped me with a gesture. Then picking up a piece of clayey stone he went up to a black basaltic rock and traced on it the single word—

"ATLANTIS."

What a flash of lightning shot through my mind!Atlantis, the ancient Meropis of Theopompus, the Atlantis of Plato, the continent disbelieved in by Origen, Jamblichus, D'Anville, Malte-Brun, and Humboldt, who placed its disappearance amongst legendary tales; believed in by Possidonius, Pliny, Ammianus, Marcellinus, Tertullian, Engel, Sherer, Tournefort, Buffon, and D'Avezac, was there before my eyes bearing upon it the unexceptionable testimony of its catastrophe! This, then, was the engulfed region that existed beyond Europe, Asia, and Lybia, beyond the columns of Hercules, where the powerful Atlantides lived, against whom the first wars of Ancient Greece were waged!

The historian who put into writing the grand doings of the heroic times was Plato himself. His dialogue of Timotheus and Critias was, thus to speak, written under the inspiration of Solon, poet and legislator.

One day Solon was talking with some wise old men of Sais, a town already eight hundred years old, as the annals engraved on the sacred walls of its temples testified. One of these old men related the history of another town, a thousand years older. This first Athenian city, nine hundred centuries old, had been invaded and in part destroyed by the Atlantides. These Atlantides, said he, occupied an immense continent, larger than Africa and Asia joined together, which covered a surface between the twelfth and fortieth degree of north latitude. Their dominion extended even as far as Egypt. They wished to impose it upon Greece, but were obliged to retire before the indomitable resistance of the Hellenes. Centuries went by. A cataclysm occurred with inundations and earthquakes. One night and one day sufficed for the extinction of this Atlantis, of which the highest summits, the Madeiras, Azores, Canaries, and Cape Verde Islands still emerge.

Such were the historical souvenirs that Captain Nemo's inscription awoke in my mind. Thus, then, led by the strangest fate, I was treading on one of the mountains of this continent! I was touching with my hand these ruins a thousand times secular and contemporaneous with the geological epochs. I was walking where the contemporaries of the first man had walked. I was crushing under my heavy soles the skeletons of animals of fabulous times, which these trees, now mineralized, formerly covered with their shade.

Ah! why did time fail me? I should have liked to descend the abrupt sides of this mountain, and go over the whole of the immense continent that doubtless joined Africa to America, and to visit the great antediluvian cities. There, perhaps, before my gaze, stretched Makhinios the warlike, Eusebius the pious, whose gigantic inhabitants lived entire centuries, and who were strong enough to pile up these blocks which still resisted the action of the water. One day, perhaps, some eruptive phenomenon would bring these engulfed regions back to the surface of the waves. Sounds that announced a profound struggle of the elements have been heard, and volcanic cinders projected out of the water have been found. All this ground, as far as the Equator, is still worked by underground forces. And who knows if in some distant epoch, increased by the volcanic dejections and by successive strata of lava, the summits of ignivome mountains will not appear on the surface of the Atlantic?

Whilst I was thus dreaming, trying to fix every detail of the grand scene in my memory, Captain Nemo, leaning against a moss-covered fragment of ruin, remained motionless as if petrified in mute ecstasy. Was he dreaming about the long-gone generations and asking them the secret of human destiny? Was it here that this strange man came to refresh his historical memories and live again that ancient existence?—he who would have no modern one. What would I not have given to know his thoughts, to share and understand them!

We remained in the same place for a whole hour, contemplating the vast plain in the light of the lava that sometimes was surprisingly intense. The interior bubblings made rapid tremblings pass over the outside of the mountain. Deep noises, clearly transmitted by the liquid medium, were echoed with majestic amplitude.

At that moment the moon appeared for an instant through the mass of waters and threw her pale rays over the engulfed continent. It was only a gleam, but its effect was indescribable. The captain rose, gave a last look at the immense plain, and then, with his hand, signed to me to follow him.

We rapidly descended the mountain. When we had once passed the mineral forest I perceived the lantern of the *Nautilus* shining like a star.

The captain walked straight towards it, and we were back on board as the first tints of dawn whitened the surface of the ocean.

THE OCEAN CHRIST[1]

Anatole France
(1844-1924)

THAT year many of the fishers of Saint-Valéry had been drowned at sea. Their bodies were found on the beach cast up by the waves with the wreckage of their boats; and for nine days, up the steep road leading to the church were to be seen coffins borne by hand and followed by widows, who were weeping beneath their great black-hooded cloaks, like women in the Bible.

Thus were the skipper Jean Lenoël and his son Désiré laid in the great nave, beneath the vaulted roof from which they had once hung a ship in full rigging as an offering to Our Lady. They were righteous men and God-fearing. Monsieur Guillaume Truphème, priest of Saint-Valéry, having pronounced the Absolution, said in a tearful voice:

"Never were laid in consecrated ground, there to await the judgment of God, better men and better Christians than Jean Lenoël and his son Désiré."

And while barques and their skippers perished near the coast, in the high seas great vessels foundered. Not a day passed that the ocean did not bring in some flotsam of wreck. Now one morning some children who were steering a boat saw a figure lying on the sea. It was a figure of Jesus Christ, life-size, carved in wood, painted in natural colouring, and looking as if it were very old. The Good Lord was floating upon the sea with arms outstretched. The children towed the figure

[1] From Winifred Stephens's translation of *Crainquebille and Other Tales*.

ashore and brought it up into Saint-Valéry. The head was encircled with the crown of thorns. The feet and hands were pierced. But the nails were missing as well as the cross. The arms were still outstretched ready for sacrifice and blessing, just as he appeared to Joseph of Arimathea and the holy women when they were burying Him.

The children gave it to Monsieur le Curé Truphème, who said to them:

"This image of the Saviour is of ancient workmanship. He who made it must have died long ago. Although to-day in the shops of Amiens and Paris excellent statues are sold for a hundred francs and more, we must admit that the earlier sculptors were not without merit. But what delights me most is the thought that if Jesus Christ be thus come with open arms to Saint-Valéry, it is in order to bless the parish, which has been so cruelly tried, and in order to announce that He has compassion on the poor folk who go a-fishing at the risk of their lives. He is the God who walked upon the sea and blessed the nets of Cephas."

And Monsieur le Curé Truphème, having had the Christ placed in the church on the cloth of the high altar, went off to order from the carpenter Lemerre a beautiful cross in heart of oak.

When it was made, the Saviour was nailed to it with brand new nails, and it was erected in the nave above the churchwarden's pew.

Then it was noticed that His eyes were filled with mercy and seemed to glisten with tears of heavenly pity.

One of the churchwardens, who was present at the putting up of the crucifix, fancied he saw tears streaming down the divine face. The next morning when Monsieur le Curé with a choir-boy entered the church to say his mass, he was astonished to find the cross above the churchwarden's pew empty and the Christ lying upon the altar.

As soon as he had celebrated the divine sacrifice he had the carpenter called and asked him why he had taken the Christ down from His cross. But the carpenter replied that he had not touched it. Then, after having questioned the beadle and the sidesmen, Monsieur Truphème made certain that no one had entered the church since the crucifix had been placed over the churchwarden's pew.

Thereupon he felt that these things were miraculous, and he meditated upon them discreetly. The following Sunday in his exhortation he spoke of them to his parishioners, and he called upon them to contribute by their gifts to the erection of a new cross more beautiful than the first and more worthy to bear the Redeemer of the world.

The poor fishers of Saint-Valéry gave as much money as they could and the widows brought their wedding rings. Wherefore Monsieur Truphème was able to go at once to Abbeville and to order a cross of ebony, highly polished and surmounted by a scroll with the inscription I.N.R.I. in letters of gold. Two months later it was erected in the place of the former and the Christ was nailed to it between the lance and the sponge.

But Jesus left this cross as He had left the other; and as soon as night fell He went and stretched Himself upon the altar.

Monsieur le Curé, when He found Him there in the morning, fell on his knees and prayed for a long while. The fame of this miracle spread throughout the neighbourhood, and the ladies of Amiens made a collection for the Christ of Saint-Valéry. Monsieur Truphème received money and jewels from Paris, and the wife of the Minister of Marine, Madame Hyde de Neuville, sent him a heart of diamonds. Of all these treasures, in the space of two years, a goldsmith of La Rue St Sulpice, fashioned a cross of gold and precious stones which was set up with great pomp in the church of Saint-Valéry on the second Sunday after Easter in the year 18—. But He who had not refused the cross of sorrow, fled from this cross of gold and again stretched Himself upon the white linen of the altar.

For fear of offending Him, He was left there this time; and He had lain upon the altar for more than two years, when Pierre, son of Pierre Caillou, came to tell Monsieur le Curé Truphème that he had found the true cross of Our Lord on the beach.

Pierre was an innocent; and, because he had not sense enough to earn a livelihood, people gave him bread out of charity; he was liked because he never did any harm. But he wandered in his talk and no one listened to him.

Nevertheless Monsieur Truphème, who had never ceased meditating on the Ocean Christ, was struck by what the poor imbecile had just said. With the beadle and two sidesmen he went to the spot, where the child said he had seen a cross, and there he found two planks studded with nails, which had long been washed by the sea and which did indeed form a cross.

They were the remains of some old shipwreck. On one of these boards could still be read two letters painted in black, a J and an L; and there was no doubt that this was a fragment of Jean Lenoël's barque, he who with his son Désiré had been lost at sea five years before.

At the sight of this, the beadle and the sidesmen began to laugh at the innocent who had taken the broken planks of a boat for the cross of Jesus Christ. But Monsieur le Curé Truphème checked their merriment. He had meditated much and prayed long since the Ocean Christ had arrived among the fisherfolk, and the mystery of infinite charity began to dawn upon him. He knelt down upon the sand, repeated the prayer for the faithful departed, and then told the beadle and the sidesmen to carry the flotsam on their shoulders and to place it in the church. When this had been done he raised the Christ from the altar, placed it on the planks of the boat and himself nailed it to them, with the nails that the ocean had corroded.

By the priest's command, the very next day this cross took the place of the cross of gold and precious stones over the churchwarden's pew. The Ocean Christ has never left it. He has chosen to remain nailed to the planks on which men died invoking His name and that of His Mother. There, with parted lips, august and afflicted, He seems to say:

"My cross is made of all men's woes, for I am in truth the God of the poor and the heavy-laden."

ICELAND FISHERMEN[1]

Pierre Loti

(1850-1923)

THEIR smack was named *La Marie,* and her master was Captain Guermeur. Every year she set sail for the big dangerous fisheries, in the frigid regions where the summers have no night. She was a very old ship, as old as the statuette of her patron saint itself. Her heavy oaken-built planks were rough and worn, impregnated with ooze and brine, but still strong and stout, and smelling strongly of tar. At anchor she looked an old unwieldy tub from her so massive build, but when blew the mighty western gales, her lightness returned, like a sea-gull awakened bv the wind. Then she had her own style of tumbling over the rollers, and rebounding more lightly than many newer ones, launched with all your new fangles.

As for the crew of six men and the boy, they were "Icelanders," the valiant race of seafarers whose homes are at Paimpol and Tréguier, and who from father to son are destined for the cod fisheries.

They had hardly ever seen a summer in France. At the end of each winter, they, with other fishers, received the parting blessing in the harbour of Paimpol. And for that *fête* day an altar, always the same, and imitating a rocky grotto, was erected on the quay; and over it, in the midst of anchors, oars, and nets, was enthroned the Virgin Mary, calm, and beaming with affection, the patroness of sailors;she would be brought from her chapel for the occasion, and had looked upon generation after generation with her same lifeless eyes, blessing the happy for whom the season would be lucky, and the others who would never return.

The Host, followed by a slow procession of wives, mothers, sweethearts, and sisters, was borne round the harbour, where the boats bound for Iceland, bedecked in all colours, saluted it on its way. The priest halted before each, giving them his holy blessing; and then the fleet started, leaving the country desolate of husbands,

---

[1] Reprinted from Clara Cadiot's translation of *An Iceland Freshman.*

lovers, and sons; and as the shores faded from their view, the crews sang together in low, full voices, the hymns sacred to "the Star of the Ocean."

II

About a month later, around Iceland, the weather was of that rare kind which the sailors call a dead calm; in other words, in the air nothing moved, as if all the breezes were exhausted and their task done.

The sky was covered with a white veil, which darkened towards its lower border near the horizon, and gradually passed into dull grey leaden tints; over this the still waters threw a pale light, which fatigued the eyes and chilled the gazer through and through. All at once, liquid designs played over the surface, such light evanescent rings as one forms by breathing on a mirror. The sheen of the waters seemed covered with a net of faint patterns, which intermingled and reformed, rapidly disappearing. Everlasting night, or everlasting day, one could scarcely say what it was; the sun, which pointed to no special hour of the day, remained fixed, as if presiding over the fading glory of dead things; it appeared but as a mere ring, being almost without substance, and magnified enormously by a shifting halo.

Yann and Sylvestre, leaning against one another, sang "Jean-Francois de Nantes," the song without an end, amused by its very monotony, looking at one another from the corner of their eyes as if laughing at the childish fun, with which they recommenced the verses over and over again, trying to put fresh spirit into them each time. Their cheeks glowed ruddily under the sharp freshness of the morning; the pure air they breathed was strengthening, and they inhaled it deep down in their chests, the very fountain of all vigorous existence. And yet, around them, was a semblance of non-existence, of a world either finished or not yet created; the light itself had no warmth; all things seemed without motion, and as if chilled for eternity under the great ghostly eye which represented the sun.

The *Marie* projected over the sea a shadow long and black as night, or rather appearing deep green in the midst of the polished surface, which reflected all the purity of the heavens; in this shadowed part, which had no glitter, could be plainly distinguished through the transparency, myriads upon myriads of fish, all alike, gliding slowly in the same direction, as if bent towards the goal of their perpetual travels. They were cods, performing their evolutions all as parts of a single body, stretched full length in the same direction, exactly parallel, offering the effect of grey streaks, unceasingly agitated by a quick motion which gave a look of fluidity to the mass of dumb lives. Sometimes, with a sudden quick movement of the tail, all turned round at the same time, showing the sheen of their silvered sides; and the same movement was repeated throughout the entire shoal by slow undulations, as if a thousand metal blades had each thrown a tiny flash of lightning from under the surface.

The sun, already low, lowered further; so night had decidedly come.

As the great ball of flame descended into the leaden-coloured zones which surrounded the sea, it grew yellow, and its outer rim became more clear and solid. Now it could be looked straight at, as if it were but the moon. Yet it still gave out light, and looked quite near in the immensity; it seemed that by going in a ship, only as far as the edge of the horizon, one might collide with the great mournful globe, floating in the air just a few yards above the water.

Fishing was going on well; looking into the calm water, one could see exactly what took place; how the cods came to bite, with a greedy spring, then feeling themselves hooked, wriggled about, as if to hook themselves still firmer. And every moment, with rapid action, the fishermen hauled in their lines, hand over hand, throwing the fish to the man who was to clean them and flatten them out.

The Paimpol fleet was scattered over the quiet mirror, animating the desert. Here and there appeared distant sails, unfurled for mere form's sake, considering there was no breeze. They were like clear white outlines upon the greys of the horizon. In this dead calm, fishing off Iceland seemed so easy and tranquil a trade that ladies' yachting was no name for it.

"Jean François de Nantes"
Jean François,
Jean François!"

So they sang, like a couple of children . . .

A slight breeze sprang up, fresher yet to inhale, and began to tarnish the surface of the still waters in patches; it traced designs in a bluish green tint over the shining mirror, and scattering in trails, these fanned out or branched off like a coral tree; all very rapidly with a low murmur; it was like a signal of awakening foretelling the end of this intense torpor. The sky, its veil being rent asunder, grew clear; the vapours fell down on the horizon, massing in heaps like slate-coloured wadding, as if to form a soft bank to the sea. The two ever-during mirrors between which the fishermen lived, the one on high and the one beneath, recovered their deep lucidity, as if the mists tarnishing them had been brushed away.

The weather was changing in a rapid way which foretold no good . . . .

Far-off Iceland also reappeared, as if she would fain come near them; showing her great mountains of bare stones more distinctly than ever.

And there arose a new Iceland of similar colour, which little by little took a more definite form, and none the less was purely illusive, its gigantic mountains merely a condensation of mists. The sun, sinking low, seemed incapable of ever rising again over all things, though glowing through this phantom island so tangibly that it seemed placed in front of it. Incomprehensible sight! no longer was it surrounded by a halo, but its disc had become firmly spread, rather like some faded yellow planet slowly decaying and suddenly checked there in the heart of chaos . . . .

III

The Northern sun had taken another aspect and changed its colour, opening the new day by a sinister morn. Completely free from its veil, it gave forth its grand rays, crossing the sky in fitful flashes, foretelling nasty weather. During the last few days it had been too fine to last. The winds blew upon that swarm of boats, as if to clear the sea of them; and they began to disperse and flee, like an army put to rout, before the warning written in the air, beyond possibility to misread. Harder and harder it blew, making men and ships quake alike.

And the still tiny waves began to run one after another and to melt together; at first they were frosted over with white foam spread out in patches; and then, with a whizzing sound, arose smoke as though they burned and scorched, and the whistling grew louder every moment. Fish-catching was no longer thought of; it was their work on deck. The fishing-lines had been drawn in, and all hurried to make sail and some to seek for shelter in the fjords, whilst yet others preferred to round the southern point of Iceland, finding it safer to stand for the open sea, with the free space about them, and run before the stern wind. They could still see each other a while: here and there, above the trough of the sea, sails wagged as poor wearied birds fleeing; the masts tipped, but ever and anon righted, like the weighted pith figures which similarly resumed an erect attitude when released after being blown down.

The illimitable cloudy roof, erstwhile compacted towards the western horizon, in an island Form, began to break up on high and sent its fragments over the surface. It seemed indestructible, for vainly did the winds stretch it, pull and toss it asunder, continually tearing away dark strips, which they waved over the pale yellow sky, gradually becoming intensely and icily livid. Ever more strongly grew the wind which threw all things in turmoil.

The waves, curling up in scrolls, continued to run after each other, to reassemble and climb on one another, and between them the hollows deepened.

In a few hours, everything was belaboured and overthrown in these regions which had been so calm the day before, and instead of the past silence, the uproar was deafening. The present agitation was a dissolving view, unconscientious and useless, and quickly accomplished. What was the object of it all? What a mystery of blind destruction it was!

The clouds continued to stream out on high, out of the west continually, racing and darkening all. A few yellow clefts remained, through which the sun shot its last rays in volleys. And the now greenish water was striped more thickly with snowy froth.

By midday the *Marie* was made completely snug for dirty weather; her hatches battened down, and her sails storm-reefed; she bounded lightly and elastic; for all the horrid confusion, she seemed to be playing, like the porpoises, also amused in storms. With her foresail taken in, she simply scudded before the wind.

It had become quite dark overhead, where stretched the heavily crushing vault. Studded with shapeless gloomy spots, it appeared a set dome, unless a steadier gaze ascertained that everything was in the full rush of motion; endless grey veils were drawn along, unceasingly followed by others, from the profundities of the sky-line—draperies of darkness, pulled from a never-ending roll.

The *Marie* fled faster and faster before the wind; and time fled also—before some invisible and mysterious power. The gale, the sea, the *Marie,* and the clouds were all lashed into one great madness of hasty flight towards the same point. The fastest of all was the wind; then the huge seething billows, heavier and slower, toiling after; and, lastly, the smack, dragged into the general whirl. The waves tracked her down with their white crests, tumbling onward in continual motion, and she though always being caught up to and outrun—still managed to elude them by means of the eddying waters she spurned in her wake, upon which they vented their fury. In this similitude of flight the sensation particularly experienced was of buoyancy, the delight of being carried along without effort or trouble, in a springy sort of way. The *Marie* mounted over the waves without any shaking, as if the wind had lifted her clean up; and her subsequent descent was a slide. She almost slid backwards, though, at times, the mountains lowering before her as if continuing to run, and then she suddenly found herself dropped into one of the measureless hollows which evaded her also; without injury she sounded its horrible depths, amid a loud splashing of water, which did not even sprinkle her decks, but was blown on and on like everything else, evaporating in finer and finer spray until it was thinned away to nothing. In the trough it was darker, and when each wave had passed the men looked behind them to see if the next to appear were higher; it came upon them with furious contortions, and curling crests, over its transparent emerald body, seeming to shriek: “Only let me catch you, and I’ll swallow you whole !” But this never came to pass, for, as a feather, the billows softly bore them up and then down as gently; they felt it pass under them, with all its boiling surf and thunderous roar. And so on continually, but the sea getting heavier and heavier. One after another rushed the waves, more and more gigantic, like a long chain of mountains, with yawning valleys. And the madness of all this movement, under the ever-darkening sky, accelerated the height of the intolerable clamour.

ITALY

THE LAST VOYAGE OF ULYSSES[1]

Dante Alighieri
(1265-1321)

WE DEPARTED thence; and, by the stairs which the rocky bourns had given us to descend before, my Guide remounted and drew me up. And pursuing our solitary way among the jaggs and branches of the cliff, the foot without the hand sped not.

I sorrowed then, and sorrow now again when I direct my memory to what I saw; and curb my genius more than I am wont, lest it run where Virtue guides it not; so that, if kindly star or something better have given to me the good, I may not grudge myself that gift.

As many fire-flies as the peasant—who is resting on the hill at the time that he who brightens the world least hides his face from us, when as the fly yields to the gnat—sees down along the valley, there perchance where he gathers grapes and tills: with flames thus numerous the eighth chasm was all gleaming; as I perceived so soon as I came to where the bottom showed itself. And as he who was avenged by the bears, saw Elijah's chariot at its departure, when the horses rose erect to heaven; for he could not so follow it with his eyes as to see other than the flame alone, like a little cloud, ascending up: thus moved each of those flames along the gullet of the loss, for none of them shews the theft, and every flame steals a sinner.

I stood upon the bridge, having risen so to look that, if I had not caught a rock, I should have fallen down without being pushed. And the Guide, who saw me thus intent, said:

"Within those fires are the spirits; each swathes himself with that which burns him."

"Master," I replied, "from hearing thee I feel more certain; but had already discerned it to be so, and already wished to say to thee: Who is in that fire, which comes so parted at the top, as if it rose from the pile where Eteocles was put with his brother?"

He answered me: "Within it there, Ulysses is tortured, and Diomed; and thus they run together in punishments, as erst in wrath. And in their flame they groan for the ambush of the horse that made the door by which the noble seed of the Romans came forth. Within it they lament the artifice whereby Deidamia in death still sorrows for Achilles; and there they suffer penalty for the Palladium."

[1] From *The Divine Comedy.* Translated by John A. Carlyle.

"If they within those sparks can speak," said I, "Master! I pray thee much, and repray that my prayer may equal a thousand, deny me not to wait until the horned flame comes hither. Thou seest how with desire I bend me towards it."

And he to me: "Thy request is worthy of much praise, and therefore I accept it. But do thou refrain thy tongue. Let me speak, for I have conceived what thou wishest; and they, perhaps, because they were Greeks, might disdain thy words."

After the flame had come where time and place seemed fitting to my Guide, I heard him speak in this manner:

"O ye, two in one fire! If I merited of you whilst I lived, if I merited of you much or little, when on earth I wrote the High Verses, move ye not; but let the one of you tell where he wandering went to die."

The greater horn of the ancient flame began to shake itself, murmuring, just like a flame that struggles with the wind. Then carrying to and fro the top, as if it were the tongue that spake, threw forth a voice, and said:

"When I departed from Circe, who beyond a year detained me there near Gaeta, ere Æneas thus had named it, neither fondness for my son, nor reverence for my aged father, nor the due love that should have cheered Penelope, could conquer in me the ardour that I had to gain experience of the world, and of human vice and worth: I ventured into the deep open sea, with but one ship, and with that small company which had not deserted me. Both the shores I saw as far as Spain, far as Morocco; and saw Sardinia and the other isles which that sea bathes round.

"I and my companions were old and slow, when we came to that narrow pass where Hercules assigned his landmarks to hinder man from venturing farther. On the right hand, I left Seville; on the other, had already left Ceuta.

"O brothers!' I said, 'who through a hundred thousand dangers have reached the West, deny not, to this the brief vigil of your senses that remains, experience of the unpeopled world behind the Sun. Consider your origin: ye were not formed to live like brutes, but to follow virtue and knowledge.'

"With this brief speech I made my companions so eager for the voyage that I could hardly then have checked them. And, turning the poop towards morning, we of our oars made wings for the foolish flight, always gaining on the left. Night already saw the other pole, with all its stars; and ours so low that it rose not from the ocean floor. Five times the light beneath the Moon had been rekindled and quenched as oft, since we had entered on the arduous passage, when there appeared to us a Mountain, dim with distance; and to me it seemed the highest I had ever seen. We joyed, and soon our joy was turned to grief; for a tempest rose from the new land, and struck the forepart of our ship. Three times it made her whirl round with all the waves; at the fourth, made the poop rise and the prow go down, as pleased Another, till the sea was closed above us."

which I saw yesterday could neither be painted with the brush nor described in words. It was a phenomenon unique and unheard of in any age, and beyond the power of any poet to depict, unless we except Homer's description of a storm in Greek waters, Virgil's of that off Sicily, and Lucan's of one on the coast of Epirus. If ever I have time, the Neapolitan storm will be the subject of my poem. One cannot, however, rightly call it Neapolitan, for it was universal on the Tyrrhenian coast, and in the Adriatic; but to me it seems natural to speak of it thus, since it found me once again, and much against my will, in Naples.

To be brief, if, owing to the haste of the bearer of this letter to leave the city, I have too little time to write to you fully of the event, I beg you to believe that a more horrible catastrophe was never seen.

Many days ago, the Bishop of a small island near Naples, had foretold this scourge of God by astrological signs, but as usual, the astrologers did not arrive at the exact truth, and they predicted a most terrible earthquake for the twenty-fifth of November, which was to cause the destruction of the whole of Naples. This prophecy had gained so much credence that the greater part of the townsfolk put aside every other consideration, and thought only of imploring mercy from God and pardon for their sins, being convinced that very shortly they must die. On the other hand, many scoffed at the prediction, declaring that little faith was to be put in astrologers, especially as only a few days before there had been several earthquake shocks.

Between fear and hope, but rather more hopeful than fearful, I went back to my dwelling before sunset on the evening of the twenty-fourth, having seen nearly all the women of the city, more mindful of the danger which threatened them than of modesty, with bare feet, flowing hair, their children in their arms, going round from church to church, weeping and calling upon God for mercy. When night fell the sky was more serene than usual, so my servants went to bed soon after supper. I myself, determined to wait, in order to observe the setting of the moon which I thought was in the seventh phase, so I opened the window looking to the west, and before midnight, saw her hide herself behind the hill of San Martino, her face covered with darkness and clouds. Then I shut the window, and lay down on my bed, and, having lain awake for a good long time, I was just beginning to sleep when I was awakened by a rumbling noise and an earthquake, which not only flung open the windows, and put out the light which I am accustomed to keep burning at night, but shook my room to its foundations. Wakened thus suddenly from sleep, I was assailed by the fear of immediate death, and went out into the cloister of the monastery where I was living. There, in the darkness, unable to see except by the chance light of some lamp, we sought our friends, and tried to bring comfort to each other. Meanwhile, terrified at such an awful storm, the monks and the Prior, a man of great sanctity, had gone into the church to sing Matins; and presently, carrying the crucifix and relics of the Saints with numbers of lighted tapers, weeping as they devoutly chanted the prayers, they came to the cloister where we were. At this point I plucked up a little spirit, and went into the church with them, and there, all of us prone on the ground, we did not cease to call aloud upon the mercy of God, expecting from moment to moment that the church would fall in upon us.

It would be much too long a story if I were to try to tell the full horror of that infernal night, and although the truth is more astounding than I can say, I suspect that my words will seem exaggerated. What mountains of waves! What awful winds! What thunder! What ghastly crashing sounds in the sky! What horrible earth tremors! What a fearful roaring of the sea, and what cries from all that great concourse of people! It seemed as if by some magic art the length of the night were doubled, but, at length, came the dawn. Even then, so black was the sky that we could only guess from a faint glimmer of light that day was at hand. Then the priests vested themselves for Mass, and we, who had not yet sufficient courage to raise our eyes to heaven, still prostrate, persevered in our laments and our prayers.

Now when the day broke, although it was still so dark that it seemed more like night, the tumult of the people in the upper part of the town began to diminish, and there arose a much greater clamour down near the sea, and we soon heard horses galloping along the street, and could not conceive the cause thereof. At last, my despair giving place to audacity, I too mounted my horse, and set forth to see what was going forward, or die!

Great God! Who had ever heard tell of such things! Aged sailors say that nothing like it had ever been seen or heard of. In the midst of the harbour, one could see floating the bodies of great numbers of unfortunate men who, while struggling desperately to reach the shore, had been so battered and dashed by the furious violence of the sea, that they looked like a flock of helpless sheep, all getting in each other's way. The whole great harbour was full of drowned or drowning people; some with their heads cut open, some with broken arms, and others with their entrails gushing out. Meanwhile the shrieks of the men and women who lived in the houses near the shore were not less awful than the terrific roar of the sea itself, and where only the day before we had walked along the sand, we saw tremendous waves, more dangerous than the breakers round the lighthouse at Messina. A thousand Neapolitan horsemen, nay, more than a thousand, had ridden down to this spot, as if to follow the obsequies of their native land, and I, having joined their troop, began to be in better heart, knowing that at least I should die in their company. But suddenly there arose an appalling sound, and, as the very ground under our feet began to sink into a chasm that opened beneath the waters, we fled, and went further up from the sea.

owner whom they knew to be very rich, as men addicted to plunder and rapine, they resolved to make her their prize. Landing some of their men, therefore, well armed with crossbows and other weapons, they posted them so as to prevent any of the crew issuing out of the bark, unless at the cost of their lives; whilst the rest getting into the long-boat, and the sea being favourable, soon boarded Landolfo's vessel, and took all his people, and everything in it, without the loss of a man, leaving him nothing but a waistcoat; and after they had cleared out the vessel, they sank her. The day following, the wind having shifted, they made sail for the west, and had a good voyage all that day; but night coming on, the wind became boisterous again, and the storm was such that the two carracks were parted, whilst that wherein poor Landolfo was, drove with the utmost violence upon the coast of Cephalonia, and was smashed like a glass flung against the wall. The sea being covered in a moment with all sorts of merchandise, and with chests, tables, and fragments of the wreck, all those of the crew who could swim strove, in spite of the darkness and the fury of the waves, to lay hold of such things as chanced to float near them. Amongst these was the unfortunate Landolfo, who, though he had wished for death a thousand times the day before, rather than return home a beggar, was terrified now that he saw death at hand, and got hold of a plank, like the rest, in hopes that if his fate were delayed, God would send him some means for his escape. Bestriding the plank as well as he could, and driven to and fro by the wind, he supported himself till daylight; and then looking round him he could see nothing but clouds and water, and a chest driving towards him, to his great alarm, for sometimes it came so near that he was afraid it would dash against him, and then he would endeavour, with the little strength he had left, to put it by with his hand; at length a great blast of wind sent it with such violence against the plank on which he floated, as to overset it, and plunge him over head and ears into the water. He rose again, however, and swimming with the strength of fear rather than with his own, he found himself at such a distance from the plank that he was afraid he could not recover it. Getting therefore to the chest, which was nearer, he laid his breast upon it as well as he could, and used his arms for paddles. In this manner was he carried up and down, with nothing to eat, but drinking more than he desired, neither knowing where he was, nor seeing anything but water for a day and a night.

The next morning (whether it was through God or the force of the winds) Landolfo who was well nigh become a sponge, grappling the chest with both arms, with the usual tenacity of drowning men, drew near to the island of Corfu, at a spot where, by good fortune, a poor woman was scouring her dishes with salt water and sand. When she saw him approach, and could discover in him nothing in the shape of a man, she screamed, and started back in terror. He was too exhausted to be able to speak, and scarcely could he see much; but as the waves carried him towards the shore, the woman could distinguish the shape of the chest. Looking more narrowly, she saw an arm laid over it, and then a face, and knew at once what was the matter. Moved by compassion, she stepped a little way into the sea, which was now calm, and seizing the half-drowned wretch by the hair of his head, drew both him and the chest to land, where, with much trouble, she unfolded his arms from the chest, which she set upon the head of her daughter, who was with her. She herself carried Landolfo like a little child to the town, put him on a stove, and chafed and washed him with warm water, by which means the vital warmth began to return, and his strength partially revived. In due time she took him from the stove, comforted him with wine and good cordials, and kept him some days till he knew where he was; she then restored him his chest, and told him he might now provide for his departure.

He had forgotten all about the chest, but took it from the hands of the woman, supposing that, small as its worth might be, it might serve for his support for a short time. Finding it very light, he was somewhat disheartened; however, whilst the good woman was out of the way, he broke it open, and found a great quantity of precious stones, some of which were polished and set. Having some judgment of such matters, and seeing that these gems were of immense value, he was now thoroughly comforted, and praised God for not having yet forsaken him. However, as he had been twice buffeted by fortune already, and was fearful of a third mishap, he judged that great caution was requisite to bring these things safe home; he wrapped them up, therefore, in old rags, as well as he could, and told the woman that he had no further use for the chest, but that she might keep it if she would give him a sack in its stead, which she was very glad to do. And now, returning her a thousand thanks, he departed with his sack over his shoulder, and passed over in a bark to Brindisi, and thence to Trani, where he met with merchants of his own town, who clothed him out of charity, after he had told them all that had befallen him, only omitting all mention of the cask of jewels. They also lent him a horse, and sent company with him to Ravello, whither he said he wished to return. Arriving there in safety, he gave thanks to God; and now he inquired more narrowly into his sack than he had done before, and found so many valuable jewels, that, rating them at the lowest prices, he was twice as rich as when he left home. Finding means, therefore, to dispose of them, he sent a sum of money to the woman at Corfu, who had taken him out of the sea, and treated him so kindly; and also to the merchants at Trani for clothing him; the remainder he kept, without having any more mind to trade, and lived handsomely upon it the rest of his life.

HOW PRINCE GERBINO FOUGHT THE GALLEY OF THE KING OF TUNIS[1]

Giovanni Boccaccio
(1313-1375)

GUIGLIELMO, the second king of Sicily (as their histories relate) had two children, a son named Ruggieri, and a daughter called Constantia. Ruggieri died before his father, leaving a son, called Gerbino, whom his grandfather took care to bring up, and he became a most accomplished prince; nor did his fame confine itself within the bounds of his own country, but was echoed through numerous parts of the world, especially in Barbary, which was then tributary to the King of Sicily. Amongst others, who had heard of his singular worth and character, was a daughter of the king of Tunis, who, in the opinion of all that ever saw her, was as beautiful a woman as ever lived, with a soul equally noble and perfect. The lady, inquiring always after people of worth, received from all hands a most extraordinary account of Gerbino's merit and noble exploits, which were so pleasing to her, that, conceiving within her own mind the idea of his person, she became violently in love, and was never more pleased than when he was the subject of discourse. On the other hand, no less had her fame reached Sicily, as well as other countries, and was particularly agreeable to the prince, who had conceived the same love for her. Being desirous of all things of seeing her, he charged some of his friends, till he could obtain leave from his grandfather to go himself to Tunis, to make his love known privately to her, in the best manner they were able, and to bring him some tidings concerning her. This was managed very dexterously by one of them, who went under the character of a jeweller. The princess received him with great cheerfulness and satisfaction, declaring a mutual regard for the prince, and as a proof of it, she sent him a present of one of her richest jewels. He received it with great joy, and wrote several letters, presenting her with things of great value, and pledging himself to wait upon her in person, when fortune afforded him an opportunity.

Things being carried so far, and farther than ought to have been, it happened, that the princess's father promised her in marriage to the King of Granada, to her infinite sorrow, and could she have found opportunity, she would gladly have fled from her father to the prince. He, in like manner, hearing of this contract, was afflicted beyond measure, and resolved, if it should happen that she was sent by sea, to take her away by force. The King of Tunis, hearing something of Gerbino's love, and what he designed, and well knowing his resolution and great valour,

[1] From W.K. Kelly's translation of *The Decameron.*

when the time came that she was to depart, sent to the King of Sicily to acquaint him with his design, and to desire a safe conduct; and that monarch, knowing nothing of his grandson's affections towards the lady, nor thinking that the safe conduct was desired upon that account, readily granted it, in token whereof he sent one of his gloves to the King of Tunis. The latter then fitted out a stately ship at Carthage, and providing it with everything necessary to transport his daughter to Granada, waited only for the time that had been appointed. The young lady, who was aware of all this, sent one of her servants in secret to Palermo, to acquaint the prince that she was to sail in a few days, and that it would now appear whether he was a person of such valour as had been always reported, or had that love for her which he had often declared. The message was faithfully delivered; and the prince knowing, at the same time, that his grandfather had granted a safe conduct, was at a loss how to act; but reflecting upon the lady's words, and that he might not appear a dastard, he hired two light ships at Messina, which he took care to have well manned, and sailed with them to the coast of Sardinia, expecting that the ship which had his mistress on board must take that course. In a few days that expectation was answered, and he saw the ship sailing with a light wind near the place where he was stationed. Thereupon he thus addressed his companions:

"Gentlemen, if you are the men I take you to be, there is none of you, I imagine, but must have felt the extraordinary power of love, without which, as I judge by myself, there can be no valour or worth in mortal. If then you have ever been, or are now, in love, you will the more easily comprehend the nature of my design. It is love that makes me call upon you; and the object of it is in the ship before you. Besides that, there is store of riches, which, if you fight manfully, you may easily obtain. For my part I desire nothing but the lady, for whose sake I have taken up arms; everything else shall be yours. Let us go then boldly to the attack; fortune seems to favour our undertaking; they lie still, unable to get along for want of wind."

The prince had no occasion to make use of such an exhortation; for his people, eager for rapine, were ready enough to his orders. They declared their approbation then with a great shout, whilst the trumpets sounded, and they all armed themselves, and rowed towards the ship. In like manner, the other ship's crew, seeing two galleys come towards them, and that there was no possibility of escaping by flight, stood resolutely upon their defence. The prince being come sufficiently near, ordered that the masters of the vessel should come on board, unless they meant to fight. The Saracens, understanding who the assailants were, and what their demand was, told them, that it was contrary to treaty, to the royal faith plighted to them, in token of which they showed King Guiglielmo's glove; and they flatly declared, that they would neither surrender themselves, nor part with anything in the ship till they were forced to do so. The prince, now seeing the storm, it at least indicated that strong kind of sirocco, which, saturated with an unhealthy humidity, and blowing from the marshes of Sardinia, is often fatal.

When the three fugitives had reached the fields of Fontanaccia, Frusciante said to the others, "I am going to leave you here, and turn to the left towards Arcaccio."

The two friends continued on their way. They opened and shut after them the four gates, through which one must pass to reach *Muro a secco.* This wall, made of nothing but pieces of rock undressed, divides the cultivated lands of Fontanaccia from the uncultivated lands, which extend to the seashore. Once there, the "Solitario" took off his poncho, and exchanged his white hat for a cap of his son Menotti's. He gave Barberini the hat and cloak he had just taken off, and then, having assured himself that there was no one on the other side of the wall, he mounted and cleared it with astonishing agility.

A remembrance of his adventurous youth gave him wings, and he felt himself twenty years younger. Besides, were not his sons and his comrades-in-arms already engaged in a struggle against the mercenaries of a monkish power? Could he keep quiet, and content himself with the pruning of his trees and the disgraceful existence of the "Moderati"?

When the "Solitario" had successfully cleared the wall, he said to Barberini: "It is still too light; let us stay here a moment, and smoke half a cigar."

Thereupon he drew from his pocket a match-box, a valued souvenir of the kind Lady Shaftesbury, lit a Cavour, and handed the match to his companion, who held a cigarette in readiness. This long and black Tuscan cigar, which costs about a half-penny, the "Solitario" generally cuts in two, and smokes but half at a time.

The shades of night soon began to fall; but in the east there appeared a feeble brightness, forerunner of the queen of night, then silently approaching.

"In three-quarters of an hour the moon will rise behind the mountains!" remarked the "Solitario." "We must not delay any longer."

The two companions set out again, and proceeded to the harbour.

There Giovanni was at his post. Aided by Barberini he got the *beccacino* afloat. The *beccacino* is our smallest kind of boat, used only for duck-shooting. It is so shallow that the one person who gets into it must lie down so as to make it go with a single oar.

The "Solitario" got into this at once, and stretched himself upon his poncho. When Giovanni had launched the canoe, and was assured that all was safe, he himself got into his *becca, a* boat built exactly like the *beccacino,* only larger, and, humming an air, he rowed towards the yacht.

"Stop! who goes there?" shouted to the Sardinian the soldiers of the gunboat, who were thus degraded to the *rôle* of police subordinates. But Giovanni paused neither in his patriotic song nor his progress.

At length, at the third summons, he replied, "I am going on board." For though in the darkness he could hardly be hit by a musket-shot, yet, to a man unaccustomed to them, bullets are somewhat alarming; and Giovanni, though else brave and courageous enough, was such a man. Besides, he would certainly have been hit sooner or later if he had not answered.

The *"Solitario,"* in the meantime making his *beccacino* go, now with the pole, and now (like the American canoes) with the paddle, proceeded by the shore of Paviano, between the harbour of Stagnatello and the headland of Arcaccio; and, in truth, the humming-bird (when he flies about the perfumed flowers of the torrid zone, and, like the busy bee, sucks their sweets) makes more noise than was made by the *beccacino* rapidly gliding, light as a feather, over the waves of the Tyrrhenian Sea.

When he reached the headland of Arcaccio, the "Solitario" distinguished among the huge boulders the form of his faithful Frusciante, fantastic in the twilight.

"Nothing new as far as the rocks of Arcaccio," cried Frusciante, speaking as softly as possible.

"Then I am safe !" replied the "Solitario," propelling his boat with increasing rapidity towards the steep cliffs, until he reached a certain point, whence he threw a piercing look over the little Isle of Rabbits, the most southern of the three islands which compose the harbour of Stagnatello. Then he promptly urged his barque in a north-westerly direction towards the high seas.

When the "Solitario" observed how strong the light of the moon had become, he rowed vigorously, and, helped by the sirocco, the little canoe passed the strait "Della Moneta" with a speed which would have excited the envy of a steamer.

By moonlight, and at a certain distance, every rock which rises above the sea level looks more or less like a boat, and as the commander of Rattazzi's squadron, to increase the number of the boats of the warships with which he was besieging Caprera, had seized all the small craft of Maddalena, it seemed as if the little archipelago "Della Moneta" swarmed with sloops and skiffs, all engaged solely in the hindering of one man from doing his duty.

As soon as the "Solitario" had reached the little island[1] situated near the north-east coast of Maddalena, he steered the *beccacino* into the labyrinth of reefs which guard the shore like a bulwark, and, from his hiding-place, he carefully scrutinized the coast-line, which was well illumined by the moon.

It is a fact that the majority of the employés of nearly all Governments, in the daytime, and when they are, or think they are, in the presence of their employers, display the utmost zeal in the fulfilment of their duties, but at night, when their

---

[1] The island Dei Giardinelli.

Uncle Crucifix came in to see how they had got on, to make his offer, so, with his eyes shut; and Goosefoot came, too, screaming and scolding about the right price, and the just price, and so on; then they didn't mind his screaming, because, after all, it was a pity to quarrel with old friends; and then La Longa would go on counting out sou by sou the money which Goosefoot had brought in his handkerchief, saying, "These are for the house; these are for the every-day expenses," and so on. Mena would help, too, to pound the salt and to count the barrels, and she should get back her blue jacket and her coral necklace that had been pawned to Uncle Crucifix; and the women could go back to their own church again, for if any young man happened to look after Mena, her dowry was getting ready.

"For my part," said 'Ntoni, rowing slowly, slowly round and round, so that the current should not drive him out of the circle of the net, while the old man pondered silently over all these things, "for my part, all I wish is that hussy Barbara may be left to gnaw her elbows when we have got back our own again, and may live to repent shutting the door in my face."

"In the storm one knows the good pilot," said the old man. "When we are once more what we have always been, every one will bear a smooth face for us, and will open their doors to us once more."

"There were two who did not shut their doors," said Alessio, "Nunziata and our cousin Anna."

"In prison, in poverty and in sickness one finds one's friends; for that may the Lord help them, too, and all the mouths they have to feed!"

"When Nunziata goes out on the downs to gather wood, or when the rolls of linen are too heavy for her, I go and help her too, poor little thing," said Alessio.

"Come and help now to pull in this side, for this time Saint Francis has really sent us the gift of God!" And the boy pulled and puffed, with his feet braced against the side of the boat, so that one would have thought he was doing it all himself.

Meanwhile 'Ntoni lay stretched on the deck singing to himself, with his hands under his head, watching the white gulls flying against-the blue sky, which had no end, it rose so pure and so high, and the *Providenza* rushed on the green waves rolling in from farther than the eye could see.

"What is the reason," said Alessio, "that the sea is sometimes blue and sometimes green and then white, then again black as the sand of the beach, and is never all one colour, as water should be?"

"It is the will of God," replied the grandfather, "so the mariner can tell when he may safely put out to sea, and when it is best to stay on shore."

"Those gulls have a fine time of it, flying in the air; they need not fear the waves when the wind is high."

"But they have nothing to eat, either, poor beasts."

"So every one has need of good weather, like Nunziata, who can't go to the fountain when it rains," concluded Alessio.

"Neither good nor bad weather lasts forever," observed the old man. But when bad weather came, and the mistral blew, and the corks went dancing on the water all day long as if the devil were playing the violin for them, or if the sea was white as milk, or bubbling up as if it were boiling, and the rain came pouring down upon them until evening, so that no wraps were proof against it, and the sea went frying all about them like oil in the pan, then it was another pair of shoes—and 'Ntoni was in no humour for singing, with his hood down to his nose, bailing out the *Providenza*, that filled faster than he could clear out the water, and the grandpapa went on repeating, "White sea, sirocco there'll be!" or "Curly sea, fresh wind!" as if he had come there only to learn proverbs; and with these blessed proverbs, too, he'd stand in the evening at the window looking out for the weather, with his nose in the air, and say, "When the moon is red it means wind; when it is clear, fine weather; when it is pale it means rain."

"If you know it is going to rain," said 'Ntoni, one day, "why do we go out, while we might stay in bed an hour or two longer?"

"'Water from the sky, sardines in the net,'" answered the old man.

Later on 'Ntoni began to curse and swear, with the water half up to his knees.

"This evening," said his grandfather, "Maruzza will have a good fire ready for us, and we shall soon be quite dry."

And at dusk when the *Providenza*, with her hull full of the gifts of God, turned towards home, with her sail puffing out like Donna Rosolina's best petticoat, and the lights of the village came twinkling one by one from behind the dark rocks as if they were beckoning to each other, Padron 'Ntoni showed his boys the bright fire which burned in La Longa's kitchen at the bottom of the tiny court in the narrow black street; for the wall was low, and from the sea the whole house was visible, with the tiles built into a shed for the hens, and the oven on the other side of the door.

"Don't you see what a blaze La Longa has got up for us?" said he, in high spirits; and La Longa was waiting for them, with the baskets ready. When they were brought back empty, there wasn't much talking; but instead, if there were not enough, and Alessio had to run up to the house for more, the grandfather would put his hands to his mouth and shout, "Mena! Oh, Mena!" And Mena knew well what it meant, and they all came down in procession—she, Lia, and Nunziata, too, with all her chicks behind her; then there was great joy, and nobody minded cold or rain, and before the blazing fire they sat talking of the gifts of God which Saint Francis had sent them, and of what they would do with the money.

But in this desperate game, men's lives are risked for a few pounds of fish; and once the Malavoglia were within a hair's-breadth of losing theirs all at once, as

Bastianazzo had, for the sake of gain, when they were off Agnone as the day drew to a close, and the sky was so dark that they could not even see Etna, and the winds blew and swept up the waves so close about the boat that it seemed as if they had voices and could speak.

"Ugly weather," said Padron 'Ntoni. "The wind turns like a silly wench's head, and the face of the sea looks like Goosefoot's when he is hatching some hateful trick."

The sea was as black as the beach, though the sun had not yet gone down, and every now and then it hissed and seethed like a pot.

"Now the gulls have all gone to sleep," said Alessio.

"By this time they ought to have lighted the beacon at Catania," said 'Ntoni, "but I can't see it."

"Keep the rudder always north-east," ordered the grandfather, "in half an hour it will be darker than an oven."

"On such evenings as this it is better to be at Santuzza's tavern."

"Or asleep in your bed, eh?" said the old man; "then you should be a clerk, like Don Silvestro."

The poor old fellow had been groaning all day with pain. "The weather is going to change," he said, "I feel it in my bones."

All of a sudden it grew so black that one couldn't even see to swear.

Only the waves, as they rolled past the *Providenza*, shone like grinning teeth ready to devour her; and no one dared to speak a word in presence of the sea, that moaned over all its waste of waters.

"I've an idea," said 'Ntoni, suddenly, "that we had better give the fish we've caught to-day to the devil."

"Silence!" said his grandfather; and the stern voice out of that darkness made him shrink together like a leaf on the bench where he sat.

They heard the wind whistle in the sails of the *Providenza* and the ropes ring like the strings of a guitar. Suddenly the wind began to scream like the steam-engine when the train comes out from the tunnel in the mountain above Trezza, and there came a great wave from nobody knew, where, and the *Providenza* rattled like a sack of nuts, and sprang up into the air and then rolled over.

"Down with the sail—down!" cried Padron 'Ntoni. "Cut away, cut away!"

'Ntoni, with the knife in his mouth, scrambled like a cat out on the yard, and standing on the very end to balance himself, hung over the howling waves that leaped up to swallow him.

"Hold on, hold on!" cried the old man to him, through all the thunder of the waves that strove to tear him down, and tossed about the *Providenza* and all that was inside her, and flung the boat on her side, so that the water was up to their knees. "Cut away, cut away!" called out the grandfather again.

"Sacrament!" exclaimed 'Ntoni; "and what shall we do without the sail, then?"

"Stop swearing; we are in the hands of God now."

Alessio, who was grasping the rudder with all his force, heard what his grandfather said, and began to scream, "Mamma, mamma, mamma!"

"Hush !" cried his brother, as well as he could for the knife in his teeth. "Hush, or I'll give you a kick."

"Make the holy sign, and be quiet," echoed the grandfather so that the boy dared not make another sound.

Suddenly the sail fell all at once in a heap, and 'Ntoni drew it in, furling it light, quick as a flash.

"You know your trade well, as your father did before you," said his grandfather. "You, too, are a Malavoglia."

The boat righted and gave one leap, then began to leap about again among the waves.

"This way the rudder, this way; now it wants a strong arm," said Padron 'Ntoni; and though the boy, too, clung to it like a cat, the boat still sprang about, and there came great waves sweeping over it that drove them against the helm, with force enough nearly to knock the breath out of them both.

"The oars!" cried 'Ntoni; "Pull hard, Alessio; you're strong enough when it comes to eating; just now the oars are worth more than the helm."

The boat creaked and groaned with the strain of the oars pulled by those strong young arms; the boy, standing with his feet braced against the deck, put all his soul into his oar as well as his brother.

"Hold hard!" cried the old man, who could hardly be heard at the other side of the boat, over the roaring of the wind and the waves. "Hold on, Alessio!"

"Yes, grandfather, I do," replied the boy.

"Are you afraid ?" asked 'Ntoni.

"No, he's not," answered his grandfather for him; "but we must commend ourselves to God."

"Holy devil!" exclaimed 'Ntoni. "Here one ought to have arms of iron, like the steam-engine. The sea is getting the best of it."

The grandfather was silent, listening to the blast.

"Mamma must by this time have come to the shore to watch for us."

"Don't talk about Mamma now," said the old man; "it is better not to think about her."

"Where are we now?" asked 'Ntoni after some time, hardly able to speak for fatigue.

"In God's hands," answered the grandfather.

"Then let me cry!" exclaimed Alessio, who could bear it no longer; and he began to scream aloud and to call for his mother at the top of his voice, in the midst of the noise of the wind and of the sea, and neither of them had the heart to scold him.

"It's all very well your howling, but nobody can hear you, and you had best be still," said his brother at last, in a voice so changed and strange that he hardly knew it himself. "Now hush!" he went on; "it is best for you and best for us."

"The sail!" ordered Padron 'Ntoni. "Put her head to the wind, and then leave it in the hands of God."

The wind hindered them terribly, but at last they got the sail set, and the *Providenza* began to dance over the crests of the waves, leaning to one side like a wounded bird.

The Malavoglia kept close together on one side, clinging to the rail.

At that moment no one spoke, for when the sea speaks in that tone no one else dares to utter a word.

Only Padron 'Ntoni said, "Over there they are saying the rosary for us."

And no one spoke again, and they flew along through the wild tempest and the night, that had come on as black as pitch.

"The light on the mole!" cried 'Ntoni; "do you see it?"

"To the right!" shouted Padron 'Ntoni; "to the right! It is not the light on the mole. We are driving on shore! Furl, furl!"

"I can't," cried 'Ntoni; "the rope's too wet." His voice was hardly to be heard through the storm, so tired he was. "The knife, the knife! Quick, Alessio!"

"Cut away, cut away!"

At that moment a crash was heard; the *Providenza* righted suddenly, like a still spring let loose, and they were within one of being flung into the sea; the spar with the sail fell across the deck, snapped tike a straw. They heard a voice which cried out as if some one were hurt to death.

"Who is it? Who called out?" demanded 'Ntoni, aiding himself with his teeth and the knife to clear away the rigging of the sail, which had fallen with the mast across the deck, and covered everything. Suddenly a blast of wind took up the sail and swept it whistling away into the night. Then the brothers were able to disengage the wreck of the mast, and to fling it into the sea. The boat rose up, but Padron 'Ntoni did not rise, nor did he answer when 'Ntoni called to him.

SPAIN

THE FIRST VOYAGE TAKEN BY THE ADMIRAL DON CRISTOBAL COLON WHEN HE DISCOVERED THE INDIES[1]

Christopher Columbus
(c. 1446-1506)

BECAUSE, O most Christian, and very high, very excellent and puissant Princes, King and Queen of the Spains and of the islands of the Sea, our Lords, in this present year of 1492, acting on the information that I had given to your Highnesses touching the lands of India, resolved to send me, Cristobal Colon, to the said parts of India, and ordered that I should not go by land to the eastward, but by way of the west, whither up to this day we do not know for certain that any one has gone.

Thus, in the month of January, your Highnesses gave orders to me that with a sufficient fleet I should go to the said parts of India, and for this they made great concessions to me, and ennobled me, so that henceforward I should be called Don, and should be chief Admiral of the Ocean Sea, perpetual Viceroy and Governor of all the islands and continents that I should discover and gain, and that I might hereafter discover and gain in the Ocean Sea, and that my eldest son should succeed, and so on from generation to generation for ever.

I left the city of Granada on the 12th of May, in the same year of 1492, being Saturday, and came to the town of Palos which is a seaport; where I equipped three vessels well suited for such service; and departed from that port, well supplied with provisions and with many sailors, on the 3rd day of August of the same year, being Friday, half an hour before sunrise, taking the route to the islands of Canaria, belonging to your Highnesses, which are in the said Ocean Sea, that I might thence take my departure for navigating until I should arrive at the Indies. As part of my duty I thought it well to write an account of all the voyage very punctually, noting from day to day all that I should do and see, that should happen, as will be seen further on. Also, Lords Princes, I resolved to describe each night what passed in the day, and to note each day how I navigated at night. I propose to construct a new chart for navigating, on which I shall delineate all the sea and lands of the Ocean in their proper positions under their bearings; and further, I propose to prepare a book, and to put down all as it were in a picture, by latitude from the equator, and western longitude. Above all, I shall have accomplished much, for I shall forget

[1] From Sir Clements R. Markham's translation of *The Journal of Christopher Columbus.*

sleep, and shall work at the business of navigation, that so the service may be performed; all which will entail great labour.

Friday, 3rd of August. We departed on Friday, the 3rd of August, in the year 1492, from the bar of Saltes, at 8 o'clock, and proceeded with a strong sea breeze until sunset, towards the south, for 60 miles, equal to 15 leagues; afterwards S.W. and W.S.W., which was the course for the Canaries.

Saturday, 4th of August. They steered S.W. ¼ S.

Sunday, 5th of August. They continued their course day and night more than 40 leagues.

Monday, 6th of August. The rudder of the caravel *Pinta* became unshipped, and Martin Alonso Pinzon, who was in command, believed or suspected that it was by contrivance of Gomes Rascon and Cristobal Quintero, to whom the caravel belonged, for they dreaded to go on that voyage. The Admiral says that before they sailed, these men had been displaying a certain backwardness, so to speak. The Admiral was much disturbed at not being able to help the said caravel without danger, and he says that he was eased of some anxiety when he reflected that Martin Alonso Pinzon was a man of energy and ingenuity. They made, during the day and night, 29 leagues.

Tuesday, 7th of August. The rudder of the Pinta was shipped and secured, and they proceeded on a course for the island of Lanzarote, one of the Canaries. They made, during the day and night, 25 leagues.

Wednesday, 8th of August. Opinions respecting their position varied among the pilots of the three caravels; but that of the Admiral proved to be nearer the truth. He wished to go to Gran Canaria, to leave the caravel Pinta, because she was disabled by the faulty hanging of her rudder, and was making water. He intended to obtain another there if one could be found. They could not reach the place that day.

Thursday, 9th of August. The Admiral was not able to reach Gomera until the night of Sunday, while Martin Alonso remained on that coast of Gran Canaria by order of the Admiral, because his vessel could not be navigated. Afterwards the Admiral took her to Canaria, and they repaired the Pinta very thoroughly through the pains and labour of the Admiral of Martin Alonso and the rest. Finally they came to Gomera. They saw a great fire issue from the mountain of the island of Tenerife, which is of great height. They rigged the Pinta with square sails, for she was lateen rigged; and the Admiral reached Gomera on Sunday the 2nd of September, with the Pinta repaired.

The Admiral says that many honourable Spanish gentlemen who were at Gomera with Dona Ines Peraza, mother of Guillen Peraza (who was afterwards the first Count of Gomera), and who were natives of the island of Hierro, declared that every year they saw land to the west of the Canaries; and others, natives of

Gomera, affirmed the same on oath. The Admiral here says that he remembers, when in Portugal in the year 1484, a man came to the King from the island of Madeira, to beg for a caravel to go to this land that was seen, who swore that it could be seen every year, and always in the same way. He also says that he recollects the same thing being affirmed in the islands of the Azores; and all these lands were described as in the same direction, and as being like each other, and of the same size. Having taken in water, wood, and meat, and all else that the men had who were left at Gomera by the Admiral when he went to the island of Canaria to repair the caravel Pinta, he finally made sail from the said island of Gomera, with his three caravels, on Thursday the 6th day of September.

Thursday, 6th of September. He departed on that day from the port of Gomera in the morning, and shaped a course to go on his voyage; having received tidings from a caravel that came from the island of Hierro that three Portuguese caravels were off that island with the object of taking him. There was a calm all that day and night, and in the morning he found himself between Gomera and Tenerife.

Friday, 7th of September. The calm continued all Friday and Saturday, until the third hour of the night.

Saturday, 8th of September. At the third hour of Saturday night it began to blow from the N.E., and the Admiral shaped a course to the west. He took in much sea over the bows, which retarded progress, and 9 leagues were made in that day and night.

Sunday, 9th of September. This day the Admiral made 19 leagues, and he arranged to reckon less than the number run, because if the voyage were of long duration, the people would not be so terrified and disheartened. In the night he made 120 miles, at the rate of 12 miles an hour, which are 30 leagues. The sailors steered badly, letting the ship fall off to N.E., and even more, respecting which the Admiral complained many times.

Monday, 10th of September. In this day and night he made 60 leagues, at the rate of 10 miles an hour, which are 2 ½ leagues; but he only counted 48 leagues, that the people might not be alarmed if the voyage should be long.

Tuesday, 11th of September. That day they sailed on their course, which was west, and made 20 leagues and more. They saw a large piece of the mast of a ship of 120 tons, but were unable to get it. In the night they made nearly 20 leagues, but only counted 16, for the reason already given.

Wednesday, 12th of September. That day, steering their course, they made 33 leagues during the day and night, counting less.

Thursday, 13th of September. That day and night, steering their course, which was west, they made 33 leagues, counting 3 or 4 less. The currents were against them. On this day, at the commencement of the night, the needles turned a half point to north-west, and in the morning they turned somewhat more north-west.

Friday, 14th of September. That day they navigated, on their westerly course, day and night, 20 leagues, counting a little less. Here those of the caravel *Nina* reported that they had seen a tern and a boatswain bird, and these birds never go more than 25 leagues from the land.

Saturday, 15th of September. That day and night they made 27 leagues and rather more on their west course; and in the early part of the night there fell from heaven into the sea a marvellous flame of fire, at a distance of about 4 or 5 leagues from them.

Sunday, 16th of September. That day and night they steered their course west, making 39 leagues, but the Admiral only counted 36. There were some clouds and small rain. The Admiral says that on that day, and ever afterwards, they met with very temperate breezes, so that there was great pleasure in enjoying the mornings, nothing being wanted but the song of nightingales. He says that the weather was like April in Andalusia. Here they began to see many tufts of grass which were very green, and appeared to have been quite recently torn from the land. From this they judged that they were near some island, but not the main land, according to the Admiral, "because," as he says, "I make the main land to be more distant."

Monday, 17th of September. They proceeded on their west course, and made over 50 leagues in the day and night, but the Admiral only counted 47. They were aided by the current. They saw much very fine grass and herbs from rocks, which came from the west. They, therefore, considered that they were near land. The pilots observed the north point, and found that the needles turned a full point to the west of north. So the mariners were alarmed and dejected, and did not give their reason. But the Admiral knew, and ordered that the north should be again observed at dawn. They then found that the needles were true. The cause was that the star makes the movement, and not the needles. At dawn, on that Monday, they saw much more weed appearing, like herbs from rivers, in which they found a live crab, which the Admiral kept. He says that these crabs are certain signs of land. The sea-water was found to be less salt than it had been since leaving the Canaries. The breezes were always soft. Every one was pleased, and the best sailers went ahead to sight the first land. They saw many tunny fish, and the crew of the *Niña* killed one. The Admiral here says that these signs of land came from the west, "in which direction I trust in that high God in whose hands are all victories that very soon we shall sight land." In that morning he says that a white bird was seen which has not the habit of sleeping on the sea, called *rabo dejunco* (boatswainbird).

Tuesday, 18th of September. This day and night they made over 55 leagues, the Admiral only counting 48. In all these days the sea was very smooth, like the river at Seville. This day Martin Alonso, with the *Pinta,* which was a fast sailer, did not wait, for he said to the Admiral, from his caravel, that he had seen a great multitude of birds flying westward, that he hoped to see land that night, and that he therefore pressed onward. A great cloud appeared in the north, which is a sign of the proximity of land.

Wednesday, 19th of September. The Admiral continued on his course, and during the day and night he made but 25 leagues because it was calm. He counted 22. This day, at 10 o'clock, a booby came to the ship, and in the afternoon another arrived, these birds not generally going more than 20 leagues from the land. There was also some drizzling rain without wind, which is a sure sign of land. The Admiral did not wish to cause delay by beating to windward to ascertain whether land was near, but he considered it certain that there were islands both to the north and south of his position. For his desire was to press onwards to the Indies, the weather being fine. For on his return, God willing, he could see all. These are his own words. Here the pilots found their positions.

He of the *Niña* made the Canaries 440 leagues distant, the *Pinta* 420. The pilot of the Admiral's ship made the distance exactly 400 leagues.

Thursday, 20th of September. This day the course was W.b.N., and as her head was all round the compass owing to the calm that prevailed, the ships made only 7 or 8 leagues. Two boobies came to the ship, and afterwards another, a sign of the proximity of land. They saw much weed, although none was seen on the previous day. They caught a bird with the hand, which was like a tern. But it was a river-bird, not a sea-bird, the feet being like those of a gull. At dawn two or three land-birds came singing to the ship, and they disappeared before sunset. Afterwards a booby came from W.N.W., and flew to the S.W. which was a sign that it left land in the W.N.W.; for these birds sleep on shore, and go to sea in the mornings in search of food, not extending their flight more than 20 leagues from the land.

Friday, 21st of September. Most of the day it was calm, and later there was a little wind. During the day and night they did not make good more than 13 leagues. At dawn they saw so much weed that the sea appeared to be covered with it, and it came from the west. A booby was seen. The sea was very smooth, like a river, and the air the best in the world. They saw a whale, which is a sign that they were near land, because they always keep near the shore.

Saturday, 22nd of September. They shaped a course W.N.W. more or less, her head turning from one to the other point, and made 30 leagues. Scarcely any weed was seen. They saw some sandpipers and another bird. Here the Admiral says: "This contrary wind was very necessary for me, because my people were much excited at the thought that in these seas no wind ever blew in the direction of Spain." Part of the day there was no weed, and later it was very thick.

Sunday, 23rd of September. They shaped a course N.W., and at times more northerly; occasionally they were on their course, which was west, and they made about 22 leagues. They saw a dove and a booby, another river-bird, and some white birds. There was a great deal of weed, and they found crabs in it. The sea being smooth and calm, the crew began to murmur, saying that here there was no great sea, and that the wind would never blow so that they could return to Spain. Afterwards the sea rose very much, without wind, which astonished them. The Admiral here says: "Thus the high sea was very necessary to me, such as had not appeared but in the time of the Jews when they went out of Egypt and murmured against Moses, who delivered them out of captivity."

Monday, 24th of September. The Admiral went on his west course all day and night, making 14 leagues. He counted 12. A booby came to the ship, and many sandpipers.

Tuesday, 25th of September. This day began with a calm, and afterwards there was wind. They were on their west course until night. The Admiral conversed with Martin Alonso Pinzon, captain of the other caravel *Pinta,* respecting a chart which he had sent to the caravel three days before, on which, as it would appear, the Admiral had certain islands depicted in that sea. Martin Alonso said that the ships were in the position on which the islands were placed, and the Admiral replied that so it appeared to him; but it might be that they had not fallen in with them, owing to the currents which had always set the ships to the N.E., and that they had not made so much as the pilots reported. The Admiral then asked for the chart to be returned, and it was sent back on a line. The Admiral then began to plot the position on it, with the pilot and mariners. At sunset Martin Alonso went up on the poop of his ship, and with much joy called to the Admiral, claiming the reward as he had sighted land. When the Admiral heard this positively declared, he says that he gave thanks to the Lord on his knees, while Martin Alonso said the *Gloria in excelsis* with his people. The Admiral's crew did the same. Those of the *Niña* all went up on the mast and into the rigging, and declared that it was land. It so seemed to the Admiral, and that it was distant 25 leagues. They all continued to declare it was land until night. The Admiral ordered the course to be altered from W. to S.W., in which direction the land had appeared. That day they made 4 leagues on a west course, and 17 S.W. during the night, in all 21; but the people were told that 13 was the distance made good; for it was always feigned to them that the distances were less, so that the voyage might not appear so long. Thus two reckonings were kept on this voyage, the shorter being feigned, and the longer being the true one. The sea was very smooth, so that many sailors bathed alongside. They saw many *dorados* and other fish.

Wednesday, 26th of September. The Admiral continued on the west course until after noon. Then he altered course to S.W., until he made out that what had been said to be land was only clouds. Day and night they made 31 leagues, counting 24 for the people. The sea was like a river, the air pleasant and very mild.

Thursday, 27th of September. The course west, and distance made good during day and night 24 leagues, 20 being counted for the people. Many *dorados* came. One was killed. A boatswain bird came.

Friday, 28th of September. The course was west, and the distance, owing to calms, only 14 leagues in day and night, 13 leagues being counted. They met with little weed; but caught two *dorados,* and more in the other ships.

Saturday, 29th of September. The course was west, and they made 24 leagues, counting 21 for the people. Owing to calms, the distance made good during day and night was not much. They saw a bird called *rabiforcado* (man-o'-war bird), which makes the boobies vomit what they have swallowed, and eats it, maintaining itself on nothing else. It is a sea-bird, but does not sleep on the sea, and does not go more than 20 leagues from the land. There are many of them at the Cape Verde Islands. Afterwards they saw two boobies. The air was very mild and agreeable, and the Admiral says that nothing was wanting but to hear the nightingale. The sea smooth as a river. Later, three boobies and a man-o'-war bird were seen three times. There was much weed.

Sunday, 30th of September. The western course was steered, and during the day and night, owing to calms, only 14 leagues were made, 11 being counted. Four boatswain-birds came to the ship, which is a great sign of land, for so many birds of this kind together is a sign that they are not straying or lost. They also twice saw four boobies. There was much weed. *Note* that the stars which are called *las guardias* (the Pointers), when night comes on, are near the western point, and when dawn breaks they are near the N.E. point; so that, during the whole night, they do not appear to move more than three lines or 9 hours, and this on each night. The Admiral says this, and also that at nightfall the needles vary a point westerly, while at dawn they agree exactly with the star. From this it would appear that the north star has a movement like the other stars, while the needles always point correctly.

Monday, 1st of October. Course west, and 25 leagues made good, counted for the crew as 20 leagues. There was a heavy shower of rain. At dawn the Admiral's pilot made the distance from Hierro 578 leagues to the west. The reduced reckoning which the Admiral showed to the crew made it 584 leagues; but the truth which the Admiral observed and kept secret was 707.

Tuesday, 2nd of October. Course west, and during the day and night 39 leagues were made good, counted for the crew as 30. The sea always smooth. Many thanks be given to God, says the Admiral, that the wind is coming from east to west, contrary to its usual course. Many fish werc seen, and one was killed. A white bird was also seen that appeared to be a gull.

Wednesday, 3rd of October. They navigated on the usual course, and made good 47 leagues, counted as 40. Sandpipers appeared, and much weed, some of it very old and some quite fresh and having fruit. They saw no birds. The Admiral, therefore, thought that they had left the islands behind them which were depicted on the charts. The Admiral here says that he did not wish to keep the ships beating about during the last week, and in the last few days when there were so many signs of land, although he had information of certain islands in this region. For he wished to avoid delay, his object being to reach the Indies. He says that to delay would not be wise.

Thursday, 4th of October. Course west, and 63 leagues made good during the day and night, counted as 46. More than forty sandpipers came to the ship in a flock, and two boobies, and a ship's boy hit one with a stone. There also came a man-o'-war bird, and a white bird like a gull.

Friday, 5th of October. The Admiral steered his course, going 11 miles an hour, and during the day and night they made good 57 leagues, as the wind increased somewhat during the night: 45 were counted. The sea was smooth and quiet. "To God," he says, "be many thanks given, the air being pleasant and temperate, with no weed, many sandpipers, and flying-fish coming on the deck in numbers."

Saturday, 6th of October. The Admiral continued his west course, and during day and night they made good 40 leagues, 33 being counted. This night Martin Alonso said that it would be well to steer south of west, and it appeared to the Admiral that Martin Alonso did not say this with respect to the island of Cipango. He saw that if an error was made the land would not be reached so quickly, and that consequently it would be better to go at once to the continent and afterwards to the islands.

Sunday, 7th of October. The west course was continued; for two hours they went at the rate of 12 miles an hour, and afterwards 8 miles an hour. They made good 23 leagues, counting 18 for the people. This day, at sunrise, the caravel *Niña,* which went ahead, being the best sailer, and pushed forward as much as possible to sight the land first, so as to enjoy the reward which the Sovereigns had promised to whoever should see it first, hoisted a flag at the mast-head and fired a gun, as a signal that she had sighted land, for such was the Admiral's order. He had also ordered that, at sunrise and sunset, all the ships should join him; because those two times are most proper for seeing the greatest distance, the haze clearing away. No land was seen during the afternoon, as reported by the caravel *Niña,* and they passed a great number of birds flying from N. to S.W. This gave rise to the belief that the birds were either going to sleep on land, or were flying from the winter which might be supposed to be near in the land whence they were coming. The Admiral was aware that most of the islands held by the Portuguese were discovered by the flight of birds. For this reason he resolved to give up the west course, and to shape a course W.S.W. for the two following days. He began the new course one hour before sunset. They made good, during the night about 5 leagues, and 23 in the day, altogether 28 leagues.

Monday, 8th of October. The course was W.S.W., and 11½ or 12 leagues were made good in the day and night; and at times it appears that they went at the rate of 15 miles an hour during the night (if the handwriting be not deceptive[1]). The sea was like the river at Seville. "Thanks be to God," says the Admiral, "the air is very soft like the April at Seville; and it is a pleasure to be here, so balmy are the breezes." The weed seemed to be very fresh. There were many land-birds, and they took one that was flying to the S.W. Terns, ducks, and a booby were also seen.

Tuesday, 9th of October. The course was S.W., and they made 5 leagues. The wind then changed, and the Admiral steered W. by N. 4 leagues. Altogether, in day and night, they made 11 leagues by day and 20½ by night; counted as 17 leagues altogether. Throughout the night birds were heard passing.

Wednesday, 10th of October. The course was W.S.W., and they went at the rate of 10 miles an hour, occasionally 12 miles, and sometimes 7. During the day and night they made *59* leagues, counted as no more than 44. Here the people could endure no longer. They complained of the length of the voyage. But the Admiral cheered them up in the best way he could, giving them good hopes of the advantages they might gain from it. He added that, however much they might complain, he had to go to the Indies, and that he would go on until he found them, with the help of the Lord.

Thursday, 11th of October. The course was W.S.W. and there was more sea than there had been during the whole of the voyage. They saw sandpipers, and a green reed near the ship. Those of the caravel *Pinta* saw a cane and a pole, and they took up another small pole which appeared to have been worked with iron; also another bit of cane, a land-plant, and a small board. The crew of the caravel *Niña* also saw signs of land, ahd a small branch covered with berries. Every one breathed afresh and rejoiced at these signs. The run until sunset was 26 leagues.

After sunset the Admiral returned to his original west course and they went along at the rate of 12 miles an hour. Up to two hours after midnight they had gone 90 miles, equal to 22½ leagues. As the caravel *Pinta* was a better sailer, and went ahead of the Admiral, she found the land, and made the signals ordered by the Admiral. The land was first seen by a sailor named Rodrigo de Triana. But the Admiral, at ten in the previous night, being on the castle of the poop, saw a light, though it was so uncertain that he could not affirm it was land. He called Pero Gutierrez, a gentleman of the King's bed-chamber, and said that there seemed to be a light, and that he should look at it. He did so, and saw it. The Admiral said the same to Rodrigo Sanchez of Segovia, whom the King and Queen had sent with the fleet as inspector, but he could see nothing because he was not in a place whence anything could be seen. After the Admiral had spoken he saw the light

---

[1] Note by Las Casas.

once or twice, and it was like a wax candle rising and falling. It seemed to few to be an indication of land; but the Admiral made certain that land was close. When they said the *Salve,* which all the sailors were accustomed to sing in their way, the Admiral asked and admonished the men to keep a good look-out on the forecastle, and to watch well for land; and to him who should first cry out that he saw land, he would give a silk doublet, besides the rewards promised by the Sovereigns, which were 10,000 maravedis to him who should first see it. At two hours after midnight the land was sighted at a distance of two leagues. They shortened sail, and lay under the mainsail without the bonnets. The vessels were hove to, waiting for daylight; and on Friday they arrived at a small island of the Lucayos, called, in the language of the Indians, *Guanahani.* Presently they saw naked people. The Admiral went on shore in the armed boat, and Martin Alonso Pinzon, and Vicente Yañez, his brother, who was captain of the *Niña.* The Admiral took the royal standard, and the captains went with two banners of the green cross, which the Admiral took in all the ships as a sign, with an F and a Y and a crown over each letter, one on one side of the cross and the other on the other. Having landed, they saw trees very green, and much water, and fruits of diverse kinds. The Admiral called to the two captains and to the others who leaped. on shore, and to Rodrigo Escovedo, secretary of the whole fleet, and to Rodrigo Sanchez of Segovia, and said that they should bear faithful testimony that he, in presence of all, had taken, as he now took, possession of the said island for the King and for the Queen, his Lords.

HOW VASCO NUÑEZ DE BALBOA DISCOVERED THE PACIFIC[1]

TO FURTHER what the Admiral Columbus had begun, God raised an instrument in the person of Vasco Nuñez de Balboa, one of the first discoverers of this new world; a man of good understanding, as he showed upon the occasion which I shall now relate.

He was with others, upon the discovery with General Encisco, the Governor: they came to a place called Uraba, and as they entered the port, by negligence of the steersman, the Governor's ship struck upon a sand, and was lost, nothing being saved out of her but the lives of the men, who got into the boats, but naked, and in danger of perishing for want of provisions. Vasco de Nuñez said, that he remembered there was not far off a river, the banks of which were inhabited by much people: he guided them thither: and the thing being found to be as he had

[1] From *Pinkerton's Voyages.*

said, he gained great reputation among them all. They came thither, and found the Indians in arms against the Castilians, whose name was already become odious to those nations: they made a vow to Our Lady, to dedicate to her the first settlement and church to the honour of her image, under the title of Sancta Maria la Antigua, or the Ancient St Mary, which to this day is venerated in Seville; and to send her many rich gifts of gold and silver, which one of them, as a pilgrim, should carry in the name of the rest. Being encouraged by this vow, they fell upon the Indians, and obtained the victory.

Presently they made a settlement, and built a town dedicated to the Virgin, calling it Sancta Maria el Antigua of Dairen, because that was the name of that river. After this, to accomplish their vow, they sent the promised presents to the devout image of the Virgin.

The good opinion of Vasco de Nuñez increasing, thus daily, and having cunningly ordered it so, that Encisco resigned his governorship, they chose Vasco Nuñez in his room: at first with an associate; but he found means in time to be alone, as it was necessary he should, in point of command, being to overcome such difficulties as were to be met with at every turn: and, indeed, he knew how to make himself be both feared and beloved, having a very good spirit of government.

In the new discoveries he undertook, he came first to the lands of the Cacique Ponea, and not finding him at home, he destroyed them: he passed on to the lands of the Cacique Careta, who not caring to enter into war, received him peacefully, and treated him as a friend. This Cacique Careta had a kinsman, who was a lord, that lived further in the country, and his name was Suran; who persuaded another neighbouring Prince, called Comagre, to make a friendship with the Castilians: this Prince had a very fine palace, which astonished them; and particularly when they saw, in a kind of chapel or oratory, some dead bodies lying, covered with rich mantles, and many jewels of gold and pearls; and being asked, whose bodies these were, they answered, of their predecessors; and that, to preserve them from corruption, they had dried them with fire. The King caressed the Castilians, and gave them great presents: he had seven sons, and one of them, more liberal, gave the Spaniards a present of near four thousand pesos of fine gold, and some pieces of rare workmanship: they weighed it, and taking the King's fifths, they began to divide the remainder. In the division, two soldiers fell out about their shares; the Cacique's son, who had made the present, hearing the noise, could not bear it, but coming to them, struck the balance where the gold was weighing, and threw it all upon the ground, saying:

"Is it possible you should value so much a thing that so little deserves your esteem? and that you should leave the repose of your houses, and pass so many seas, exposed to such dangers, to trouble those who live quiet in their own country? Have some shame, Christians, and do not value these things: but if you are resolved to search gold, I will show you a country where you may satisfy yourselves."

And, pointing with his finger to the south, he told them they should see there another sea, when they had passed over certain high mountains where they should see other people, who could go with sails and oars as they did: and that passing that sea, they should meet with vast quantities of gold, whereof the natives made all their utensils; and that he would be their guide, and conduct them with his father's vassals: but that it would be requisite they should be more in number, because they were powerful kings, who could hinder their passage: giving them by this the first notice of Peru and its riches.

This was the first knowledge and light which the Spaniards got of the South Sea, and of the gold and riches of its coasts, which gave them all great joy; so that they were impatient to see the hour of breaking through all obstacles, to see that sea never before heard of, and enjoy the riches of it. Vasco Nuñez immediately disposed all things, and went out of Dairen, in the beginning of September in the year 1513, and going along the seaside, to the habitation of the friendly Cacique Careta, he went towards the mountains by the lands of the Cacique Ponea, who, though at first he endeavoured to oppose their passage, yet being advised by the Indians of Careta who accompanied the Castilians, he presented them with gold and provisions, and gave them guides; they, in return, giving him looking-glasses, needles, knives, and other baubles, which they valued very much.

Then they began to mount the mountain, through the country of a Cacique called Quareca, who appeared in arms, and attacked the Spaniards: he had a long robe of cotton, but all his men were naked. They began to skirmish, and threaten, by their actions, to hinder the passage; but no sooner did they hear the noise, and feel the effects of the muskets, and find some to fall, but they turned their backs, flying like a herd of deer, frighted to see the fire, and hear the sound of the vollies, which appeared thunder to them, and thought the Spaniards had thunderbolts at their command: so they left the passage free to them.

The Indians of Careta had said, that from their country to the top of the highest mountain, there was the time of six suns: for by that they meant so many days' journey; but the ways were so bad, that they employed five and twenty days to get to the top.

A little before they were at the highest, Vasco Nuñez de Balboa, caused a halt to be made, desiring to have the glory of having himself been the first man that ever saw the South Sea. And so it was: he goes alone, discovers that vast ocean, and the large bays of the South Sea, called Pacifick: and upon his knees, with tears in his eyes, lifts up his eyes to Heaven, giving thanks to the great Creator of all things, for having brought him from such remote parts to contemplate that which none of his ancestors had ever seen: he made a sign after this to his companions to come up, and so they all run in haste, pushing one another on; and when they were on the top, where there is a full prospect of the sea, it is not to be imagined the content they all received in admiring that vast and smooth liquid crystal, which not being animated, did not on its side give leaps of joy, nor go out of its bed to the tops of the mountains, to welcome those who came to deliver it from the tyranny the devil exercised over it, by infesting it with storms and tempests, and infecting the air with the breath of idolatry, which was breathed in all those parts, both east, west, and north, and south.

Vasco Nuñez de Balboa, having performed his devotions, and thanked Our Lord with all his companions, for so great a favour done him, as to bring them to that place, he then bethought himself of his second obligation, which was to his King; in conformity to which, he took possession, in His Majesty's name, for the Crowns of Castile and Leon, of the place where he was and of the sea which he discovered from thence; cutting for this purpose many trees and making great crosses which he set up, and writ upon them the names of Their Majesties.

HOW FERNAN DE MAGALHAES SAILED INTO THE SOUTHERN SEA AND THE MANNER OF HIS DEATH[1]

Anthony Pigapheta

(1491-1535)

I

ANTHONY PIGAPHETA, *Patrician of Vicenza, and Knight of Rhodes, to the very illustrious and very excellent* Lord Philip de Villers Lisleaden, *the famous Grand Master of Rhodes, his most respected Lord.*

Since there are several curious persons (very illustrious and very reverend lord) who not only are pleased to listen to and learn the great and wonderful things which God has permitted me to see and suffer in the long and perilous navigation, which I have performed (and which is written hereafter), but also they desire to learn the methods and fashions of the road which I have taken to go thither, therefore, my lord, it will please you to hear that finding myself in Spain in the year of the Nativity of our Lord, one thousand five hundred and nineteen, at the court of the most serene king of the Romans, and knowing both by the reading of many

[1] From Lord Stanley of Alderley's translation of *The First Voyage Round the World of Magellan.*

books and by the report of many lettered and well informed persons, the very great and awful things of the ocean, I deliberated, with the favour of the Emperor to experiment and go and see with my eyes a part of these things.

Now in order to decypher the commencement of my voyage (very illustrious lord); having heard that there was in the city of Seville, a small armade to the number of five ships, ready to perform this long voyage, that is to say, to find the islands of Maluco, from whence the spices come:of which armade the captain-general was Fernand de Magaglianes, a Portuguese gentleman, commander of *St James of the Sword,* who had performed several voyages in the ocean sea (in which he had behaved very honourably as a good man), I set out from Barcelona and came by sea as far as Malaga, and thence I went away by land until I arrived at the said city of Seville. There I remained for the space of three months, waiting till the said armade was in order and readiness to perform its voyage.

Finally (very illustrious lord), after all provisions had been made, and the vessels were in order, the captain-general, a discreet and virtuous man, careful of his honour, would not commence his voyage without first making some good and wholesome ordinances, such as it is the good custom to make for those who go to sea. Nevertheless he did not entirely declare the voyage which he was going to make, so that his men should not from amazement and fear be unwilling to accompany him. These ordinances he made over in writing to each master of the ships, and commanded them to be observed and inviolably kept.

Firstly, the said captain-general willed that the vessel in which he himself was should go before the other vessels, and that the others should follow it; therefore he carried by night on the poop of his ship a torch or faggot of burning wood, which they called farol, which burned all the night, so that his ships should not lose sight of him. Sometimes he set a lantern, sometimes a thick cord of reeds was lighted, which was called trenche. When the captain had made one of his signals to his people, they answered in the same way. In that manner they knew whether the ships were following and keeping together or not. And when he wished to take a tack on account of the change of weather, or if the wind was contrary, or if he wished to make less way, he had two lights shown; and if he wished the others to lower their small sail, which was a part of the sail attached to the great sail, he showed three lights. Also by the three lights, notwithstanding that the wind was fair for going faster, he signalled that the studding sail should be lowered; so that the great sail might be quicker and more easily struck and furled when bad weather should suddenly set in, on account of some squall or otherwise. Likewise when the captain wished the other ships to lower the sail he had four lights shown which shortly after he had put out and then showed a single one, which was a signal that he wished to stop there and turn, so that the other ships might do as he did. Withal, when he discovered any land, or shoal, that is to say, a rock at sea, he made several lights to be shown or had a bombard fired off. And to know whether all the ships followed him and were coming together, he showed one light only besides the farol, and then each of the ships showed another light, which was an answering signal.

Besides the above-mentioned ordinances for carrying on seamanship as is fitting, and to avoid the dangers which may come upon those who do not keep watch, the said captain ordered that three watches should be kept at night. The first was at the beginning of the night, the second at midnight, and the third towards break of day, which is commonly called *La diane*, otherwise the star of the break of day.

Monday, the day of St Lawrence, the 10th of August, in the year above mentioned, the fleet, provided with what was necessary for it, and carrying crews of different nations, to the number of two hundred and thirty-seven men in all the five ships, was ready to set sail from the mole of Seville; and firing all the artillery, we made sail only on the foremast, and came to the end of a river named Betis, which is now called Guadalcavir. And passing by many little villages along the said river, at last we arrived at a castle, which belongs to the Duke of Medina Sidonia, named St Lucar, where there is a port from which to enter the ocean sea.

Tuesday, the 20th September of the said year, we set sail from St Lucar, making the course of the south-west otherwise named Labeiche; and on the twenty-sixth of the said month we arrived at an island of great Canaria, named Teneriphe, which is in twenty-eight degrees latitude; there we remained three days and a half to take in provisions and other things which were wanted. After that we set sail thence and came to a port named Monterose, where we sojourned two days to supply ourselves with pitch, which is a thing necessary for ships.

Monday, the third of October of the said year, at the hour of midnight, we set sail, making the course auster, which the lavantine mariners call Siroc, entering into the ocean sea. We passed the Cape Verd and the neighbouring islands in fourteen-and-a-half degrees, and we navigated for several days by the coast of Guinea or Ethiopia; where there is a mountain called Sierra Leona, which is in eight degrees latitude according to the art and science of cosmography and asytology. Sometimes we had the wind contrary and at other times sufficiently good, and rains without wind. In this manner we navigated with rain for the space of sixty days until the equinoctial line, which was a thing very strange and unaccustomed to be seen, according to the saying of some old men and those who had navigated here several times. Nevertheless, before reaching this equinoctial line we had in fourteen degrees a variety of bad weather and bad winds, as much on account of squalls as for the head winds and currents which came in such a manner that we could no longer advance. In order that our ships might not perish nor broach to (as it often happens when the squalls come together), we struck our sails, and in that manner we went about the sea hither and thither until the fair weather came. During the calm there came large fishes near the ships which they called *Tiburoni* (sharks), which have teeth of a terrible kind, and eat people when they find them in the sea either alive or dead. During these storms the body of St Anselme appeared to us several times; amongst others, one night that it was very dark on account of the bad weather, the said saint appeared in the form of a fire lighted at the summit of the mainmast, and remained there near two hours and a half, which comforted us greatly, for we were in tears, only expecting the hour of perishing; and when that holy light was going away from us it gave out so great a brilliancy in the eyes of each, that we were near a quarter-of-an-hour like people blinded, and calling out for mercy. For without any doubt nobody hoped to escape from that storm. It is to be noted that all and as many times as that light which represents the said St Anselme shows itself and descends upon a vessel which is in a storm at sea, that vessel never is lost.

After that we had passed the equinoctial line, towards the south, we lost the star of the tramontana, and we navigated between the south and Garbin, which is the collateral wind (or point) between south and west; and we crossed as far as a country named Verzin, which is in twentyfour degrees and a half of the Antarctic sky. At this place we had refreshments of victuals, like fowls and meat of calves, also a variety of fruits, called *battate, pigne* (pine-apples), sweet, of singular goodness, and many other things, which I have omitted mentioning, not to be too long.

We entered into this port the day of Saint Lucy (13th December) before Christmas, and departing from it, and following our course, we went as far as thirty-four degrees and a third towards the antarctic pole; there we found, near a river, men whom they call "cannibals," who eat human flesh, and one of these men, great as a giant, came to the captain's ship to ascertain and ask if the others might come. This man had a voice like a bull, and whilst this man was at the ship his companions carried off all their goods which they had to a castle further off, from fear of us. Seeing that, we landed a hundred men from the ships, and went after them to try and catch some others; however they gained in running away. This kind of people did more with one step than we could do at a bound.

This place was formerly called the Cape of St Mary, and it was thought there that from thence there was a passage to the Sea of Sur; that is to say, the South Sea. And it is not found that any ship has ever discovered anything more, having passed beyond the said cape. And now it is no longer a cape, but it is a river which has a mouth seventeen leagues in width, by which it enters into the sea.

Afterwards following the same course towards the Antarctic pole, going along the land, we found two islands full of geese and goslings, and sea wolves.

Departing thence as far as forty-nine degrees and a half in the Antarctic heavens (as we were in the winter), we entered into a port to pass the winter, and remained there two whole months without ever seeing anybody. However, one day, without anyone expecting it, we saw a giant, who was on the shore of the sea, quite naked, and was dancing and leaping, and singing, and whilst singing he put the sand and dust on his head. Our captain sent one of his men towards him, whom he charged to sing and leap like the other to reassure him, and show him friendship. This he did, and immediately the sailor led this giant to a little island where the captain was waiting for him; and when he was before us he began to be astonished, and to be afraid, and he raised one finger on high, thinking that we came from heaven. He was so tall that the tallest of us only came up to his waist; however he was well built. He had a large face, painted red all round, and his eyes also were painted yellow around them, and he had two hearts painted on his cheeks; he had but little hair on his head, and it was painted white. When he was brought before the captain, he was clothed with the skin of a certain beast, which skin was very skilfully sewed. This beast has its head and ears the size of a mule, and the neck and body of the fashion of a camel, the legs of a deer, and the tail like that of a horse, and it neighs like a horse. The captain caused food and drink to be given to this giant, then they showed him some things, amongst others a steel mirror. When the giant saw his likeness in it, he was greatly terrified, leaping backwards, and made three or four of our men fall down.

We remained in this port, which was called the Port of St Julian, about five months, during which there happened to us many strange things, of which I will tell a part. One was, that immediately that we entered into this port, the masters of the other four ships plotted treason against the captain-general, in order to put him to death. These were thus named: John of Carthagine, conductor of the fleet; the treasurer, Loys de Mendoza; the conductor, Anthony Cocha; and Gaspar de Casada. However, the treason was discovered, for which the treasurer was killed with stabs of a dagger, and then quartered. This Gaspar de Casada had his head cut off, and afterwards was cut into quarters; and the conductor having a few days later attempted another treason, was banished with a priest, and was put in that country called Pattagonia. The captain general would not put this conductor to death, because the Emperor Charles had made him captain of one of the ships.

Departing thence, we found in fifty-one degrees less one third (50° 40' S.), in the Antarctic, a river of fresh water, which was near causing us to be lost, from the great winds which it sent out; but God, of his favour, aided us. We were about two months in this river, as it supplied fresh water and a kind of fish an ell long, and very scaly, which is good to eat. Before going away, the captain chose that all should confess and receive the body of our Lord like good Christians.

After going and taking the course to the fifty-second degree of the said Antarctic sky, on the day of the Eleven Thousand Virgins (October 21), we found, by a miracle, a strait which we called the Cape of the Eleven Thousand Virgins, this strait is a hundred and ten leagues long, which are four hundred and forty miles, and almost as wide as less than half a league, and it issues in another sea; which is called the peaceful sea; it is surrounded by very great and high mountains covered with snow. In this place it was not possible to anchor with the anchors, because no bottom was found, on which account they were forced to put the moorings of twenty-five or thirty fathoms length on shore. This strait was a round place surrounded by mountains, as I have said, and the greater number of the sailors thought that there was no place by which to go out thence to enter into the peaceful sea. But the captain-general said that there was another strait for going out, and said that he knew it well, because he had seen it by a marine chart of the King of Portugal, which map had been made by a great pilot and mariner named Martin of Bohemia. The captain sent on before two of his ships, one named *St Anthony,* and the other the *Conception,* to seek for and discover the outlet of this strait, which was called the Cape de la Baya. And we, with the other two ships, that is to say, the flagship named *Trinitate,* and the other the *Victory,* remained waiting for them within the bay, where in the night we had a great storm, which lasted till the next day at midday, and during which we were forced to weigh the anchors and let the ships go hither and thither about the bay. The other two ships met with such a head wind that they could not weather a cape which the bay made almost at its extremity; wishing to come to us, they were near being driven to beach the ships. But, on approaching the extremity .of the bay, and whilst expecting to be lost, they saw a small mouth, which did not resemble a mouth but a corner, and (like people giving up hope) they threw themselves into it, so that by force they discovered the strait. Seeing that it was not a corner, but a strait of land, they went further on and found a bay, then going still further they found another strait and another bay larger than the first two, at which, being very joyous, they suddenly returned backwards to tell it to the captain-general. Amongst us we thought that they had perished: first because of the great storm; next, because two days had passed that we had not seen them. And being thus in doubt we saw the two ships under all sail, with ensigns spread, come towards us: these, when near us, suddenly discharged much artillery, atwhich we, very joyous, saluted them with artillery and shouts. Afterwards, all together, thanking God and the Virgin Mary, we went to seek further on.

After having entered inside this strait we found that there were two mouths, of which one trended to the Sirocco (S.E.) and the other to the Garbin (S.W.). On that account the captain again sent the two ships, *St Anthony* and *Conception,* to see if the mouth which was towards Sirocco had an outlet beyond into the said peaceful sea. One of these two ships, named *St Anthony,* would not wait for the other ship, because those who were inside wished to return to Spain: this they did, and the principal reason was on account of the pilot of the said ship being previously discontented with the said captain-general, because that before this armament was made, this pilot had gone to the Emperor to talk about having some ships to discover countries. But, on account of the arrival of the captain-general, the Emperor did not give them to this pilot. The other ship, named the *Conception,* not being able to follow that one, was always waiting for it, and fluttered hither and thither. But it lost its time, for the other took the road by night for returning.

When this happened, at night the ship of the captain and the other ship went together to discover the mouth to Garbin (S.W.), where, on always holding on our course, we found the same strait. But at the end we arrived at a river which we named the River of Sardines, because we found a great quantity of them. So we remained there four days to wait for the other two ships. A short time after we sent a boat well supplied with men and provisions to discover the cape of the other sea; these remained three days in going and coming. They told us that they had found the cape, and the sea great and wide. At the joy which the captain-general had at this he began to cry, and he gave the name of the Cape of Desire to this cape, as a thing which had been much desired for a long time.

Having done that we turned back to find the two ships which were at the other side, but we only found the *Conception,* of which ship we asked what had become of her companion. To this the captain of the said ship, named John Serrano, replied that he knew nothing of her, and that he had never seen her since she entered the mouth. However, we sought for her through all the strait, as far as the said mouth, by which she had taken her course to return. Besides that, the captain-general sent back the ship named the *Victory* as far as the entrance of the strait to see if the ship was there, and he told the people of this ship that if they did not find the ship they were looking for, they were to place an ensign on the summit of a small hill, with a letter inside a pot placed in the ground near the ensign, so that if the ship should by chance return, it might see that ensign, and also find the letter which would give information of the course which the captain was holding. This manner of acting had been ordained by the captain from the commencement, in order to effect the junction of any ship which might be separated from the others. So the people of the said ship did what the captain had commanded them, and more; for they set two ensigns with letters; one of the ensigns was placed on a small hill at the first bay, the other on an islet in the third bay, where there were many sea wolves and large birds. The captain-general waited for them with the other ship near the river named Isles: and he caused a cross to be set upon a small island in front of that river, which was between high mountains covered with snow. This river comes and falls into the sea near the other river of the Sardines.

If we had not found this strait the captain-general had made up his mind to go as far as seventy-five degrees towards the Antarctic pole; where at that height in the summer time there is no night, or very little: in a similar manner in the winter there is no day-light, or very little, and so that every one may believe this, when we were in this strait the night lasted only three hours, and this was in the month of October.

The land of this strait on the left-hand side looked towards the Sirocco wind, which is the wind collateral to the Levant and South; we called this strait Pathagonico. In it we found at every half league a good port and place for anchoring, good waters, wood all of cedar, and fish like sardines, missiglioni, and a very sweet herb named *appio* (celery). There is also some of the same kind which is bitter. This herb grows near the springs, and from not finding anything else we ate of it for several days. I think that there is not in the world a more beautiful country, or better strait than this one.

Wednesday, the twenty-eighth of November, 1520, we came forth out of the said strait, and entered into the Pacific Sea, where we remained three months and twenty days without taking in provisions or other refreshments, and we only ate old biscuit reduced to powder, and full of grubs, and stinking from the dirt which the rats had made on it when eating the good biscuit, and we drank water that was yellow and stinking. We also ate the ox hides which were under the main-yard, so that the yard should not break the rigging: they were very hard on account of the sun, rain, and wind, and we left them for four or five days in the sea, and then we put them a little on the embers, and so ate them; also the sawdust of wood, and rats which cost half-a-crown each, moreover enough of them were not to be got. Besides the above-named evils, this misfortune which I will mention was the worst, it was that the upper and lower gums of most of our men grew so much that they could not eat, and in this way so many suffered that nineteen died. Besides those who died, twenty-five or thirty fell ill of divers sicknesses, both in the arms and legs, and other places, in such manner that very few remained healthy. However, thanks be to the Lord, I had no sickness. During those three months and twenty days we went in an open sea, while we ran fully four thousand leagues in the Pacific sea. This was well named Pacific, for during this same time we met with no storm, and saw no land except two small uninhabited islands, in which we found only birds and trees. We named them the Unfortunate Islands; they are two hundred leagues apart from one another, and there is no place to anchor, as there is no bottom. There we saw many sharks, which are a kind of large fish which they call *Tiburoni.* The first Isle is in fifteen degrees of austral latitude, and the other island is in nine degrees. With the said wind we ran each day fifty or sixty leagues, or more; now with the wind astern, sometimes on a wind or otherwise. And if our Lord and his Mother had not aided us in giving us good weather to refresh ourselves with provisions and other things, we should all have died of hunger in this very vast sea, and I think that never man will undertake to perform such a voyage.

II

Friday, the 26th of April, Zula, who was one of the principal men or chiefs in the island of Matan, sent to the captain a son of his with two goats to make a present of them, and to say that if he did not do all that he had promised, the cause of that was another chief named Silapulapu, who would not in any way obey the King of Spain, and had prevented him from doing so: but that if the captain would send him the following night one boat full of men to give him assistance, he would fight and subdue his rival. On the receipt of this message, the captain decided to go himself with three boats. We entreated him much not to go to this enterprise in person, but he as a good shepherd would not abandon his flock.

We set out from Zubu at midnight, we were sixty men armed with corslets and helmets; there were with us the Christian king, the prince, and some of the chief men, and many others divided among twenty or thirty balangai. We arrived at Matan three hours before daylight. The captain before attacking wished to attempt gentle means, and sent on shore the Moorish merchant to tell those islanders who were of the party of Cilapulapu, that if they would recognize the Christian king as their sovereign, and obey the King of Spain, and pay us the tribute which had been askcd, the captain would become their friend, otherwise we should prove how our lances wounded. The islanders were not terrified, they replied that if we had lances, so also had they, although only of reeds, and wood hardened with fire. They asked however that we should not attack them by night, but wait for daylight, because they were expecting reinforcements, and would be in greater number. This they said with cunning, to excite us to attack them by night, supposing that we were ready; but they wished this because they had dug ditches between their houses and the beach, and they hoped that we should fall into them.

We however waited for daylight; and then we leaped into the water up to our thighs, for on account of the shallow water and the rocks, the boats could not come close to the beach, and we had to cross two good crossbow shots through the water before reaching it. We were fortynine in number, the other eleven remained in charge of the boats. When we reached land we found the islanders fifteen hundred in number, drawn up in three squadrons; they came down upon us with terrible shouts, two squadrons attacking us on the flanks, and the third in front. The captain then divided his men in two bands. Our musketeers and crossbow men fired for half an hour from a distance, but did nothing, since the bullets and arrows, though they passed through their shields made of thin wood, and perhaps wounded their arms, yet did not stop them. The captain shouted not to fire, but he was not listened to. The islanders seeing that the shots of our guns did them little or no harm would not retire, but shouted more loudly, and springing from one side to the other to avoid our shots, they at the same time drew nearer to us, throwing arrows, javelins, spears hardened in fire, stones, and even mud, so that we could hardly defend ourselves. Some of them cast lances pointed with iron at the captain-general.

He then, in order to disperse this multitude and to terrify them, sent some of our men to set fire to their houses, but this rendered them more ferocious. Some of them ran to the fire, which consumed twenty or thirty houses, and there killed two of our men. The rest came down upon us with greater fury; they perceived that our bodies were defended, but that the legs were exposed, and they aimed at them principally. The captain had his right leg pierced by a poisoned arrow, on which account he gave orders to retreat by degrees; but almost all our men took to precipitate flight, so that there remained hardly six or eight of us with him. We were oppressed by the lances and stones which the enemy hurled at us, and could make no more resistance. The bombards which we had in the boat were of no assistance to us, for the shoal water kept them too far from the beach. We went thither, retreating little by little, and still fighting, and we had already got to the distance of a crossbow shot from the shore, having the water up to our knees, the islanders following and picking up again the spears which they had already cast, and they threw the same spear five or six times; as they knew the captain they aimed specially at him, and twice they knocked the helmet off his head. He, with a few of us, like a good knight, remained at his post without choosing to retreat further. Thus we fought for more than an hour, until an Indian succeeded in thrusting a cane lance into the captain's face. He then, being irritated, pierced the Indian's breast with his lance, and left it in his body, and trying to draw his sword, he was unable to draw it more than half way, on account of a javelin wound which he had received in the right arm. The enemies seeing this, all rushed against him, and one of them with a great sword, like a great scimetar gave him a great blow on the left leg, which brought the captain down on his face; then the Indians threw themselves upon him, and ran him through with lances and scimetars, and all the other arms which they had, so that they deprived of life our mirror, light, comfort, and true guide. Whilst the Indians were thus overpowering him, several times he turned round towards us to see if we were all in safety, as though his obstinate fight had no other object than to give an opportunity for the retreat of his men. We who fought to extremity, and who were covered with wounds, seeing that he was dead, proceeded to the boats which were on the point of going away. This fatal battle was fought on the 27th of April of on a Saturday; a day which the captain had chosen himself, because he had a special devotion to it. There perished with him eight of our men, and four of the Indians, who had become Christians; we had also many wounded, amongst whom I must reckon myself. The enemy lost only fifteen men.

He died; but I hope that your illustrious highness will not allow his memory to be lost, so much the more since I see revived in you the virtue of so great a captain, since one of his principal virtues was constance in the most adverse fortune. In the midst of the sea he was able to endure hunger better than we. Most versed in nautical charts, he knew better than any other the true art of navigation, of which it is a certain proof that he knew by his genius, and his intrepidity, without anyone having given him the example, how to attempt the circuit of the globe, which he had almost completed.

THE CAPTIVE'S ESCAPE[1]

Miguel de Cervantes Saavedra (1547-1616)

IN LESS than fifteen days our renegado had bought a very good bark, capable of holding above thirty persons; and, to make sure work, and give the business a colour, he made a short voyage to a place called Sargel, thirty leagues from Algiers towards Oran, to which there is a great trade for dried figs. Two or three times he made this trip, in company of the Tagarin. You must know, that each time he passed with his bark, he cast anchor in a little creek, not two bow-shots distant from the garden, where Zoraida expected us: and there the renegado designedly set himself, together with the Moors that rowed, either to perform the zala, or to practise by way of jest what he intended to execute in earnest; and with this view he would go to Zoraida's garden, and beg some fruit, which her father would give him, without knowing who he was. His design was, as he afterwards told me, to speak to Zoraida and tell her that he was the person, who, by my direction, was to carry her to Christendom, and that she might be easy and secure: but it was impossible for him to do it, the Moorish women never suffering themselves to be seen either by Moor or Turk, unless when commanded by their husbands and fathers. But I should have been sorry if he had talked to her, because it might have frightened her, to see that the business was intrusted to a renegado. But God, who ordered it otherwise, gave the renegado no opportunity of effecting his good design: who, finding how securely he went to and from Sargel, and that he lay at anchor, when, how, and where, he pleased, and that the Tagarin, his partner, had no will of his own, but approved whatever he directed; that I was ransomed, and

[1] From the translation of *Don Quixote* by Charles Jarvis.

that there wanted nothing but to find some Christians to help to row; he bid me consider who I would bring with me, besides those already ransomed, and bespeak them for the first Friday; for that was the time he fixed for our departure. Upon this I spoke to twelve Spaniards, all able men at the oar, and such as could most easily get out of the city unsuspected: and it was no easy matter to find so many at that juncture; for there were twenty corsairs out pirating, and they had taken almost all the rowers with them; and these had not been found, but that their master did not go out that summer, having a galiot to finish, that was then upon the stocks. I said nothing more to them, but that they should steal out of the town one by one, the next Friday in the dusk of the evening, and wait for me somewhere about Agimorato's garden. I gave this direction to each of them separately, with this caution, that, if they should see any other Christians there, they should only say, I ordered them to stay for me in that place.

"This point being taken care of, one thing was yet wanting, and that the most necessary of all; which was, to inform Zoraida how matters stood, that she might be in readiness, and on the watch, so as not to be frightened if we rushed upon her on a sudden, before the time she could think that the vessel from Christendom could be arrived. And therefore I resolved to go to the garden, and try if I could speak to her: and under pretence of gathering some herbs, one day before our departure I went thither, and the first person I met was her father, who spoke to me in a language, which all over Barbary, and even at Constantinople, is spoken among captives and Moors, and is neither Morisco nor Castilian, nor of any other nation, but a medley of all languages, and generally understood. He, I say, in that jargon, asked me what I came to look for in that garden, and to whom I belonged? I answered him, I was a slave of Arnauté Mamai, who, I knew, was a very great friend of his; and that I came for a few herbs of several sorts to make a sallad. He then asked me if I was upon ransom or not, and how much my master demanded for me? While we were thus talking, the fair Zoraida, who had espied me some time before, came out of the house: and, as the Moorish women make no scruple of appearing before the Christians, nor are at all shy towards them, as I have already observed, she made no difficulty of coming where I stood with her father, who, seeing her walking slowly towards us, called to her, and bid her come on. It would be too hard a task for me, at this time, to express the great beauty, the finery and richness of attire, with which my beloved Zoraida appeared then before my eyes. More pearls, if I may say so, hung about her beauteous neck, and more jewels were in her ears and hair, than she had hairs on her head. In short, she came extremely adorned, and extremely beautiful; to me at least she seemed the most so of any thing I had ever beheld: which, together with my obligations to her, made me think her an angel from heaven, descended for my pleasure and relief.

"When she was come up to us, her father told her, in her own tongue, that I was a captive belonging to his friend Arnauté Mamai, and that I came to look for a sallad. She took up the discourse, and in the aforesaid medley of languages, asked me whether I was a gentleman, and why I did not ransom myself. I told her I was already ransomed, and by the price she might guess what my master thought of me, since he had got fifteen hundred pieces of eight for me. To which she answered: 'Truely had you belonged to my father, he should not have parted with you for twice that sum: for you Christians always falsify in your accounts of yourselves, pretending to be poor, in order to cheat the Moors.'—'It may very well be so, madam,' answered I; 'but in truth, I dealt sincerely with my master, and ever did and shall do the same by everybody in the world.' 'And when you go away ?' said Zoraida. 'To-morrow I believe,' said I: 'for there is a French vessel which sails to-morrow, and I intend to go in her.'—'Would it not be better,' replied Zoraida, 'to stay until some ships come from Spain, and go with them, and not with those of France, who are not your friends?'—'No, madam,' answered I; 'but should the news we have of a Spanish ship's coming suddenly prove true, I would perhaps stay a little for it, though it is more likely I shall depart to-morrow: for the desire I have to be in my own country, and with the persons I love, is so great, that it will not suffer me to wait for any other conveniency, though ever so much better.'—'You are married, doubtless, in your own country?' said Zoraida, 'and therefore you are so desirous to be gone, and be at home with your wife?'—'No,' replied I, 'I am not married; but I have given my word to marry as soon as I get thither.'—'And is the lady whom you have promised beautiful?' said Zoraida. 'So beautiful,' answered I, 'that to compliment her, and tell you the truth, she is very like yourself.' Her father laughed heartily at this, and said: 'Really, Christian, she must be beautiful indeed, if she resembles my daughter, who is accounted the handsomest woman in all this kingdom: observe her well, and you will see I speak the truth.' Zoraida's father served us as an interpreter to most of this conversation, as understanding Spanish; for though she spoke the bastard language in use there, as I told you, yet she expressed her meaning more by signs than by words.

"While we were thus engaged in discourse, a Moor came running to us, crying aloud that four Turks had leaped over the pales or wall of the garden, and were gathering the fruit, though it was not yet ripe. The old man was put into a fright, and so was Zoraida: for the Moors are naturally afraid of the Turks, especially of their soldiers, who are insolent and imperious. Therefore Zoraida's father said to her; 'Daughter, retire into the house, and lock yourself in, while I go and talk to these dogs; and you, Christian, gather your herbs, and be gone in peace, and Alla send you safe to your own country.' I bowed myself, and he went his way to find the Turks, leaving me alone with Zoraida, who also made as if she was going whither her father bid her. But scarcely was he got out of sight among the trees of the garden, when she turned back to me, with her eyes full of tears, and said: 'Amexi, Christiano, amexi?' that is, *'Are you going away, Christian, are you going away?'* I answered, 'Yes, madam, but not without you: expect me the next Juma, and be not frightened when you see us; for we shall certainly get to Christendom.' I said this in such a manner, that she understood me very well; and throwing her arm about my neck, she began to walk softly and trembling towards the house: and fortune would have it, which might have proved fatal, if heaven had not ordained otherwise, that, while we were going in the posture and manner I told you, her arm being about my neck, her father returning from driving away the Turks, saw us in that posture, and we were sensible that he discovered us. But Zoraida had the discretion and presence of mind not to take her arm from about my neck, but rather held me closer; and leaning her head against my breast, and bending her knees a little, gave plain signs of fainting away: and I also made as if I held her up only to keep her from falling. Her father came running to us, and seeing his daughter in that posture, asked what ailed her. But she not answering, he said: 'Without doubt, these dogs have frightened her into a swoon': and taking her from me, he inclined her gently to his bosom. And she fetching a deep sigh, and her eyes still full of tears, said again: 'Amexi, Christiano, amexi': *Begone, Christian, begone.* To which her father answered: 'There is no occasion, child, why the Christian should go away: he has done you no harm, and the Turks are gone off: let nothing frighten you; there is no danger.' 'Sir,' said I to her father, 'they have frightened her, as you say; but, since she bids me be gone, I will not disturb her: God be with you, and with your leave, I will come again, if we have occasion for herbs.' I now took my leave of them both, and she, seeming as if her soul had been rent from her, went away with her father. And I, under pretence of gathering herbs, walked over and took a view of the whole garden at my leisure, observing carefully all the inlets and outlets, and the strength of the house, and every conveniency which might tend to facilitate our business.

"When I had so done, I went and gave an account to the renegado and my companions of all that had passed, longing eagerly for the hour when, without fear of surprise, I might enjoy the happiness which fortune presented me in the beautiful Zoraida. In a word, time passed on, and the day appointed, and by us so much wished for, came; and we all observing the order and method which after mature deliberation and long debate we had agreed on, had the desired success. For the Friday following the day when I talked with Zoraida in the garden, Morrenago, for that was the renegado's name, at the close of the evening cast anchor with the bark almost opposite to whereZoraida dwelt. The Christians who were to be employed at the oar were ready and hidden in several places thereabouts. They were all in suspense, their hearts beating in expectation of my coming, being eager to surprise the bark which lay before their eyes: for they knew nothing of what was concerted with the renegado, but thought they were to regain their liberty by mere force, and by killing the Moors who were on board the vessel. As soon, therefore, as I and my friends appeared, all they that were hidden came out and joined us one after another. It was now the time when the city gates were shut, and nobody appeared abroad in all that quarter. Being met together, we were in some doubt whether it would be better to go first to Zoraida, or secure the Moors who rowed the vessel. While we were in this uncertainty, our renegado came to us, asking us what we staid for; for now was the time, all his Moors being thoughtless of danger, and most of them asleep. We told him what we demurred about, and he said, that the thing of the most importance was, first to seize the vessel, which might be done with all imaginable ease, and without any manner of danger; and then we might presently go and fetch Zoraida. We all approved of what he said, and so, without further delay, he being our guide, we came to the vessel; and he leaping in first, drew a cutlass, and said in Morisco: 'Let not one man of you stir, unless he has a mind it should cost him his life.' By this time all the Christians were got on board; and the Moors, who were timorous fellows, hearing the master speak thus, were in a great fright; and, without making any resistance, for indeed they had few or no arms, silently suffered themselves to be bound, which was done very expeditiously, the Christians threatening the Moors that if they raised any manner of cry, or made the least noise, they would in that instant put them all to the sword.

"This being done, and half our number remaining on board to guard them, the rest of us, the renegado being still our leader, went to Agimorato's garden, and as good luck would have it, the door opened as easily to us as if it had not been locked: and we came up to the house with great stillness and silence, and without being perceived by anyone. The lovely Zoraida was expecting us at a window, and when she knew it was I, she staid not a moment, but came down in an instant, and opening the door, appeared to us all so beautiful and richly attired that I cannot easily express it. As soon as I saw her I took her hand and kissed it: the renegado did the same, and my two comrades also, and the rest, who knew not the meaning of it, followed our example, thinking we only meant to express our thanks and acknowledgments to her as the instrument of our deliverance. The renegado asked her in Morisco, whether her father was in the house: she answered he was, and asleep. 'Then we must awaken him,' replied the renegado, 'and carry him with us, and all that he has of value in this beautiful villa.'—'No' said she, 'my father must by no means be touched, and there is nothing considerable here but what I have with me, which is sufficient to make you all rich and content: stay a little, and you shall see.' And so saying, she went in again, and bid us be quiet, and make no noise, for she would come back immediately. I asked the renegado what she said: he told me, and I bid him be sure to do just as Zoraida would have him, who was now returned with a little trunk so full of gold crowns, that she could hardly carry it.

"Ill fortune would have it, that her father in the meantime happened to awake, and hearing a noise in the garden, looked out at the window, and presently found there were Christians in it. Immediately he cried out as loud as he could in Arabic, 'Christians, Christians, thieves, thieves!' which outcry put all into the utmost terror and confusion. But the renegado seeing the danger we were in and considering how much it imported him to go through with the enterprise before it was discovered, ran up with the greatest speed to the room where Agimorato was; and with him ran up several others: but I did not dare to quit Zoraida, who had sunk into my arms almost in a swoon. In short, they that went up acquitted themselves so well, that in a moment they came down with Agimorato, having tied his hands, and stopped his mouth with a handkerchief, so that he could not speak a word, and threatening, if he made the least noise, that it should cost him his life. When his daughter saw him she covered her eyes, that she might avoid his sight, and her father was astonished at finding her, not knowing how willingly she had put herself into our hands. But at that time, it being of the utmost consequence to us to fly, we got as speedily as we could to the bark, where our comrades already expected us with impatience, fearing we had met with some cross accident. Scarcely two hours of the night were passed, when we were all got on board, and then we untied the hands of Zoraida's father, and took the handkerchief out of his mouth: but the renegado warned him again not to speak a word; for if he did they would take away his life. When he saw his daughter there, he began to weep most tenderly, and especially when he perceived that I held her closely embraced, and that she, without making any show of opposition, complaint, or coyness, sat so still and quiet: nevertheless he held his peace, lest we should put the renegado's threats in execution.

"Zoraida now finding herself in the bark, and that we began to handle our oars, and seeing her father there, and the rest of the Moors, who were bound, spoke to the renegado, to desire me to do her the favour to loose those Moors, and set her father at liberty; for she would sooner throw herself into the sea, than see a father, who loved her so tenderly, carried away captive before her eyes, and upon her account. The renegado told me what she desired, and I answered that I was entirely satisfied it should be so: but he replied it was not convenient; for should they be set on shore there, they would presently raise the country and alarm the city, and cause some light frigates to be sent out in quest of us, and so we should be beset both by sea and land, and it would be impossible for us to escape: but what might be done was, to give them their liberty at the first Christian country we should touch at. We all came into this opinion, and Zoraida also was satisfied when we told her what we had determined, and the reasons why we could not at present comply with her request. And then immediately, with joyful silence and cheerful diligence, each of our brave rowers handled his oar, and recommending ourselves to God with all our hearts, we began to make toward the island of Majorca, which is the nearest Christian land. But the north wind beginning to blow fresh, and the sea being somewhat rough, it was not possible for us to steer the course of Majorca, and we were forced to keep along shore towards Oran, not without great apprehensions of being discovered from the town of Sargel, which lies on that coast, about sixty miles from Algiers. We were afraid, likewise, of meeting in our passage with some of those galiots which came usually with merchandise from Tetuan; though, each relying on his own courage and that of his comrades in general, we presumed that, if we should meet a galiot, provided it were not a cruiser, we should be so far from being ruined, that we should probably take a vessel in which we might more securely pursue our course. While we proceeded in our voyage, Zoraida kept her head between my hands, that she might not look on her father; and I could perceive she was continually calling upon Lela Marien to assist us.

"We had rowed about thirty miles, when day-break came upon us, and we found ourselves not above three musket-shot distant from the shore, which seemed to be quite a desert, and without any creature to discover us: however, by mere dint of rowing, we made a little out to sea, which was by this time become more calm; and when we had advanced about two leagues, it was ordered they should row by turns, whilst we took a little refreshment, the bark being well provided, but the rowers said, that it was not a time to take any rest, and that they would by no means quit their oars, but would eat and row, if those who were unemployed would bring the victuals to them. They did so; and now the wind began to blow a brisk gale, which forced us to set up our sails, lay down our oars, and steer directly to Oran, it being impossible to hold any other course. All this was done with great expedition; and we sailed above eight miles an hour, without any other fear than that of meeting some corsair. We gave the Moorish prisoners something to eat, and the renegado comforted them, telling them they were not slaves, and that they should have their liberty given them the first opportunity, and he said the same to Zoraida's father, who answered: 'I might, perhaps, expect or hope for any other favour from your liberality and generous usage, O Christians; but as to giving me my liberty, think me not so simple as to imagine it; for you would never have exposed yourselves to the hazard of taking it from me, to restore it me so freely, especially since you know who I am, and the advantage that may accrue to you by my ransom; which do but name, and from this moment I promise you whatever you demand for myself and for this my unhappy daughter, or else for her alone, who is the greater and better part of my soul.' In saying this he began to weep so bitterly, that it moved us all to compassion, and forced Zoraida to look up at him; who seeing him weep in that manner, was so melted, that she got up from me, and ran to embrace her father; and laying her face to his, they began so tender a lamentation that many of us could not forbear keeping them company. But when her father observed that she was adorned with her best attire, and had so many jewels about her, he said to her in his language: 'How comes it, daughter, that yesterday evening, before this terrible misfortune befell us, I saw you in your ordinary household dress, and now, I see you set off with the best clothes that I could possibly give you, when fortune was more favourable to us?' The renegado interpreted to us all that the Moor said to his daughter, who answered him not a word: but when he saw in a corner of the vessel the little trunk in which she used to keep her jewels, which he knew very well he had left in Algiers, and had not brought with him to the garden, he was still more confounded, and asked her how that trunk had come to our hands, and what was in it; to which the renegado, without staying until Zoraida spoke, answered—'Trouble not yourself, Signor, about asking your daughter so many questions; for with one word I can satisfy them all: and therefore be it known to you, that she is a Christian, and has been the instrument to file off our chains, and give us the liberty we enjoy: she is here with her own consent, and well pleased, I believe, to find herself in this condition, like one who goes out of darkness into light, from death to life, and from suffering to glory.'—'Is this true, daughter?' said the Moor. 'It is,' answered Zoraida. 'In effect then,' replied the old man, 'you are become a Christian, and are she who has put her father into the power of his enemies?' To which Zoraida answered: '1 am indeed a Christian; but not she who has reduced you to this condition: for my desire never was to do you harm, but only myself good.' 'And what good have you done yourself, my daughter?' 'Ask that,' answered she, 'of Lela Marien, who can tell you better than I can.'

"The Moor had scarcely heard this when, with incredible precipitation, he threw himself headlong into the sea, and without doubt had been drowned, if the wide and cumbersome garments he wore had not kept him a little while above water. Zoraida cried out to save him; and we all presently ran, and laying hold of his garments dragged him out, half drowned and senseless; at which sight Zoraida was so affected, that she set up a tender and sorrowful lamentation over him, as if he had been dead. We turned him with his mouth downward, and he voided a great deal of water, and in about two hours came to himself.

"In the mean time the wind being changed, we were obliged to ply our oars to avoid running upon the shore: but by good fortune we came to a creek by the side of a small promontory, or head, which by the Moors is called the cave of Cava Rumia, that is to say, in our language, *The Wicked Christian Woman;* for the Moors have a tradition, that Cava, who occasioned the loss of Spain, lies burried there; Cava signifying in their language a *wicked woman,* and Rumia, *a Christian;*

and farther, they reckon it an ill omen to be forced to anchor there; and otherwise they never do so: though to us it proved, not the shelter of a wicked woman, but a safe harbour and retreat, considering how high the sea ran. We placed scouts on shore, and never dropped our oars: we eat of what the renegado had provided, and prayed to God and to Our Lady very devoutly for assistance and protection, that we might give a happy ending to so fortunate a beginning. Order was given, at Zoraida's entreaty, to set her father on shore with the rest of the Moors, who, until now, had been fast bound; for she had not the heart, nor could her tender feelings brook, to see her father and her countrymen carried off prisoners before her face. We promised her it should be done at our going off, since there was no danger in leaving them in so desolate a place. Our prayers were not in vain: heaven heard them; for the wind presently changed in our favour, and the sea was calm, inviting us to return and prosecute our intended voyage.

"Seeing this, we unbound the Moors, and set them one by one on shore, at which they were greatly surprised: but when we came to disembark Zoraida's father, who was now perfectly in his senses, he said: 'Why, Christians, think you, is this wicked woman desirous of my being set at liberty? Think you it is out of any filial piety she has towards me? No, certainly, but it is on account of the disturbance my presence would give her when she has a mind to put her evil inclinations in practice. And think not that she is moved to change her religion because she thinks yours is preferable to ours: no, but because she knows that libertinism is more allowed in your country than in ours.' And turning to Zoraida, whilst I and another Christian held him fast by both arms, lest he should commit some outrage, he said: 'O infamous girl, and illadvised maiden! whither goest thou blindfold and precipitate, in the power of these dogs, our natural enemies? Cursed be the hour in which I begat thee, and cursed be the indulgence and luxury in which I brought thee up!' But perceiving he was not likely to give over in haste, I hurried him ashore, and from thence he continued his execrations and wailings, praying to Mahomet that he would beseech God to destroy, confound, and make an end of us: and when, being under sail, we could no longer hear his words, we saw his actions; which were, tearing his beard, plucking off his hair, and rolling himself on the ground: and once he raised his voice so high, that we could hear him say: 'Come back, beloved daughter, come back to shore; for I forgive thee all:let those men keep the money they already have, and do thou come back, and comfort thy disconsolate father, who must lose his life in this desert land, if thou forsakest him.' All this Zoraida heard; all this she felt and bewailed; but could not speak nor answer him a word. So I comforted Zoraida, and we all minded our voyage, which was now made so easy to us by a favourable wind, that we made no doubt of being next morning upon the coast of Spain.

"But as good seldom or never comes pure and unmixed, without being accompanied or followed by some ill, it happened, that being now got far out to sea, and the third hour of the night well nigh past; being under full sail, and the oars being lashed, for the fair wind eased us of the labour of making use of them,—by the light of the moon, which shone very bright, we discovered a round vessel with all her sails out a little ahead of us, but so very near that we were forced to strike sail to avoid running foul of her; and they also put the helm hard up to give us room to go by. The men had posted themselves on the quarter-deck to ask who we were, whither we were going, and from whence we came: but asking us in French, our renegado said, 'Let no one answer; for these, without doubt, are French corsairs, to whom all is fish that comes to net.' Upon this caution nobody spoke a word: and having sailed a little on, their vessel being under the wind, on a sudden they let fly two pieces of artillery, and both, as it appeared, with chain-shot, for one cut our mast through the middle, which, with the sail, fell into the sea, and the other at the same instant came through the middle of our bark, so as to lay it quite open without wounding any of us. But finding ourselves sinking, we all began to cry aloud for help, and to beg of those in the ship to take us in, for we were drowning. They then struck their sails, and hoisting out the boat or pinnace, with about twelve Frenchmen in her, well armed with muskets, and their matches lighted, they came up close to us, and seeing how few we were, and that the vessel was sinking, they took us in, telling us, that this had befallen us because of our incivility in returning them no answer. Our renegado took the trunk, in which was Zoraida's treasure, and without being perceived by any one, threw it overboard into the sea. In short, we all passed into the French ship, where, after they had informed themselves of whatever they had a mind to know concerning us, immediately, as if they had been our capital enemies, they stripped us of every thing, and Zoraida even of the bracelets she wore upon her ancles: but the uneasiness they gave her, gave me less than the apprehension I was in, lest they should proceed from plundering her of her rich and precious jewels, to the depriving her of the jewel of most worth, and that which she valued most. But the desires of this sort of men seldom extend farther than money, with which their avarice is never satisfied, as was evident at that time; for they would have taken away the very clothes we wore as slaves, if they had thought they could have made anything of them. Some of them were of opinion it would be best to throw us all overboard, wrapped up in a sail: for their design was to trade in some of the Spanish ports, pretending to be of Brittany; and should they carry us with them thither, they would be seized on and punished, upon discovery of the robbery. But the captain, who had rifled my dear Zoraida, said he was contented with the prize he had already got, and that he would not touch at any port of Spain, but pass the Straits of Gibraltar by night, or as he could, and make the best of his way for Rochelle, from whence he came; and therefore, in conclusion, they agreed to give us their ship-boat, and what was necessary for so short a voyage as we had to make: which they did the next day in view of the Spanish coast; at which sight all our troubles and miseries were forgotten as entirely as if they had never happened to us; so great is the pleasure of regaining one's lost liberty. It was about noon when they put us into the boat, giving us two barrels of water and some biscuit; and the captain, moved by I know not what compassion, gave the beautiful Zoraida at her going off, about forty crowns in gold, and would not permit his soldiers to strip her of these very clothes she has now on.

"We went on board, giving them thanks for the favour they did us and showing ourselves rather pleased than dissatisfied. They stood out to sea, steering towards the Straits; and we, without minding any other north-star than the land before us, rowed so hard that we were at sunset so near it that we might easily, we thought, get thither before the night should be far spent: but the moon not shining, and the sky being cloudy, as we did not know the coast we were up on, we did not think it safe to land, as several among us would have had us, though it were among the rocks, and far from any town; for by that means they said, we should avoid the danger we ought to fear from the corsairs of Tetuan, who are over-night in Barbary, and the next morning on the coast of Spain, where they commonly pick up some prize, and return to sleep at their own homes. However, it was agreed at last that we should row gently towards the shore, and if the sea proved calm, we should land wherever we could. We did so; and a little before midnight we arrived at the foot of a very large and high mountain, not so close to the shore but there was room enough for our landing commodiously. We ran our boat into the sand; we all got on shore and kissed the ground, and, with tears of joy and satisfaction, gave thanks to God our Lord for the un-paralleled mercy he had shown us in our voyage.

THE INVINCIBLE ARMADA[1]

James Anthony Froude

(1818-1894)

ALL being thus in order, the Duke of Medina Sidonia sailed from Lisbon on the 19th-29th of May. The northerly breeze which prevails on the coast of Portugal was unusually strong. The galleons standing high out of the water, and carrying small canvas in proportion to their size, worked badly to windward. They

[1] From *The History of England*.

were three weeks in reaching Finisterre where, the wind having freshened to a gale, they were scattered, some standing out to sea, some into the Bay of Biscay. Their orders, in the event of such a casualty, had been to make for Ferrol. The wind shifting suddenly to the west, those that had gone into the Bay could not immediately reach it, and were driven into Santander. The officers, however, were, on the whole, well satisfied with the qualities which the ships had displayed. A mast or two had been sprung, a few yards and bowsprits had been carried away; but beyond loss of time there had been no serious damage.

The weather moderating, the fleet was again collected in the Bay of Ferrol by the 6th-16th of July. All repairs were completed by the 11th-21st, and the next day, the 12th-22nd, the Armada took leave of Spain for the last time.

The scene as the fleet passed out of the harbour must have been singularly beautiful. It was a treacherous interval of real summer. The early sun was lighting the long chain of the Galician mountains, marking with shadows the cleft defiles, and shining softly on the white walls and vineyards of Coruña. The wind was light, and falling towards a calm; the great galleons drifted slowly with the tide on the purple water, the long streamers trailing from the trucks, the red crosses, the emblem of the crusade, shewing bright upon the hanging sails. The fruit boats were bringing off the last fresh supplies, and the pinnaces hastening to the ships with the last loiterers on shore. Out of thirty thousand men who that morning stood upon the decks of the proud Armada, twenty thousand and more were never again to see the hills of Spain. Of the remnant who in two short months crept back ragged and torn, all but a few hundred returned only to die.

The Spaniards, though a great people, were usually over conscious of their greatness, and boasted too loudly of their fame and prowess; but among the soldiers and sailors of the doomed expedition against England, the national vainglory was singularly silent. They were the flower of the country, culled and chosen over the entire Peninsula, and they were going with a modest nobility upon a service which they knew to be dangerous, but which they believed to be peculiarly sacred. Every one, seaman, officer, and soldier, had confessed and communicated before he went on board. Gambling, swearing, profane language of all kinds had been peremptorily forbidden. Private quarrels and differences had been made up or suspended. The loose women who accompanied Spanish armies, and sometimes Spanish ships to sea, had been ordered away, and no unclean thing or person permitted to defile the Armada; and in every vessel, and in the whole fleet, the strictest order was prescribed and observed. Medina Sidonia led the way in the *San Martin,* showing lights at night, and firing guns when the weather was hazy. Mount's Bay was to be the next place of rendezvous if they were again separated.

On the first evening the wind dropped to a calm. The morning after, the 13th-

23rd, a fair fresh breeze came up from the south and southwest; the ships ran flowingly before it; and in two days and nights they had crossed the bay, and were off Ushant. The fastest of the pinnaces was dispatched from thence to Parma, with a letter bidding him expect the Duke's immediate coming.

But they had now entered the latitude of the storms which through the whole season had raged round the English shore. The same night a south west gale overtook them. They lay to, not daring to run further. The four galleys unable to keep the sea were driven in upon the French coast, and wrecked. The *Santa Ana,* a galleon of eight hundred tons, went down, carrying with her ninety seamen, three hundred soldiers, and fifty thousand ducats in gold. The weather was believed to be under the peculiar care of God, and this first misfortune was of evil omen for the future. The storm lasted two days, and then the sky cleared, and again gathering into order, they proceeded on their way. On the 19th-29th, they were in the mouth of the Channel. At daybreak on the morning of the 20th-30th the Lizard was under their lee, and an English fishing-boat was hanging near them, counting their numbers. They gave chase; but the boat shot away down wind and disappeared. They captured another an hour or two later, from which they learnt the English fleet was in Plymouth, and Medina Sidonia called a council of war, to consider whether they should go in, and fall upon it while at anchor. Philip's orders, however, were peremptory that they should turn neither right nor left, and make straight for Margate roads and Parma. The Duke was unenterprising, and consciously unequal to his work; and already bending under his responsibilities he hesitated to add to them.

Had he decided otherwise it would have made no difference, for the opportunity was not allowed him. Long before the Spaniards saw the Lizard they had themselves been seen, and on the evening of the 19th-29th, the beacons along the coast had told England that the hour of its trial was come.

TRAFALGAR[1]

Beneto Perez Galdos
(1845-1920)

IT WAS the 18th of October. I can have no doubt as to the date because the fleet sailed out of the bay next day. We rose very early and went down to the quay, where a boat was waiting to carry us on board.

[1] From Clara Bell's translation of *Trafalgar*.

Imagine, if you can, my surprise—nay, surprise do I say?—my enthusiasm, my rapture, when I found myself on board the *Santísima Trinidad,* the largest vessel on the main, that floating fortress of timber which, seen from a distance, had appeared to my fancy some portentous and supernatural creature; such a monster as alone was worthy of the majesty of the seas. Each time our boat passed under the side of a ship I examined it with a sort of religious astonishment, wondering to see the hulls so huge that from the ramparts had looked so small; and in the wild enthusiasm that possessed me I ran the greatest danger of falling into the water as I gazed in ecstasy at a figurehead—an object which fascinated me more than anything else.

At last we reached the *Santísima Trinidad.* As we approached, the colossal mass loomed larger and larger, and when the launch pulled up alongside, lost in the black transparent void made where its vast shadow fell upon the water—when I saw the huge hulk lying motionless on the dark waves which gently plashed against the side—when I looked up and saw the three tiers of cannon with their threatening muzzles thrust through the portholes—my excitement was changed to fear; I turned pale and sat silent and motionless by my master's side.

But when we went up the side and stood on deck my spirits rose. The intricate and lofty rigging, the busy scene on the quarter-deck, the open view of the sky and bay, the perfect order of everything on deck, from the hammocks lashed in a row to the bulwarks, to the capstans, shells, windsails, and hatchways; the variety of uniforms—everything I saw, in short, amazed me to such a degree that for some time I stood blankly gazing at the stupendous structure, heedless of all else ....

The *Santísima Trinidad* had four decks; the largest ships in the world had but three. This giant, constructed in Havana, in 1769, of the finest woods of Cuba, could reckon thirty-six years of honourable service. She measured 220 feet from stem to stern, 58 feet in the waist, that is to say in width, and 28 feet deep from the keel to the deck, measurements which no other vessel at the time could approach. Her huge ribs, which were a perfect forest, supported four decks. When she was first built 116 portholes gaped in her sides which were thick walls of timber; after she was enlarged in 1796 she had 130, and when she was newly fitted in 1805 she was made to carry 140 guns, cannons and carronades. The interior was a marvel of arrangement; there were decks for the guns, the forecastle for the crew, holds for stores of all kinds, state-cabins for the officers, the galley, the cock-pit and other offices. I was quite bewildered as I ran through the passages and endless nooks of this floating fortress. The stern cabins on the main deck were a little palace within, and outside like some fantastic castle; the galleries, the flag-turrets at the corners of the poop—exactly like the oriels of a Gothic tower—looked like huge cages open to the sea, whence the eye could command three quarters of the horizon.

Nothing could be grander than the rigging—those gigantic masts thrust up to heaven like a menace to the storm. It was difficult to believe that the wind could have strength enough to fill those vast sails. The eye lost its way and became weary in gazing at the maze of the rigging with the shrouds, stays, braces, halyards, and other ropes used to haul and reef the various sails . . . .

In the cabin I found my master eagerly conversing with the captain in command of the ship, Don Francisco Xavier de Uriarte, and the commander of the squadron, Don Baltasar Hidalgo de Cisneros. From what I overheard I could have no doubt that the French admiral had ordered the fleets to put to sea the next morning . . . .

The fleet was to sail out of the bay next morning—what joy! To ride the seas in this immense vessel—the largest in the world; to witness a fight at sea; to see what a battle was like, how cannon were fired, how the enemy's ships were taken—what a splendid triumph!and then to return to Cadiz covered with glory. To say afterwards to all who cared to hear: "Yes, I was there, I was on board, I saw it all . . ." To tell Rosita too, describing the glorious scene, winning her attention, her curiosity, her interest. To say to her: "Oh yes! I was in the most dangerous places and I was not afraid:"—and to see her turn pale with alarm, or faint, as she heard my tale of the horrors of the battle—and then to look down in contempt on all who would ask me: "Tell us, Gabrielito, was it so terrible after all?" All this was more than enough to fire my imagination, and I may frankly say that I would not, that day, have changed places with Nelson himself.

The morning of the 19th dawned, the day I hailed so eagerly; indeed it had not yet dawned when I found myself at the stern of the vessel with my master, who wanted to look on at the working of the ship. After clearing the decks the business of starting the ship began. The huge topsails were hoisted, and the heavy windlass, turning with a shrill clatter, dragged the anchor up from the bottom of the bay. The sailors clambered along the yards, while others handled the braces, obedient to the boatswain's call; and all the ship's voices, hitherto mute, filled the air with threatening outcries. The whistles, the bell, the discordant medley of men's voices, mixed with the creaking of the blocks, the humming of the ropes, the flapping of the sails as they thrashed the mast before they caught the wind—all these various sounds filled the air as the huge ship got under way. The bright ripples seemed to caress her sides, and the majestic monster made her way out of the bay without the slightest roll or even lurch, with a slow and solemn advance which was only perceptible to those on board by watching the apparent motion of the merchantmen lying at anchor and the landscape beyond.

At this moment I stood looking back at the scene behind us. And what a scene it was! Thirty-two men-of-war, five frigates, and two brigantines, Spanish and French together—some in front, some behind, and some abreast of us—were bursting into sail, as it were, and riding before the light breeze. 1 never saw a lovelier morning. The sun flooded those lovely shores with light; a faint purple tinge coloured the sea to the east, and the chain of hills which bound the horizon on the side of the town seemed to be on fire in the sunrise; the sky was perfectly clear excepting where, in the east, a few rose and golden clouds floated above the horizon. The blue sea was calm, and over that sea and beneath that sky the forty ships with their white sails rode forward, one of the noblest fleets that human eyes ever rested on.

The vessels did not all sail with equal speed. Some got ahead, others were slow to get under way; some gained upon us, while we passed others. The solemnity of their advance, the height of their masts, covered with canvas, and a vague and obscure harmony which my childish ears fancied they could detect proceeding from those glorious hulls—a kind of hymn, which was no doubt the effect of my own imagination—the loveliness of the day, the crispness of the air, the beauty of the sea, which seemed to be dancing with joy outside the gulf at the approach of the vessels—all formed the grandest picture that the mind of man can conceive of.

Cadiz, itself, like a moving panorama, unfolded itself before our eyes, displaying in turn every aspect of its vast amphitheatre. The low sun, illuminating the glass in its myriad windows, sprinkled it with living sparks of gold, and its buildings lay so purely white above the blue water that it looked as if it might have been that moment called into being, or raised from the sea like the fanciful city of San Genaro. I could see the wall extending from the mole as far as the fort of Santa Catalina; I could distinguish the bastions of Bonete and Orejon, and recognize the *Calete*; and my pride rose as I reflected what I had risen from and where I now was. At the same time the sound of the bells of the waking city came to my ears like some mysterious music, calling the inhabitants to early mass, with all the confused clamour of the bells of a large town. Now they seemed to me to ring gladly, and send good wishes after us—I listened to them as if they were human voices bidding us God-speed; then again they tolled sadly and dolefully—a knell of misfortune; and as we sailed further and further away their music grew fainter till it was lost in space.

The fleet slowly made its way out of the bay—some of the ships taking several hours in getting fairly to sea. Marcial meanwhile made his comments on each, watching their behaviour, laughing them to scorn if they were clumsy, and encouraging them with paternal advice if they were swift and well-handled.

"What a lump that Don Federico is!" he exclaimed as he looked at the *Príncipe de Asturias* commanded by Gravina. "There goes Mr Corneta,[1]" he exclaimed as

[1] Admiral Villeneuve.

he saw the *Bucentaure* with Villeneuve on board. "He was a clever man that called you the *Rayo!*" (Thunderbolt) he cried ironically, as he watched the ship so named, which was the least manageable of all the fleet. "Well done *Papá Ignacio!*" he added, pointing to the *Santa Ana* commanded by Alava.

"Hoist your topsail properly, senseless oaf!" he went on, addressing Dumanoir's ship, *Le Formidable.* "That Frenchman keeps a hairdresser to crimp the topsail and to clew up the sails with curling tongs."

Towards evening the sky clouded over, and as night fell we could see Cadiz, already at a great distance, gradually vanish in the mist till the last faint outline became one with the darkness. The fleet then steered to the southward.

All night I kept close to Marcial, as soon as I had seen my master comfortably settled in his cabin. The old sailor, eagerly listened to by a couple of veteran comrades and admirers, was explaining Villeneuve's plan of battle.

"Mr Corneta," said he, "has divided the fleet into four lines. The vanguard led by Alava consists of six vessels; the centre, likewise of six, is commanded by *Mr Corneta* in person; the rear, again of six, is under Dumanoir, and the reserve of twelve ships is led by Don Federico. This seems to me not badly planned. I imagine that the French and Spanish ships are mixed, in order that they may not leave us impaled on the bull's horns, as they did at Finisterre.

"From what Don Alfonso tells me the Frenchman says that if the enemy comes up to leeward we are to form in line of battle and attack at once... This is very pretty talk in the state-room; but do you think the *Señorito*[1] will be such a booby as to come up to leeward of us? Oh yes—his lordship has not much brains in his figure-head and is sure to let himself be caught in that trap! Well! we shall see—if we see, what the Frenchman expects.—But do you just tell me: if we Spanish want to scuttle a few of those English ships, are we not strong enough and many enough to do it? Then why in the world need we ally ourselves with the French, who would not allow us to do anything we had a mind to, but would have us dancing attendance at the end of their tow-line? Whenever we have had to work with them they have got us into mischief and we have had the worst of it. Well—may God and the Holy Virgin *del Cármen* be on our side, and rid us of our French friends for ever and ever, Amen.". . .

On the morning of the 20th there was a stiff breeze blowing and the vessels kept at some distance From each other; but as the wind had moderated soon after noon the admiral signalled that the ships were to form in five lines—the van, centre, and rear, and two lines of reserve. I was enchanted with watching the docile monsters, obediently taking their places; for, although the conditions of naval manœuvres did not admit of great rapidity nor of perfect uniformity in the line, it was

[1] Nelson.

impossible to see them without admiration. The wind was from the south west, according to Marcial, and the fleet, catching the breeze on the starboard quarter, ran towards the straits. During the night a few lights were seen, and by dawn on the 21st we saw twenty-seven ships to windward, among which Marcial pointed out three as three-deckers. By eight o'clock the thirty-three vessels of the enemy's fleet were in sight, forming two columns. Our fleet displayed a wide Front, and to all appearance Nelson's two columns, advancing in a wedge, were coming down upon us so as to cut our lines through the centre and rear.

This was the position of the hostile fleets when the *Bucentaure* signalled that we were to put about; maybe you do not understand this. It means that we were to turn completely round and that whereas the wind was on our port side it would now be on the starboard, so that we should sail in the opposite direction. The ships' heads were now turned northwards and this manœuvre, which was intended to place us to windward of Cadiz so that we might reach it in case of disaster, was severely criticized on board the Trinidad, especially by Marcial, who said:

"The line of battle is all broken up; it was bad before and is worse now."

In point of fact what had been the vanguard was now in the rear and the reserve ships, which, as I heard said, were the best, were hindmost of all. The wind had fallen and the ships, being of various tonnage and inefficiently manned, the new line could not form with due precision; some of the vessels moved quickly and rushed forward; others went slowly, hanging back or losing their course, and forming a wide gap that broke the line before the enemy took the trouble of doing it.

"Reform the line," was now the signal; but, though a good ship answers her helm with wonderful docility, it is not so easy to manage as a horse. As he stood watching the movements of the ships nearest to us, Marcial observed:

"The line is wider than the Milky Way. If the *Señorito* cuts through it,

Heaven help us! we shall not be able to sail in any sort of order; they will shave our heads for us if they fire upon us. They are going to give us a dose through the centre, and how can the *San Juan* and the *Bahama* come up to support us from the rear—or the *Neptuno* and the *Rayo* which are in front. Besides, here we are to leeward, and the 'great-coats' can pick and choose where they will attack us, while all we can do is to defend ourselves as best we may. All I have to say is: God get us well out of the scrape and deliver us from the French for ever and ever, Amen."

The sun had now nearly reached the meridian and the enemy was coming down upon us.

"And is this a proper hour to begin a battle?" asked the old sailor indignantly. "Twelve o'clock in the day!"

But he did not dare to express his views publicly and these discussions were confined to a small circle into which I, with my eternal and insatiable curiosity, had squeezed myself. I do not know why, but it seemed to me that there was an expression of dissatisfaction on every face. The officers on the quarter-deck, and the sailors and non-commissioned officers at the bows, stood watching the ships to leeward, quite out of the line of battle, four of which ought to have been in the centre.

I forgot to mention one preliminary in which I myself had borne a hand. Early in the morning the decks were cleared for action, and when all was ready for serving the guns and working the ship, I heard someone say: "The sand—bring the sand." Marcial pulled me by the ear, and taking me to one of the hatchways set me in a line with some of the pressed men, ship's boys, and other supernumeraries. A number of sailors were posted on the ladders from the hatchway to the hold and between decks, and in this way were hauling up sacks of sand. Each man handed one to the man next to him and so it was passed on without much labour. A great quantity of sacks were thus brought up from hand to hand, and to my great astonishment they were emptied out on the upper deck, the poop, and the forecastle, the sand being spread about so as to cover all the planking; and the same thing was done between decks. My curiosity prompted me to ask the boy who stood next to me what this was for.

"For the blood," he said very coolly.

"For the blood!" I exclaimed unable to repress a shudder. I looked at the sand—I looked at the men who were busily employed at this task —and for a moment I felt I was a coward. However, my imagination reverted to the ideas which had previously filled it, and relieved my mind of its alarms; I thought no more of anything but victory and a happy issue.

Everything was ready for serving the guns, and the ammunition was passed up from the store-rooms to the decks by a chain of men, like that which had brought up the sand-bags.

The English advanced to attack us in two sections. One came straight down upon us, and at its head, which was the point of the wedge, sailed a large ship carrying the admiral's flag. This; as I afterwards learned, was the *Victory,* commanded by Nelson. At the head of the other line was the *Royal Sovereign,* commanded by Collingwood. All these names, and the strategical plan of the battle, were not known to me till later . . . .

It was now a quarter to twelve. The fatal moment was approaching. The anxiety was general, and I do not speak merely from what was going on in my own mind, for I was absorbed in watching the ship which was said to contain Nelson, and for some time was hardly aware of what was going on round me.

Suddenly a terrible order was given by our captain—the boatswains repeated it; the sailors flew to the tops; the blocks and ropes creaked, the topsails flapped in the wind.

"Take in sail!" cried Marcial, with a good round oath. "The infernal idiot is making us work back."

And then I understood that the *Trinidad* was to slacken her speed so as to run alongside of the *Bucentaure,* because the *Victory* seemed to be taking measures to run in between those two ships and so cut the line in the middle . . . .

So far as I am concerned, in all my life my soul has never gone through any experiences to compare with those of that hour. In spite of my youth, I was quite capable of understanding the gravity of the occasion, and for the first time in my life, my mind was filled with grand ideas, lofty aspirations, and heroic thoughts. A conviction that we must conquer was so firmly rooted in my mind that I felt quite pitiful towards the English, and wondered to see them so eagerly advancing to certain destruction. For the first time too I fully understood the ideal of patriotism, and my heart responded to the thought with a glow of feeling such as I had never experienced before. Until now my mother country had been embodied in my mind in the persons of its rulers—such as the King and his famous minister, for whom I felt different degrees of respect. As 1 knew no more of history than I had picked up in the streets, it was to me a matter of course that everybody's enthusiasm must be fired by knowing that the Spaniards had, once upon a time, killed a great number of Moors, and, since then, swarms of French and of English. I considered my countrymen as models of valour; but valour, as I conceived of it, was as like barbarity as one egg is like another; and with such ideas as these, patriotism had been to me nothing more than boastful pride in belonging to a race of exterminators of Moors.

But in the pause that preceded the battle I understood the full significance of that divine word; the conception of nationality, of devotion to a mother-country, was suddenly born in my soul, lighting it up, as it were, and revealing a thousand wonderful possibilities—as the rising sun dissipates the darkness that has hidden a beautiful landscape. I thought of my native land as a vast place full of people all united in brotherly regard—of society as divided into families, married couples to be held together, and children to be educated—of honour, to be cherished and defended; I imagined an unspoken agreement among all these human beings to help and protect each other against any attack from without, and I understood that these vessels had been constructed by them all for the defence of their native land; that is to say, for the soil on which they lived, the fields watered by their sweat, the homes where their ancestors had dwelt, the gardens where their children played, the colonies discovered and conquered by their forefathers, the harbours where their ships found shelter after long voyages—the magazines where they stored their wealth—the Church which was the mausoleum of those they had loved, the dwelling-place of their saints, and the ark of their belief—the public places where they might take their pleasure, the private homes where the venerable household gods, handed down from generation to generation, seemed to symbolize the perpetuity of the nation—their family hearth round which the smoke-dyed walls seem still to re-echo with the time-honoured legends with which the grand dame soothes the flightiness or the naughtiness of the little ones, the street where friendly faces meet and smile—the field, the sea, the sky—everything which from the moment of birth makes up the sum of existence, from the crib of a pet animal to the time-honoured throne of the king; every object into which the soul seems to go forth to live, as if the.body that clothes it were too narrow a shell.

I believed too that the disputes between Spain and France or England were always about something that those countries ought to give up to us, and in which Spain could not, on the whole, be wrong. Her self-defence seemed to me as legitimate as the aggression was brutal; and as I had always heard that justice must triumph, I never doubted of victory. Looking up at our red and yellow flag—the colours nearest to that of fire—I felt my bosom swell, and could not restrain a few tears of enthusiasm and excitement; I thought of Cadiz, of Vejer, of the whole Spanish nation assembled, as it were, on a vast platform and looking on with eager anxiety; and all this tide of emotion lifted up my heart to God to whom I put up a prayer, which was neither a *Paternoster* nor an *Ave,* but a gush of inspiration that came to me at the moment.

A sudden shock startled me from my ecstasy, terrifying me with its violent vibration. The first broadside had been fired.

A vessel in the rear had been the first to fire on the *Royal Sovereign,* commanded by Collingwood, and while that ship carried on the fight with the *Santa Ana* the *Victory* came down on us. On board the *Trinidad* every one was anxious to open fire; but our captain would not give the word till he saw a favourable opportunity. Meanwhile, as if the ships were in such close communication that a slow-match was lighted from one to the other, the fire ran along from the *Santa Ana* in the middle, to each end of the line.

The *Victory* fired first on the *Redoubtable,* and being repulsed, came up to the windward of the *Trinidad.* The moment had come for us; a hundred voices cried "Fire!"—loudly echoing the word of command, and fifty round-shot were hurled against the flank of the English man-of-war. For a minute I could see nothing of the enemy for the smoke, while he, as if blind with rage, came straight down upon us before the wind. Just within gun-shot he put the ship about and gave us a broadside. In the interval between our firing and theirs, our crew, who had taken note of the damage done to the enemy, had gained in enthusiasm. The guns were rapidly served, though not without some hitches owing to want of experience in some of the gunners. Marcial would have been only too glad to undertake the management of one of the cannon, but his mutilated body was not equal to the heroism of his spirit. He was forced to be satisfied with superintending the delivery of the charges and encouraging the gunners by word and gesture.

The *Bucentaure,* just at our stern, was, like us, firing on the *Victory,* and the *Téméraire,* another powerful English vessel. It seemed as though the *Victory* must fall into our hands, for the *Trinidad's* fire had cut her tackle to pieces, and we saw with pride that her mizzen-mast had gone by the board.

In the excitement of this first onslaught I scarcely perceived that some of our men were wounded or killed. I had chosen a place where I thought I should be least in the way, and never took my eyes off the captain who stood on the quarter-deck, issuing his orders with heroic coolness; and I wondered to see my master, no less calm though less enthusiastic, encouraging the officers and men in his quavering voice.

"Ah!" said I to myself, "if only Doña Francisca could see him now!" I am bound to confess that at times I felt desperately frightened, and would gladly have hidden myself at the very bottom of the hold, while at others I was filled with an almost delirious courage, when I longed to see the glorious spectacle from the most dangerous posts. However, I will set aside my own insignificant individuality and relate the most terrible crisis of our fight with the *Victory.* The *Trinidad* was doing her immense mischief when the *Téméraire,* by a wonderfully clever manœuvre, slipped in between the two vessels thus sheltering her consort from our fire. She then proceeded to cut through the line behind the *Trinidad,* and as the *Bucentaure,* under fire, had got so close alongside of the *Trinidad* that their yards touched, there was a wide space beyond into which the *Téméraire* rushed down and, going about immediately, came up on our lee and delivered a broadside on that quarter, till then untouched. At the same time the *Neptune,* another large English ship, ran in where the *Victory* had previously been, while the *Victory* veered round so that, in a few minutes, the *Trinidad* was surrounded by the enemy and riddled on all sides.

From my master's face, from Uriarte's heroic fury, and from a volley of oaths delivered by Marcial and his friends, I understood that we were lost and the idea of defeat was anguish to my soul. The line of the combined fleets was broken at several points, and the bad order in which they had formed after turning round, gave place to the most disastrous confusion. We were surrounded by the enemy whose artillery kept up a perfect hail of round and grape-shot on our ship, and on the *Bucentaure* as well. The *Augustin,* the *Héros,* and the *Leandro* were engaged at some distance from us where they had rather more sea-room, while the *Trinidad,* and the Admiral's ship, utterly hemmed in and driven to extremities by the genius of the great Nelson, were fighting heroically—no longer in hopes of a victory which was impossible, but anxious, at any rate, to perish gloriously.

The white hairs which now cover my old head almost stand on end as I remember those terrible hours, from two to four in the afternoon. I think of those five ships, not as mere machines of war obeying the will of men, but as living giants, huge creatures fighting on their own account, carried into action by their sails as though they were active limbs and using the fearful artillery they bore in their sides for their personal defence. As I looked at them then, my fancy could not help personifying them, and to this hour I feel as though I could see them coming up, defying each other, going about to fire a broadside, rushing furiously up to board, drawing back to gather more force, mocking or threatening the enemy; I can fancy them expressing their sufferings when wounded or loftily breathing their last, like a gladiator who in his agony forgets not the dignity which beseems him;—I can imagine that I hear the voices of the crews like the murmur of an oppressed sufferer, sometimes eager with enthusiasm, sometimes a dull roar of desperation the precursor of destruction, sometimes a hymn of triumph in anticipation of victory, or a hideous storm of voices lost in space and giving way to the awful silence of disgrace and defeat.

The scene on board the *Santísima Trinidad* was nothing short of infernal. All attempt at working the ship had been abandoned, for it did not and could not move. The only thing to be done was to serve the guns with the utmost rapidity, and to do as much damage to the enemy as they had done to us. The English small-shot rent the sails just as if huge and invisible nails were tearing slits in them. The splinters of timber and of masts, the stout cables cut through as if they were straws, the capstans, spindles, and other heavy machinery torn from their place by the enemy's fire, strewed the deck so that there was scarcely room to move. Every minute men, till then full of life, fell on deck or into the sea; the blasphemy of those who were fighting mingled with the cries of the wounded till it was impossible to say whether the dying were defying God or the living crying to him for mercy while they fought . . . .

Blood was flowing in rivulets on the upper and lower decks and in spite of the sand the motion of the ship carried it from side to side making sinister patterns on the boards. The cannon-balls, fired at such a short range, mutilated those they killed in a terrible manner, and I saw more than one man still standing with his head blown away, the force of the shock not having been great enough to fling the victim into the sea, whose waters would have extinguished almost painlessly the last sensation of existence. Other balls struck a mast or against the bulwarks, carrying off a hail of hot splinters that pierced and stung like arrows. The rifle-shots from the tops and the round-shot from the carronades dealt a more lingering and painful death, and there was hardly a man to be seen who did not bear the marks, more or less severe, of the foe's iron and lead.

The crew—the soul of the ship—being thus thrashed by the storm of battle and utterly unable to deal equal destruction saw death at hand though resolved to die with the courage of despair; and the ship itself—the glorious body—shivered under the cannonade. I could feel her shudder under the fearful blows; her timbers cracked, her beams creaked, her ribs groaned like limbs on the rack, and the deck trembled under my feet with audible throbs, as though the whole huge creature was indignant at the sufferings of her crew. Meanwhile the water was pouring in at a hundred holes in the riddled hull, and the hold was fast filling.

The *Bucentaure,* the Admiral's vessel, surrendered before our very eyes. Villeneuve struck to the *Victory.* When once the leader of the fleet was gone, what hope was there for the other ships? The French flag vanished from the gallant vessel's mast and she ceased firing. The *San Augustin* and the *Héros* still persevered, and the *Rayo* and *Neptuno,* of the van, made an effort to rescue us from the enemy that was battering us. I could see what was going on in the immediate neighbourhood of the *Trinidad,* though nothing was to be seen of the rest of the line. The wind had fallen to a calm and the smoke settled down over our heads shrouding everything in its dense white wreaths which it was impossible for eye to pierce. We could catch a glimpse now and then of a distant ship, mysteriously magnified by some inexplicable optical effect; I believe indeed that the terror of that supreme moment exaggerated every impression.

Presently this dense cloud was dispersed for an instant—but in what a fearful manner! A tremendous explosion, louder than all the thousand guns of the fleet fired at once, paralysed every man and filled every soul with dread; and just as the ear was stunned by the terrific roar an intense flash lighted up the two fleets, rending the veil of smoke and revealing the whole panorama of the battle. This catastrophe had taken place on the side towards the South where the rear line had been posted.

"A ship blown up!" said one to another. But opinion differed as to whether it was the *Santa Ana,* the *Argonauta,* the *Ildefonso,* or the *Bahama.* We afterwards learnt that it was a Frenchman, the *Achilie.* The explosion scattered in a myriad fragments what had a few moments before been a noble ship of 74 guns and 600 men. But a few seconds after we had already forgotten the explosion in thinking only of ourselves.

The *Bucentaure* having struck, the enemy's fire was directed on us, and our fate was sealed. The enthusiasm of the first hour was by this extinct in my soul; my heart quaked with terror that paralysed my limbs and smothered every other emotion excepting curiosity. This I found so irresistible that I could not keep away from places where the danger was greatest. My small assistance was of no great use now, for the wounded were too numerous to be carried below and the guns had to be served by those who had some little strength left. Among these was Marcial who was here, there, and everywhere, shouting and working to the best of his small ability, acting as boatswain, gunner, sailor, and carpenter all at once, doing everything that happened to be needed at this awful moment. No one could have believed that, with hardly more than half a body, he could have done the work of so many men. A splinter had struck him on the head and the blood had stained his face and given him a most horrible appearance. I could see his lips move as he licked the blood from them and then he spit it out viciously over the side, as if he thought he could thus punish the enemy.

What astonished me most, and indeed shocked me somewhat, was that Marcial even in this scene of horror could still cut a good-humoured joke; whether to encourage his dejected comrades or only to keep his own courage up 1 do not know. The foremast fell with a tremendous crash, covering the whole of the fore-deck with rigging, and Marcial called out to me:

"Bring the hatchets, boy; we must stow this lumber in Davy Jones' locker," and in two minutes the ropes were cut and the mast went overboard.

Then, seeing that the enemy's fire grew hotter, he shouted to the purser's mate, who had come up to serve a gun:

"Daddy, order up some drink for those 'great coats,' and then they will let us alone."

To a soldier, who was lying like a dead creature with the pain of his wounds and the misery of sea-sickness, he exclaimed as he whisked the slow-match under his nose:

"Take a whiff of orange-flower, man, to cure your faintness. Would you like to take a turn in a boat? Nelson has invited us to take a glass of grog with him."

This took place amidships; looking up at the quarter-deck I saw that Cisneros was killed; two sailors hastily carried him down into his cabin. My master remained immoveable at his post, but his left arm was bleeding severely. I ran up to help him, but before I could reach the spot an officer had gone to him to persuade him to retire to his state-room. He had not spoken two words when a ball shot away half his head and his blood sprinkled my face. Don Alonso withdrew, as pale as the corpse which fell on the quarter-deck. When my master had gone down the commander was left standing alone, so perfectly cool that I could not help gazing at him for a few minutes, astounded by such courage. His head was uncovered, his face very white, but his eyes flashed and his attitude was full of energy, and he stood at his post, commanding the desperate strife, though the battle was lost past retrieval. Even this fearful disaster must be conducted with due order, and the captain's duty was still to keep discipline over heroism. His voice still controlled his men in this struggle between honour and death. An officer who was serving in the first battery came up for orders, and before he could speak he was lying dead at the feet of his chief; another officer of marines who was standing by his side fell wounded on the deck, and at last Uriarte stood quite alone on the quarter-deck, which was strewn with the dead and wounded. Even then he never took his eyes off the English ships and the working of our guns—the horrible scene on the poop and in the roundhouse, where his comrades and subalterns lay dying, could not quell his noble spirit nor shake his firm determination to face the fire till he too should fail. As I recall the fortitude and stoical calmness of Don Francisco Xavier de Uriarte, I understand all that is told us of the heroes of antiquity. At that time the word Sublime was as yet unknown to me, but I felt that there must be, in every language under heaven, some human utterance to express that greatness of soul which I here saw incarnate and which revealed itself to me as a special grace vouchsafed by God to miserable humanity.

By this time most of our guns were silenced, more than half of our men being incapable of serving them. I might not, however, have been aware of the fact, but that being impelled by curiosity I went out of the cabin once more and heard a voice saying in a tone of thunder:

"Gabrielillo, come here."

It was Marcial who was calling me; I ran to his side and found him trying to work one of the guns which had been left silent for lack of men. A ball had shot away the half of his wooden leg, which made him exclaim:

"Well! so long as I can manage to keep the one of flesh and bone . . . .!"

Two sailors lay dead by the gun; a third, though horribly wounded, still tried to go on working it.

"Let be, mate!" said Marcial. "You cannot even light the match," and taking the linstock from his hand, he put it into mine, saying, "Take it, Gabrielillo. If you are afraid you had better jump overboard."

He loaded the cannon as quickly as he was able, helped by a ship's boy who happened to come up; we ran it forward: "Fire!" was the word. I applied the match and the gun went off.

We repeated this operation a second and a third time, and the roar of the cannon fired by my own hand produced an extraordinary effect on my nerves. The feeling that I was no longer a spectator but an actor in this stupendous tragedy for the moment blew all my alarms to the winds; I was eager and excited or at any rate determined to appear so. That moment revealed to me the truth that heroism is often simply the pride of honour. Marcial's eye—the eyes of the world were upon me; I must bear myself worthy of their gaze.

"Oh!" I exclaimed to myself with an impulse of pride, "If only my young mistress could see me now!. . . Bravely firing cannon like a man!" Two dozen of English were the least I might have sent to the other world.

These grand visions, however, did not last long for Marcial, enfeebled by age, was beginning to sink with exhaustion; he breathed hard as he wiped away the blood which flowed profusely from his head, and at last his arms dropped by his side, and closing his eyes, he exclaimed:

"I can do no more; the powder is rising to my head. Gabrielillo, fetch me some water."

I ran to obey him, and when I had brought the water he drank it eagerly. This seemed to give him fresh energy; we were just about to load once more when a tremendous shock petrified us as we stood. The main-mast, cut through by repeated shots, fell amidships and across the mizzen; the ship was completely covered with the wreck, and the confusion was appalling.

I happily was so far under shelter that I got no harm but a slight blow on the head which, though it stunned me for a moment, did not prevent my thrusting aside the fragments of rope and timber which had fallen above me. The sailors and marines were struggling to clear away the vast mass of lumber, but from this moment only the lower deck guns could be used at all. I got clear as best I could and went to look for Marcial, but I did not find him, and casting my eyes up at the quarter-deck, I saw that the captain was no longer at his post. He had fallen senseless, badly wounded in the head by a splinter, and two sailors were just about to carry him down to the stateroom. I was running forward to assist when a piece of shell hit me on the shoulder, terrifying me excessively, for I made sure my wound was mortal and that I was at my last gasp. My alarm did not hinder me from going into the cabin; I tottered from loss of blood and for a few minutes lay in a dead faint. I was roused from my short swoon by hearing the rattle of the cannon below and then a voice shouting vehemently:

"Board her! bring pikes!—axes!"

And then the confusion was so complete that it was impossible to distinguish human voices from the rest of the hideous uproar. However, somehow—I know not how—without thoroughly waking from my drowsy state, I became aware that all was given up for lost and that the officers had met in the cabin to agree to strike; nor was this the work of my fancy, bewildered as I was, for I heard a voice exclaiming: "The *Trinidad* never strikes!" I felt sure that it was Marcial's voice; but at any rate some one said it.

When I recovered perfect consciousness, I saw my master sunk on one of the sofas in the cabin, his face hidden in his hands, prostrate with despair, and paying no heed to his wound.

I went to the heart-broken old man, who could find no way of expressing his grief but by embracing me like a father, as if we were both together on the brink of the grave. He, at any rate, was convinced that he must soon die of grief, though his wound was by no means serious. I comforted him as best I might, assuring him that if the battle were indeed lost it was not because I had failed to b tter the English to the best of my power; and I went on to say that we should be more fortunate next time but my childish arguments failed to soothe him.

Going out presently in search of water for my master, I witnessed the very act of lowering the flag which was flying at the gaff, that being one of the few spars, with the remains of the mizzen-mast, that remained standing. The glorious flag, the emblem of our honour, pierced and tattered as it was, which had gathered so many fighting-men under its folds, ran down the rope never to be unfurled again. The idea of stricken pride, of a brave spirit giving way before a superior force, can find no more appropriate symbol to represent it than that of a flying standard which sinks and disappears like a setting sun. And our flag thus slowly descending that fatal evening, at the moment when we surrendered, seemed to shed a parting ray of glory.

The firing ceased, and the English took possession of the conquered vessel.

THE FISHERMEN OF RODILLERO[1]

Armando Palacio Valdes

THE weather became so bad, and the men so mistrustful of it, that the skippers met together and decided that three of them should keep watch each night to note carefully the state of sea and sky, and, according to their observations, decide whether to call out the men or not. Moreover, as they usually went out before daybreak, it was agreed that the boat which went out first or was ahead of the others, should set a light at the prow in case it seemed dangerous to go on; this would serve as a signal to the other boats to put back to harbour.

Two nights before the event we are about to tell of, it fell to José to keep watch with two of the others. The sky, they saw, gave promise of bad weather, and they did not want to call out the men. But as it was now some days since they had been out, and the pinch of hunger was beginning to be felt, there was some murmuring in the inn at this decision. During the day the weather improved a little, but not much. That night three other skippers kept watch, who hesitated a long time before giving the boy the order for calling out the crews, for the outlook had seldom been less promising. At last they did give it, thinking of the people's misery, or, maybe, in fear of the grumblers.

José was one of the first to reach the shore.

"Ave Maria, how awful !" he cried, looking at the sky. "What a night to put to sea!"

Too wise to alarm his fellows, and too brave to refuse to go out, he kept silent, and, helped by his men, launched the boat. As it was the nearest, it was the first ready and afloat. And the crew, once aboard, took the oars. There were more men

---

[1] From *José*. Translated by Elizabeth D'Oyley.

in the boat than there would be in summer; as always happened, firstly, because in winter there was no other work for them, and secondly, because more oars were needed on account of the frequent calms. In José's boat there were fourteen.

A mile from shore José gave the order to hoist sail. Asturian boats always carry five sails, which are—in order of size—the mainsail, spritsail, foresail, foretopsail, and the *uncion* which are differently grouped according to the force of the wind. The *uncion*, the smallest, bears this terrible name, because it is the only one hoisted when the boat is on the point of being lost.

"What sail shall we set, José?" one of the men asked.

"Foresails," he answered, shortly.

Amidships the seamen ran up the spritsail, and the foresail at the prow, which was the meaning of José's order.

The night was dark, but not impenetrable. Here and there the sky was clear. Big dark clouds sailed swiftly, plainly showing that on high the wind blew strongly, though they felt little of it below. It was this that made José—whose eyes were fixed upon the sky—uneasy and preoccupied. The men, too, were silent and apprehensive; the cold paralysed their hands and dread—which they could not hide—their tongues. They cast frequent glances aloft and each time saw the clouds racing with greater fury. The sea was oily and sinister.

A quarter of an hour went by, and then José broke the silence with a sudden exclamation.

"What a filthy night!Not fit for a dog to be out!"

"You're right !" three or four of the men made haste to say. "Dirty weather—more fit for pigs than Christians."

"Don't go on for us, José," one of them ended. "Put back, if you want to."

José did not answer. He was silent for a few minutes: then, raising himself suddenly, he said with decision.

"Light that lantern, boy! About ship!"

The boy lit the lantern and set it in the prow with evident relief; and with equal relief the men obeyed the order.

The boat tacked, bearing towards Rodillero. And at once, far off, they saw the lanterns of the boats come alight, one after the other, signifying that all had seen the signal and were putting back to harbour.

"As if we could do anything else!" said one of the men.

"Who on earth would go to sea of his own free will to-day ?" another exclaimed.

"Why the devil did those fools Nicholas and Toribio call us out?" The tongues of all were loosened, and, as they talked, making for home, José saw to leeward the shape of a boat, passing not far from his, without a light at the prow.

"Easy, lads!" he said. "What the devil's that? Where's that boat making for?"

"You may well ask!"

The skipper got to his feet, and making a trumpet of his hands, shouted:

"Ahoy there !"

"What d'you want, José?" the skipper of the other boat answered, recognizing him by his voice.

"Where are you making for, Hermanegildo?" asked José, who had recognized him too.

"The fishing ground," the other answered, coming as near as he could.

"Why didn't you light your lantern when I did?"

"Because I know these folks well. They'll show you their lights and pay no damn heed to you. How much d'you bet me all the boats will be at the fishing ground at daybreak?"

"Damn his cheek!" muttered José, and turning to his crew:—"Go about! Some day when we least expect it we'll have to pay for this folly." With a bad grace the seamen obeyed the command.

"Haven't I told you many a time, José," said Bernardo, "that in these parts anyone will willingly lose one eye as long as his neighbour loses two?"

The skipper did not answer.

"The best of it is," said another, "those fools yonder think we'll cheat them, when the truth is we're all wanting to know what the other fellow's up to."

"The joke'll be when we meet at dawn!" a third added.

"You'll see! When something happens one of these days," said José again, "they'll soon find somebody to blame."

"Always the way!" Bernardo answered with mock gravity.

Silence reigned in the boat after that. The men scanned the horizon.

The skipper kept a close watch upon the weather and with more and more uneasiness, despite the fact that for one moment the sky seemed to clear entirely. But it soon clouded over again. Yet even now the wind did not blow hard, except up above. Towards daybreak it grew quieter. The dawn was sadder and greyer than usual. With difficulty the light filtered through a threefold bank of clouds.

When they reached the fishing ground, they saw in fact nearly all the Rodillero boats, which had already thrown their lines into the sea and were fishing not very far from one another. As soon as they had furled their sails, they, too, made one of them, and in two hours' time they had caught a few bream; but not many. About ten o'clock the sky darkened and a shower fell, bringing with it a little wind. Half an hour later came another, and the wind grew stronger. Then a few of the boats gathered in their tackle, and hoisting sail, headed for land. One after the other the rest followed.

"We didn't need baggage for this trip," said one of José's men sullenly, clewing up the fore-topsail.

They were some ten or twelve leagues from the coast. Before they had covered two miles, over in the west they saw the sky darkening ominously. So dark it was that the men looked from one to the other apprehensively.

"*Madre del alma*, look what's coming," cried one.

For safety, José had at the start ordered the hoisting of the foresails only, that is, the foresail amidships and the foretopsail at the prow. He gazed steadily westward. The blackness was coming closer rapidly. When he felt upon his cheek the coolness that foreruns a squall, he jumped to his feet, shouting:

"Let go sheets and halyards!"

Quickly the men obeyed, though they did not realize how great the danger was. The sails fell heavily on to the thwarts—in the nick of time, for a violent gust of wind went whistling between the masts and hurled the boat forward. The men threw a grateful look at José.

"How did you smell the damned blast ?" said one. Then looking seaward, they saw that one of the boats had foundered, and once again they turned their glance upon José, pale as the dead.

"Did you see, José?" one of them asked in a husky shaken voice.

The skipper closed his eyes as a sign of assent. But the boy in the bow, seeing what had happened, began to cry aloud:

"Holy Virgin! what's to become of us? Holy Mother! what's to become of us?"

José, faced him, his eyes flashing with anger.

"Stow that, you little devil, or I'll pitch you overboard !"

And the little lad, terrified, fell silent.

"Up with the foretops'l and the *uncion!*" José ordered.

Quickly it was done. As much as possible José let the boat fall off to leeward, taking care not to lose sight of the coast line of Rodillero; and with extraordinary swiftness the boat gathered way, for the wind blew fiercely, growing stronger each moment. Not many minutes had gone when a heavy sea got up, so that they could no longer see the direction the other boats were taking. Now and again it rained heavily. The boat shipped a good deal of water, and several of the men had to be always baling. But José paid more heed to the wind, than to the water. It blew so fitfully and treacherously that should he relax his attention for a moment the boat would most surely capsize. Twice again he had to strike sail hastily to prevent it: and at last seeing the impossibility of carrying even the two sails, he gave orders for the hoisting of the *uncion* only. The men looked at him in consternation and the hands of many of them trembled as they obeyed.

"We must put her before the wind," said José, his voice already hoarse with shouting. "We can't make Rodillero. We'll put into Sarrio."

"It looks to me as if we won't make Sarrio either," an old man answered in a low voice.

"Don't lose heart, lads! Courage! This is nothing!" the skipper answered with energy.

From the moment when they gave up all idea of making Rodillero and put the boat before the wind, he could do no more, especially as they were carrying so very little sail. But the sea began to alarm them. Helped by the oily swell of the night before, it had become in truth a mountainous sea, terrible and awe-inspiring. The waves broke so heavily and so unceasingly against the stern that at last José was forced to bear away a little. In spite of this the men never ceased to bale. The sea grew heavier. The waves every moment higher. The boat disappeared beneath them and by a miracle rose again. One sea carried away the rudder. Quickly José seized the one they had in reserve, but even as he was hooking it in place, another blow wrenched it from his hands and the boat shipped a heavy sea.

The boy broke into sobs, crying out again;

"*Madre de mi alma*, we're lost!"

José threw the tiller—which still remained on board—at his head.

"Shut up, you young fool, or I'll kill you!"

And seeing signs of fear in the faces of some of the crew, he flung a fierce look at them;

"The first man who cries out—I'll wring his neck!"

This roughness was needed: if panic fell upon them and they ceased for one moment to bale, they would most surely founder.

In place of the rudder, José put an oar over the stern. With sails set, it is utterly impossible to steer with an oar, but as they were carrying nothing but the *uncion,* he could, by dint of great effort, make the boat answer to it. At each buffet of the sea they shipped a great quantity of water, and in spite of the fact that one man, working steadily, could with a bucket bale out a pipe of water in eight or ten minutes, it was impossible to clear the boat; almost always the water remained knee-high. And José never ceased for a moment to shout with the little voice left him:

"Bale, lads! Bale! Courage, lads! Bale! Bale !"

One wave carried away Bernardo's cap.

"Go on!" he cried angrily. "My head 'll go next!"

Their case was desperate. And although they tried to hide it, fear had taken hold of them all. Then it was that José, seeing their strength must soon give out, said:

"Boys, we're in a tight corner. Would you like to call upon the Holy Christ of Rodillero to save us?"

"Yes, José," they all answered with the haste of despair.

"Very well; if you like, we'll offer to go barefooted to hear Mass. But this must give us courage. There must be no cowardice. Courage! And bale, lads, bale!"

The vow put new heart into them and in faith they went on with their work. In a few minutes they had flung out most of the water and the boat rode easier. Then José noticed that the mainmast was hampering them.

"We must unship the mainmast," he said, and pushed forward in haste to grasp it.

But in that instant they saw with terror an immense wave coming down on them, high as a mountain and black as a cave.

"José, this is beyond a joke!" cried out Bernardo, resigning himself to death.

The wave struck the boat with such force that it flung José upon his face and hurled him against the thwarts. The boat was awash, almost swamped. But José, nearly stunned as he was, struggled doggedly to his feet, crying out:

"Bale!Bale! It's nothing!"

What was passing in Rodillero?

The few boats that had obeyed José's signal returned to harbour before morning. Their crews felt shamed and disheartened when they saw how miserably they had been taken in, especially when their womenfolk bantered them.

"Must you always play the fool? When will you know the kind of people you have to deal with? *Hombre de Dios!* You'll see what sort of a sea we get to-day! You'll see!"

The men held their tongues as usual, knowing that right was on their side. But they swore within themselves not to fall again into the same snare.

At daybreak they changed their opinion a little. The sea had so drear an aspect and the weather looked so bad that their idleness did not greatly trouble them. When, shrouded in a shower, the first blast of the North East wind was felt in the village, some of them went back to their wives, with a smile.

"What d'you think of it now? You'd like me to be at sea now, would you?"

It was the women's turn then to hold their tongues. The second blast, much fiercer than the first, put the whole neighbourhood in commotion. Men and women hurried to the shore, and from there, despite the rain that fell in torrents, mounted to San Esteban. Fear showed itself so quickly that the superstitious unrest which had reigned in the place all winter was easy to be seen. From the corners of their eyes the women watched the old seamen screwing up their faces anxiously.

"Is there any danger, Uncle Pipe?" some of them thrust forward to ask.

"It's not up to much ... But the sea hasn't yet said 'Here I am!'" It said it, nevertheless, sooner than they expected. The storm broke suddenly, furiously. In an instant the sea rose in a way truly terrifying, and began to break upon the Hoesos de San Pedro, the reefs nearest to the coast. Soon it was breaking also on the Cobanin, the nearest reefs on the other side of the bay. The crowd standing on the heights of San Esteban, watched the progress of the storm in terror. Some of the women began to cry.

Nevertheless there was no need to worry as yet—so said the experienced seamen. The harbour was quite open. As long as the boats did not capsize (and this was the men's own lookout; they must trust to their own skill to avoid it) they could put into Rodillero without danger. But some one cried out:

"And what about the great waves? Will they have time to bale?"

"Time enough!" a dour-looking fisherman said. "One would think we'd never seen a high sea before! There never was a village like this for getting excited over nothing!"

The energy with which he said these words silenced the doubters and a little lightened the hearts of the women. Unhappily his triumph was short lived: a few minutes later the waves broke over the Tornio, another of the reefs that formed the bar.

Near the chapel of San Esteban stood a hut in which lived a peasant who was employed by the coastguard service for a very small yearly wage, to light the beacons which served as signals on days or nights of danger. This peasant, although he had been to sea only a few times, knew it as well as any sailor. After watching it closely for some time and often hesitating, he took from the hut yard a load of furze and dry broom, put it on the highest part of the headland and set fire to it. It was the first signal for the fishermen.

Elisa who was among the crowd, close to her godmother, felt her heart contract at sight of the beacon. She called to mind the terrible curse of the sacristan's wife; and all the sad forebodings and superstitious fears that lay sleeping in her soul awoke suddenly. Yet for shame's sake she managed to control herself; but she began to hasten from group to group, listening with ill-concealed anxiety to the remarks of the seamen. What she heard terrified her.

Little was said; all watched intently. The wind whipped their faces with the last raindrops of the squall. The sea grew rapidly. After breaking over the Huesos de San Pedro, the Cobanin and the Torno, it burst upon another reef further from the coast.

"It's breaking on the Furada! . . . Manuel, you can light your perch beacon," cried one of the seamen.

Manuel ran to the hut once again, brought out another load of furze and set fire to it close to the first. This was the signal of immediate danger. If those at sea did not make haste to harbour, they ran the risk of its being closed against them.

"Any boat in sight, Rafael?" asked a young girl, two large tears rolling down her cheeks.

"Not yet. We can't see much for the spray."

Not a sail showed on the horizon. Anguish so held the watchers that some minutes passed before a voice was raised among them. Every gaze was riveted upon the Carrero, a short space left free *by* the bar of Rodillero, where the boats had safe entry when the sea was choppy. Elisa's forehead was cold and damp with sweat, and she clung tightly to her godmother to prevent herself from failing.

A quarter of an hour went by. Suddenly a cry went up from the crowd, a cry weaker, but more mournful than the roar of the sea. A wave had just broken upon the Carrero. The bar was now nothing but a fringe of foam. The barbour was closed.

Manuel, pale and silent, went in search of another load of furze and set fire to it, beside the other two. The rain had ceased and the beacons, fanned by the wind, flared up.

Elisa trembled at the sound of that cry, and urged by an irresistible impulse, she hurried away, ran down the pathway through the pines, crossed the deserted village, mounted the avenue to the church and came, spent and panting, to the door. For a moment she paused to take breath; then, making the sign of the cross, she dropped to her knees, and so made her way up to the high altar; but instead of halting there, she turned to the right and began to mount painfully the winding stairway which led to the chapel of the Christ. It was the stairway of penitence and its steps were worn by the knees of the devout. Elisa's when she reached the top were dropping blood.

The chapel was a dusky place, its walls covered with images and offerings, with a grated window opening upon the church, through which the faithful could see the venerated image on the days when Mass was said at its altar. The Holy Christ was there, covered as usual by a velvet curtain. With a hand that trembled Elisa drew aside the curtain and prostrated herself. A little while later many of the other women came in, and in like manner knelt down in silence. From time to time, an irrepressible sob broke upon the mystery and majesty of the place.

The sea grew calmer by the afternoon. Thanks to this, a good many of the boats managed, though at great risk, to put into Rodillero. Later, others came in, but when night fell there were still five missing. One of them was José's. The seamen, who had no doubt as to their fate, for they had seen one boat founder, dared not utter a word; the countless questions put to them they answered evasively. No one knew anything; no one had seen anything. The shore remained thronged with people late into the night, but as the hours went by, despair grew. Little by little the beach was deserted, only the families of the men still at sea remaining. At last these, too, almost gave up hope, and leaving the shore went back to the village utterly heart-broken.

That awful night! There still rings in my ears the heart-rending sobs of unhappy wives and of children crying for their father. The village looked drear—terrible. People hastened through the street in groups, gathering about the house doors, all talking with raised voices. The inns were open, and there the men argued hotly, blaming one another for this disaster. From time to time a dishevelled woman, stricken with grief, would cross the street, uttering cries so horrible as to make one's hair stand on end. Even from within the houses came the sound of groans and sobs.

The first moment of dismay and anguish was followed by one of calm, more sorrowful yet, if that were possible. The people were shut within doors, and grief had now more the look of resignation. Within those humble homes how many tears were shed! In one, a poor old woman, whose two sons were out at sea, uttered such piercing shrieks that the few who passed along the street stood still in horror. In another, an unhappy wife who had lost her husband was sobbing in a corner while two little children of three or four were playing and eating nuts. When day dawned, the village seemed a place of the dead. The priest had the bells rung, calling all to church, and he arranged to celebrate next day a requiem mass for the repose of the souls of those who had been lost.

But towards midday a rumour went about—though none knew who brought it—that some of the Rodillero boats had put into the port of Banzones, some seven leagues away. Such tidings caused an immense sensation in the neighbourhood. Hope, already dead, was born again in every heart. Bustle and noise filled the street once again. Swift messengers were sent to find out the truth, and many were the comments and surmises that went about. The day and night passed in anguish and pitiful anxiety. Pale and weeping, the poor women ran from group to group, longing to find in the men's talk something that might give them hope.

At last, at twelve o'clock, came the news that the boats which had reached Banzones were no more than two. Which? The messengers did not know or did not want to say. Nevertheless in a little while news began to leak out that one of them was José's and the other Toribio's.

Then, in the afternoon, came a boy, breathless, bare-headed, covered with sweat.

"Here they are! Here they are!"

"Who?"

"Lots of them! Lots of them! Lots are coming!" he managed to say, with difficulty for breath failed him. "They must be in Antromero now." Then a change indescribable swept over the village. Without a single exception every one came out of doors, made a great uproar in the street for a few moments, and then in one body hastened from the place. They took the way to Antromero, along the seashore, in a state of excitement and anguish it is impossible to describe. The men talked busily, speculating upon the way their comrades had managed to save themselves. The women went in silence, dragging along the children who in vain pleaded that they were tired. Half a league further on they came upon an opening from where they could see in the distance a group of fishermen coming towards them with their oars on their shoulders. A loud cry went up from the crowd.

Waving their caps, the fishermen gave an answering Hurrah! From one to the other the cries went, until, hastening towards each other, they met.

It was a sight both joyous and terrible. As the large and small groups mingled, cries of joy and cries of grief broke out together. The women, wide-eyed, sought their lost ones and not finding them, burst into piteous sobs, and dropping to the ground, wrung their hands in agony. Others, more fortunate, finding much loved husbands and sons, flung themselves fiercely upon them, and remained pressed against their breasts as if nothing on earth could ever tear them away. The men, the centre of this fervent welcome, strove to hide their emotion with a smile, but the tears rolled down their cheeks in spite of them.

Elisa, who was among the crowd, felt such a tightening in her throat when she saw José that she thought she would stifle. She covered her face with her hands and burst into sobs, striving to make no sound. José, nearly strangled by his mother's arms, sought eagerly over her shoulder for his betrothed. Elisa lifted her face to his, and looking into each other's eyes their lips met.

The first moments of emotion passed, and the great crowd of people turned with slow step towards the village. Each one of the men was surrounded by a group of his comrades, all eager to learn every detail of the boat's fortune. Behind came the women; sometimes, just to assure themselves that they were still alive, they would call their men by name and when they turned in answer, found nothing to say to them.

That same afternoon it was arranged that they should give thanks to God on the day following by a solemn *fiesta*. It chanced that almost all the rescued men had made the same vow—to hear Mass barefooted at the altar of the Christ. It was a now very common in Rodillero in moments of danger and one which had come down from father to son. And so, upon the following morning they met upon the seashore, and from there each crew with its skipper at the head, set out slowly for the church, all bare-looted and bare-headed. They went in silence, their faces grave, their quiet eyes showing the simple and ardent faith of those who know little of this life save its sorrows. Behind came the women, the children and the few gentlefolk of the village, silent too, overcome by emotion at the sight of these men, so strong and so rugged, thus humbling themselves like children. The widows and orphans of those who had been lost went, too, to pray for the repose of their dead. They had put on whatever bit of black they had been able to find at the moment—a kerchief, an apron, a cap.

And in the little church of Rodillero the miraculous Christ awaited them, hanging from the cross, with open arms. He too had suffered shipwreck and had been saved from the sea by the piety of a few fishermen; he too had experienced the sadness and loneliness of the ocean and the bitterness of its waves. They knelt down, dropping their heads upon their breasts while their lips murmured prayers learnt in childhood and never said with more fervour. The candles surrounding the sacred image flickered sadly. From the crowd came a soft murmur. The voice of the officiating priest, shaken and tremulous, broke from time to time the majestic silence of the church.

When Mass was ended, Elisa and José met in the church porch and smiled tenderly upon each other; and with that innocent and pardonable egoism which belongs to love, forgot in a moment all the sadness that was about them; side by side, in eager and happy talk, they went down the village street, and before they had reached the house, had fixed upon the day of their wedding.

PORTUGAL

HOW THE PAGE OF PRINCE HENRY THE NAVIGATOR BROUGHT HOME THE SHIP[1]

Gomez Eannes de Zurara

AH, IN what brief words did I find enregistered the record of the death of such a noble knight as was this Nuno Tristam, of whose sudden end I purpose to speak. And of a surety I could not pass it by without tears, did I not know, almost by divine forecast, the eternal delight his soul tasteth, for it seemeth to me that I should be reckoned as covetous by all true Catholics were I to bewail the death of one whom it hath pleased God to make a sharer in His immortality ....

Now this noble knight was perfectly informed of the great desire and purpose of our virtuous Prince, being one who from such an early youth had been brought up in his household; and seeing how the Prince was toiling to send his ships to the land of the Negroes and much further yet, if he might accomplish it; and hearing that some caravels had already passed the river of Nile, and the things that were reported from there; it seemed to him that if he were not to make himself one of that elect company and to render service to the Infant his lord in that land in any good thing that might be done or encountered there, he could not obtain the name of a good man and true.

Wherefore he straightway made him ready a caravel, and having it armed, he began his voyage and stayed not in any part, but pursued his course toward the land of the Negroes. And passing by Cape Verde, he went sixty leagues further on and came unto a river, in the which it seemed to him that there ought to be some inhabited places. Wherefore he caused to be launched two small boats he was carrying, and in them there entered twenty-two men, to wit, ten in one and twelve in the other. And as they began to take their way up the river, the tide was rising with the which they entered, and they made for some habitations that they espied on the right hand. And it came to pass that before they went on shore, there appeared from the other side twelve boats, in the which there would be as many as seventy or eighty Guineas, all Negroes, with bows in their hands. And because the water was rising, one of the boats of the Guineas crossed to the other side and put on shore those it was carrying, and thence they began to shoot arrows at our men in the boats. And the others who remained in the boats bestirred themselves as much as they could to get at our men, and as soon as they perceived themselves

[1] From the translation of *The Chronicle of the Discovery and Conquest of Guinea* by C.R. Beazley and Edgar Prestage.

to be within reach, they discharged that accursed ammunition of theirs all full of poison upon the bodies of our countrymen. And so they held on in pursuit of them until they had reached the caravel which was lying outside the river in the open sea; and they were all hit by those poisoned arrows in such wise that before they came on board four of them died in the boats.

And so, wounded as they were, they made fast their small boats to the ship, and commenced to make ready for their voyage, seeing their case how perilous it was; but they were not able to lift their anchors for the multitude of arrows with which they were attacked, and they were constrained to cut the cables so that not one remained. And so they began to make sail, leaving the boats behind, for they could not hoist them up. And it came to pass that of the twenty-two men that left the ship only two escaped, to wit, one André Diaz and another Alvaro da Costa, both esquires of the Infant and natives of the City of Evora; and the remaining nineteen died, for that poison was so artfully composed that a slight wound, if it only let blood, brought men to their last end. And there died that noble Knight Nuno Tristam, very desirous as he was of this present life, in that there was no place left him to buy his death like a brave man. And there died also another Knight called John Correa, and one Duarte Dollanda, and Estevam Dalmeida, and Diego Machado, men of noble birth and young in years, brought up by the Infant in his household; as well as other esquires and foot-soldiers of the same upbringing; and seamen and others of the ship's company.

Suffice it to say that they numbered in all twenty-one, for of the seven that had remained in the caravel, two were also wounded as they were trying to raise the anchors. But whom will you have to make ready this ship that she may pursue her voyage and depart from among that evil race? For the two esquires who remained, as we said, did not wholly escape from that peril, for being wounded they came near unto death, and lay ill quite twenty days, not being able to render any aid to the others who were toiling to direct the caravel. And these latter were not more than five in number, to wit, a sailor lad very little acquainted with the act of navigating, and a boy of the Infant's household called Airas Tinoco, who went as purser, and a Guinea boy who had been captured with the first prisoners taken in that land, and two other boys, both quite young, who were living with some of those esquires that died there. Of a surety, compassion is due to their great toil at that hour. They went weeping and sorrowing for the death of such a captain and of the others their comrades and friends, and were from that time in fear of the hateful enemies they knew to be near them, from whose deadly wounds so many and such brave men had died in a very brief space. And especially they sorrowed because they found so slight a remedy whereby to seek their safety; for the sailor lad in whom they were all putting their hope, confessed openly his scant knowledge, saying that he knew not how to direct the course of a ship or to work at anything of that kind in such wise as to be serviceable; but only if directed by another he would do what he could, as he was bidden.

O Thou great and supreme succour of all the forsaken and afflicted who dost never desert those that cry out to Thee in their most great necessity, and who now didst hear the cries of these men who made their moan to Thee, fixing their eyes on the height of the clouds and calling upon Thee to hasten to their aid; clearly didst Thou show that Thou heardest their prayers when in such a brief space Thou didst send them heavenly aid. For Thou didst give courage and understanding to a youth who had been born and brought up in Olivenca, an inland town far removed from the sea; and he, enlightened by divine grace, piloted the ship, and bade the seamen steer directly to the North, declining a little to the East, namely, to the wind that is called North-east, for he thought that there lay the kingdom of Portugal, towards which they wished to make their voyage. And as they were going thus on their way, after a part of the day was over, they went to see Nuno Tristam and the other wounded men, and they found them dead, so that they were obliged to throw them into the sea; and on that day they threw in fifteen, and four remained in the boats, and two they threw in the next day. But I write not of the feelings that would be theirs when they cast those bodies upon the multitude of waters, burying their flesh in the bellies of fish. For what importeth it to us if our bodies lack sepulture? since in our flesh we shall see our Saviour, according to the determination of Holy Scripture, for it is the same thing whether we lie in the sea or the land, and whether we be eaten of fishes or of birds. Our chief concern is in those works of ours by which after our death we shall find the truth of all these matters that here we see in figure .... Therefore we can say with justice to these men: "Beati mortui qui in Domino moriuntur." And moreover, all who read this history will obtain a reward from God, if they make a memorial of the death of these men in their prayers, for inasmuch as they died in the service of God and their lord, their death is happy.

Now this youth whom I have mentioned was that same Airas Tinoco of whom I spoke above, and in him God put such grace that for two months together he directed the course of that ship; but all were doubtful what their end would be, for in all those two months they never caught sight of land. And at the end of this time they sighted a pinnace which was on warlike business, and they had great fear at the sight, for they thought it belonged to Moors; but after they found it pertained to a Galician pirate whose name was Pero Falcom, a new joy came upon them, and much more so when they were told that they were off the coast of Portugal, opposite a place belonging to the Mastership of Santiago, called Sines. And so they arrived at Lagos, and thence they went to the Infant to tell him of the tragical fortune of their voyage, and laid before him a multitude of arrows by the which their companions had died.

THE STORY OF GASPAR AND MIGUEL CORTE REAL[1]

Damiao de Goes

GASPAR CORTE REAL, son of Joam Vaz Corte Real, was an enterprising man, valorous, and eager to gain honour. He proposed to undertake the discovery of lands towards the north, because many discoveries had been made to the south. Thus he obtained favour for his undertaking from the King, whose servant he was when Duke of Beja, and armed one ship which was well supplied with men and all necessaries. He sailed from the port of Lisbon in the beginning of the summer of 1500. In this voyage he discovered, in that direction of the north, a land which was very cool and with great woods, as are all lands that lie in that direction. He gave it the name of Green Land. The people are very barbarous and wild, almost like those of the land of Sancta Cruz. At first they are white, but they are so cut up by the cold that they lose their whiteness with age, and remain brown. They are of medium height, very agile, and great archers, using sticks hardened by fire instead of darts, with which they make as good a cast as if it was tipped with fine steel. They dress in the skins of animals which abound in that land ....

Returning to Gaspar Corte Real, after he had discovered that land, and coasted along a great part of it, he returned to this kingdom. Presently, in the year 1501, being desirous of discovering more of this province, and of becoming better acquainted with its advantages, he departed from Lisbon on the 15th of May; but it is not known what happened to him in this voyage, for he never more appeared, nor were there any tidings of him.

The delay and the suspicion that began to arise of his fate caused Miguel Corte Real, Chief Porter of the King, for the great love he bore his brother, to determine to go in search of him. He left Lisbon on the 10th of May, 1502, with two ships, but there were never any tidings of them. The King felt the loss of these two brothers very much, and, of his own royal and pious motion, in the year 1503, he ordered two armed ships to be fitted out at his own cost, to go in search of them. But it could never be ascertained how either the one or the other was lost. To that part of the province of Green Land where it was believed that the brothers were lost the name was given of the Land of the Corte Reals.

These two brothers, Gaspar and Miguel Corte Real, had another brother, whose name was Vasque Anes Corte Real, who was Controller of the King's Household, of his Council, Captain-Governour of the Islands of St George and Terceira, and Alcalde Mayor of the city of Tavilla. He was a very good knight and

[1] From Sir Clements R. Markham's translation of *The Journal of Christopher Columbus.*

Christian, a man of exemplary life, and one who dispensed many charities, both publicly and in secret. His son and heir is Emanuel Corte Real, also of the King's Council and Captain of the same islands, who now lives. This Vasque Anes Corte Real, unable to persuade himself that his brothers were dead, determined to fit out ships at his own cost, and go in search of them, in the year 1503. But, on requesting the King to excuse his absence, His Majesty could not consent that he should proceed further in that business, holding that it was useless, and that all had been done that could be done.

HOW VASCO DA GAMA CAME TO THE LAND OF CALICUT[1]

Luiz de Camoês

(1524-1579)

THE heathen king eagerly welcomed the hardy navigators, anxious to win the friendship of the Christian king and so powerful a people, and sad that fate had not made him a nearer neighbour to the fertile land of Europe. With dances and games and other festivities and rich banquets, he daily entertained the Portuguese.

But their Captain, seeing that he made too long a stay, and that now a favourable wind invited him to depart on the long sea voyage that was still before them, took leave of the king with many expressions of friendship. So they set sail for the lands of the East, which they had sought so long, and his new pilot showed him the true course without any treacherous design.

And now they sailed in Indian seas and came in sight of the region where the sun rose, and had almost attained their goal; but cruel Bacchus enraged by the good fortune of the Portuguese, gave free rein to his fierce wrath. He saw that Heaven had determined to make of Lisbon another Rome, and he was unable to prevent what had been decreed by an omnipotent power. In despair he left Olympus, and descended to earth in search of a remedy, and entered the watery realm of the God of the Sea.

In the lowest depths of the deep-sunk caverns, where the sea lies hid and whence the waves issue when the sea answers to the wind's fury, dwell Neptune and the festive Nereids and other ocean Gods. There, in a plain of finest sand, rise lofty towers of transparent crystal or diamond, so brightly do they gleam. The doors are of fine gold inlaid with pearls and wrought with lovely sculpture. Angry

[1] Translated from *The Lusiad* by Aubrey Fitzgerald Bell.

Bacchus entered this palace, and Neptune, warned of his coming, received him at the gate, accompanied by the Nymphs who marvel at the coming of the God of Wine to this watery realm.

"Neptune," said he, "be not amazed at this my visit, for fortune plagues even the great and powerful; but bid the Gods of the Sea assemble before I say more, if you are willing to hear me; they will hear of great misfortunes, and indeed it concerns them nearly."

Neptune, considering that it must be indeed some strange event, at once sent Triton to call the Gods of the farther and the nearer seas—Triton, the son of King Neptune and Salacia, a dark and uncouth youth of large stature, his father's messenger; his hair and beard fell over his shoulders unkempt, matted with slime and mussels; on his head for cap he wore a lobster's shell. His naked limbs were rough with innumerable shells and crabs, oysters and crayfish. And now as he blew his curving shell, his voice sounded from sea to sea, and all the company of the Gods began to come towards the palace of the God.

Oceanus came with all his sons and daughters; Nereus, who married Doris and peopled all the sea with Nymphs; and the seer Proteus also came, leaving his sea-flocks to graze in their bitter pastures, although he knew already what was Bacchus' wish. Thither also came the lovely spouse of Neptune, daughter of Heaven and Vesta, of grave and cheerful mien, and so fair that the sea grew calm in wonder: her transparent robe allowed her crystal form to be seen; and Amphitrite, lovely as the flowers, conducted by the dolphin who had introduced her to King Neptune's love: her eyes shine brighter than the sun. Both queens come hand in hand, acknowledging one lord. And she, who fleeing from the rage of Athamas, became a Goddess, brought her son, numbered among the Gods; along the shore he runs, playing with the fair sea-shells, and sometimes lovely Panopaea carried him on her neck. The God, too, who from a man was transformed by powerful herbs into a fish, and attained a glorious divinity, came, still bewailing the evil trick played by Circe upon his love, the lovely Scylla.

At length they are all seated in the great hall, noble and divine, the Goddesses on richest daises, the Gods on seats of crystal. They were welcomed by Poseidon who sat enthroned with the Theban God; and all the house was filled with richest incense of Arabia. When the tumult of the Gods and their reception had subsided, Bacchus began to unfold his troubles to them, with grieved and angry mien, devising violent death for the Portuguese.

"O Prince, who rulest in thy might the angry sea from pole to pole, and hemmest the peoples of all the earth in their appointed bounds; and thou, Father Ocean, who surroundest the whole world and only allowest men to exist outside thy frontier; and you Gods of the Sea, who in your mighty realm permit no injury to pass unavenged: how is it that you are careless now ? You see how a weak race of men, called Lusians after one who owns my sovereignty, with proud and lofty heart are overcoming me and you and all the world. You see how they sail across your sea more than ever was done by ancient Rome, and outrage your kingdom and break your laws."

More would he have spoken, but tears impede his speech, tears that from water change the Gods to fire. Their anger permitted no further counsel or delay: they send word from Neptune to great Æolus, bidding him loose the fury of all the winds and drive all navigators from the seas. Proteus, indeed, would gladly have spoken first and uttered some deep prophecy, but so great a tumult of the Gods arose that Tethys cried to him angrily:

"Neptune knows well what order he has sent."

And now the proud son of Hippotes released the raging winds from their prison, and incited them against those brave and daring men. Suddenly the sky grew dark, and the winds with renewed strength and fury begin to overthrow towers and hills and houses.

While this council of the Gods was held in the depths of the ocean, the glad though weary fleet was continuing its long voyage with gentle wind over the tranquil sea. It was night, at the hour when the first watch were about to awake those who were to take their place; yawning and sleepy they stand against the rigging in the bitter cold, and rubbing their eyes tell many a tale to ward off sleep. But suddenly the boatswain, who had been observing the sky, blows his whistle, summoning all the seamen from their sleep: he points to a black cloud, from which the wind blew strongly, and bade them furl the topgallant sails. Hardly had this been done when a fierce and sudden squall fell on them.

"Down with the mainsail," roared the boatswain.

But the furious winds gave them no time to obey; in one fell rush they tear it to pieces with a sound of shattering worlds. A sudden fear and dismay overcame the men, for they were now shipping heavy seas.

"Throw everything overboard," cried the boatswain, "and the rest work the pumps without ceasing."

The brave soldiers ran to the pumps, but the ship, rolling in that dreadful sea, hurled them from side to side. Three strong and seasoned seamen scarce sufficed to hold the helm, and neither strength nor skill availed. The winds could not have been more fierce and cruel if it had been their intent to overthrow the strong tower of Babel: in the towering seas the strong ship is a speck and seems to survive by miracle. The great ship in which Paulo da Gama sailed was full of water; her mast broken in twain, and her crew are imploring the Saviour of the world. Those in Coelho's ship were not in less affliction, although their boatswain had been able to furl the mainsail before the blast struck it.

Now the raging waves carry them up to the clouds; now they seem to see the lowest depths of the abyss; the four winds vied to unhinge the world; the black and dreadful night is lit with lightning flashes. The halcyons along the rocky coast sang again their sorrowful song of old, caused by the raging waters, and the lovelorn dolphins sought their caverns, fleeing from the tempest and relentless winds which gave them no peace even in the ocean depths. Never were such thunderbolts forged against the fierce pride of the giants by the grim smith who wrought gleaming armour for his son-in-law; nor was such lightning hurled athwart the world by the great Thunderer in the mighty flood from which two alone escaped to convert stones into men. Many a mountain was overthrown by the angry waves, many an ancient tree torn up by the roots, and the astonished sand of the depths was hurled to heaven.

Vasco da Gama, when he saw ruin appear as he had nearly reached his goal, and the sea raging heaven-high, hell-deep, in the confusion and danger betook himself to the only remaining refuge, to the Power which can achieve even the impossible.

"O heavenly Power, that rulest over skies and sea and earth, Thou who gavest to Israel a passage through the Red Sea, who didst rescue Paul from wreck and whirlpool, and, with his sons, save the second founder of the flooded empty world; since we have passed safe through a new Scylla and Charybdis, over new shoals and whirlpools, and along fell Acroceraunian cliffs, why after so many dangers dost Thou now forsake us, seeing that this our voyage is undertaken in Thy service? O happy they who fell fighting in Morocco for the faith, whose honoured memory is a new life after death !"

But as he spoke, the raging winds increased the tempest, roaring like angry bulls and whistling in the rigging; fierce lightning flashed without ceasing, and the fell thunder seemed to declare that the very sky had fallen on the earth, and all the elements were waging war.

But now love's morning star shone clear on the horizon, the harbinger of day, and the Goddess who guides it through the Heavens was revisiting with joyous mien the earth and broad seas; the Goddess from whom sword-girt Orion flees; but when she saw the sea and the fleet which she held dear, she felt both fear and anger.

"This," she said, "is the work of Bacchus, but may it be mine always to prevent his fell designs."

So saying, she descends swiftly into the depths of the sea, bidding her Nymphs crown themselves with roses; for she would woo the sullen company of the winds with sight of the fair Nymphs, lovelier even than the stars. And so it was; for at sight of them, their former strength of battle weakened, and they willing are to obey the Nymphs' behests. And fairest Orithia thus addresses Boreas:

"Think not, fierce Boreas, ever to persuade me that thy love to me was a constant love, for that is marked by gentleness, not fury. If thou dost not at once check this raging storm, my love for thee must be changed into fear."

Even so the lovely Galatea spoke to fierce Notus, who in joy at this sign of her love is eager to obey her. In like manner the other Nymphs tamed their lovers, and all the rage and fury bowed down before fair Venus, who promised ever to favour their loves in return for their oath to be loyal to her during this voyage. And now clear morning shone along the hills where Ganges murmurs to the sea, when from the maintopmast the seamen discovered land to starboard; and fear departed from them, since they had escaped the storm and raging seas; and cheerfully the pilot from Melinde said:

"The land must be the land of Calicut."

HOW THE SÃO THOMÉ WAS WRECKED OFF THE TERRA DOS FUMOS[1]

Diogo do Couto
(1542-1616)

WHEN Manoel de Sousa Coutinho was Governor of India, Estevam da Veiga left Cochin in the ship *São Thomé* in January 1589, and steering a course outside the Shallows, made for the island of Diogo Rodrigues, twenty degrees south, where he met a south-east wind so violent, that in great seas the ship rode at the mercy of the wind, and was so beaten about that she sprang a leak in the prow, so that the tow of the calking hung out and let some water in; but this was soon remedied. The wind now calmed, and they continued their course to a latitude of twenty-six degrees off the Island of S. Lourenco, and here, ninety or a hundred leagues from land, the ship began to leak worse and in a more dangerous place—under the floorheads, where it is more difficult to stop than in any other place. The seamen cleared this part of the ship, and found the leak, which was very large, both the tow and the leaden bands nailed over it having been forced out, owing to the badness of the calking, through which many ships are lost: there is great carelessness in this respect, and the workmen are very unscrupulous, as though they were not responsible for the lives and property embarked in these ships. The force of the leak was such that a man's hand had not strength to stay it. As it could not be stopped without cutting away the flanks of the ship, this was done against the opinion of many, but they soon desisted, since this is, as it were, the key of the whole ship, and there were no nails to mend the hole made (for most

[1] Translated from *Historia Tragico-Maritima* by Aubrey Fitzgerald Bell

of these ships are sent out anyhow in order to save a few shillings). They then stopped the hole as best they could with knives and large nails and other articles, and pressing many small sacks of rice against the sides of the ship, and crushing them together in a mass, threw sand over the sacks of rice to strengthen them against the force of the water.

With this the ship became easier, and the water less, and they continued their voyage in good weather to a latitude of thirty-two and a half degrees south, 150 leagues from the Bay of Alagoa and eighty from Natal, the nearest land. Here on the 11th of March a south-west wind struck them, so that they took in the greater part of their sail, and took a northerly direction in great stress of wind and seas, so that the water poured in through the old leak; there were soon three or four feet in the hold and there was great work in throwing overboard everything on the lower deck in order to keep the hatchways clear; and all with their hands on the pumps spent the night without rest; but the water rose another foot, and, flooding the ballast in the hold, reached the barrels and cargo which began to roll from one side of the ship to the other and knock against her side with such force as to shake the whole ship. And as the water was still rising, the seamen placed some lateen yards above the hatchways in prow and stern, and here arranged many small barrels which could be let down and brought up with ease. And there was no one, beginning with Dom Paulo de Lima, who was in the ship with his wife, and Bernardim de Carvalho, Captain Estevam da Veiga, Gregorio Botelho, father-in-law of Guterres de Monroy, who was taking his daughter to be married at home, and other passengers, gentlemen and monks—nobody was exempt from working day and night at the pumps and at the barrels, without leaving them even for meals; for the priests went up and down the deck with biscuits, preserves, and water, giving to all both material and spiritual comfort.

Nevertheless the water kept on rising, and they therefore determined to make for land and cast themselves upon it; and they set the small sails to the prow without daring to touch the mainsail, since to leave the pumps even for an instant would be enough to sink them. And as they made for land, it being now the 14th of March, the hold was entirely filled with water, and the pumps were choked with the pepper that was carried into the hold, and they ceased working them in despair; but those noblemen, monks, and honourable gentlemen kept working with great spirit, and encouraged the rest to do likewise, persuading them not to take their hands off the pumps, for that was their only hope. The seamen spent that day in clearing the pumps, and lining the openings with tin so that they should not again be choked. And as it was necessary to lighten the ship as much as possible, they entrusted this work to certain persons who threw overboard the wealth in the ship, and the extremely valuable porcelain, all of which had been won with much toil and who knows by what means.

Next day, the fifteenth of the month, the deck above the hold was under water, and the wind blew from the south-west, and from time to time in fearful and violent squalls. Everything indeed was against them; even the helm ceased to steer, and the ship lay like a hulk without sails, for they were all rent, and the seamen attended to nothing so as not to cease work at the pumps, in which lay their only hope. All this night was passed in great trouble and despair, for everything around them seemed to tell of death: beneath them they saw the ship full of water, and above them the sky which seemed to conspire against them, and was shrouded in blackest gloom and darkness. The wind whistled on every side, seeming to pipe out "Death, death"; below, the water came rushing in above, the sky poured water down on them as though it would drown them in another flood. Inside the ship nothing could be heard but sighs, groans, cries and lamentation and prayers for mercy to God, who appeared to be angered against them on account of the sins of some of those who were in the ship.

Next day at dawn, giving up all hope, they began to set about lowering the boat, and for this it was necessary to make a space by clearing away some of the barrels. And between decks it seemed that all the spirits of the damned were let loose, and with the thud of things floating from side to side and knocking against one another it sounded like the Last Judgment. The seamen and others made ready the boat rapidly, but with great difficulty, owing to the rocking of the ship between sea and sea, the seas entering through the gangway which was open for throwing the cargo overboard. Their direction was now north-east, for the pilot was of opinion that they were very near land, and that day at sunset a sailor declared that he had sighted it, and called out from the maintopmast: "Land! land!" The pilot did not know if there were reefs on that coast, and therefore stood off and took a course north-east in order to make the land in daylight, and save all the people who had come through this night of toil and affliction. At dawn next day they saw no land, and let down the boat with great difficulty, because, before it was clear of the ship, men leapt into it like madmen, in spite of the fact that Dom Paulo de Lima stood in the boat, sword in hand, in order to prevent the crew from going off in it and leaving him; yet for all the ruthless slashing with swords and cutlasses, so many entered the boat that it would have sunk as soon as it touched the water. At length with great pains Dom Paulo was able to make some of those in it return to the ship, promising them that the boat would take off all it possibly could.

The boat was then brought to the stern of the ship to take in over the ship's side women, monks and noblemen; but the ship rolled so that there was danger of the boat capsizing, and it put off a little, and orders were given that the women should be strapped on bales of cloth: they were thus taken into the boat over the ship's side after being plunged in the sea and in pitiable plight.

The ordering of all this and of the ship fell on Bernardim de Carvalho, for as for Dom Paulo de Lima, as a God-fearing Christian, he believed that the wreck was a punishment for his sins, and was so downcast that he did not seem to be the same man who in great risks and danger had never for a minute lost his calm and courage, which now altogether failed him. The first to be taken into the boat was his wife; then Dona Mariana, wife of Guterres de Monroy; and Dona Joana de Mendoca, widow of Goncalo Gomez de Azevedo, who, though young and with many hopes in the world, was going home to enter a convent; a woman of great virtue, who in all this voyage set an admirable example to every one. She had with her a daughter less than two years old: she had her in her arms and was imploring God for mercy when, in order to strap her to a bale, it became necessary to take the child from her and give it to its nurse. After the women, the priests were taken off, and then Bernardim de Carvalho, and last of all the ship's master and boatswain, who were busy throwing into the boat barrels of biscuit and water and with that it could contain no more and put off.

Dona Joana de Mendoca, seeing that her child had remained on board, on its nurse's neck, who showed it to her with many tears and cries, spoke imploringly in such affliction that she moved the hearts of all to go back to the ship and ask the nurse for the child, bidding her strap it to a bale and throw it down; but she never would, saying that they must take her too, otherwise she would not give it up; and they were never able to persuade her although her mistress entreated her with tears and prayers which might have moved a tiger if a tiger had held the child in its arms. And because they might not delay and the girl was obstinate and the ship was lurching terribly and threatened to capsize the boat, they were obliged to put off, which they did with great pity for the poor mother, who kept her eyes fixed on her daughter with that sorrowful affection with which men look their last on those they love. And seeing that she must leave her child, although she would rather have remained on board with it in her arms than leave it to the mercy of the cruel waves which seemed ready to swallow it, she turned her back on the ship, and raising her eyes to heaven offered her infant daughter in sacrifice as a second Isaac, praying for mercy for herself since her innocent daughter needed none. This sight filled them all with great sorrow, although each of those in the boat was himself in sore need of his neighbour's pity.

When the boat was some little way from the ship, they waited for the Dominican Frei Nicolao do Rosario, who had refused to enter the boat without confessing all those who remained on the ship, that, having no material. comfort, spiritual consolation might not be denied them also; and thus he confessed and comforted them with great charity and absolved them of their sins. It was not possible for the boat to go near and take him off by force, and he was determined to remain and comfort those on board the ship, but at last Dom Paulo de Lima and the others in the boat induced him to jump into the sea and swim to the boat, and he was received by all with joy, since his virtue and example in all that voyage had made them respect and love him. After they had taken him in they made for the land.

After the departure of the boat, those on the ship, placing their hope in God alone, made some rafts as best they could, but God had ordained that they should perish there and they were all sunk, as were two small boats launched from the stern. And really it seemed a punishment of God, for all the people in the ship might easily have been saved if those in the boat had not thought of themselves alone: they could have put everybody, with water and provisions, on great rafts which the boat would then have towed ashore, for the land was so near that they had sight of it next morning; and the ship lasted for twenty-four hours after the pumps had ceased working.

When the boat began to make for land, the seamen found it so full and so low in the water that they began to implore some of those in it to throw themselves into the sea in order to save the rest; the nobles agreed to this course and left the choice of those who must die to the seamen; and they at once threw overboard six persons, who plunged into the depths and were no more seen. The rest looked on amazed, as in a dream; and after these six persons had gone, there remained in the boat one hundred and four. The tide kept pushing the boat out to sea, for it was very heavy and they were too worn out to row; and at midnight they found themselves not far from the ship and rowed up to her, and saw many lights moving on board, for those in the ship spent the night in processions and litanies, holding lighted candles in their hands and imploring the mercy of God with cries and supplications so loud that they could be heard from the boat. At dawn the boat went close up to the ship and had speech with those on board, and encouraged them to make rafts, and offered to wait to accompany them. Those on board answered with loud shouts and lamentation, beseeching for pity with so deep a passion as to fill every one with fear and awe, for the scene was all the more terrible because it was not yet fully light.

When day broke, three or four sailors in the boat swam to the ship to take off food and muskets; they found the deck under water and the people all demented in expectation of death, and in the raised part of the stern there was still a beautiful altar to the Virgin; round it were huddled the slaves with hair dishevelled, supplicating Our Lady for mercy; and in front of them all was Dona Joana's nurse, with the child still in her arms, unwitting of its danger. The sailors threw into the sea some barrels of water and biscuit and one barrel of wine which were taken into the boat. The boat made some efforts to go up to the ship and put on board some of those who made it too heavy to be seaworthy. The sailors returned to the boat without Dona Joana's child, for indeed most of them are inhuman and cruel by nature.

Being unable to reach the ship, they pulled away and left it to the seamen to act as they considered best; and these proceeded to throw certain persons overboard, among them being a certain Diogo Fernandez, a good man of little spirit, who was returning from the post of factor in Ceylon; a soldier named Diogo de Seixas; Diogo Duarte, a merchant; and Diogo Lopes Bayam, who had spent many years in Balagate, where the native ruler had given him an income of three thousand crusados because he was a man of skill and resource, who traded in horses between Goa and Balagate, and brought him secret news; and it was suspected that he was doubtful in the faith, for which reason he was sent home. Before they threw him into the sea, he gave Frei Nicolao a sack of precious stones which were said to be worth ten or twelve thousand crusados. And together with these men they threw into the sea some slaves, who were all immediately swallowed up by those cruel waves.

After this abominable cruelty on the part of the seamen, for which God soon punished them, since all or most of them perished in despair on land, the boat began to row ashore, and when they were some way from the ship, at ten o'clock in the morning, they saw her plunge terribly and disappear in an instant from their sight. The boat hoisted a sail, and made for the nearest land, the wind blowing from the east; and in the afternoon of the 20th of March they came in sight of land with great rejoicing, if hearts so stricken might rejoice.

MODERN GREECE

SEA[1]

Antrea Karkavitsas

MY FATHER—may the wave that buried him be holy oil for him—never meant to make a sailor of me.

"Keep away, my boy," he said, "keep away from the lying monster! She has no faith nor mercy. Worship her as you will—honour her—she never moves from her own aim. Don't look at her deceiving smile, promising her countless wealth. Sooner or later she will dig a grave for you, or she will cast you on the world a useless ruin, with nothing to own but your skin and bones. Sea or woman—it's all the same!"

These were the words of a man who had spent a whole life on a ship's deck, a man whose father and grandfather and great-grandfather had died by the mast. And he was not alone in this opinion. The other old men of the island, veterans of the ships, and the younger people whose hands were still callous, whenever they took their seats in the coffeehouse to smoke their water pipes, would waggle their heads sadly and say with a sigh:

"There's no more bread to be gained from the sea. Let me have just a root of vine on the solid earth and I would throw a black stone behind me."

The truth was that many of them had money enough to own not only a vine but a whole island. Yet they would spend it all on the sea. They competed against each other to see who could build the biggest vessel or who would be a captain first. I, who often heard their words and saw their acts, contrary to and inconsistent with their words, could not understand the mystery.

Some God's breath, I said to myself, some power sent from infinity was coming down to drag with it all those souls and hurl them captives against their wills into the open sea, just as the raging north wind beating on the bare cliffs bites off the weathered pieces and hurls them down in a mass of fragments.

But the same impulse was pushing me, too, that way. Ever since my childhood days, I loved the sea. You might say I took my first steps in the water. My first toy was a box of beans with a little stick set up in the centre for a mast, with two pieces of thread for hawsers and a sheet of paper for a sail and my imagination made of this little box a triple-decked bark. I put it to sea with emotion and imagined myself in it. Of course, as soon as I took my hand off, my bark sank to the bottom, but I was not slow in building another of timber. My dockyard was at the little harbour of St Nicholas. I put my boat to sea and I followed it, swimming to the entrance

[1] Translated by Demetra Vaka and Aristides Phoutrides.

of the harbour, where the current swept it far away from me. Later I became first in rowing and first in swimming. All I lacked was a fish's scales.

"Bravo!" said the old sailors to me with their good-natured smiles as they saw me ripping the water like a dolphin. "You will put us all to shame!"

I was proud because of these words and I hoped that some day I would fulfill their prophecy. I remember it was my seventh year at school when I closed my books forever. I found nothing in them that would respond to my longings, while everything else about me, living or not, whispered to me a thousand tales: The sailors with their faces bronzed by the sun; the old men with their reminiscences; the piled timber with its story told at sight; the lasses with their songs:

> How handsome is my little mate when wet with the sea-spray,
> He puts on his change of snow-white clothes and takes the helm in hand.

This song I heard ever since my cradle days and it seemed to me like a hymn sung by my island to lure its inhabitants to the life of the sea. My dream, too, was some day to be a mate and wet with the sea-spray, to hold the helm in hand. Surely I would be handsome then and strong—a real man. I would be the pride of my island and I would be loved by every lass.

Yes, I did love the sea! At times I saw her spreading from the headland far away and mingling with the blue firmament, like a sapphire floor, smooth, calm, and silent with a secret that I longed to know. At times I saw her in a fury, spattering the shore angrily with white foam, toppling over the reefs, scaling the caves of the great rocks with a restless thundering roar, as if she sought to penetrate the earth's fiery womb and to extinguish the flames that burned there. This intoxicated me, and I ran to play with her, to make her angry and provoke her, so that she might rush against me and chase me, and lash my body with her spray—tease her as we like to tease wild beasts bound with chains. Then, when I saw a ship lifting anchor and sailing out of the harbour into the open sea and heard the cheering chanties of the sailors labouring at the capstan sheets and the farewells of the women, my soul would fly like a lonely bird after it. The sails of dark grey, swelling with the wind, the stays stretching like delicate lines against the horizon, the golden trucks leaving behind them a trail of light in the blue sky, called out to me to go with them, promising new lands, new men, riches, joys, strange kisses that, though I knew it not, were stored in my heart as the inherited pleasures of my fathers. So, day and night, my soul longed for nothing else but the day of sailing away. Even when the news of a shipwreck reached the island, and the death of the drowned men lay heavy on everybody's heart, and silent grief spread from the frowning faces to the inanimate pebbles of the beach; even when I met the orphans of the dead in the streets, like gilded pieces of wood among the ruins of a once prosperous home, and saw the women clothed in black, and the bereaved sweethearts left disconsolate, and heard the survivors of the shipwreck tell of their misfortune—even then I was sorry and jealous that I had not been with them to see my own sweetheart in her wild majesty and to wrestle with her, wrestle unto death.

At last I could no longer control myself. My father had sailed away with his schooner. My uncle, Kaligeres, was just about to set sail for the Black Sea. I fell on his neck; and my mother, too, fearing I might get sick intervened in my behalf. He consented to take me along.

"I will take you, "he said "but you'll have to work. A sailing ship needs care, it's no fishing boat for food and sleep."

I was always afraid of my uncle. He was as rude and mean to me as he was to his sailors. Men avoided working under him.

Better slaving in Algiers
Than with Captain Kaligeres,

they would say to show his heartlessness. He would "bake a fish on their lips" not only in the work he exacted but even in the food and the pay he gave them. Whatever there was of old salt junk, mouldy dry cod, bitter flour, weevilly biscuit and chalky cheese could be found in Kaligeres' stores to be used for his sailors. He would never speak, except to command, to swear, or to abuse somebody. Only men who despaired of any other chance would offer themselves to him. So I knew well I was not going to indulge in caresses and good times. But the lure of the sea made me disregard everything.

"Only take me aboard," I said, "and I'll work as much as you want." To make my word good, I plunged into work. I made the futtock shrouds my play. The higher I had to go the more eager I was to climb up first. Perhaps my uncle wished to make it especially hard for me from the beginning, and to acquaint me with the endless trials of a sailor's life in order to make me change my mind. He surely kept me going, from deck-washing to deck-scrubbing, from sail-mending to rope-twisting, from letting go and clewing up the sails to stowing them; from the quay to the capstan, from loading to unloading, from caulking to painting. I had to be first in everything. First be it! What did I care? I was satisfied to climb high to the topyard and with my big toes grasping the backstay to look down into space and watch the sea open a way and retreat before me as my humble subject. Drunk with joy, I compared myself to a proud bird winging its way triumphantly across the skies. I was in a magic trance. I looked with pity on the rest of the world, on the men who lived on dry land. They seemed to me like ants, creeping snakes, or slow-moving tortoises condemned to wear their shells forever as a useless burden.

"Bah!" I would say with contempt. "They think they live!" On such a surge of enthusiasm I heard one day the Captain's voice roar like a peal of thunder beside me:

"Let go the sails! Clew up and let go all!"

I was frightened, and ran to follow the other sailors without understanding exactly what the trouble was. Every one to his post, and I to mine. They flew to the jibs; I followed them. They climbed up to the yards. I was among them, making fast and stowing every sail. Within five minutes the bark was a skeleton of spars. In front of his cabin the captain stood shouting and abusing and cursing. I looked at him, but damned if I knew what he was talking about.

"What in hell is the matter?" I asked the man next to me as we were making the sky-sail fast.

"The squall—don't you see the water spout!"

The waterspout! A shiver ran down my back. I had often heard of its awful wonders; how it sweeps everything away in its path, how it makes tatters of sails, breaks down masts, and downs all things that sail the sea. There was not only one, but three or four. Two of them rose towards Batum. The others were on our port bow, sweeping over the waters from grey distance where sky and sea met. Ahead, Caucasus, a frowning monstrous mass, showing his darkened coast walled with great cliffs like bare teeth ready to tear a world. Above us, the sky draped with thick heavy curtains of clouds; below, the sea, blackish-grey, trembling from end to end like a living thing shuddering with fear. For the first time I saw my sweetheart frightened.

The one waterspout was high and arched like an elephant's proboscis, and hung over the waters, a black, motionless monster. The other, at first like an immense thick pillar rising straight up, was suddenly broken in two like a column of smoke; its lower half was shattered into a thousand fragments, while the upper half hung from the clouds like a manyforked serpent's tongue. I saw the serpent moving on, stretching his neck, now this way and now that, brandishing his tongues as if seeking something on the face of the waters, and then suddenly flinging his body backward and gathering it in coils to nestle among the clouds. But a third one, black and grey and as thick as the trunk of a plane-tree a thousand years old, stood motionless for some time sucking up the water and swelling in size; and then, tottering like a menacing beast, it started sweeping against us, a monstrous mass of terror.

"Down, there! Get down!" I heard a voice from the deck calling to me.

Turning around, I saw that all the others had climbed down while I had been clinging fast to the topmast, watching the strange miracle. I slid down to the captain. With bulging eyes he was glaring at the apparition. In his right hand he held a black-handled knife, and stood behind the mainmast as if it were a bulwark.

Near by the mate was hurriedly filling up the rusty "trompone"[1] and around him stood the stunned sailors, staring now at the sea, now at the sky.

The waterspout was approaching on winged feet, sucking up the water and then spitting it out skyward in a black roaring fog. It seemed as if it would sweep everything off the boat, or as if it would lift it up bodily. It came within two fathoms of us—cylindrical, luminous, golden and green like smoked crystal, its piston working inside its heart, as if it were endeavouring to extinguish some huge conflagration up in heaven. "Now !" commanded the captain.

The mate sent the contents of the "trompone" into it. Old nails, lead, oakum all were absorbed in it. It seemed to totter. That stopped: it tried to move. Twice it swooped about, and again stood, uniting sea and sky.

"We failed," the captain said bitterly to the mate.

"Yes, we did. And now draw the pentagram, captain, and let the sin be upon my head."

"God forgive me!" murmured the captain, making the sign of the cross.

With the black-handled knife he traced the pentagram upon the mast, saying thrice: "In the beginning was the Word, and the Word was God, and God was the Word."

He stuck the knife in the middle of the pentagram as if he were nailing it to the very entrails of the monster.

A blast was heard as if a cannon had been discharged, and a gigantic wave broke over our deck. At the same instant the Caucasus was illuminated by a lightning flash, and reverberated thunderously as the monster broke. And the frightened sea foamed and raged over its whole immense surface.

"Aloft the sails!" commanded the captain quickly. "Top-sails! Jibs! Top-gallants! Royals!"

We spread our sails, and soon the bark was on its course again.

II

Three weeks later we anchored at Constantinople, with a cargo on board. There I received the first letter from my mother, a first letter that came like a first stab at my inexperienced heart.

"Yanne, my boy," said the old woman, "when you come back to the island with St Nicholas' help and my blessing, you will not be any longer a captain's son as you were on the day you sailed away—your father is gone with his schooner and all our fortune! The Black Sea has swallowed them all. Now you have nothing left

[1] An ancient Turkish term for a hell-mouthed gun or small cannon was a "tromboni."

but this one-story house, me, a helpless woman, and God. May your arms be strong. Work, my boy, and respect your uncle. If you have anything left over from your earnings, send it to me to buy oil and burn a candle before the Saint for your father's soul."

I crossed my hands and looked with tearful eyes at the sea. The words of the letter seemed to me like an echo of my father's words. He had been a captain, owner of his own vessel for many years, and now his widow had to depend on my savings to make a wheat offering[1] for the dead man's soul! His wheat offering, not to speak of the poor widow's own needs! Meanwhile, who knows against what reefs his iron-strong arms are dashing, what gulls are tearing his flesh, or what waves are bleaching his fleshless bones!

How significant were his last words! We had met for the last time just as we were sailing into the port of Theodosia, when he saw me high on the top-yard stowing the skysail. He crossed himself and stood dumb with emotion. He had not expected such a thing.

"Why do you look at him, Captain Angele?" Kaligeres shouted to him as we sailed by. "I wouldn't exchange him for your best hand."

At the same moment I was praying earnestly that the sea might open and swallow me. I could not rest so long as I felt his stern eyes fixed on me. I ran hurriedly from one end to another, as if I were too busy to stop. Down into the forecastle I would go, and up the futtook-shrouds; or I would pass from the capstan to the poop and do anything to avoid him. He understood my confusion, and did not rise from his seat; but from the place where he sat he followed me with a sad, complaining eye as if he was looking on a deathbed.

Next day he met me as I was going to town with the other men. As soon as I caught sight of him, I tried to hide, but he nodded, and even from the distance his nod was so commanding that my legs refused to obey my will.

"My boy, whatever was the matter with you? Have you thought over what you are trying to do?"

For the first time I knew there was gentleness in my father's voice; but I did not hesitate.

"Father," I said with courage, "I did think it over. Maybe my act is foolish and bad; but I can't help it. I can't live otherwise. The sea calls me; don't try to stop me. Else I might go where you will never see me again."

He made the sign of the cross, puzzled by my determination. He looked straight into my eyes for some time, then he shook his head and said:

---

[1] Boiled wheat seasoned with sugar, cinnamon, burned flour nuts, etc., and placed on a tray before the altar. The priest prays for the forgiveness of the dead person's sins and the wheat is distributed among all present, who take it saying, "God forgive him," and eat it.

"Very well, my boy; do whatever God prompts you to. I have done my part. Remember, I have spared neither words nor money. You will have no reason to curse me in the future. Go with my blessing."

His last blessing was my first regret. The sea did not reward my love on my first trip.

I was now truly a hired man for Captain Kaligeres, to earn my own bread and my mother's, who had been a captain's wife. Yet in spite of her advice, I could neither respect him nor work for my uncle any longer. If I must be a hired sailor, I thought, thank God there are other vessels. I would much rather get a shower of abuse from a stranger than from my own kin. A stranger would be more likely to respect my name. And so I made up my mind, if all was well, to disembark at the first port.

"Out for a better job? You will see!" said Kaligeres, who guessed my thoughts.

One day I went to ask a little olive oil for my food.

"No," he said, "that's for the man who stands by the wheel."

I went a second time and a third. The same answer. It wasn't enough for him to feed us with every decaying thing; he had to strike even olive oil off our rations. His avarice and his heartlessness were his most detestable traits. I decided to get back at him once, and one day when I was at the wheel and he was out of sight, I took the picture of St Nicholas from the chart-house, where a lamp filled with olive oil burned before it, tied it to the wheel and left the deck. The bark, like a crazy person, wandered all over the sea.

"Yanne !" shouted the captain, "who is at the wheel ?"

"He who eats the oil!" I answered.

All the crew split themselves laughing and that angered him.

"Get out!" he said. "Pack your things and go!"

"All right. Give me my pay."

He took me into the chart-house and opened his account book. He reckoned up my dues in his usual manner.

"I hired you on such a day. The next day you came aboard; the day after, you brought your clothes, and one day later you started work. Not so ?"

He cheated me altogether, out of five days' pay. Still, it might have been worse.

"Just as you say," I said.

And so, with two pounds in my pocket, I landed in Messene.

III

From now on I lived like a real sailor. A life of toil and turmoil. Antlike as far as being always busy, but never ant-like in saving. How could you ever save with such living from hand to mouth? One pair of shoes took one month's wages. A

IV

Three years went by, spent with Mary up in Trapi, my father-in-law's village. Three years of real life. I learned how to handle a pick, and worked with my wife in the orchard, the vineyard and the field. With work and love, I never felt the passing of time. When we did not dig together we chased each other under the citron trees like birds just learning how to fly. Her word followed on my word; her kiss on mine. I learned how to dig around the citron trees, how to prune the vines, and how to plough the field. Then I knew how to pick the citrons in the fall, how to gather the grapes when vintage time came in August, and how to reap the wheat-field in the month of harvest. I earned fifty talera from my citrons yearly, twenty from my vine, and forty from my wheat, besides the seed I kept for next year's crop and the provisions for my own home use. It was the first time that I really knew what earning was, and realized that my labour was received gratefully and rewarded with plenty. The speechless earth tried in a thousand manners, colours, shapes, fragrances, fruits, and flowers to speak and thank me for taking care of it.

If I ploughed, the furrow remained faithfully where I opened it. It would receive the seed and hide it diligently from the flying things; then it would keep it warm and damp until the day when it would show it before my eyes fresh with dew, green with living sap, and finally mature with gold. The earth seemed to say: "See how I have brought it up!" If I lightened the burden of a vine by pruning it, the vine would seem to burst into tears with emotion, and shaking with delight would open its eyes like bright butterflies and suddenly bring forth its heavy burden of new clusters. If I trimmed the citron tree, it would rise lithe with grace and dazzling with beauty, and with its tufted branches would build wonderful shady arches to cool our bodies from the noon-day heat and to shower fragrances on our sleep at night, while its light golden fruit would refresh our very being.

Yes, it is the earth God has blessed with feeling, and not that senseless monster which effaces your track as soon as the keel has opened it, jealous of the least sign that anyone might try to leave on eternity. Praise the sea all you may; flatter it, sing of it; its answer is a thrust for you to get away, a murmur of discontent at your presence, or an untamed tiger's roar when it tries to open a grave for you. Cain, after his crime, should have been condemned to a seaman's life.

At sunset we would walk back to the village. Mary would go ahead in the midst of her playful goats, who shook their bells as they frisked about merrily. I would follow with the pick on my shoulder, leading behind me the mule loaded with logs for fuel. Then, at home, while Mary lighted the fire to make supper, I would light my pipe and sit down comfortably at the threshold in the midst of a gay honeysuckle that spread lustily over the walls in the midst of scented royal mints and spearmints and sweet marjorams, generous little plants that asked for nothing but a handful of proper earth and a drop of water to bathe us with fragrance and grace.

From this place I would exchange greetings with passing neighbours, greetings that trickled from the very heart.

"Good evening!"

"Good evening to you!"

"Good night!"

"Good luck to you!"

I did not have to look anxiously at the sky any longer. I did not have to consider the position of the moon, the trembling light of the stars, the course of the wind, the rise of the Pleiades. And late at night, when I cast anchor in my love's arms, what bay or what luring port could ever give me such happiness!

So two years passed, and now we were in the third. One Sunday in February I went with my wife to my old town of St Nicholas by the sea. Her cousin, Captain Malamos, was christening his brig, and had invited us to the joyful occasion. It was a beautiful day, which was the first awakening of my old longing. The dock was covered with timber, masts, beams, splinters, and wood-shavings. The air was filled with the smell of the sea brine, the scent of freshly cut timber, the heavy odour of tar, pitch, and ropes. There were hills of hemp and piles of steel pieces. From one end of the beach to the other there was an array of little rowboats beautifully painted, brigs careened, luggers stripped of all rigging and old hulls covered with barnacles and seaweed. There were skeletons of cutters, schooners, and brigantines, some with just the keel and the sea-steps, others ribbed and planked up to the gunwale, others only halfway up. Any tool a seaman might wish for was there; and any seaman's dreams, ambitions, simple longings, and great hopes could be found on that gold-sanded beach, expressed vividly in some wooden structure by some ship-builder's hands. The guests—the whole island, it seemed—old men and young boys, old women and young girls, moved in their Sunday clothes from one ship's frame to another. The boys hopped from place to place. The men handled their parts with knowing pride, and often they spoke to them as if they were living things. The veterans of the sea sized up each ship's worth, estimated its speed, measured its tonnage, recounted the profits it might bring, and gave their advice to the master builder on everything. At last, they concluded by wishing the owner of each ship that its nails might turn to gold for him.

Captain Malamos' brig was in its dock; its fine and lovely hull, with its many props on both sides, looked like a huge centipede sleeping on the sandy beach. Its prow curved like a delicately wrought sabre; its stern was girded with garlands of flowers. A glistening meadow of pure azure, the sea, spread before it, shimmering playfully and reaching for the ship's feet with little tongues of rippling water. She sprinkled it with her lukewarm spray, made it fragrant with her salt breath, and sang to it a secret confiding song: "Come," she sang, "come and lie on my bosom. I will give you life with my kiss; I will breathe a soul into you and will make you fly on strong wings. Why do you lie there, a mass of soulless timber, like something heavy with sleep? Are you not weary of the torpor of the forest and its life of no will? Shame on you! Come out into the sun, and the air, and the light! Come to wrestle with the wave and ride victor over it! With raised breast meet the strong wind and tear him into tatters. You will be the whale's envy, the dolphin's mate, the sea-gulls' comfort, the sailor's song, your captain's pride. Come, my golden one, come!" and the ship seemed to feel the spell of the sea and began to creak, eager to leave its bed where it lay in idleness.

All about, the guests were crowding. Captain Malamos stood by with a smooth-shaved, smiling face, dressed in his best, with a broad scarf about his waist. Near him, his wife, in a dress of silk, looked like a bride. They seemed to live their wedding-day once more, while a violin, a mandolin, and a drum played their gay melodies, with a spirit that seemed determined to carry the glad tidings to the ends of the earth.

Would you believe it? I was not happy in the least. As I sat toward the end nearest the sea, I would see the water's little ripples reaching at my feet, and a certain sadness wrung my heart. My first sweetheart, whom I had not seen for years, was now facing me again, young and beautiful, clothed in her raiment of sapphire blue. Her face smiled with perfect gladness; and I thought that she had her eyes fixed on me and that she spoke words of regretful complaint:

"Faithless one! Deceiver! Coward!"

"Get thee behind me, Satan!" I said to myself, and made the sign of the cross.

I wanted to get away but my feet refused. My body seemed like a mass of lead that was stuck to the rock; and my eyes, my ears, my soul were a helpless prey to the wave which continued to sing its sad complaint:

"Faithless one! Deceiver! Coward!"

Tears almost came to my eyes. My hatred for the sea, her tyranny, her crimes, the sleepless nights and my fruitless labour, all, vanished from my mind like bad dreams. I remembered only my first joys, the glad intoxication of the sea, the charm of wandering over her, the magic shiver of her dangers, the sheer enjoyment of escaping them, the recklessness of a sailor's life. All these joys I had abandoned for the sake of a woman.

"Well, what makes you so thoughtful, life of mine?" I heard a voice beside me. I turned and saw Mary, beautiful and smiling, with her lithe body, her fresh lips, her full breast, her shining eyes, and her coal-black hair. I felt confused and guilty as if I had been caught in the act of deceiving her.

"Nothing," I murmured; "nothing! Lend me a hand to get up. I feel dizzy."

I took her hand and grasped her with intense eagerness as if I were in danger of falling into the cold darkness of an abyss. The priest, in his vestments, was reading his prayers over the new ship. The ship-builder began giving his commands:

"Let go the stern prop! Let go the prow! Loosen the sides, now!"

One after another the props fell from the hull and the brig began to shake as if still stiff from sleep and hesitating to plunge forward into its new life. The boys who had climbed on deck were running from stern to prow and from starboard to port, making a noise like a flock of sheep.

The hands had taken their places beside the hull in order to push it into the sea. The master-builder commanded again:

"Let go!"

At the united effort of so many breasts, the ship groaned, shook once more, and finally glided, like a duck, into the water with its youthful crew on deck.

"Good luck to it, Captain Malamos! Good luck to it. May her nails turn to gold for you!" the crowd of seamen shouted, and sprinkled the captain and his wife with handfuls of spray.

But at that moment one of the boys on deck stumbled as he ran and fell senseless overboard. On the same instant, I plunged into the sea with my clothes on. With the second dive I pulled the boy to the surface. I saved the boy, but the meshes of the sea were tight about me, and none could save me. From that time on I could neither sleep nor rest. Joy had left me forever. That plunge into the sea, her warm water that had embraced me, was now dragging my soul a slave behind it. I remembered its touch was like warm kisses that sent an electric current down my back. With my open eyes I saw before me a bride clothed in blue; young, glad, and tender, nodding to me from the distance to follow her. I could hear her call: "Come! Come!"

I could not work any longer. I tried to go back to my orchard, field and vineyard, but all seemed to me walled-in and narrow. The shade of the citron tree was heavy and cold. The vine-twigs with their knots seemed disgustingly ugly, like a lobster's legs. The furrows of the field, cheap. So I spent day after day on the beach plunging into the water. I felt its touch with shivers of delight. I caught hungrily its salt breath, and I wallowed in bliss among the seaweeds as on a bed of soft feathers and silk. I would spend hours picking sea-urchins and crabs. Often I would go down to the harbour, and with some hesitation draw near the groups of sailors to hear them talk about their rigs, and travels, and storms, and shipwrecks. They would hardly look at me. You see, I was only a peasant, an old farmer, while they were sailors, dolphins of the sea. What could a poplar have to do with rhubarb? How could it stoop from its height to see the little weed at its feet? They could not even count me as present in their company. The younger sailors would look at me with wonder, as if to say: "Where does this ghost come from?" The older men who once had been my friends and my mates would occasionally deign to address me with a jest:

"Now, Yanne, you have your hawsers pretty tight. You don't have to worry about wind or sea. You've cast anchor for good!"

Their eyes had such an expression of pity that I could read in them what they did not speak in words: "You are a dead man! You don't belong to the living world any longer!" So I turned to the beach to tell my troubles to the waves. In the end, I turned back to my early years and consoled myself with little ships which I built with my hands. My skill was mature now, and I could make them with oak masts and actual stays and sails, while my imagination was again aflame and made tripledecked barks out of them. I was a child again.

Mary watched me and wondered about my change. Often she thought I was turning insane and prayed to Virgin Mary to help me. She made more than one vow to the Holy Virgin of Tenos, and went with bare feet on many pilgrimages to the neighbouring country shrines. She had prayers read over my clothes, and often, beating her breast with anxiety, she called on the saints and tried to secure their help in bringing me back to my senses again.

"Mary," I said to her once, "there's nothing that will help. Neither saints nor vows can cure my trouble. I am a child of the sea. It calls and I must go. Sooner or later I must return to my old trade. Else I cannot live."

As soon as she heard it she put on mourning. At last she knew the serpent that had been biting her so long in secret.

"Your trade!" she cried; "to be a sailor—and poor again!"

"Yes, a sailor! I can't help it. The sea is calling me!"

But she could not understand. She would not hear of it. She cried and prayed. She threw her arms about me, pressed me to her bosom, and covered me with kisses, clinging to me with despair, anxious in her jealousy to make me see the toil of the sea, its dangers, and shipwrecks. She would abuse the sea, find a thousand faults with it, and curse it as if it were her rival. But all was in vain. Neither her arms nor her kisses could bind me any longer. Everything seemed cold and wearisome, even my bed.

One evening, about sunset, as I was sitting on the rocks by the sea, plunged in my usual thought, I saw before me a brig sailing by, with all her sails drawing. It looked like a cliff of light rising suddenly from the midst of the sea. All her spars and stays were painted with wonderful distinctness against the blue sky. I saw the jibs, the courses, the top-sails, the top-gallants, the trucks. I believed I could even see the billet-head. My eyes seemed to get a supernatural power, so that they could turn timber to crystal and reach the very depths of the ship I could see the captain's cabin adorned with the picture of St Nicholas and his neverfailing candle. I could see the sailors' bunks, hear their simple talk, and sense their sour smell. I could see the galley, the water-barrels, the pump, the capstan. My soul, like a homesick bird, had perched on the full-rigged ship. I heard the wind whistling through the stays and shrouds, singing with a harmony more than divine of a seaman's life; and before my eyes passed on winged feet virgins with fair hair and black hair, virgins with blue eyes and dark eyes, and virgins with flowers, showing their bare breasts and sending me distant kisses. Then I saw noisy ports, taverns filled with smoke and wine-cups and resounding with sweet-voiced guitars and tambourines. Suddenly I saw a sailor pointing at me and heard him say to his companion:

"There goes one who renounced the sea for fear of it!"

I sprang up like a madman. Never for fear! Never, I thought, and ran back to the house. Mary had gone out to the brook. So much the better. I took a purse from under my pillow, cast a last glance on the bed, and with a pack of clothes on my shoulder, I disappeared like a thief. It was dark when I reached St Nicholas, but without losing any time I jumped into a boat and rowed to the brig.

Life has been a phantom for me ever since. If you ask me if I regret it, I would not know what to answer. But even should I go back to my island now, I could never rest.

The sea claims me.

HOLLAND

THE FLYING DUTCHMAN[1]

Auguste Jal

ONCE upon a time, a good many years ago, there was a ship's captain who feared neither God nor His Saints. He is said to have been a Dutchman, but I do not know, nor does it greatly matter, from what town he came. He happened once to be making a voyage to the South. All went well until he came near to the Cape of Good Hope, where he ran into a head wind strong enough to blow the horns off a bull. The ship was in great danger, and every one began to say to the Captain:

"Captain, we must turn back. If you insist on continuing to try to round the Cape we shall be lost. We shall inevitably perish, and there is no priest on board to give us absolution."

But the Captain laughed at the fears of his crew and passengers, and began to sing songs so horrible and blasphemous that they might well have attracted the lightning to his mast a hundred times over. Then he calmly smoked his pipe and drank his beer as though he was seated in a tavern at home. His people renewed their entreaties to him to turn back, but the more they implored him the more obstinate he became. His masts were broken, his sails had been carried away, but he merely laughed as a man might who has had a piece of good news.

So the Captain continued to treat with equal contempt the violence of the storm, the protests of the crew and the fears of the passengers, and when his men attempted to force him to make for the shelter of a bay near by, he flung the ringleader overboard. But even as he did so, the clouds opened and a Form alighted on the quarter deck of the ship. This Form is said to have been the Almighty Himself. The crew and passengers were stricken with fear, but the Captain went on smoking his pipe, and did not even touch his cap when the Form addressed him. "Captain," said the Form, "you are very stubborn."

"And you're a rascal," cried the Captain. "Who wants a peaceful passage? I don't. I'm asking nothing from you, so clear out of this unless you want your brains blown out."

The Form gave no other answer than a shrug of the shoulders.

The Captain then snatched up a pistol, cocked it and fired; but the bullet, instead of reaching its target, pierced his hand. His fury knew no bounds. He leaped up

[1] This translation is taken from J.G. Lockhart's *Mysteries of the Sea.*

to strike the Form in the face with his fist, but his arm dropped limply to his side, as though paralyzed. In his impotent rage he cursed and blasphemed and called the good God all sorts of impious names.

But the Form said to him:

"Henceforth you are accursed, condemned to sail on for ever without rest or anchorage or port of any kind. You shall have neither beer nor tobacco. Gall shall be your drink and red-hot iron your meat. Of your crew your cabin-boy alone shall remain with you; horns shall grow out of his forehead, and he shall have the muzzle of a tiger and skin rougher than that of a dog-fish."

The Captain groaned, but the Form continued:

"It shall ever be your watch, and when you wish, you will not be able to sleep, for directly you close your eyes a sword shall pierce your body. And since it is your delight to torment sailors, you shall torment them."

The Captain smiled.

"For you shall be the evil spirit of the sea. You shall traverse all latitudes without respite or repose, and your ship shall bring misfortune to all who sight it."

"Amen to that!" cried the Captain with a shout of laughter.

"And on the Day of Judgment Satan shall claim you."

"A fig for Satan!" was all the Captain answered.

The Almighty disappeared, and the Dutchman found himself alone with his cabin-boy, who was already changed as had been predicted. The rest of his crew had vanished.

From that day forward the Flying Dutchman has sailed the seas, and it is his pleasure to plague poor mariners. He casts away their ship on an uncharted shoal, sets them on a false course and then shipwrecks them. He turns their wine sour and all their food into beans. Sometimes he will send letters on board the ships he meets, and if the Captain tries to read them he is lost. Or an empty boat will draw alongside the Phantom Ship and disappear, a sure sign of ill-fortune. He can change at will the appearance of his ship, so as not to be recognized; and round him he has collected a crew as cursed as himself, all the criminals, pirates and cowards of the sea.

HOW WILLIAM THE SILENT OPENED THE GATES OF THE SEA[1]

John Lothrop Motley
(1814-1877)

ON THE 26th of May (1574) Valdez reappeared before the place, at the head of eight thousand Walloons and Germans, and Leyden was now destined to pass through a fiery ordeal. This city was one of the most beautiful in the Netherlands. Placed in the midst of broad and fruitful pastures, which had been reclaimed by the hand of industry from the bottom of the sea, it was fringed with smiling villages, blooming gardens, fruitful orchards. The ancient and, at last, decrepit Rhine, flowing languidly towards its sandy death-bed, had been multiplied into innumerable artificial currents by which the city was completely interlaced. Those watery streets were shaded by lime-trees, poplars, and willows, and crossed by one hundred and forty-five bridges, mostly of hammered stone. Upon an artificial elevation, in the centre of the city, rose a ruined tower of unknown antiquity. By some it was considered to be of Roman origin, while others preferred to regard it as a work of the Anglo-Saxon Hengist raised to commemorate his conquest of England. Surrounded by fruit-trees and overgrown in the centre with oaks, it afforded, from its mouldering battlements, a charming prospect over a wide expanse of level country, with the spires of neighbouring cities rising in every direction. It was from this commanding height, during the long and terrible summer days which were approaching, that many an eye was to be strained anxiously seaward, watching if yet the ocean had begun to roll over the land.

Valdez lost no time. . . . In the course of a few days, Leyden was thoroughly invested, no less than sixty-two redoubts, some of them having remained undestroyed from the previous siege, now girdling the city, while the besiegers already numbered nearly eight thousand, a force to be daily increased. On the other hand, there were no troops in the town, save a small corps of *"free-booters,"* and five companies of the burgher guard.

The main reliance of the city, under God, was on the stout hearts of its inhabitants within the walls, and on the sleepless energy of William the Silent without. The Prince, hastening to comfort and encourage the citizens, although he had been justly irritated by their negligence in having omitted to provide more sufficiently against the emergency while there had yet been time, now reminded them that they were not about to contend for themselves alone, but that the fate

[1] From *The Rise of the Dutch Republic.*

of their country and of unborn generations would, in all human probability, depend on the issue about to be tried. Eternal glory would be their portion if they manifested a courage worthy of their race and of the sacred cause of religion and liberty. He implored them to hold out at least three months, assuring them that he would, within that time, devise the means of their deliverance.

By the end of June, the city was placed on a strict allowance of food, all the provisions being purchased by the authorities at an equitable price. Half a pound of meat and half a pound of bread was allotted to a full-grown man, and to the rest a due proportion. The city being strictly invested, no communication, save by carrier pigeons, and by a few swift and skilful messengers, called jumpers, was possible. Sorties and fierce combats were, however, of daily occurrence, and a handsome bounty was offered to any man who brought into the city gates the head of a Spaniard. The reward was paid many times, but the population was becoming so excited and so apt, that the authorities felt it dangerous to permit the continuance of these conflicts. Lest the city, little by little, should lose its few disciplined defenders, it was now proclaimed, by sound of church bell, that in future no man should leave the gates.

The Prince had his headquarters at Delft and at Rotterdam. Between those two cities, an important fortress, called Polderwaert, secured him in the control of the alluvial quadrangle, watered on two sides by the Yssel and the Meuse. On the 29th June, the Spaniards, feeling its value, had made an unsuccessful effort to carry this fort by storm. They had been beaten off, with the loss of several hundred men, the Prince remaining in possession of the position, from which alone he could hope to relieve Leyden. He still held in his hand the keys with which he could unlock the ocean gates and let the waters in upon the land, and he had long been convinced that nothing could save the city but to break the dykes. Leyden was not upon the sea, but he could send the sea to Leyden, although an army fit to encounter the besieging force under Valdez could not be levied. The battle of Mookerheyde had, for the present, quite settled the question of land relief, but it was possible to besiege the besiegers with the waves of the ocean. The Spaniards occupied the coast from the Hague to Vlaardingen, but the dykes along the Meuse and the Yssel were in possession of the Prince. He determined that these should be pierced, while, at the same time, the great sluices at Rotterdam, Schiedam, and Delftshaven should be opened. The damage to the fields, villages, and growing crops would be enormous, but he felt that no other course could rescue Leyden, and with it the whole of Holland, from destruction. His clear expositions and impassioned eloquence at last overcame all resistance. By the middle of July the estates fully consented to his plan, and its execution was immediately undertaken. "Better a drowned land than a lost land," cried the patriots, with enthusiasm, as they devoted their fertile fields to desolation.

Meantime, Valdez, on the 30th of July, issued most urgent and ample offers of pardon to the citizens, if they would consent to open their gates and accept the King's authority; but his overtures were received with silent contempt, notwithstanding that the population were already approaching the starvation point. Although not yet fully informed of the active measures taken by the Prince, yet they still chose to rely upon his energy and their own fortitude, rather than upon the honeyed words which had formerly been heard at the gates of Harlem and of Naarden. On the 3rd of August, the Prince, accompanied by Paul Buys, chief of the commission appointed to execute the enterprise, went in person along the Yssel, as far as Kappelle, and superintended the rupture of the dykes in sixteen places. The gates at Schiedam and Rotterdam were opened, and the ocean began to pour over the land. While waiting for the waters to rise, provisions were rapidly collected, according to an edict of the Prince, in all the principal towns of the neighbourhood, and some two hundred vessels, of various sizes, had also been got ready at Rotterdam, Delfthaven, and other ports.

The citizens of Leyden were, however, already becoming impatient, for their bread was gone, and of its substitute, malt cake, they had but slender provision. On the 12th of August they received a letter from the Prince, encouraging them to resistance, and assuring them of a speedy relief, and on the 21st they addressed a despatch to him in reply, stating that they had now fulfilled their original promise, for they had held out two months with food, and another month without food. If not soon assisted, human strength could do no more; their malt cake would last but four days, and after that was gone, there was nothing left but starvation. Upon the same day, however, they received a letter, dictated by the Prince, who now lay in bed at Rotterdam with a violent fever, assuring them that the dykes were all pierced, and that the water was rising upon the "Land-scheiding," the great outward barrier which separated the city from the sea. He said nothing, however, of his own illness, which would have cast a deep shadow over the joy which now broke forth among the burghers.

The letter was read publicly in the market-place, and to increase the cheerfulness, Burgomaster Van der Werf, knowing the sensibility of his countrymen to music, ordered the city musicians to perambulate the streets, playing lively melodies and martial airs. Salvos of cannon were likewise fired, and the starving city for a brief space put on the aspect of a holiday, much to the astonishment of the besieging forces, who were not yet aware of the Prince's efforts. They perceived very soon, however, as the water everywhere about Leyden had risen to the depth of ten inches, that they stood in a perilous position. It was no trifling danger to be thus attacked by the waves of the ocean, which seemed about to obey with docility the command of William the Silent. Valdez became anxious and uncomfortable at the strange aspect of affairs; for the besieging army was now in its turn beleaguered, and by a stronger power than man's. He consulted with the most experienced of his officers, with the country people, with the most distinguished among the Glippers, and derived encouragement from their views concerning the Prince's plan. They pronounced it utterly futile and hopeless. The Glippers knew the country well, and ridiculed the desperate project in unmeasured terms.

Even in the city itself, a dull distrust had succeeded to the first vivid gleam of hope, while the few royalists among the population boldly taunted their fellow citizens to their faces with the absurd vision of relief which they had so fondly welcomed. "Go up to the tower, ye Beggars," was the frequent and taunting cry, "go up to the tower, and tell us if ye can see the ocean coming over the dry land to your relief" and day after day they did go up to the ancient tower of Hengist, with heavy heart and anxious eyes, watching, hoping, praying, fearing, and at last almost despairing of relief by God or man. On the 27th they addressed a desponding letter to the estates, complaining that the city had been forgotten in its utmost need, and on the same day a prompt and warm-hearted reply was received, in which the citizens were assured that every human effort was to be made for their relief. "Rather," said the estates, "will we see our whole land and all our possessions perish in the waves, than forsake thee, Leyden. We know full well, moreover, that with Leyden, all Holland must perish also." They excused themselves for not having more frequently written, upon the ground that the whole management of the measures for their relief had been entrusted to the Prince, by whom alone all the details had been administered, and all the correspondence conducted.

The fever of the Prince had, meanwhile, reached its height. He lay at Rotterdam, utterly prostrate in body, and with mind agitated nearly to delirium, by the perpetual and almost unassisted schemes which he was constructing. Leyden lay, as it were, anxious and despairing at his feet, and it was impossible for him to close his ears to her cry. Therefore, from his sick bed he continued to dictate words of counsel and encouragement to the city; to Admiral Boisot, commanding the fleet, minute directions and precautions.

On the 1st of September, Admiral Boisot arrived out of Zealand with a small number of vessels, and with eight hundred veteran sailors. A wild and ferocious crew were those eight hundred Zealanders. Scarred, hacked, and even maimed, in the unceasing conflicts in which their lives had passed; wearing crescents in their caps, with the inscription, "Rather Turkish than Popish"; renowned far and wide, as much for their ferocity as for their nautical skill; the appearance of these wildest of the "Sea-beggars" was both eccentric and terrific. They were known never to give or to take quarter, for they went to *mortal* combat only and had sworn to spare neither noble nor simple, neither king, kaiser, nor pope, should they fall into their power.

More than two hundred vessels had been now assembled, carrying generally ten pieces of cannon, with from ten to eighteen oars, and manned with twenty-five hundred veterans, experienced both on land and water. The work was now undertaken in earnest. The distance from Leyden to the outer dyke, over whose ruins the ocean had already been admitted, was nearly fifteen miles. This reclaimed territory, however, was not maintained against the sea by these external barriers alone. The flotilla made its way with ease to the Land-scheiding, a strong dyke within five miles of Leyden, but here its progress was arrested. The approach to the city was surrounded by many strong ramparts, one within the other, by which it was defended against its ancient enemy, the ocean, precisely like the circumvallations by means of which it was now assailed by its more recent enemy, the Spaniard. To enable the fleet, however, to sail over the land, it was necessary to break through this two-fold series of defences. Between the Land-scheiding and Leyden were several dykes which kept out the water; upon the level territory, thus encircled, were many villages, together with a chain of sixty-two forts, which completely occupied the land. All these villages and fortresses were held by the veteran troops of the King; the besieging force being about four times as strong as that which was coming to the rescue.

The Prince had given orders that the Land-scheiding, which was still one-and-a-half foot above water, should be taken possession of, at every hazard. On the night of the 10th and 11th of September this was accomplished by surprise, and in a masterly manner. The few Spaniards who had been stationed upon the dyke were all despatched or driven off, and the patriots fortified themselves upon it, without the loss of a man. As the day dawned the Spaniards saw the fatal error which they had committed in leaving this bulwark so freely defended, and from two villages which stood close to the dyke, the troops now rushed in considerable force to recover what they had lost. A hot action succeeded, but the patriots had too securely established themselves. They completely defeated the enemy, who retired, leaving hundreds of dead on the field, and the patriots in complete possession of the Land-scheiding. This first action was sanguinary and desperate. It gave an earnest of what these people, who came to relieve their brethren, by sacrificing their property and their lives, were determined to effect.

The great dyke having been thus occupied, no time was lost in breaking it through in several places, a work which was accomplished under the very eyes of the enemy. The fleet sailed through the gaps; but after their passage had been effected in good order, the Admiral found, to his surprise, that it was not the only rampart to be carried. The Prince had been informed, by those who claimed to know the country, that, when once the Land-scheiding had been passed, the water would flood the country as far as Leyden, but the "Greenway," another long dyke, three-quarters of a mile further inward, now rose at least a foot above the water, to oppose their further progress. Fortunately, by a second and still more culpable carelessness, this dyke had been left by the Spaniards in as unprotected a state as the first had been. Promptly and audaciously Admiral Boisot took possession of this barrier also, levelled it in many places, and brought his flotilla, in triumph, over its ruins. Again, however, he was doomed to disappointment. A large mere, called the Fresh-water Lake, was known to extend itself directly in his path about midway between the Land-scheiding and the city. To this piece of water, into which he expected to have instantly floated, his only passage lay through one deep canal. The sea which had thus far borne him on, now diffusing itself over a very wide surface, and under the influence of an adverse wind, had become too shallow for his ships. The canal alone was deep enough, but it led directly towards a bridge, strongly occupied by the enemy. Hostile troops, moreover, to the amount of three thousand, occupied both sides of the canal. The bold Boisot, nevertheless, determined to force his passage, if possible. Selecting a few of his strongest vessels, his heaviest artillery, and his bravest sailors, he led the van himself, in a desperate attempt to make his way to the mere. He opened a hot fire upon the bridge, then converted into a fortress, while his men engaged in hand-to-hand combat with a succession of skirmishers from the troops along the canal. After losing a few men, and ascertaining the impregnable position of the enemy, he was obliged to withdraw, defeated, and almost despairing.

A week had elapsed since the great dyke had been pierced, and the flotilla now lay motionless in shallow water, having accomplished less than two miles. The wind, too, was easterly, causing the sea rather to sink than to rise. Everything wore a gloomy aspect, when, fortunately, on the 18th, the wind shifted to the north-west, and for three days blew a gale. The waters rose rapidly, and before the second day was closed the armada was afloat again. Some fugitives from Zoetermeer village now arrived, and informed the Admiral that, by making a detour to the right, he could completely circumvent the bridge and the mere. They guided him, accordingly, to a comparatively low dyke, which led between the villages of Zoetermeer and Benthuyzen. A strong force of Spaniards was stationed in each place, but, seized with a panic, instead of sallying to defend the barrier, they fled inwardly towards Leyden, and halted at the village of North Aa. It was natural that they should be amazed. Nothing is more appalling to the imagination than the rising ocean tide, when man feels himself within its power; and here were the waters hourly deepening and closing around them, devouring the earth beneath their feet, while on the waves rode a flotilla, manned by a determined race, whose courage and ferocity were known throughout the world.

Three barriers, one within the other, had now been passed, and the flotilla, advancing with the advancing waves, and driving the enemy steadily before it, was drawing nearer to the beleaguered city. As one circle after another was passed, the besieging army found itself compressed within a constantly contracting field. The *Ark of Delft,* an enormous vessel, with shot-proof bulwarks, and moved by paddle-wheels turned by a crank, now arrived at Zoetermeer, and was soon followed by the whole fleet. After a brief delay, sufficient to allow the few remaining villagers to escape, both Zoetermeer and Benthuyzen, with the fortifications, were set on fire, and abandoned to their fate. The blaze lighted up the desolate and watery waste around, and was seen at Leyden, where it was hailed as the beacon of hope. Without further impediment, the armada proceeded to North Aa, the enemy retreating from this position also, and flying to Zoeterwoude, a strongly-fortified village, but a mile and three quarters from the city walls. It was now swarming with troops, for the bulk of the besieging army had gradually been driven into a narrow circle of forts, within the immediate neighbourhood of Leyden. Besides Zoeterwoude, the two posts where they were principally established were Lammen and Leyderdorp, each within three hundred rods of the town. At Leyderdorp were the head-quarters of Valdez; Colonel Borgia commanded in the very strong fortress of Lammen.

The fleet was, however, delayed at North Aa by another barrier called the "Kirk-way." The waters, too, spreading once more over a wider space, and diminishing under an east wind, which had again arisen, no longer permitted their progress, so that very soon the whole armada was stranded anew. The waters fell to the depth of nine inches, while the vessels required eighteen and twenty. Day after day the fleet lay motionless upon the shallow sea. Orange, rising from his sick bed as soon as he could stand, now came on board the fleet. His presence diffused universal joy; his words inspired his desponding army with fresh hope. He rebuked the impatient spirits who, weary of their compulsory idleness, had shown symptoms of ill-timed ferocity, and those eight hundred mad Zealanders, so frantic in their hatred to the foreigners, who had so long profaned their land, were as docile as children to the Prince. He reconnoitred the whole ground, and issued orders for the immediate destruction of the Kirk-way, the last important barrier which separated the fleet from Leyden. Then, after a long conference with Admiral Boisot, he returned to Delft.

Meantime, the besieged city was at its last gasp. The burghers had been in a state of uncertainty for many days; being aware that the fleet had set forth for their relief, but knowing full well the thousand obstacles which it had to surmount. They had guessed its progress by the illumination from the blazing villages; they had heard its salvos of artillery, on its arrival at North Aa; but since then, all had been dark and mournful again, hope and fear, in sickening alternation, distracting every breast. They knew that the wind was unfavourable, and at the dawn of each day every eye was turned wistfully to the vanes of the steeples. So long as the easterly breeze prevailed, they felt, as they anxiously stood on towers and housetops, that they must look in vain for the welcome ocean. Yet, while thus patiently waiting, they were literally starving; for even the misery endured at Harlem had not reached that depth and intensity of agony to which Leyden was now reduced. Bread, malt-cake, horseflesh, had entirely disappeared; dogs, cats, rats, and other vermin were esteemed luxuries. A small number of cows, kept as long as possible for their milk, still remained; but a few were killed from day to day, and distributed in minute proportions, hardly sufficient to support life among the famishing population. In many a house the watchmen, in their rounds, found a whole family of corpses, father, mother, children, side by side, for a disorder called the plague, naturally engendered of hardship and famine, now came, as if in kindness, to abridge the agony of the people. The pestilence stalked at noonday through the city, and the doomed inhabitants fell like grass beneath its scythe. From six thousand to eight thousand human beings sank before this scourge alone, yet the people resolutely held out—women and men mutually encouraging each other to resist the entrance of their foreign foe—an evil more horrible than pest or famine.

The missives from Valdez, who saw more vividly than the besieged could do, the uncertainty of his own position, now poured daily into the city, the enemy becoming more prodigal of his vows, as he felt that the ocean might yet save the victims from his grasp. The inhabitants, in their ignorance, had gradually abandoned their hopes of relief, but they spurned the summons to surrender. Leyden was sublime in its despair. A few murmurs were, however, occasionally heard at the steadfastness of the magistrates, and a dead body was placed at the door of the burgomaster, as a silent witness against his inflexibility. A party of the more faint-hearted even assailed the heroic Adrian van der Werf with threats and reproaches as he passed through the streets. A crowd had gathered around him, as he reached a triangular place in the centre of the town, into which many of the principal streets emptied themselves, and upon one side of which stood the church of Saint Pancras, with its high brick tower surmounted by two pointed turrets, and with two ancient lime-trees at its entrance. There stood the burgomaster, a tall, haggard, imposing figure, with dark visage, and a tranquil but commanding eye. He waved his broad-leaved felt hat for silence, and then exclaimed, in language which has been almost literally preserved, "What would ye, my friends? Why do ye murmur that we do not break our vows and surrender the city to the Spaniards? a fate more horrible than the agony which she now endures. I tell you I have made an oath to hold the city and may God give me strength to keep my oath! I can die but once; whether by your hands, the enemy's, or by the hand of God. My own fate is indifferent to me, not so that of the city entrusted to my care. I know that we shall starve if not soon relieved; but starvation is preferable to the dishonoured death which is the only alternative. Your menaces move me not; my life is at your disposal, here is my sword, plunge it into my breast, and divide my flesh among you. Take my body to appease your hunger, but expect no surrender, so long as I remain alive."

The words of the stout burgomaster inspired a new courage in the hearts of those who heard him, and a shout of applause and defiance arose from the famishing but enthusiastic crowd. They left the place after exchanging new vows of fidelity with their magistrate, and again ascended tower and battlement to watch for the coming fleet. From the ramparts they hurled renewed defiance at the enemy. "Ye call us rateaters and dog-eaters," they cried, "and it is true. So long, then, as ye hear dog bark or cat mew within the walls, ye may know that the city holds out. And when all has perished but ourselves, be sure that we will each devour our left arms, retaining our right to defend our women, our liberty, and our religion, against the foreign tyrant. Should God, in his wrath, doom us to destruction, and deny us all relief, even then will we maintain ourselves for ever against your entrance. When the last hour has come, with our hands we will set fire to the city, and perish, men, women, and children together, in the flames, rather than suffer our homes to be polluted, and our liberties to be crushed."

Such words of defiance, thundered daily from the battlements, sufficiently informed Valdez as to his chance of conquering the city, either by force or fraud, but at the same time, he felt comparatively relieved by the inactivity of Boisot's fleet, which still lay stranded at North Aa. "As well," shouted the Spaniards, derisively, to the citizens, "as well can the Prince of Orange pluck the stars from the sky as bring the ocean to the walls of Leyden for your relief."

On the 28th of September, a dove flew into the city, bringing a letter from Admiral Boisot. In this despatch, the position of the fleet at North Aa was described in encouraging terms, and the inhabitants were assured that in a very few days at furthest, the long-expected relief would enter their gates. The letter was read publicly upon the market-place, and the bells were rung for joy. Nevertheless, on the morrow, the vanes pointed to the east, the waters, so far from rising, continued to sink, and Admiral Boisot was almost in despair. He wrote to the Prince, that if the springtide, now to be expected, should not, together with a strong and favourable wind, come immediately to their relief, it would be in vain to attempt anything further, and that the expedition would, of necessity, be abandoned. The tempest came to their relief. A violent equinoctial gale, on the night of the 1st and 2nd of October, came storming from the north-west, shifting after a few hours full eight points, and then blowing still more violently from the south-west. The waters of the North Sea were piled in vast masses upon the southern coast of Holland, and then dashed furiously landward, the ocean rising over the earth, and sweeping with unrestrained power across the ruined dykes.

In the course of twenty-four hours the fleet at North Aa, instead of nine inches, had more than two feet of water. No time was lost. The Kirk-way, which had been broken through according to the Prince's instructions, was now completely overflowed, and the fleet sailed at midnight, in the midst of the storm and darkness. A few sentinel vessels of the enemy challenged them as they steadily rowed towards Zoeterwoude. The answer was a flash from Boisot's cannon, lighting up the black waste of waters. There was a fierce naval midnight battle; a strange spectacle among the branches of those quiet orchards, and with the chimney stacks of half-submerged farm-houses rising around the contending vessels. The neighbouring village of Zoeterwoude shook with the discharges of the Zealanders' cannon, and the Spaniards assembled in that fortress knew that the rebel Admiral was at last afloat and on his course. The enemy's vessels were soon sunk, their crews hurled into the waves. On went the fleet, sweeping over the broad waters which lay between Zoeterwoude and Zwieten. As they approached some shallows, which led into the great mere, the Zealanders dashed into the sea, and with sheer strength shouldered every vessel through. Two obstacles lay still in their path—the forts of Zoeterwoude and Lammen, distant from the city five hundred and two hundred and fifty yards respectively. Strong redoubts, both well supplied with troops and artillery, they were likely to give a rough reception to the light flotilla, but the panic, which had hitherto driven their foes before the advancing patriots, had reached Zoeterwoude. Hardly was the fleet in sight when the Spaniards in the early morning poured out from the fortress, and fled precipitately to the left, along a road which led in a westerly direction towards The Hague. Their narrow path was rapidly vanishing in the waves, and hundreds sank beneath the constantly-deepening and treacherous flood. The wild Zealanders, too, sprang from their vessels upon the crumbling dyke and drove their retreating foes into the sea. They hurled their harpoons at them, with an accuracy acquired in many a polar chase; they plunged into the waves in the keen pursuit, attacking them with boat-hook and dagger. The numbers who thus fell beneath these corsairs, who neither gave nor took quarter, were never counted, but probably not less than a thousand perished. The rest effected their escape to The Hague.

The first fortress was thus seized, dismantled, set on fire, and passed, and a few strokes of the oars brought the whole fleet close to Lammen. This last obstacle rose formidable and frowning directly across their path. Swarming as it was with soldiers, and bristling with artillery, it seemed to defy the armada either to carry it by storm or to pass under its guns into the city. It appeared that the enterprise was, after all, to founder within sight of the long expecting and expected haven. Boisot anchored his fleet within a respectful distance, and spent what remained of the day in carefully reconnoitring the fort, which seemed only too strong. In conjunction with Leyderdorp, the headquarters of Valdez, a mile and a half distant on the right, and within a mile of the city, it seemed so insuperable an impediment that Boisot wrote in despondent tones to the Prince of Orange. He announced his intention of carrying the fort, if it were possible, on the following morning, but if obliged to retreat, he observed, with something like despair, that there would be nothing for it but to wait for another gale of wind. If the waters should rise sufficiently to allow them to make a wide detour, it might be possible, if, in the meantime, Leyden did not starve or surrender, to enter its gates from the opposite side.

Meantime, the citizens had grown wild with expectation. A dove had been despatched by Boisot, informing them of his precise position, and a number of citizens accompanied the burgomaster, at nightfall, toward the tower of Hengist— "Yonder," cried the magistrate, stretching out his hand towards Lammen, "yonder, behind that fort, are bread and meat, and brethren in thousands. Shall all this be destroyed by the Spanish guns, or shall we rush to the rescue of our friends?" "We will tear the fortress to fragments with our teeth and nails," was the reply, "before the relief, so long expected, shall be wrested from us." It was resolved that a sortie, in conjunction with the operations of Boisot, should be made against Lammen with the earliest dawn. Night descended upon the scene, a pitch dark night, full of anxiety to the Spaniards, to the armada, to Leyden. Strange sights and sounds occurred at different moments to bewilder the anxious sentinels. A long procession of lights issuing from the fort was seen to flit across the black face of the waters, in the dead of night, and the whole of the city wall, between the Cow-gate and the Tower of Burgundy, fell with a loud crash. The horror-struck citizens thought that the Spaniards were upon them at last; the Spaniards imagined the noise to indicate a desperate sortie of the citizens. Everything was vague and mysterious.

Day dawned, at length, after the feverish night, and the Admiral prepared for the assault. Within the fortress reigned a death-like stillness, which inspired a sickening suspicion. Had the city, indeed, been carried in the night; had the massacre already commenced; had all this labour and audacity been expended in vain? Suddenly a man was descried, wading breast-high through the water from Lammen towards the fleet, while at the same time, one solitary boy was seen to wave his cap from the summit of the fort. After a moment of doubt, the happy mystery was solved. The Spaniards had fled, panic-struck, during the darkness. Their position would still have enabled them, with firmness, to frustrate the enterprise of the patriots, but the hand of God, which had sent the ocean and the tempest to the deliverance of Leyden, had struck her enemies with terror likewise. The lights which had been seen moving during the night were the lanterns of the retreating Spaniards, and the boy who was now waving his triumphant signal from the battlements had alone witnessed the spectacle. So confident was he in the conclusion to which it led him, that he had volunteered at daybreak to go thither all alone. The magistrates, fearing a trap, hesitated for a moment to believe the truth, which soon, however, became quite evident. Valdez, flying himself from Leyderdorp, had ordered Colonel Borgia to retire with all his troops from Lammen. Thus, the Spaniards had retreated at the very moment that an extraordinary accident had laid bare a whole side of the city for their entrance. The noise of the wall, as it fell, only inspired them with fresh alarm; for they believed that the citizens had sallied forth in the darkness, to aid the advancing flood in the work of destruction. All obstacles being now removed, the fleet of Boisot swept by Lammen, and entered the city on the morning of the 3rd of October. Leyden was relieved.

THE MAN WHO FIRST ROUNDED THE HORN[1]

John Callander
(d. 1789)

THE States General of the United Provinces having granted to the East-India Company an exclusive charter, prohibiting thereby all their subjects, except the said Company, from carrying on any trade to the eastward beyond the Cape of Good Hope, or westward through the Streights of Magellan, in any countries either known or unknown, under very high penalties; this prohibiton gave very great distaste to many rich merchants, who were desirous of fitting out ships and making discoveries at their own costs, and could not help thinking it a little hard, that the Government should thus, against the laws of nature, bar those passages which Providence had left free. Amongst the number of these merchants, there was one of Amsterdam, who then resided at Egmont, very rich, well-acquainted with business, and who had an earnest desire to employ a part of that wealth, which he had acquired by trade, in acquiring fame as a discoverer. With this view he applied himself to William Cornelison Schouten, of Horn, a man in easy circumstances, and who was deservedly famous for his great skill in maritime affairs, and for his perfect knowledge in the trade to the Indies, having been thrice there himself, in the different characters of master, pilot, and supercargo, or, as the phrase in those days was, of Merchant. The great question proposed by Mr le Maire to this intelligent man was, Whether he did not think it possible to find another passage into the South Seas than by the Streights of Magellan; and whether, if this was possible, it was not highly likely, that the countries to the south of that passage might afford as rich commodities as either the East or West Indies? Mr Schouten answered, That there was great reason to believe such a passage

[1] From *Callander's Voyages.*

might be found, and still stronger reason to confirm what he conjectured as to the riches of these southern countries.

After many conversations upon this subject, they came at last to a resolution of attempting such a discovery, from a full persuasion, that the States General could not intend, by their exclusive charter to the East-India Company, to preclude their subjects from discovering countries on the south by a new route, distinct from either of those mentioned in that charter. In consequence of this agreement, it was stipulated, that le Maire and his friends should advance one moiety towards the necessary expence of the voyage, and Schouten and his friends the other. In pursuance of this scheme, Isaac le Maire advanced his part of the money; and Cornelison Schouten, with the assistance of the following persons, viz. Peter Clementson, Burgomaster of Horn; John Janson Molenwert, one of the Schepen or Aldermen of the same place; John Clementson Keis, Senator of the said town; and Cornelius Segetson, a merchant of Horn, laid down the rest. It is certain that so many people of substance would never have embarked in such a project if they had so much as suspected that the East-India Company had a right to confiscate their vessels and effects whenever they had it in their power.

As soon therefore as these matters were adjusted, which was in the spring of the year 1615, the Company, engaged in this undertaking, began to apply themselves to the carrying it into execution, proposing to equip for that purpose a larger and a less vessel, to sail from Horn at the proper season of the year. And that all parties might be thoroughly satisfied, it was determined, that William Cornelison Schouten, on account of his age and experience, should have the command of the larger ship, with the sole direction of the voyage, and that James le Maire, the eldest son of Isaac le Maire, should be the first supercargo. The Company were so eager in the prosecution of their design, and so attentive to whatever might be necessary to promote it, that in the space of two months all things were ready, and a sufficient number of men engaged for navigating both ships. But, as secrecy was absolutely necessary, the seamen were articled in general terms to go wherever their masters and supercargoes should require; and, in consideration of so unusual a condition, their wages were advanced considerably; which was a circumstance of such consequence, and there were in those days so many adventurous spirits, that they did not find it at all difficult to make up their intended complement; which gave them an opportunity of chusing none but experienced mariners, on whose skill and fidelity they could depend; a circumstance of the utmost consequence in a voyage of this nature, where the tempers of men were sure to be thoroughly tried.

These extraordinary preparations, but, above all, the mighty secrecy that was observed, caused a great noise, not only at Amsterdam, but all over Holland, where people reasoned on the intention of this voyage, according to the several degrees of their capacity and experience, some fancying they were bound to one place, some to another; but the common people thought they hit upon the proper title, in calling them the Goldfinders; whereas the merchants, who were better versed in such matters, called them, with greater propriety, the South Company, and indeed that was their true designation; for the real design of Isaac le Maire, was to discover those southern regions, to which few people had hitherto travelled even in imagination, and which, by an unaccountable indolence, remain, in a great measure, undiscovered to this day.

In the beginning of the month of May 1615, the South Company drew their men together; and, on the 16th of that month, they were mustered before the magistrates of Horn, took their leave of their friends and relations, and prepared to embark on board their ships.

The biggest of these vessels was called *The Unity,* of the burden of 360 tons, carrying nineteen pieces of cannon, and twelve swivels. She had on board likewise a pinnace to sail, and another to row, a launch for landing of men, and a small boat, with all other necessaries whatever for so long a voyage; and of this vessel William Cornelison Schouten was master and pilot, and Jaques le Maire supercargo. The lesser ship was called *The Horn,* of the burden of 110 tons, carrying eight cannon and four swivels, John Cornelison Schouten master, and Aris Clawson supercargo. The crew of the former consisted of sixty-five men, and the latter of twenty-two only. The *Unity* sailed May 25th, for the Texel, where the *Horn* likewise arrived June 3rd following, that being judged the properest season of the year for them to proceed on their voyage. On June 14th they sailed out of the Texel, and passing, in sight of Dunkirk, between Dover and Calais, anchored on the 17th in the Downs, when William Cornelison Schouten went on shore at Dover, in order to get fresh water, and to hire an English gunner; which accordingly he did, and that day sent him on board. They sailed again in the evening, and met with several large Dutch ships laden with salt. In the night between the 21st and 22d, they were grievously ruffled by a storm; which obliged them to put into the Isle of Wight for shelter, where Captain Schouten endeavoured, if possible, to have hired a carpenter, but without success, which obliged them to sail on the 25th for Plymouth, where he arrived on the 27th, and there hired a carpenter of Maydenblick.

On July 28th, they sailed from Plymouth with a north-north-east wind, and very fair weather. On the 29th, Captain Schouten made a signal for all officers to come on board; when it was resolved in a council, to settle the rate of their sea-allowance in such a manner, as that the men might have no reason to complain, and their officers be in no apprehensions of their wanting provisions during the course of so long a voyage. The rate they fixed in the following proportions; viz, a can of beer a man every day, four pounds of biscuit, half a pound of butter, and as much sweet suet, for the week, together with five large Dutch cheeses, that were to serve them the whole voyage. This was exclusive of flesh or fish: And we may, from hence, form some notion of the frugality the Dutch victualled with in those days, and from which they have deviated very little ever since. They likewise made the necessary orders for the due regulation of the voyage, directing, that, in case of landing men, one of the masters should always command; that, in ports where they went to trade, the supercargo should go on shore, and have the sole direction of the commerce: That, on board, every officer should be strict in the execution of his duty; but without putting unnecessary hardships on the men, or interfering with other officers in their commands: That none of the officers should hold any conversation with the seamen, in relation to the design of the voyage, which being solely in the breast of the first captain and supercargo, conjectures must be fruitless, and might be dangerous; that any embezzlement of provisions, stores, or merchandize, should be severely punished; and, in case of their being reduced to short allowance, then offences of this nature to be punished with death; that the two supercargoes should keep clear and distinct journals of all proceedings, for the use of the Company, that it might plainly appear, how far every man had done his duty, and to what degree the end of the voyage had been answered. All these rules were very exactly observed, and particularly the last; so that, from these journals, kept by the supercargoes, this account has been taken. On July 8th, being in the latitude of 39 degrees 25 minutes, their carpenter's mate died. On the 9th and 10th, with a north-north-east wind, and a stiff gale, they stood on their course, without putting in to Porto Santo, or Madeira, of which they had sight on the 11th. The reason was, that having, as they conceived, victuals sufficient for the voyage, they determined not to lose time, by going needlessly on shore, especially since hitherto their men were vigorous, and in good health; which resolution was founded on an observation made by Captain Schouten, that many voyages had been lost, by lingering in port without any urgent cause, when the winds and seasons were fair, and their course might have been prosecuted without delay.

On July 13, they sailed between the island Teneriff and the grand Canary, with a stiff north-north-east wind, and a swift current. About the 15th, the same wind and current following them still, they passed the Tropic of Cancer. The 20th, in the morning, they fell in with the north side of Cape Verd. At sun-rising the Cape lay west by south from them; so that the north-north-east wind would not suffer them to get beyond it; but kept them there at anchor all that night. The 25th, the Moorish Alcaid came on board them, with whom they agreed at the price of eight states of iron for a supply of fresh water. They left the Cape August 1, and the 21st of the same month they saw the high land of Sierra Leona, and also the island of Madrabomba, which lies on the south point of the high land of Sierra Leona, and north from the shallows of St Anne's island. This land of Sierra Leona is the highest of all that lies between Cape Verd and the coast of Guinea, so that the point is very easy to be known. Here they would have landed, running up to the point over the baixos, or shallows, of St Anne's at ten, nine, eight, seven, and five fathoms water, it being still deeper to the north, but shallower to the east; so that in the evening, they anchored with a high-water at four fathoms and a half soft ground, and at night at three fathoms and a half.

The 22nd, William Schouten, in the Horn, led the way off the shallows, steering north-north-east, with a north-west wind, by which course they were intirely disengaged from the Baixos, and got into thirteen fathoms water. From hence they went to the islands of Madrabomba, which are very high, and lie all three on a row south-west and north-east, half a league from Sierra Leona, to the seaward. Here they had shallow water at four and five fathoms, and soft muddy ground. They anchored a league from the island, which appeared to be very full of bogs and marshes, and all over waste like a wilderness, scarce fit to entertain any other inhabitants than wild beasts, and indeed not seeming to have any other. Going ashore on the 23rd, they found a river there, the mouth of which was so stopped up with sands, and cliffs of rocks, that no ship could get into it; yet, within, the water was sufficiently deep, and the breadth such too, as to give a ship free scope to turn and wind herself about, as she should have occasion. Here they saw tortoises, crocodiles, monkies, wild oxen, and a sort of birds, which made a noise, barking like dogs. They met with no fruit but lemons, some few trees of which they found after a tedious search. The 29th, about noon, they got above the islands of Madrabomba westward, along to the north part of the high land, till they had twelve and fifteen fathoms water, and, in the evening, got about the point.

On the 30th, being assisted both by wind and current, they arrived before the village that looks upon the road of Sierra Leona, where they anchored at eight fathoms water, a little from the shore, in a very sandy bottom. The village consisted of about eight or nine poor houses covered with straw: The Moors, that dwelt there, were willing to come aboard, only demanding pledges to be left ashore, to secure their safe return; because a French ship that came thither before, had perfidiously carried off two of them: So Aris Clawson the merchant went ashore, and staid there amongst them, driving a small trade with them for lemons and bananas, which they exchanged for glass-beads; and in the mean time they came on board, bringing an interpreter with them, who spoke all sorts of languages. Here they had good opportunity of furnishing themselves with fresh water, which pouring down in large quantities from a very high hill, they had nothing to do but to place their barrels under the fall of the water to receive it. There were also vast woods of lemon trees here, which made lemons so cheap to them, that, for a few beads and knives, they might have had 10,000. September 1, they drove away before the stream, and anchored that evening at the mouth of the sea, before a small river. Here they took an antelope in the woods, with lemons and palmitoes; and had good success in their fishing. The third the master brought in a great shoal of fish, that were of the shape of a shoemaker's knife, and as many lemons as came to 150 for every man's share.

The 4th, they sailed from Sierra Leona, early in the morning. October 5, they made 4 degrees 27 minutes south latitude; and the same day at noon, they were strangely surprised with a very violent stroke given to one of their ships in the lower part of it. No adversary appeared, no rock was in the way to be encountered with; but, while this amused them, the sea all about them began to change its colour, and looked as if some great fountain of blood had been opened into it; this sudden alteration of the water being no less surprising to them, than the striking of the ship; but the cause both of the one and the other they were equally ignorant of, till they came to Port Desire, and there set the ship upon the strand to make her clean; for then they found a large horn, both in form and magnitude resembling an elephant's tooth, sticking fast in the bottom of the ship. A very firm and solid body it was, and seemed to be equally so all over, there being nothing of a cavity, or a light and spungy matter in the midst of it, but all over as dense and compact a substance, as that in the exterior parts. It had pierced through three very stout planks of the ship, and razed one of the ribs of her; so that it stuck at least half a foot deep in the planks; and there was about as much that appeared without the great hole up to the place where it was broken off. And now the riddle was completely solved, this horn being the spoil of some seamonster, that had thus rudely assaulted the ship with that piercing weapon; and, after the thrust, not being able to draw it out again, had there broke it, which was attended with such a plentiful effusion of blood, as had discoloured the sea to that degree.

Having now sailed so far, that none in the ships, but the master, knew where they were, or whither they intended, upon the 25th they discovered their designs to the rest of the company, of going to find out a new southern passage into the great Pacific Sea. This they had kept very close to themselves before, but now thought it time to reveal the scheme, there being no danger of defeating it; and the company seemed to be very well pleased with it, hoping to light on some golden country or other, to make them amends for all their trouble and danger. The 26th, they made 6 degrees 25 minutes south latitude, sailing mostly southwards, till they had made 10 degrees 30 minutes. November 1, they had the sun north of them at noon. The 3rd, in the afternoon, they had sight of Martin Vad's island, called Ascension, under 20 degrees; and here they observed the compass to vary to the north-east 12 degrees. The 21st, they came under 38 degrees 25 minutes, and had a deep water, whose bottom they could reach with their lead. Here the variations of the compass was 17 degrees to the north-east. December 6, they had a prospect of land, not very high, but flat and white; and, quickly after, fell in with the north side of Port Desire, and, that night, anchored within one league and an half from the shore, in ten fathoms water, with an ebb that ran southwards as strongly as the sea runs between Flushing Heads.

The 7th, keeping a south course, at noon they came before the haven of Port Desire, which lies under 47 degrees 40 minutes. At the entry of it they had very high water; neither did any of those cliffs appear, which Van Noort had described, and which he left northwards in sailing into the haven. If there were any, they were all under water; but the cliffs lay open and visible enough towards the south point, which therefore, might be those which Noort intended. Upon this they went on, sailing so far southward, as to miss the right channel. They came into a crooked bay, where, at high-water, they had but four fathoms and a half, and at low water but fourteen feet; by which means the *Unity* lay with her stern fast aground, and, if a brisk gale from the north-east had blown, she must infallibly have been lost; but, the wind blowing west from the land, she recovered again. Here they found plenty of eggs, amongst the cliffs: and the bay afforded them muscles, and smelts of sixteen inches in length, and therefore they called it Smelt-Bay. Their shallop went to the Penguin islands, and came back with 150 penguins, and two sea-lions.

The 8th, before noon, they sailed out of the Smelt-Bay, and anchored just before Port Desire. The shallop was employed before hand to sound the depth of the channel; which proving to be twelve or thirteen fathoms, they boldly entered, having a north-east wind to carry them along: But after a little more than a league's sailing, the wind began to veer about, and they anchored at twenty fathoms; but the bottom they were upon being only slippery stones, and the wind now blowing hard at north-west, their anchors could not preserve them from driving with that rough wind upon the southern shore; so both these ships were likely to be wrecked together. The *Unity* lay with her side upon the cliffs; but still kept the water, and, by the fall of the sea, was gradually slidden down lower and lower into it; but the *Horn* stuck so that her keel was above a fathom out of water, and a man might have walked dry under it at low water. She was, for some time, obliged to the north-west wind, that, by blowing hard upon her side, kept her from falling over; but, that support being gone, with the wind that gave it, she sunk down upon that side at least three feet lower than the keel: Upon which sight they gave her over for lost; and yet the succeeding flood, which came on with still weather, set her upright again; and both she and her companion got clear of that danger. The 9th, they went farther into the river, and came to King's island, which they found full of black sea-mews, and almost covered over with their eggs. A man, without straining to reach, might have taken between fifty and sixty nests with his hand, each of which have three or four eggs a-piece; so that they were quickly furnished with some thousands of them. The 11th the boat went in search of good water lower down the river, on the south-side; but found it all of a brackish unpleasant taste. They saw ostriches here, and a sort of beasts like harts, with wonderful long necks, and extremely wild. Upon the high hills they found great heaps of stones, under which some monstrous carcases had been buried. There were bones of ten and eleven feet long. In all probability they were (if of rational creatures) some bones of the giants of that country. No water was to be found here for several days together; so that, though they had plenty of good fish and fowl, they could meet with no drink to wash it down.

On the 17th, they laid the *Unity* dry upon King's Island in order to clean her, which they performed very successfully. On the 18th, they likewise hauled the *Horn* on shore, for the same purpose, and placed her about 200 yards from the other ship. On the 19th, a very dreadful accident happened; for, while they were busy cleaning both ships, in order to which it was necessary to light a fire of dry reeds under the *Horn,* it so fell out, that the flame got into the ship, and set it on fire; and, as they were fifty feet from the water-side, they were forced to stand still and see her burn, without being able to do anything towards extinguishing it. On the 20th, at high water, they launched the *Unity,* and the next day carried on board her all the wood, iron-work, anchors, and pieces of cannon, and whatever else they could save out of the *Horn.* On the 25th, the sailors found certain holes full of fresh water, which was white and thick, but well tasted, a great quantity of which they carried on board in small casks upon their shoulders. They met here with great numbers of sea-lions; the young ones they eat, and found them pretty good food. The sea-lion is a creature as big as a small horse; their heads resemble lions exactly; on their necks they have long manes of a tough strong hair; but this is to be understood of the helions only: For the she-lion is without hair and not above half as big as the male. They are a bold fierce animal, not to be destroyed but by musket-shot.

January 13, they sailed out of Port Desire; but having a calm, they anchored before the haven, till the rising of the wind invited them to pursue their voyage. The 18th, being in 51 degrees, they saw the Sebaldin islands; which they observed to lie in that position and distance from the Strait, that De Weert had determined. The 20th, being then in 53 degrees, they observed the great current that runs south-west; and now they reckoned about twenty leagues to the southwards of the Magellanic Straits. The 23rd they had an uncertain shifting wind, and the water appeared white, as if they had been within the land. They held their course south by west, and the same day saw land, bearing west and westsouth-west from them, and quickly after to the south. Then attempting, by an east-south-east course, to get beyond the land, the hard north wind, that blew then, constrained them to take in their topsails. The 24th, in the forenoon, they saw land a starboard, about a league's distance, stretching out east and south, with very high hills, all covered with ice; and then other land bearing east from it, high and rugged as the former. They guessed the lands they had in these two prospects lay about eight leagues asunder, and that there might be a good passage between them, because of a pretty brisk current, that ran southward along by them. About noon, they made 54 degrees 46 minutes, and then began to make towards the aforementioned opening; but the succeeding calm prevented it. Here they saw an incredible number of penguins, and such huge shoals of whales, that they were forced to proceed with great caution for fear they should run their ship upon them.

The 25th, in the forenoon, they got up close by the east land, which, upon the north side, reaches east-south-east as far as the eye can follow it. This they called States Land; and to that which lay west, they gave the name of Maurice Land. They observed there were good roads and sandy bays, good store of fish, penguins, and porpoises, and some sorts of fowls; but the land adjacent seemed quite bare of trees and woods. They had a north wind at their entrance into this passage, and directed their course south-south-west; so that, going pretty briskly on, at noon they made 55 degrees 36 minutes, and then held a south-west course, having a good stiff gale to blow them forwards. The land upon the south side of the passage, at the west end of Maurice Land, appeared to run west-south-west, and south-west as far as they could see it, and all very craggy uneven ground.

In the evening, having a south-west wind, they steered southwards, meeting with mighty waves, that came rolling along before the wind, and the depth of the water to the leeward from them, which appeared by some very evident signs, gave them a full assurance, that the great South Sea was now before them, into which they had almost made their way by a passage of their own discovering. The sea-mews thereabouts were larger than swans, and their wings, when extended to the full length, spread about the compass of a fathom. They would come and very tamely sit down upon the ship, and suffer themselves to be taken by hand, without any endeavours to fly away. The 26th, they made 57 degrees, and were there ruffled by a brisk storm out of the west and south-west. The water was also very high, and blue. They still held all this day their course to the southward, but changed it at night for a north-west one; in which quarter they discovered very high land. The 27th, they were under 56 degrees 51 minutes, the weather very cold, with hail and rain, the wind west and west by south. They went a southern course, and then crossed northwards with their main-sails. The 28th, they hoisted up their topsails, and had great billows out of the west, with a west and then a north-east wind, and therewith held their course south and then west and west by south, which brought them under 56 degrees 48 minutes.

The 29th they had a north-east wind, and held their course south-west which gave them the prospect of two islands, beset round with cliffs, and lying west-south-west from them; they got up to them at noon, but could not sail above them, and therefore held their course to the north. They gave them the name of Barnevelt's Islands, and found their latitude to be 57 degrees south. Taking a north-west course, from hence in the evening, they saw land again, lying north-west, and northnorth-west from them; this was the high hilly land, covered with snow, that lay southward from the Magellanic Straits, ending in a sharp point, which they called Cape Horn, and lying in 57 degrees 48 minutes. They held their course now westward, in which course they found a strong current which ran that way too, yet had the wind in the north, and great billows rolling out of the west upon them. The 30th, the billows and the current still ran as before; and now they gathered a full assurance from hence, that the way was open into the South Sea: This day they made the latitude of 57 degrees, 34 minutes. The 31st, they sailed west, with the wind in the north, and made 58 degrees; but the wind turning to the west and west-south-west, they passed Cape Horn, losing all sight of land, and still meeting the billows rolling out of the west, which, together with the blueness of the water, made them quickly expect the main South Sea. February 1, a storm blowing out of the south-west, they sailed with their main-sails north-west and west-north-west. The 2d, with a westerly wind, they sailed to the southward, and made 57 degrees 58 minutes, the variation being there 12 degrees north-ward. The 3rd, they made 59 degrees 25 minutes, with a hard west wind, but saw no signs of any land to the south: and the next day 56 degrees 43 minutes, turning to and fro with very uncertain south-west winds, and finding 11 degrees of north-east variation. The 5th, by reason of a strong westerly current, and a hollow water, they could bear no sail, but were forced to drive with the wind.

The 12th they plainly discerned the Magellanic Streights, lying east of them; and therefore, now being secure of their happy new discovery, they rendered thanks to good Fortune in a cup of wine, which went three times round the company. And now this new-found passage had a name given it, which was that of Maire's Streights, though that honour (in justice) ought to have been done to William Schouten, by whose happy conduct the Streights were discovered.

GERMANY

A WHALING VOYAGE INTO SPITZBERGEN[1]

Frederick Martens of Hamburg

I

WE SET sail the 15th of April, 1671, about noon, from the Elbe. The wind was north-east; at night, when we came by the Hilgeland, it bore to north-north-east. The name of the ship was *Jonas in the Whale,* Peter Peterson, of Friseland, master.

The 27th, we had storms, hail and snow, with very cold weather, the wind north-east, and by east; we were in seventy-one degrees, and came to the ice, and turned back again. The Island of John Maien bore from us south-west and by west, as near as we could guess within ten miles. We might have seen the Island plain enough, but the air was haizy, and full of fogs and snow, so that we could not see far. About noon it blew a storm, whereupon we took down our topsails, and, furling our mainsail, drove with the missensail towards south-east.

The 29th, it was foggy all day, the wind north-east, and by north; we came to the ice, and sailed from it again.

The 30th, the first Sunday after Easter, was foggy, with rain and snow, the wind at north; at night we came to the ice, but sailed from it again; the sea was tempestuous, and tossed our ship very much.

The 3rd of May was cold, snowy, with hail, and misty sunshine; the wind north-west and by west; the sun set no more, we saw it as well by night as by day.

The 4th, we had snow, hail, and gloomy sunshine, with cold weather, but not excessive; the wind at north-west; the weather every day unconstant. Here we saw abundance of scales; they jumped out of the water before the ship, and, which was strange, they would stand half out of the water, and, as it were, dance together.

The 5th, in the forenoon, it was moderately cold, and sunshine, but toward noon darkish and cloudy, with snow and great frost; the wind north-west and by north. We saw daily many ships, sailing about the ice; I observed that as they passed by one another, they hailed one another, crying *Holla,* and asked each other how many fish they had caught; but they would not stick sometimes to tell more than they had. When it was windy, that they could not hear one another, they waived their hats to signifie the number caught. But when they have their full fraight of whales, they put up their great flag as a sign thereof: then if any hath a message to be sent, he delivers it to them.

[1] From an anonymous translation of 1694 of *A Voyage into Spitzbergen and Greenland.*

The 7th we had moderate frosts, clouds, and snow, with rain. In the evening we sailed to the ice, the wind was quite contrary to us, and the ice too small, wherefore we sailed from it. In the afternoon we saw Spitzbergen, the south point of the North Foreland: we supposed it the true Harbour. The land appeared like a dark cloud, full of white streeks; we turned to the West again, that it, according to the compass, which is also to be understood of the ice and harbour.

The 9th was the same weather and cold as before, the wind south-west and by west. In the afternoon a fin-fish swam by our ship, which we took at first to be a whale, before we saw the high fins of his tail and came near to it. We had let down our sloop from the ship, but that labour was lost, for he was not worth taking.

On the 14th, the wind was north-west, fine weather with sunshine; we were within seventy-five degrees and twenty-two minutes. We told twenty ships about us; the sea was very even, and we hardly felt any wind, and yet it was very cold. In this place the sea becomes smooth presently again after a storm, chiefly when the wind blows from the ice; but when it blows off the sea, it always makes a great sea. The same day we saw a whale, not far off from our ship; we put out four boats from on board after him, but this labour was also in vain, for he run under the water and we saw him no more.

On the 20th, it was exceeding cold, so that the very sea was all frozen over; yet it was so calm and still that we could hardly perceive the wind, which was north; there were nine ships in our company, which sailed about the ice; we found still, the longer we sailed the bigger the ice.

On the 21st (which was the fourth Sunday after Easter), we sailed into the ice in the forenoon, with another Hamburgher-ship called the *Lepeler,* with eight Hollanders. We fixed our ship with ice-hooks to a large ice-field, when the sun was south-west and by south; we numbered thirty ships in the sea; they lay, as it were, in an harbour or haven. Thus, they venture their ships in the ice at great hazard.

On the 30th, it was fair weather in the morning, snowy about noon, the wind was south-west, and very calm. We rowed in the great sloop, before the ship, farther into the ice. In the morning we heard a whale blow when the sun was in the east, and brought the whale to the ship when the sun was at south-west and by east; the same day we cut the fat from it, and filled with it seventy barrels (which they call kardels). By this fish we found abundance of birds, most of them were mallemucks (that is to say, foolish gnats), which were so greedy of their food, that we killed them with sticks. This fish was found out by the birds, for we saw everywhere by them in the sea where the whale had been, for he was wounded by an harpooning iron that stuck still in his flesh, and he had also spent himself by hard swimming; he blowed also very hollow.

In the morning, June 4th, we were a-hunting again after a whale, and we came so near unto one, that the harpoonier was just going to fling his harpoon into her, but she sunk down behind and held her head out of the water, and so sunk down like a stone, and we saw her no more; it is very like that the great ice-field was full of holes in the middle, so that the whale could fetch breath underneath the ice. A great many more ships lay about this sheet of ice; one hunted the whales to the other, and so they were frighted and became very shy. So one gets as many fishes as the other, and sometimes they all get one. We were there several times a hunting that very day, and yet we got never a one.

On the 12th, it was cold and stormy all day, at night sunshine; he that takes not exact notice, knows no difference whether it be day or night.

On the 13th, in the afternoon, it was windy and foggy; we were in seventy-seven degrees; we sailed along by the ice somewhat easterly towards Spitzbergen. That night we saw more than twenty whales, that run one after another towards the ice; out of them we got our second fish, which was a male one; and this fish, when they wounded him with lances, bled very much, so that the sea was tinged by it where he swam; we brought him to the ship when the sun was in the north, for the sun is the clock to the seamen in Spitzbergen, or else they would live without order, and mistake in the usual seven weekly days.

We arrived at Spitzbergen June the 14th. First we came to the Foreland thereof, then to the seven Ice-hills or mountains, then we passed the harbours (or bays) of the Hamburghers, Magdalans, of the English men, the Danes, and sailed into the South Bay: we were followed by seven ships, three Hamburghers and four Hollanders.

That night we sailed with three boats into the English harbour or bay, and saw a whale, and flung into him three harpoons, and threw our lances into him; the whale ran underneath the small ice, and remained a great while under water before he came up again; and then ran but a very little way before he came up again; and this he repeated very often, so that we were forced to wait upon him above half an hour before he came from underneath the ice. The harpoons broke out at length, and we lost him.

On the 22nd, we had very fair weather, and pretty warm; we were by Rehenfelt (Deersfield), where the ice stood firm. We saw six whales, and got one of them that was a male and our third fish; he was killed at night when the sun stood westward: this fish was killed by one man who flung the harpoon into him; and killed him also, while the other boats were busy in pursuing or hunting after another whale. This fish run to the ice, and before he died beat about with his tail; the ice settled about him, so that the other boats could not come to this boat to assist him, till the ice separated again that they might row, when they tied one boat behind the other, and so towed the whale to the great ship, where they cut him up into the vessels, and filled with him forty-five barrels. This night the sun shined very brightly.

On the 1st July, about noon, two whales came near to our ship; we saw that they had a mind to couple together; we set our boat for them, and the harpoonier hit the female, which when the other found, he did not stay at all, but made away. The female run all along above the water, straight forward, beating about with her tail and fins, so that we durst not come near to lance her; yet one of our harpooniers was so foolhardy to venture too near the fish, which saluted him with a stroke of her tail over his back so vehemently, that he had much ado to recover his breath again. Those in the other boat, to show their valour also, hastened to the fish, which overturned their boat, so that the harpoonier was forced to dive for it, and hide his head underneath the water; the rest did the same; they thought it very long before they come out, for it was cold, so that they came quaking to the ship again. In the same morning, a whale appeared near our ship, before the wide harbour: we put out four boats from our ship after him, but two Holland ships were about half a league from us; one of them sent a boat towards us; we used great diligence and care to take him, but the fish came up just before the Dutchman's boat, and was struck by him with the harpoon. Thus he took the bread out of our mouths.

On the 5th July, in the forenoon, it was bright sunshine and pretty warm; in the afternoon it was foggy; at night sunshine again, which lasted all the night. We hunted all that day long, and in the morning we struck a whale before the Weigatt; this fish run round about under the water, and so fastened the line whereon our harpoon was about a rock, so that the harpoon lost its hold, and that fish got away. This whale did blow the water so fiercely, that one might hear it at a league's distance.

On the 6th, we had the same weather, and warm sunshine all night. Hard by us rode a Hollander, and the ship's crew busie in cutting the fat of a whale, when the fish burst with so great a bounce as if a cannon had been discharged, and bespattered the workmen all over.

On the 8th, the wind turned north-west, with snow and rain. We were forced to leave one of our anchors, and thank'd God for getting off from land, for the ice came on fiercely upon us; at night the wind was laid, and it was colder, although the sun shined.

On the 12th, we had gloomy sunshine all day. We saw but very few whales more, and those we did see were quite wild, that we could not come near them. That night it was so dark and foggy, that we could hardly see the ship's length; we might have got sea-horses enough, but we were afraid of losing our ships, for we had examples enough of them that had lost their ships, and could not come to them again, but have been forced to return home in other ships. When after this manner any have lost their ships, and cannot be seen, they discharge a cannon from the ship, or sound the trumpets, or hautboys, according as they are provided in their ships, that the men that are lost may find their ship again.

On the 13th, the ice came afloating down apace, we sailed from the south-east land to the west, and we could but just get through by the north side from the Bear Harbour or Bay. We sailed on to the Rehenfelt (or Deer Field), where the ice was already fixed to the land, so that we could but just get through; we sailed further to the Vogelsanck (bird's song). Then we turned to the east with a north-east wind, in company with twelve ships more, to see whether there were any more whales left, with *George* and *Cornelius Manglesen,* and *Michael Appel,* who sailed in four fathoms water, and touched upon the wreck of a ship that was lost there.

On the 14th, in the morning, we sailed still among the ice, the wind being north-east and by east; we had a fog all that day with sunshine, with a rainbow of two colours, white and pale yellow, and it was very cold, and we saw the sun a great deal lower.

On the 15th, it was windy, cold, and foggy the whole day; the wind turned north-west, and the ice come on in abundance, so that we could hardly sail, for it was everywhere full of small sheets of ice. At this time there were many ships beset with ice in the Deer or Muscle Bay. We sailed all along near the shoar; at night we entered the South-Harbour, where twenty-eight ships lay at anchor, eight whereof were Hamburghers, the rest Dutchmen. From that time when we sailed out of the Southhaven we kept always within sight of the land, and saw it always, except it was foggy; and so long the skippers stay by the ice to see if there are any more whales to be had.

On the 22nd day of July, in the morning, when the sun was northeast, we waied our anchors, and sailed out of the South-haven.

On the 24th, it was so warm with sunshine, that the tarr wherewith the ship was daubed over melted; we drove, it being calm, before the haven or Bay of Magdalen.

On the 25th, at night we came to the Forelands, the night was foggy, the wind south-west.

On the 28th, we turned from the side of the North Foreland towards the west, when the sun was south-east; and we did sail south-west and by west towards the sea ....

II

The fish properly called the whale, for whose sake our ships chiefly undertake the voyage to Spitzbergen, is differing from other whales in his finns and mouth, which is without teeth, but instead thereof long, black, somewhat broad and horny flakes, all jagged like hairs: he differs from the finn-fish in his finns, for the finn-fish hath a great finn on his back: but the whale properly so called, hath none on his back: and there are two finns behind his eyes of a bigness proportionable to the whale, covered with a thick black skin, delicately marbled with white strokes; or as you see in marble, trees, houses or the like things represented. In the tail of one of the fishes was marbled very delicately this number, 1222, very even and exact, as if they had been painted on it on purpose. This marbling on the whale is like veins in a piece of wood, that run streight through, or else round about the center or pith of a tree, and so go both white and yellow strokes, through the thick and the thin strokes, that is like parchment or vellam, and give to the whale an incomparable beauty and ornament. When these finns are cut up, you find underneath the thick skin bones that look like unto a man's hand, when it is opened and the fingers are expanded or spread; between these joynts there are stiff sinews, which flye up and rebound again if you fling them hard against the ground, as the sinews of great fish, as of a sturgeon, or of some four footed beasts generally do.

Their tail doth not stand up as the tails of almost any other fish, but it doth lye horizontal, as that of the finn-fish, butskopf, dolphin, and the like, and it is three, three and a half, and four fathoms broad. The head is the third part of the fish, and some have bigger heads; on the upper and under lip are short hairs before. Their lips are quite plain, somewhat bended like an S, and they end underneath the eyes before the two finns. Above the uppermost bended lip he hath black streaks; some are darkish brown, and they are crooked as the lips are. Their lips are smooth and quite black, round like the quarter of a circle; when they draw them together they lock into one another. Within, on the uppermost lip, is the whale-bone, of a brown, black, and yellow colour, with streaks of several colours, as the bones of a finn-fish. The whale bones of some of the whales are blew, and light blew, which two are reckoned to come from young whales. Just before, on the under lip, is a cavity or hole, which the upper lip fits exactly into, as a knife into a sheath. I do really believe, that he draws the water that he bloweth out through this hole, and so I have been informed also by seamen. Within his mouth is the whalebone, all hairy as horse's hair, as it is also in the finn-fish, and it hangs down from both sides all about his tongue. The whalebone of some whales is bended like unto a cimeter, and others like unto a half-moon. The lower part of the whale's mouth is commonly white: the tongue lyeth amongst the whale-bones; it is very close tyed to the undermost chap or lip; it is very large and white, with black spots at the edges.

Upon his head is the hovel or bump before the eyes and finns: at the top of this bump on each side, is a spout-hole, two over-against one another, which are bended on each side like an S, or as the hole that is cut in a violin, whereout he doth blow the water very fiercely, that it roars like a hollow wind which we hear when the wind bloweth into a cave, or against the corner of a board, or like an organ-pipe. This may be heard at a league's distance, although you do not see him by reason of the thick and foggy air. The whale bloweth or spouts the water fiercest of all when he is wounded, then it sounds as the roaring of the sea in a great storm, and as we hear the wind in a very hard storm. The head of the whale is not round at the top, but somewhat flat, and goeth down sloaping, like unto the tyling of an house, to the under lip. The under lip is broader than the whale is in any part of his body, and broadest in the middle; before and behind it is something narrower, according to the shape of the head. In one word, all the whole fish is shaped like unto a shoemakers last, if you look upon it from beneath. Behind the knob or bump where the finns are, between that and the finns, are his eyes, which are not much bigger than those of a bullock, with eyelids and hair, like men's eyes. The crystal of the eye is not much bigger than a pea, clear, white, and transparent as crystal; the colour of some is yellowish, of others quite white. The seale's are three times as big as those of the whale. The eyes of the whale are placed very low, almost at the end of the upper lip. Some bring along with them from Spitzbergen some bones, which they pretend to be the ears of the whale; but I can say nothing to this, because I never saw any; but thus much I do remember, that I have heard them say that they lye very deep. The whale doth not hear when he spouts the water, wherefore he is easiest to be struck at that time. His belly and back are quite red, and underneath the belly they are commonly white, yet some of them are coal black; most of them that I saw were white. They look very beautiful when the sun shines upon them, the small clear waves of the sea that are over him glisten like silver. Some of them are marbled on their back and tail. Where he hath been wounded there remaineth always a white scar; I understood one of our harpooniers that he once caught a whale at Spitzbergen that was white all over. Half white I have seen some, but one above the rest, which was a female, was a beautiful one; she was all over marbled black and yellow. Those that are as black are not all of the same colour, for some of them are black as velvet, others of a coal black, others of the colour of a tench.

The yard of a whale is a strong sinew, and according as they are in bigness, six, seven, or eight foot long, as I have seen myself. Where this yard is fixed the skin is doubled, so that it lies just like a knife in a sheath, where you can see nothing of the knife, but only a little of the haft. Where the yard doth begin it is four-square, consisting of many strong sinews; if you dry them they are as transparent as fish glew; out of these sinews the seamen make twisted whips. Their bones are hard, like unto them of great four-footed beasts, but porous, like unto a spunge, and filled with marrow; when that is consumed out, they will hold a great deal of water, for the holes are big like unto the wax of a honey-comb.

The other strong sinews are chiefly about the tail, where it is thinnest, for with it he turns arid winds himself as a ship is turn'd by the rudder; but his finns are his oars, and according to his bigness he rows himself along with them as swiftly as a bird flies, and doth make a long track in the sea, as a great ship doth when under sail.

BARON MUNCHAUSEN TELLS OF THE PRANKS OF A WHALE AND OF WHAT HAPPENED ON A VOYAGE TO THE INDIES[1]

Rudolf Erich Raspe

(1737-1794)

I

I EMBARKED at Portsmouth in a first-rate English man-of-war, of one hundred guns, and fourteen hundred men, for North America; nothing worth relating happened till we arrived within three hundred leagues of the river Saint Lawrence, when the ship struck with amazing force against (as we supposed) a rock; however, upon heaving the lead, we could find no bottom, even with three hundred fathom. What made this circumstance the more wonderful, and indeed beyond all comprehension, was, that the violence of the shock was such that we lost our rudder, broke our bowsprit in the middle, and split all our masts from top to bottom, two of which went by the board; a poor fellow, who was aloft, furling the main-sheet, was flung at least three leagues from the ship; but he fortunately saved his life, by laying hold of the tail of a large sea-gull, who brought him back, and lodged him on the very spot whence he was thrown. Another proof of the violence of the shock was the force with which the people between decks were driven against the floors above them; my head particularly was pressed into my stomach, where it continued some months, before it recovered its natural situation. Whilst we were all in a state of astonishment at the general and unaccountable confusion in which we were involved, the whole was suddenly explained, by the appearance of a large whale, who had been basking asleep within sixteen feet of the surface of the water. This animal was so much displeased with the disturbance which our ship had given him, (for in our passage we had with our rudder scratched his nose,) that he beat in all the gallery and part of the quarter-deck with his tail, and almost at the same instant, took the main sheet-anchor, which was suspended, as it usually is, from the head, between his teeth, and ran away with the ship, at least sixty leagues, at the rate of twelve leagues an hour, when fortunately the cable broke, and we lost both the whale and the anchor. However, upon our return to Europe some months after, we found the same whale, within a few leagues of the same spot, floating dead upon the water; it measured above half a mile in length. As we could take but a small quantity of such a monstrous animal on board, we got our boats out, and, with much difficulty, cut off his head, where, to our great joy, we found the anchor, and above 4 fathom

[1] From *Gulliver Revived.*

of the cable concealed on the left side of his mouth, just under his tongue. Perhaps this was the cause of his death, as that side of his tongue was much swelled, with a great degree of inflammation. This was the only extraordinary circumstance that happened on this voyage.

II

In a voyage which I made to the East Indies with Captain Hamilton, I took a favourite pointer with me; he was, to use a common phrase, worth his weight in gold, for he never deceived me. One day, when we were, by the best observations we could make, at least three hundred leagues from the land, my dog pointed; I observed him for near an hour with astonishment, and mentioned the circumstance to the Captain, and every officer on board, asserting, that we must be near land, for my dog smelt game; this occasioned a general laugh; but that did not alter in the least the good opinion I had of my dog. After much conversation pro and con, I boldly told the Captain, I placed more confidence in Tray's nose, than I did in the eyes of every seaman on board, and therefore boldly proposed laying the sum I had agreed to pay for my passage (viz. one hundred guineas) that we should find game within half an hour; the Captain (a good hearty fellow) laughed again, desired Mr Crawford, the surgeon, who was present, to feel my pulse; he did so, and reported me in perfect health: the following dialogue between them took place; I overheard it, though spoken low and at some distance.

CAPTAIN. His brain is turned; I cannot with honour accept his wager.
SURGEON. I am of a different opinion; he is quite sane, and depends more upon the scent of his dog, than he will upon the judgment of all the officers on board; he will certainly lose, and he richly merits it.

CAPTAIN. Such a wager cannot be fair on my side; however, I'll take him up, if I return his money afterwards.

During the above conversation, Tray continued in the same situation, and confirmed me still more in my former opinion. I proposed the wager a second time; it was then accepted.

Done and Done were scarcely said on both sides, when some sailors, who were fishing in the long-boat, which was made fast to the stern of the ship, harpooned an exceedingly large shark, which they brought on board, and began to cut up for the purpose of barrelling the oil, when, behold, they found no less than *six brace of live partridges* in this animal's stomach!

They had been so long in that situation, that one of the hens was sitting upon four eggs, and a fifth was hatching when the shark was opened!!!

This young bird we brought up, by placing it with a litter of kittens that came into the world a few minutes before! The old cat was as fond of it as any of her own four-legged progeny, and made herself very unhappy when it flew out of her reach till it returned again; as to the other partridges, there were four hens amongst them; one or more were, during the voyage, constantly sitting, and consequently we had plenty of game at the Captain's table; and in gratitude to poor Tray (for being the means of winning one hundred guineas) I ordered him the bones daily, and sometimes a whole bird.

HOW THE SEA SAVED LEYDEN[1]

Georg Ebers
(1837-1898)

PETER was sitting in front of his writing-table in his Burgomaster's dress, and with his hat on. His face was hidden in his folded arms, the two-branched candlestick stood lighted on the table. He saw nothing, heard nothing; and when she presently called him by his name he started violently, stood bolt upright, and flung his hat angrily on to the table. His hair was in disorder, his gaze unsteady, and in the dull flickering light of the candles his face was as grey as that of a corpse.

"What do you want?" he asked shortly in a hoarse voice; but for some moments she could not answer—her tongue seemed paralyzed with terror. At last she spoke.

"What has happened?" she said, and her voice betrayed her anguish. "The beginning of the end," he said gloomily.

"They have outvoted you!" cried the young woman. "Baersdorp and the rest of the cowards want to treat ?"

He drew himself up.

"Beware of what you say," he cried, in loud and threatening tones. "A man who holds out till his children die, and corpses bar the way to his own house-door, who is responsible for a thousand deaths, who for weeks has been loaded with curses, and who for more than four months has hoped for succour, who, look where he will, sees nothing but unutterable and constantly increasing wretchedness and then feels that he can no longer thrust back the saving hand held out even by the foe—"

"He is a coward, a traitor, and breaks the solemn oath he has sworn!"

"Maria!" thundered Peter, going close up to her with a threatening glare.

She stood still, drawn up to her full height, and pointing her finger at him, as she went on with keen asperity, though her voice trembled:

"You—you voted with Baersdorp! You, Peter van tier Werff, you! You have

[1] From Clara Bell's translation of *The Burgomaster's Wife*

done this, the Prince's friend, the guardian and providence of this brave town; you, the man to whom the citizens pledged their word —the son of the martyr, the champion of freedom!"

"Say no more!" he interrupted, quivering with shame and rage. "Do you know what it is to bear the burden of this woe that cries to Heaven, in the sight of God and man ?"

"I do, I do, and again I say, I do. It is to bind your heart to the rack and wheel in order to save Holland and her freedom! That is what it is! Great God! great God! You are lost indeed; you are making terms with Valdez!"

"And if I were?" said the Burgomaster with a haughty wave of his hand as if to dismiss the question.

Maria fixed her eyes on his, and exclaimed with clear decision:

"Then it would be my turn to say, Go to Delft, go to Delft; we want other men here."

Van der Werff turned paler and looked down at the floor, while she stood facing him with a frank and fearless gaze. The light fell full on her glowing countenance, and as he raised his eyes once more to hers he felt that the woman who stood before him was that same Maria, who, as his bride, had sworn to share suffering and danger with him, and stand steadfast to the end in the struggle for freedom; he felt that his "child" Maria had grown up to his own level, ay, and beyond it; he recognized for the first time in the high-souled woman before him his ally in the fight, a worthy helpmate in trouble and in danger. An overpowering yearning, an eager aspiration such as he had never before felt, surged and seethed within him, and drew him to her, and bound utterance in words.

"Maria!" he cried, "Maria, my wife, my guardian angel! We have indeed written to Valdez, but it is yet time; nothing as yet binds me, and with you, with you by my side, I can stand firm to the end." And in the middle of this day of anguish her heart overflowed with the flood of this new, unhoped-for, and unutterable joy. As she flung herself on his breast, she exclaimed: "And I with you—one with you! for ever, through this struggle, and in love beyond the grave!"

Peter felt like a man under a charm. Courage and enthusiasm once more filled his soul, for they overflowed in an unfailing stream from the brave and confident spirit of his wife.

Under the pressure of the fearful responsibility he bore and the urgency of his fellow-citizens, he had agreed in the Council to write to Valdez and crave a safe-conduct for an envoy to be sent to the States General and the Prince of Orange, to beg them to release the perishing city from its oath. Valdez spared no effort to incite the Burgomaster to farther negotiations, but Van der Werff stood firm, and the demand for release from the sacred duty of resistance never left the town. Both the Van der Does, the Town-Clerk, the Jonker van Warmond, and other staunch men, who, at the great general meeting had opposed all negotiations with the enemy, now ranged themselves on his side against their fellow-officials and the Town-Council, who, with the exception of seven only of their number, perseveringly and violently insisted on the discussion of terms.

Deep as the gloom was, and dark as was the horizon, in the midst of all this cruel misery, there were moments when a bright ray of sunshine fell on these suffering souls, and Hope unfurled her green standard. On the morning of the eleventh of September, the townsfolk of Leyden rose from their beds more radiantly joyful than a bride roused on her wedding day by the songs of her maiden companions, for in the distance the loud and persistent thunder of cannon could be heard, and the sky was dyed with crimson; to the south-west of the town there must be villages in flames, and each house, each granary, that sank into ashes, burying the hopes of honest men, was a beacon of promise to the despairing Leydeners.

The Gueux were approaching!

There, out there, where the cannon thundered and the horizon glowed, was the Land-scheiding, the dyke, which for centuries had stoutly protected the plain of Leyden against the incursions of the waves, and which now stopped the advance of the fleet that was to bring them life.

"Fall, sheltering wall! Rise, storms, and thou sea, engulf thy prey! Destroy the peasant's wealth, ruin our fields and pastures, but drown the foe or drive him hence!"

Thus sang Janus Dousa, thus cried Peter's soul, thus prayed Maria, and with her thousands of men and women.

But the blaze in the distance died away, the firing was silent. A second day went by, a third, a fourth; no messenger came, no ship of the Gueux was to be seen, and the lake lay motionless; while another awful power grew and stalked through the city with secret, stealthy, and omnipotent force—Death, with its gaunt helpmates Despair and Famine. Silently and at night the dead were carried to their graves, that the survivors might share their slender ration undiminished. From house to house the Angel of Death winged his way, and laid his hand at last on little Elizabeth, kissing her closed eyes as she slept in the noiseless night.

The faint-hearted, and those who sided with the Spaniards, assembled in mobs, one of which even made its way into the council-room, clamouring for bread. But there was not a crumb left in the stores, the authorities had nothing left to give but a morsel of cow or horse-flesh, or hides—soaked and salted hides.

On one of these days of dire extremity, Van der Werff was going down the Breede Straat; he paid no heed to the fact that a crowd of desperate men and women were following him with threats and abuse, but as he turned a corner to go to Van Hout's house, he suddenly found himself surrounded. A pale woman with a child in her arms at its last gasp, flung herself before him, holding the dying infant up to him, and crying in a hollow, feeble voice:

"Is it not enough, is it not enough? Look here, see this—it is the third! It is enough, enough!"

"Enough, enough! Bread, bread—give us bread!" thundered and growled all round him, and stones and missiles were lifted to throw, while a carpenter whom he knew, and who had always stood by the good cause, stepped close up to him, and said deliberately, in a deep voice: "We can bear it no longer. We have patiently endured famine and suffering to defy the Spaniards and to defend our Bible, but to fight with certain death is sheer madness."

Peter stood still, shocked and silent, and looked at the mother, the child, the stalwart working man, and the shrieking threatening wretches. The common woe which was crushing them and so many starving creatures burdened his soul with tenfold weight. Anguish unutterable clutched his heart, and he longed to open his arms and embrace them all as fellow-sufferers, and brethren in a future and nobler existence. He looked from one to another deeply moved; then pressing his hands to his breast he thus addressed the crowd that thronged round him:

"Here I stand. I have sworn to remain faithful, and you swore it with me. I will never break my oath, but I can die! If my death can do you any good, here I am! Bread I have none, but here is my body—take it; kill me, and tear me in pieces. Here I stand, and I will never break my oath."

The carpenter's head fell on his breast. "Come, good folks," he said; "God's will be done. We have sworn."

The Burgomaster passed on calmly to his friend's house. Dame van Hout had watched the whole scene from a window, and that same day she related it to Maria, and her eyes sparkled with enthusiasm as she added:

"I never saw a man so supremely great as he was at that moment. It is well for us that he commands within these walls; this deed will be remembered by our children and our children's children." They have, indeed, kept his memory green in faithful remembrance. During the night which followed the day when the Burgomaster had held himself so bravely, a letter arrived from the Prince, full of cheerful and encouraging news. Their illustrious chief was well again, and straining every nerve to save his brave town of Leyden. The Gueux had pierced the Land-scheiding; the ships were advancing; help was approaching; and the devoted men who brought the letter had, with their own eyes, seen the fleet that was bringing supplies and the champions of freedom, fired with zeal and valour for the struggle. The two Van der Does were nominated in the same letter to represent the Prince in the place of Van Bronkhorst. Van der Werff no longer stood alone; and when, next morning, "Father William's" letter was read to the populace, and the messenger's errand had become generally known, the spirits and confidence of the long-suffering townsfolk rose like withered grass under refreshing showers.

But there were still weary weeks of terror and misery to be gone through. In the last days of September they had to kill the cows, which till then had been spared for the benefit of the children and women in child-bed; and then—what next? Succour was at hand, for the sky was often red, and the air shook with the thunder of distant cannon; but the east wind blew steadily, and held back the water which was let in upon the land; and the ships which were trying to reach the town needed a high flood-tide.

Of all the messengers they sent forth not one returned; nothing was certain but their hideous, cruel, and increasing misery.

At last Barbara had succumbed, and was complaining of prostration and loathing for every kind of food. Maria remembered the roast pigeon which had been so welcome to their little lost Liesje, and she went to the musician to ask him whether he could bear to sacrifice another of his pets to save her sister-in-law.

She was received by his mother, who was sitting languid and feeble in an easy-chair. She could still walk, it is true, but all this anxiety and extreme want had brought on a strange shaking palsy in her hands. To Maria's question she shook her head and replied: "Ask him yourself. He has had to keep the poor little creatures shut up, for if they had been seen, they would have been shot down long since by the starving people. He still has three; the rest have flown off with various letters, but have never come back. Thank God! say I, for the scrap of food he still has by him is better in the pot than in their crops. Would you believe it? A fortnight since he paid fifty gülden out of his savings for half a sack of peas, and God only knows where he got them then. Ullrich, take Dame van der Werff up to speak to Wilhelm. I would spare you the stairs, but he is watching up there for the pigeons he has sent out, and will not come down even to meals; and God knows they are not worth coming down to."

The day was clear and sunny. Wilhelm was standing on his balcony, and looking out over the green, well-watered plain that stretched before him to the south. Behind him sat the Captain's orphan son, Andreas, writing music; but his attention was not very steady, for, whenever he had finished a line, he sat gazing into the air and watching, like his master, for the expected pigeons. He was not very much the worse for the dearth, for a certain portion of the pigeons' food had fallen to his share with his small allowance of meat.

Wilhelm was as much surprised as honoured by Maria's visit, and promised to grant her request; but it was plain that he did not find it an easy matter to say "Yes." The young woman went out on to the balcony with him, and he showed her that to the south, where formerly nothing had been visible but miles of green, there was a line—a long, level margin—above which hovered a filmy mist. The noon-day sun seemed to saturate the pale vapour with light and draw it upwards. It was the water that was pouring in through the cuts in the dykes; and the long black patches which might be seen moving on its shore must be the Spanish troops and herds of cattle which were being driven into the outermost forts, villages, and hamlets, by the encroaching tide. The Land-scheiding itself was out of sight, but the Gueux had already cut through that. If the fleet could only reach the Zoetermeer Lake, and from thence—

But Wilhelm suddenly broke off in his explanation, for Andreas sprang up, throwing down his stool and shouting:

"It is coming! the pigeon! By Roland, my former self, there it is!" It was the first time that Wilhelm had ever heard the father's favourite cry from the lips of the son; something must have excited him strangely; and in fact he was not mistaken, for the speck which his sharp eyes had espied cutting through the air was no longer a speck but already an object of discernible form—a bird—a pigeon.

Wilhelm snatched up a banner that lay on the balcony, and waved it more joyfully than ever a pictor waved his flag after winning a battle. There came the pigeon; it settled, slipped into the dovecot, and in another minute the musician appeared with a tiny letter in his hand.

"To the Burgomaster—quick!" cried Wilhelm. "Carry it at once to your husband, dear Dame, and finish what the pigeon has begun. God be praised! they are already at North Aa. This will save the poor folks from despair; and one thing more, you shall have a bird to cook; but take this corn too—barleymeal porridge is the very best remedy in Barbara's condition;—I have tried it."

In the evening, and after the organist had communicated the good news to his parents, he ordered that the blue pigeon with the white breast should be killed. "Make an end of it outside," he said; "I cannot bear to see it done."

Andreas soon came in with the dead pigeon; his lips were red, and Wilhelm could guess the reason, but he could not scold the famishing boy, and only said:

"Faugh! you ferret!"

Next morning, quite early, another pigeon flew in. The letters that they brought were read out from the window of the town-hall, and the courage of the Leydeners, now in the utmost extremity of misery, once more flickered into life, and helped them to endure the worst. One of the letters was to Van der Werff, the other to Janus Dousa; they spoke of confidence and hope; and the Prince—the faithful rock of their freedom, the friend and leader of the nation—the Prince himself was well and strong again, and had himself been to see the ships which were being sent to relieve the town. Salvation was so near—but the north-east wind would not change, and the waters did not rise.

On the Burcht and other elevated spots stood the citizens, soldiers, town-councillors and women in great numbers, all gazing into the distance. A thousand hands were uplifted in fervent prayer, and all eyes were fixed in feverish expectation and agonizing longing on the southern horizon; but the line of water did not advance, and the sun broke brightly through the mists of the autumn mornings as if in mockery, tempered the keen air, and sank to rest in the evening in a fiery glow and farreaching shafts of golden light. A cloudless blue sky o'erarched the town with pitiless calm, and decked itself at night with myriads of bright stars.

On the morning of the 29th, however, the mists seemed to pack more solidly together, the grass was dewless, a fog rose, the sharp air was tempered to a dull mildness, and the great clouds grew dense and gathered blackness. Then a light breeze rose, and rustled in the leafless branches, and suddenly a gust of wind swept over the heads of the watching crowd. It was followed by a second and a third, and at last the gale whistled and roared, and a howling storm whirled through the town, sweeping the tiles from the roofs, bending the fruit-trees in the gardens and the young elms and limetrees in the streets; tearing down the banners which the boys had stuck up on the wails, in defiance of the Spaniards; lashing the dull waters of the canals and the moat. And now—for the Lord forsaketh not his own—the weathercock veered, the blast came down from the north-west, and drove the spring-tide in the stormtossed sea up the mouth of the Maas; none could see it, but the seamen shouted out the news, and it was caught up and passed on from one to another. The stream was forced violently up its channel and over its banks; rushing through the cuttings made in the dykes to admit it, and through the yawning sluice-gates, and bearing on its mighty shoulders the ships that bore relief.

Rage, rage, thou storm; beat down, thou lashing rain; rush on, ye floods; destroy the land, engulf the houses and farms! Thousands are waiting to welcome you on the walls and towers of Leyden. They see in you the avenging and saving hosts of the Lord, and rejoice and hail you with shouts.

For two successive days the Burgomaster—with Maria and Adria, and the families of Van der Does and Van Hour—has remained, with brief intervals, among the townspeople, who are watching from the Burcht or the Cow Gate; and even Barbara, though hardly recovered, will not be kept at home, for hope has done more to revive her than the barleymeal porridge and the lean pigeon; she has dragged herself up to the musician's eyrie, for every one must see the advancing waters, as the earth gives place to them—see the moisture trickle through the grass, collect in puddles, pools, lakes, till at last it is a broad level, beaten by the thrashing rain into bubbles that break into rings and vanish. Every one wants to see with his own eyes how the Spaniards hurry hither and thither, like sheep fleeing before a wolf. Every one must hear for himself the thunder of the Gueux' cannon, the rattle of their arquebuses and musketry; men and women alike, rejoice more in the storm which threatens to sweep them away, than in the softest zephyr; and the drenching rain that soaks them is more delightful than the sun-lit showers of spring.

Beyond the stronghold of Lammen, defended by some hundred Spanish soldiers, and the tower of Croonesteyn, a keen eye could now detect the ships of the Gueux. All Thursday and Friday Wilhelm had looked in vain for a pigeon, but on Saturday his best carrier came home. It bore a letter from Admiral Boisot, begging that the men-at-arms left in the town would make a sortie on the Friday, and throw themselves upon Lammen. The storm had carried the bird out of its track; it had arrived a day too late. However, on the Saturday evening Janus Dousa and Captain van der Laen prepared to move. All who could bear arms were called out early on Sunday morning. A hapless, pale, and diminished force gathered at their Commander's call; but none would be missing, and all were prepared to yield up their lives for the rescue of the town, and of those dear to them.

The storm had moderated; the firing had ceased; the night was warm and dark. Not an eye was closed, and those who, for a few moments, were overcome by sleep were startled and alarmed by strange and mysterious noises. Wilhelm sat up on his balcony looking and listening towards the south. Now a light gust of wind would whistle round the tall house, now a shout, a cry, a trumpet-call rang through the silent night; and presently there was a crash and roar out by the Cow Gate, as though an earthquake had shaken the foundations of part of the town and hurled it to the ground. There was not a star in the sky, but in the neighbourhood of Lammen dancing lights moved in regular rows across the black darkness. It was an ominous and terrible night.

At dawn it was seen that a part of the town-wall by the Cow Gate had fallen in, and a cry of joy went up to Heaven at the sight of the breach, which was now no longer a source of danger, while the joyful news flew through the streets and alleys. Men and women, old men and children, sick and sound, came out of the houses, crowding down to the Cow Gate; now the fleet of the Gueux was to be seen rapidly coming nearer, and the town-carpenter, Thomassohn, with some others, was tearing up the piles with which the Spaniards had barred the Vliet, till at last the first ship, and then a second and a third, was close under the walls. The wild-looking hairy sailors—men with deeply-scarred, fierce, sun-burnt faces, which for years had felt no touch of any salt water but the sea spray—were laughing to the citizens and crying and sobbing like children; while they threw them up loaves and good things long unknown to them, which the poor creatures on the wall ate and ate, and could not even find a word of thanks. And then the chiefs arrived and met; Admiral Boisot fell into the arms of Van der Does and the Burgomaster, and Van Duykenburg into those of his mother, old Barbara, and many a Leydener hugged the liberators he had never set eyes on till this hour. Many, many a tear was shed, and thousands of hearts overflowed, and the Sunday bells rang out louder and clearer than was their wont, bidding the rescuer and the rescued alike to church and prayer. The wide vault of the sanctuary was too narrow for the worshippers, and when the preacher Corneliuszoon—filling the place of the worthy Vestroot, who had fallen ill himself while tending so many sufferers-exhorted the devout to thanksgiving, his words had long been anticipated, for at the very first sound of the organ the thousands who crowded the church in every part had been fired to offer up, as with one voice, thanks—thanks, and again fervent thanks!

Pater Damianus, too, returned thanks to God in the little chapel of the Carmelite Sisters, and with him Nicolas van Wibisma and many another Catholic, to whom freedom and his fatherland were dear.

After church, Adrian, with a piece of bread in one hand and his shoes in the other, waded at the head of his school-fellows across the higher meadows, which were all under water, as far as Leyderdorp, to see the deserted Spanish camp. There stood the handsome tent of the Commander-in-chief; over the bedstead hung a map of the Rhineland, which had been drawn by Beeldsnyder, a Dutchman, for the destruction of his own countrymen. The boys stood gazing at it, and a Gueux, who had once sat at a desk, and who now looked like a sea-bear, went up to them.

"See here, lads," he said, "here is the Land-scheiding. We cut through that first, but that was only half our task. We were checked at the Greenway, and here at the third dyke the Voorweg they call it—we found too hard a nut to crack; we could not get through any way. So back we had to go again, a long round by Zeegwaert and through the canal here, where we had a hard tussle, to North Aa. The Zoetermeer Lake was now behind us, but the water was too shallow, and we could get no farther. Have you seen the great *Ark of Delft?* It is a huge vessel, and is not moved by oars but by wheels which turn and push it on through the water; you will like to see it. At last the Lord sent the storm and the spring-tide, and the ships had water enough to float them. At the Kirkway we again had hot work, but we got to Lammen the day before yesterday. Many a brave man had already fallen on both sides, but when we got to Lammen, we all thought we were to fight it out in good earnest. Early this morning we meant to storm the fort, but when day dawned all was awfully still in the nest, and there was an uncanny sultriness in the air. Then we thought to ourselves, 'It is all over with Leyden; hunger has been too much for them!' But nothing of the kind! You are made of sterner stuff; and a boy came wading out to the ship—about as big as one of you—and said that in the night he had seen a long train of lights come out of the fort and march away. At first we would not believe him, but the boy was right. The crabs had found the water too hot for them, and the lights the youngster had seen were the slow matches of the Spaniards. Look, children, there is Lammen—" Adrian and his companions had gone quite close up to the map, and had interrupted the seaman's story with a loud laugh.

"What have you found there, curly-pate?" asked the Gueux.

"Look here, look here, the great Valdez has immortalized himself; and here is his name too! Our head-master would make him wear a dunce's cap, for he writes *Castelii parvi! Vale civitas, valete Castelli parvi; relicti estis propter aquam et non per vim inimicorum.* Oh, what an ass! *Castelli parvi!"*

"And what does all that mean?" asked the sailor.

"Farewell, Leyden, farewell, ye little *Castelli!* you are abandoned because of the waters and not because of the strength of the enemy. *'Parvi Castelli!"*

POLAND

THE LIGHTHOUSE KEEPER OF ASPINWALL[1]

Henryk Sienkiewicz

(1846–1916)

ON A time it happened that the lighthouse keeper in Aspinwall, not far from Panama, disappeared without a trace. Since he disappeared during a storm, it was supposed that the ill-fated man went to the very edge of the small, rocky island on which the lighthouse stood, and was swept out by a wave. This supposition seemed the more likely, as his boat was not found next day in its rocky niche. The place of lighthouse keeper had become vacant. It was necessary to fill this place at the earliest moment possible, since the lighthouse had no small significance for the local movement as well as for vessels going from New York to Panama. Mosquito Bay abounds in sandbars and banks. Among these, navigation, even in the daytime, is difficult; but at night, especially with the fogs which are so frequent on those waters warmed by the sun of the tropics, it is nearly impossible. The only guide at that time for the numerous vessels is the lighthouse.

The task of finding a new keeper fell to the United States consul living in Panama, and this task was no small one: first, because it was absolutely necessary to find a man within twelve hours; second, the man must be unusually conscientious—it was not possible, of course, to take the first comer at random; finally, there was an utter lack of candidates. Life on a tower is uncommonly difficult, and by no means enticing to people of the South, who love idleness and the freedom of vagrant life. That lighthouse keeper is almost a prisoner. He cannot leave his rocky island except on Sundays. A boat from Aspinwall brings him provisions and water once a day, and returns immediately; on the whole island, one acre in area, there is no inhabitant. The keeper lives in the lighthouse; he keeps it in order. During the day he gives signals by displaying flags of various colours to indicate changes of the barometer; in the evening he lights the lantern. This would be no great labour were it not that to reach the lantern at the summit of the tower he must pass over more than four hundred steep and very high steps; sometimes he must make this journey repeatedly during the day. In general, it is the life of a monk, and indeed more than that—the life of a hermit. It was not wonderful, therefore, that Mr Isaac Falconbridge was in no small anxiety as to where he should find a permanent successor to the recent keeper; and it is easy to understand his joy when

[1] From Jeremiah Curtln's translation of Yanko the Musician.

a successor announced himself most unexpectedly on that very day. He was a man already old, seventy years or more, but fresh, erect, with the movements and bearing of a soldier. His hair was perfectly white, his face as dark as that of a Creole; but, judging from his blue eyes, he did not belong to a people of the South. His face was somewhat downcast and sad, but honest. At the first glance he pleased Falconbridge. It remained only to examine him. Therefore the following conversation began:

"Where are you from?"

"I am a Pole."

"Where have you worked up to this time?"

"In one place and another."

"A lighthouse keeper should like to stay in one place."

"I need rest."

"Have you served? Have you testimonials of honourable government service?"

The old man drew from his bosom a piece of faded silk, resembling a strip of an old flag, unwound it, and said:

"Here are the testimonials. I received this cross in 1830. This second one is Spanish from the Carlist War; the third is the French legion; the fourth I received in Hungary. Afterward I fought in the States against the South; there they do not give crosses."

Falconbridge took the paper and began to read.

"H'm! Skavinski? Is that your name? H'm! Two flags captured in a bayonet attack. You were a gallant soldier."

"I am able to be a conscientious lighthouse keeper."

"It is necessary to ascend the tower a number of times daily. Have you sound legs ?"

"I crossed the plains on foot." (The immense steppes between the East and California are called "the plains.")

"Do you know sea service?"

"I served three years on a whaler."

"You have tried various occupations."

"The only one I have not known is quiet."

"Why is that?"

The old man shrugged his shoulders. "Such is my fate."

"Still you seem to me too old for a lighthouse keeper."

"Sir," exclaimed the candidate suddenly in a voice of emotion, "I am greatly wearied, knocked about. I have passed through much, as you see. This place is one of those which I have wished for most ardently. I am old, I need rest. I need to say to myself, 'Here you will remain; this is your port.' Ah, sir, this depends now on you alone. Another time perhaps such a place will not offer itself. What luck that I was in Panama! I entreat you—as God is dear to me, I am like a ship which if it misses the harbour will be lost. If you wish to make an old man happy—I swear to you that I am honest, but—I have enough of wandering."

The blue eyes of the old man expressed such earnest entreaty that Falconbridge, who had a good, simple heart, was touched.

"Well," said he, "I take you. You are lighthouse keeper."

The old man's face gleamed with inexpressible joy.

"I thank you."

"Can you go to the tower to-day?"

"I can."

"Then good-bye. Another word—for any failure in service you will be dismissed."

"All right."

That same evening, when the sun had descended on the other side of the isthmus, and a day of sunshine was followed by a night without twilight, the new keeper was in his place evidently, for the lighthouse was casting its bright rays on the water as usual. The night was perfectly calm, silent, genuinely tropical, filled with a transparent haze, forming around the moon a great coloured rainbow with soft, unbroken edges; the sea was moving only because the tide raised it. Skavinski on the balcony seemed from below like a small black point. He tried to collect his thoughts and take in his new position; but his mind was too much under pressure to move with regularity. He felt somewhat as a hunted beast feels when at last it has found refuge from pursuit on some inaccessible rock or in a cave. There had come to him, finally, an hour of quiet; the feeling of safety filled his soul with a certain unspeakable bliss. Now on that rock he can simply laugh at his previous wanderings, his misfortunes and failures. He was in truth like a ship whose masts, ropes, and sails had been broken and rent by a tempest, and cast from the clouds to the bottom of the sea—a ship on which the tempest had hurled waves and spat foam, but which still found its way to the harbour. The pictures of that storm passed quickly through his mind as he compared it with the calm future now beginning. A part of his wonderful adventures he had related to Falconbridge; he had not mentioned, however, thousands of other incidents. It had been his misfortune that as often as he pitched his tent and fixed his fireplace to settle down permanently, some wind tore out the stakes of his tent, whirled away the fire, and bore him on toward destruction. Looking now from the balcony of the tower at the illuminated waves, he remembered everything through which he had passed. He had campaigned in the four parts of the world, and in wandering had tried almost every occupation. Labour-loving and honest, more than once he had earned money, and had always lost it in spite of every prevision and the utmost caution. He had been a gold-miner in Australia, a diamond-digger in Africa, a rifleman in public service in the East Indies. He established a ranch in California—the drought ruined him; he tried trading with wild tribes in the interior of Brazil—his raft was wrecked on the Amazon; he himself alone, weaponless and nearly naked, wandered in the forest for many weeks living on wild fruits, exposed every moment to death from the jaws of wild beasts. He established a forge in Helena, Arkansas, and that was burned in a great fire which consumed the whole town. Next he fell into the hands of Indians in the Rocky Mountains, and only through a miracle was he saved by Canadian trappers. Then he served as a sailor on a vessel running between Bahia and Bordeaux, and as harpooner on a whaling-ship; both vessels were wrecked. He had a cigar factory in Havana, and was robbed by his partner while he himself was lying sick with the vomito. At last he came to Aspinwall, and there was to be the end of his failures—for what could reach him on that rocky island? Neither water nor fire nor men. But from men Skavinski had not suffered much; he had met good men oftener than bad ones.

But it seemed to him that all the four elements were persecuting him. Those who knew him said that he had no luck, and with that they explained everything. He himself became somewhat of a monomaniac. He believed that some mighty and vengeful hand was pursuing him everywhere, on all lands and waters. He did not like, however, to speak of this; only, at times, when some one asked him whose hand that could be, he pointed mysteriously to the Polar Star, and said, "It comes from that place." In reality his failures were so continuous that they were wonderful, and might easily drive a nail into the head, especially of the man who had experienced them. But Skavinski had the patience of an Indian, and that great calm power of resistance which comes from truth of heart. In his time he had received in Hungary a number of bayonetthrusts because he would not grasp at a stirrup which was shown as means of salvation to him, and cry for quarter. In like manner he did not bend to misfortune. He crept up against the mountain as industriously as an ant. Pushed down a hundred times, he began his journey calmly for the hundred and first time. He was in his way a most peculiar original. This old soldier, tempered, God knows, in how many fires, hardened in suffering, hammered and forged, had the heart of a child. In the time of the epidemic in Cuba, the vomito attacked him because he had given to the sick all his quinine, of which he had a considerable supply, and left not a grain to himself.

There had been in him also this wonderful quality—that after so many disappointments he was ever full of confidence, and did not lose hope that all would be well yet. In winter he grew lively, and predicted great events. He waited for these events with impatience, and lived with the thought of them whole summers. But the winters passed one after another, and Skavinski lived only to this—that they whitened his head. At last he grew old, began to lose energy; his endurance was becoming more and more like resignation, his former calmness was tending toward supersensitiveness and that tempered soldier was degenerating into a man ready to shed tears for any cause. Besides this, from time to time he was weighed down by a terrible homesickness which was roused by any circumstance—the sight of swallows, grey birds like sparrows, snow on the mountains, or melancholy music like that heard on a time. Finally, there was one idea which mastered him—the idea of rest. It mastered the old man thoroughly, and swallowed all other desires and hopes. This ceaseless wanderer could not imagine anything more to be longed for, anything more precious, than a quiet corner in which to rest, and wait in silence for the end. Perhaps specially because some whim of fate had so hurried him over all seas and lands that he could hardly catch his breath, did he imagine that the highest human happiness was simply not to wander. It is true that such modest happiness was his due; but he was so accustomed to disappointments that he thought of rest as people in general think of something which is beyond reach. He did not dare to hope for it. Meanwhile, unexpectedly, in the course of twelve hours he had gained a position which was as if chosen for him out of all the world. We are not to wonder, then, that when he lighted his lantern in the evening he became as it were dazed—that he asked himself if that was reality, and he did not dare to answer that it was. But at the same time reality convinced him with incontrovertible proofs; hence hours one after another passed while he was on the balcony. He gazed, and convinced himself. It might seem that he was looking at the sea for the first time in his life. The lens of the lantern cast into the darkness an enormous triangle of light, beyond which the eye of the old man was lost in the black distance completely, in the distance mysterious and awful. But that distance seemed to run toward the light. The long waves following one another rolled out from the darkness, and went bellowing toward the base of the island; and then their foaming backs were visible, shining rose-coloured in the light of the lantern. The incoming tide swelled more and more, and covered the sandy bars. The mysterious speech of the ocean came with a fullness more powerful and louder, at one time like the thunder of cannon, at another like the roar of great forests, at another like the distant dull sound of the voices of people. At moments it was quiet; then to the ears of the old man came some great sigh, then a kind of sobbing, and again threatening outbursts. At last the wind bore away the haze, but brought black, broken clouds, which hid the moon. From the west it began to blow more and more; the waves sprang with rage against the rock of the lighthouse, licking with foam the foundation walls. In the distance a storm was beginning to bellow. On the dark, disturbed expanse certain green lanterns gleamed from the masts of ships. These green points rose high and then sank; now they swayed to the right, and now to the left. Skavinski descended to his room. The storm began to howl. Outside, people on those ships were struggling with night, with darkness, with waves; but inside the tower it was calm and still. Even the sounds of the storm hardly came through the thick walls, and only the measured tick-tack of the clock lulled the wearied old man to his slumber.

Hours, days, and weeks began to pass. Sailors assert that sometimes when the sea is greatly roused, something from out the midst of night and darkness calls them by name. If the infinity of the sea may call out thus, perhaps when a man is growing old, calls come to him, too, from another infinity still darker and more deeply mysterious; and the more he is wearied by life the dearer are those calls to him. But to hear them quiet is needed. Besides old age loves to put itself aside, as if with a foreboding of the grave. The lighthouse had become for Skavinski such a half grave. Nothing is more monotonous than life on a beacon-tower. If young people consent to take up this service they leave it after a time. Lighthouse keepers are generally men not young, gloomy, and confined to themselves. If by chance one of them leaves his lighthouse and goes among men, he walks in the midst of them like a person roused from deep slumber. On the tower there is a lack of minute impressions which in ordinary life teach men to adapt themselves to everything. All that a lighthouse keeper comes in contact with is gigantic and devoid of definitely outlined forms. The sky is one whole, the water another; and between those two infinities the soul of man is in loneliness. That is a life in which thought is continual meditation, and out of that meditation nothing rouses the keeper, not even his work. Day is like day as two beads in a rosary, unless changes of weather form the only variety. But Skavinski felt more happiness than ever in life before. He rose with the dawn, took his breakfast, polished the lens, and then sitting on the balcony gazed into the distance of the water; and his eyes were never sated with the pictures which he saw before him. On the enormous turquoise ground of the ocean were to be seen generally flocks of swollen sails gleaming in the rays of the sun so brightly that the eyes were blinking before the excess of light. Sometimes the ships, favoured by the so-called trade winds, went in an extended line one after another, like a chain of seamews or albatrosses. The red casks indicating the channel swayed on the light wave with gentle movement. Among the sails appeared every afternoon gigantic greyish feather-like plumes of smoke. That was a steamer from New York which brought passengers and goods to Aspinwall, drawing behind it a frothy path of foam. On the other side of the balcony Skavinski saw, as if on his palm, Aspinwall and its busy harbour, and in it a forest of masts, boats, and craft; a little farther, white houses and the towers of the town. From the height of his tower the small houses were like the nests of sea-mews, the boats were like beetles, and the people moved around like small points on the white stone boulevard. From early morning a light eastern breeze brought a confused hum of human life, above which predominated the whistle of steamers. In the afternoon six o'clock came; the movements in the harbour began to cease; the mews hid themselves in the rents of the cliffs; the waves grew feeble and became in some sort lazy; and then on the land, on the sea, and on the tower came a time of stillness unbroken by anything. The yellow sands from which the waves had fallen back glittered like golden stripes on the width of the waters; the body of the tower was outlined definitely in blue. Floods of sunbeams were poured from the sky on the water and the sands and the cliff. At that time a certain lassitude full of sweetness seized the old man. He felt that the rest which he was enjoying was excellent; and when he thought that it would be continuous nothing was lacking to him.

Skavinski was intoxicated with his own happiness; and since a man adapts himself easily to improved conditions, he gained faith and confidence by degrees; for he thought that if men built houses for invalids, why should not God gather up at last His own invalids? Time passed, and confirmed him in this conviction. The old man grew accustomed to his tower, to the lantern, to the rock, to the sand-bars, to solitude. He grew accustomed also to the sea-mews which hatched in the crevices of the rock, and in the evening held meetings on the roof of the lighthouse. Skavinski threw them generally the remnants of his food; and soon they grew tame, and afterward, when he fed them, a real storm of white wings encircled him, and the old man went among the birds like a shepherd among sheep. When the tide ebbed he went to the low sand-banks, on which he collected savoury periwinkles and beautiful pearl shells of the nautilus, which receding waves had left on the sand. In the night by the moonlight and the tower he went to catch fish, which frequented the windings of the cliff in myriads. At last he was in love with his rocks and his treeless little island, grown over only with small thick plants exuding sticky resin. The distant views repaid him for the poverty of the island, however. During afternoon hours, when the air became very clear he could see the whole isthmus covered with the richest vegetation. It seemed to Skavinski at such times that he saw one gigantic garden—bunches of cocoa, and enormous musa, combined as it were in luxurious tufted bouquets, right there behind the houses of Aspinwall. Farther on, between Aspinwall and Panama, was a great forest over which every morning and evening hung a reddish haze of exhalations—a real tropical forest with its feet in stagnant water, interlaced with lianas and filled with the sound of one sea of gigantic orchids, palms, milk-trees, irontrees, gum-trees.

Through his field-glass the old man could see not only trees and the broad leaves of bananas, but even legions of monkeys and great marabous and flocks of parrots, rising at times like a rainbow cloud over the forest. Skavinski knew such forests well, for after being wrecked on the Amazon he had wandered whole weeks among similar arches and thickets. He had seen how many dangers and deaths lie concealed under those wonderful and smiling exteriors. During the nights which he had spent in them he heard close at hand the sepulchral voices of howling monkeys and the roaring of the jaguars; he saw gigantic serpents coiled like lianas on trees; he knew those slumbering forest lakes full of torpedo-fish and swarming with crocodiles; he knew under what a yoke man lives in those unexplored wildernesses in which are single leaves that exceed a man's size ten times—wildernesses swarming with blood-drinking mosquitoes, treeleeches, and gigantic poisonous spiders. He had experienced that forest life himself, had witnessed it, had passed through it; therefore it gave him the greater enjoyment to look from his height and gaze on those *matos*, admire their beauty, and be guarded from their treacherousness. His tower preserved him from every evil. He left it only for a few hours on Sunday. He put on then his blue keeper's coat with silver buttons, and hung his crosses on his breast. His milk-white head was raised with a certain pride when he heard at the door, while entering the church, the Creoles say among themselves, "We have an honourable lighthouse keeper and not a heretic, though he is a Yankee." But he returned straightway after Mass to his island, and returned happy, for he had still no faith in the mainland. On Sunday also he read the Spanish newspaper which he bought in the town, or the *New York Herald,* which he borrowed from Falconbridge; and he sought in it European news eagerly. The poor old heart on that lighthouse tower, and in another hemisphere, was beating yet for its birthplace. At times too, when the boat brought his daily supplies and water to the island, he went down from the tower to talk with Johnson, the guard. But after a while he seemed to grow shy. He ceased to go to the town, to read the papers and to go down to talk politics with Johnson. Whole weeks passed in this way, so that no one saw him and he saw no one. The only signs that the old man was living were the disappearance of the provisions left on shore, and the light of the lantern kindled every evening with the same regularity with which the sun rose in the morning from the waters of those regions. Evidently, the old man had become indifferent to the world. Homesickness was not the cause, but just this—that even homesickness had passed into resignation. The whole world began now and ended for Skavinski on his island. He had grown accustomed to the thought that he would never leave the tower till his death, and he simply forgot that there was anything else besides it. Moreover, he had become a mystic; his mild blue eyes began to stare like the eyes of a child, and were as if fixed on something at a distance. In presence of a surrounding uncommonly simple and great, the old man was losing the feeling of personality; he was ceasing to exist as an individual, was becoming merged more and more in that which inclosed him. He did not understand anything beyond his environment; he felt only unconsciously. At last it seems to him that the heavens, the water, his rock, the tower, the golden sand-banks, and the swollen sails, the sea-mews, the ebb and flow of the tide—all form a mighty unity, one enormous mysterious soul; that he is sinking in that mystery, and feels that soul which lives and lulls itself. He sinks and is rocked, forgets himself; and in that narrowing of his own individual existence, in that half-waking, half-sleeping, he has discovered a rest so great that it nearly resembles half-death.

But the awakening came.

On a certain day, when the boat brought water and a supply of provisions, Skavinski came down an hour later from the tower, and saw that besides the usual cargo there was an additional package. On the outside of this package were postage stamps of the United States, and the address: "Skavinski, Esq.," written on coarse canvas.

The old man, with aroused curiosity, cut the canvas, and saw books; he took one in his hand, looked at it, and put it back; thereupon his hands began to tremble greatly. He covered his eyes as if he did not believe them; it seemed to him as if he were dreaming. The book was Polish—what did that mean? Who could have sent the book? Clearly, it did not occur to him at the first moment that in the beginning of his lighthouse career he had read in the *Herald,* borrowed from the consul, of the formation of a Polish society in New York, and had sent at once to that society half his month's salary, for which he had, moreover, no use on the tower. The society had sent him the books with thanks. The books came in the natural way; but at the first moment the old man could not seize those thoughts. Polish books in Aspinwall, on his tower, amid his solitude—that was for him something uncommon, a certain breath from past times, a kind of miracle. Now it seemed to him, as to those sailors in the night, that something was calling him by name with a voice greatly beloved and nearly forgotten. He sat for a while with closed eyes, and was almost certain that, when he opened them, the dream would be gone.

The package, cut open, lay before him, shone upon clearly by the afternoon sun, and on it was an open book. When the old man stretched his hand toward it again, he heard in the stillness the beating of his own heart. He looked; it was poetry. On the outside stood printed in great letters the title, underneath the name of the author. The name was not strange to Skavinski; he saw that it belonged to the great poet,[1] whose productions he had read in 1830 in Paris. Afterwards, when campaigning in Algiers and Spain, he had heard from his countrymen of the growing fame of the great seer; but he was so accustomed to the musket at that time that he took no book in hand. In 1849 he went to America, and in the adventurous life which he led he hardly ever met a Pole, and never a Polish book. With great eagerness, therefore, and with a livelier beating of the heart, did he turn to the title-page. It seemed to him then that on his lonely rock some solemnity is about to take place. Indeed it was a moment of great calm and silence. The clocks of Aspinwall were striking five in the afternoon. Not a cloud darkened the clear

[1] Mickiewicz (pronounced Mitskyevich), the greatest poet of Poland.

sky; only a few sea-mews were sailing through the air. The ocean was as if cradled to sleep. The waves on the shore stammered quietly, spreading softly on the sand. In the distance the white houses of Aspinwall, and the wonderful groups of palm, were smiling. In truth, there was something there solemn, calm, and full of dignity. Suddenly, in the midst of that calm of nature, was heard the trembling voice of the old man, who read aloud as if to understand himself better:

> "Thou art like health, O my birth-land Litva![1]
> How much we should prize thee he only can know who has lost thee.
> Thy beauty in perfect adornment this day.
> I see and describe, because I am yearning for thee."

His voice failed Skavinski. The letters began to dance before his eyes; something broke in his breast, and went like a wave from his heart higher and higher, choking his voice and pressing his throat. A moment more he controlled himself, and read further:

> "O Holy Lady, who guardest bright Chenstohova,
> Who shinest in Ostrobrama and preservest
> The castle town Novgrodek with its trusty people,
> As Thou didst give me back to health in childhood,
> When by my weeping mother placed beneath Thy care
> I raised my lifeless eyelids upward,
> And straightway walked unto Thy holy threshold,
> To thank God for the life restored me,—
> So by a wonder now restore us to the bosom of our birthplace."

The swollen wave broke through the restraint of his will. The old man sobbed and threw himself on the ground; his milk-white hair was mingled with the sand of the sea. Forty years had passed since he had seen his country, and God knows how many since he heard his native speech; and now that speech had come to him itself—it had sailed to him over the ocean, and found him in solitude on another hemisphere—it so loved, so dear, so beautiful! In the sobbing which shook him there was no pain —only a suddenly aroused immense love, in the presence of which other things are as nothing. With that great weeping he had simply implored forgiveness of that beloved one, set aside because he had grown so old, had become so accustomed to his solitary rock, and had so forgotten it that in him even longing had begun to disappear. But now it returned as if by a miracle; therefore the heart leaped in him.

Moments vanished one after another; he lay there continually. The mews flew over the lighthouse, crying as if alarmed for their old friend. The hour in which

[1] Lithuania

he fed them with the remnants of his food had come; therefore, some of them flew down from the lighthouse to him; then more and more came, and began to pick and shake their wings over his head. The sound of the wings roused him. He had wept his fill, and had now a certain calm and brightness; but his eyes were as if inspired. He gave unwittingly all his provisions to the birds, which rushed at him with an uproar, and he himself took the book again. The sun had gone already behind the gardens and the forest of Panama, and was going slowly beyond the isthmus to the other ocean; but the Atlantic was full of light yet; in the open air there was still perfect vision; therefore, he read further:

> "Now bear my longing soul to those forest slopes, to those green meadows."

At last the dusk obliterates the letters on the white paper—the dusk short as a twinkle. The old man rested his head on the rock, and closed his eyes. Then "She who defends bright Chenstohova" took his soul and transported it to "those fields coloured by various grain." On the sky were burning yet those long stripes, red and golden, and on those brightnesses he was flying to beloved regions. The pine-woods were sounding in his ears; the streams of his native place were murmuring. He saw everything as it was; everything asked him, "Dost remember?" He remembers! he sees the broad fields; between the fields, woods and villages. It is night now. At this hour his lantern usually illuminates the darkness of the sea; but now he is in his native village. His old head has dropped on his breast, and he is dreaming. Pictures are passing before his eyes quickly, and a little disorderly. He does not see the house in which he was born, for war had destroyed it; he does not see his father and mother, for they died when he was a child; but still the village is as if he had left it yesterday—the line of cottages with lights in the windows, the mound, the mill, the two ponds opposite each other, and thundering all night with a chorus of frogs. Once he had been on guard in that village all night; now that past stood before him at once in a series of views. He is an Uhlan again, and he stands there on guard; at a distance is the publichouse; he looks with swimming eyes. There is thundering and singing and shouting amid the silence of the night, with voices of fiddles and bassviols "U-ha! U-ha!" Then the Uhlans knock out fire with their horseshoes, and it is wearisome for him there on his horse. The hours drag on slowly; at last the lights are quenched; now as far as the eye reaches there is mist, and mist impenetrable; now the fog rises, evidently from the fields, and embraces the whole world with a whitish cloud. You would say, a complete ocean. But that is fields; soon the land-rail will be heard in the darkness, and the bitterns will call from the reeds. The night is calm and cool—in truth, a Polish night! In the distance the pine-wood is sounding without wind, like the roll of the sea. Soon dawn will whiten the east. In fact, the cocks are beginning to crow behind the hedges.

One answers to another from cottage to cottage; the storks are screaming somewhere on high. The Uhlan feels well and bright. Some one had spoken of a battle to-morrow. Hei! that will go on, like all the others, with shouting, with fluttering of flaglets. The young blood is playing like a trumpet, though the night cools it. But it is dawning. Already night is growing pale; out of the shadows come forests, the thicket, a row of cottages, the mill, the poplars. The well is squeaking like a metal banner on a tower. What a beloved land, beautiful in the rosy gleams of the morning! Oh, the one land, the one land!

Quiet! the watchful picket hears that some one is approaching. Of course, they are coming to relieve the guard.

Suddenly some voice is heard above Skavinski:

"Here, old man! Get up! What's the matter?"

The old man opens his eyes, and looks with wonder at the person standing before him. The remnants of the dream-visions struggle in his head with reality. At last the visions pale and vanish. Before him stands Johnson, the harbour guide.

"What's this?" asked Johnson; "are you sick?"

"No."

"You didn't light the lantern. You must leave your place. A vessel from St Geromo was wrecked on the bar. It is lucky that no one was drowned, or you would go to trial. Get into the boat with me; you'll hear the rest at the Consulate."

The old man grew pale; in fact he had not lighted the lantern that night.

A few days later, Skavinski was seen on the deck of a steamer, which was going from Aspinwall to New York. The poor man had lost his place. There opened before him new roads of wandering; the wind had torn that leaf away again to whirl it over lands and seas, to sport with it till satisfied. The old man had failed greatly during those few days, and was bent over; only his eyes were gleaming. On his new road of life he held at his breast his book, which from time to time he pressed with his hand as if in fear that that too might go from him.

FINLAND

HOW VÄINÄMÖINEN WAS BORN OF THE MOTHER OF THE SEA[1]

I HAVE heard it has been said; and I know it has been sung, how alone, one by one, the nights fell upon the earth; alone, one by one, the days grew light; alone Väinämöinen was born, alone the immortal bard was revealed. A woman bore him within her womb, the daughter of Ilma gave him birth.

She was a virgin, a virgin most beautiful, Luonnaaotar, the daughter of Ilma. Long time did she remain a virgin, alone amid the vast regions of the air, the immense ethereal spaces.

But the weariness of her days pressed upon her; she grew tired of her virginity, of her lone existence amid the air's vast spaces, its sad and desolate plains.

And she descended from her heights; she flung herself upon the sea, riding the white crests of the waves.

Then the wind arose; a storm wind blew from the east; the sea grew rough and the waves mounted high.

The tempest tossed her; from wave to wave she floated on the foam crowned crests. And the breath of the wind caressed her bosom, and the sea woke life within her.

Seven centuries long, nine times the life of man, she bore her heavy burden. And he who should be born was not born, he whom none had engendered saw not as yet the day.

And the Virgin Mother of the Sea swam to the east and to the west; she swam to north-west and to south-west; she swam toward all the boundaries of the air. And within her body she suffered torment, and he who should be born was not born, he whom none had engendered saw not as yet the day.

And the virgin wept gently and said:

"Unhappy that I am! how sad are my days! Poor little one, how wandering is my life. Everywhere and always, beneath the great arch of heaven, driven onward by the wind, borne up by the waves upon the bosom of this vast ocean, upon its waves never-ending.

"Far better were it that I had remained the lonely daughter of Ilma than to float thus for ever as the Mother of the Sea. It is so cold! It is so cruel to be swept onward like an icicle in this watery waste!

"O Ukko, greatest of the Gods! thou who dost bear up the world, come to me, for much I need thy help. Haste thou, for I entreat thee. Deliver me from my

[1] Translated by Elizabeth D'Oyley from the French of L. Leouzon Le Duc's *Le Kalevala Epopée Nationale de la Finlande.*

anguish, free me from the burden within my womb. Come, O come quickly! The need of thy help groweth ever greater!"

A moment went by—one brief moment; and suddenly a broad-winged eagle took flight, cleaving the air with the loud beating of her wings as she sought a place for her nest, aplace for her habitation.

East she flew; west she flew; she flew to the north-east and to the south, but she found no place wherein to make her nest or fix her dwelling.

Again she flew, and then she paused, and thus she pondered:

"Shall I build my nest in the kingdoms of the wind or in the midst of the sea? The wind will overturn my dwelling; the sea will overwhelm it in its waves."

Then the Mother of the Sea, the Virgin of the Air, raised her knee above the waves, offering to the eagle a place for her dwelling, for her well-loved nest.

The eagle, bird most beautiful, stayed her flight: she saw the knee of the daughter of Ilma above the blue waters; and to her it seemed a green hillock, a turf of fresh growth.

Slowly she hovered in the air. Then she dropped upon the upraised knee; and there she built her nest; and in the nest she laid six eggs, six eggs of gold and a seventh of iron.

And the eagle began to brood upon her eggs: one day she sat; a second day and a third. Then the Mother of the Sea, the daughter of Ilma, felt a burning warmth upon her flesh; it seemed to her that her knee was on fire and all her nerves were melting.

Swiftly she drew back her knee; she shook her limbs; and the eggs rolled down into the water, breaking in pieces amidst the waves.

Yet they were not lost in the mud, nor did they merge into the water. Their fragments changed into things of beauty.

From the lower fragments the earth was formed; mother of all beings; from the upper pieces came the heavens sublime; from the yellow came the glorious sun; from the white, the shimmering moon; the stars came from the mottled fragments, and the black parts made the clouds.

And time went by, and year followed year, for the sun and the moon had begun to shine.

But the Mother of the Sea, Ilma's daughter, wandered yet through the great waters, borne upon the mist-clad waves. Below her the watery waste; above her the clear sky.

And in the ninth year, and the tenth summer, she raised her head above the water and began to spread Creation about her.

Wheresoever she stretched out her hand, there she made cliffs arise; wheresoever her feet touched, she made caves for the fishes; wheresoever she dived, she made the ocean's depths yet deeper; when with her thighs she touched the land, she there spread out the shores; when with her feet she touched it, there she made the salmon pools; and wheresoever her head struck it, there were the gulfs pierced.

Then she sprang up, pressing onward to the open sea. There she made rocks, and brought forth reefs for the wrecking of ships and the losing of sailors' lives.

Already the islands had risen from the waves, the pillars of the air stood up, the earth, born at a word, spread its solid mass; veins of a million tints furrowed the stones and coloured the rocks. And Väinämöinen was still unborn, the immortal bard had not yet come forth.

Väinämöinen, the old, the steadfast, dwelt within his mother's womb for the space of thirty summers, thirty winters, for ever on the unfathomable deep, upon the foaming waves.

Deeply he pondered, wondering how he could exist, how he could pass his life within this dim retreat, this narrow dwelling-place where never the light of sun or moon could reach.

And he said:

"Break my bonds, O Moon! O Sun, deliver me! And thou, Great Bear, show me how to break through these unknown doors, these unknown ways, how to win forth from this gloomy dwelling-place, this stifling cage. Bring the voyager to land, the son of man beneath the open skies, that he may see the sun and the moon, and the splendour of the Great Bear, that he may rejoice in the glory of the stars!"

But the moon did not break his bonds, neither did the sun deliver him. Then Väinämöinen grew weary of his days, his life became irksome to him. Sharply, with the nameless finger, he struck upon the door of his prison; with his left toe he forced the barrier of bone; and with his nails dragged himself beyond the threshold, upon his knees across the gateway.

And now, plunged headlong in the deep, the puissant hero is thrall to the might of the waves.

For the space of five years, six years, seven years, and eight years, he tossed from wave to wave. At last, he came to rest upon an unknown headland, upon a land barren of trees.

There, using both elbow and knee, he stood to his full height, and looked upon the sun and the moon, admired the Great Bear's splendour, and rejoiced in the glory of the stars.

Thus Väinämöinen was born, thus was the illustrious bard revealed. A woman bore him in her womb, the daughter of Ilma gave him birth.

ICELAND

ONUND TREEFOOT[1]

THERE was a man named Onund, who was the son of Ufeigh Clubfoot, the son of Ivar the Smiter; Onund was brother of Gudbiorg, the mother of Gudbrand Ball, the father of Asta, the mother of King Olaf the Saint. Onund was an Uplander by the kin of his mother; but the kin of his father dwelt chiefly about Rogaland and Hordaland. He was a great Viking, and went harrying west over the Sea. Balk of Sotanes, the son of Blæng, was with him herein, and Orm the Wealthy withal, and Hallvald was the name of the third of them. They had five ships, all well manned, and therewith they harried in the South-isles; and when they came to Barra, they found there a king, called Kiarval, and he, too, had five ships. They gave him battle, and a hard fray there was. The men of Onund were of the eagerest, and on either side many fell; but the end of it was that the king fled with only one ship. So there the men of Onund took both ships and much wealth, and abode there through the winter. For three summers they harried throughout Ireland and Scotland, and thereafter went to Norway.

In those days were there great troubles in Norway. Harald the Unshorn, son of Halfdan the Black, was pushing forth for the kingdom. Before that he was King of the Uplands; then he went north through the land, and had many battles there, and ever won the day. Thereafter he harried south in the land, and wheresoever he came, laid all under him; but when he came to Hordaland, swarms of folk came thronging against him; and their captains were Kiotvi the Wealthy, and Thorir Longchin, and those of South Rogaland, and King Sulki. Geirmund Helskin was then in the West over the Sea; nor was he in that battle, though he had a kingdom in Hordaland.

Now that autumn Onund and his fellows came from the west over the Sea; and when Thorir Longchin and King Kiotvi heard thereof, they sent men to meet them, and prayed them for help, and promised them honours. Then they entered into fellowship with Thorir and his men; for they were exceeding fain to try their strength, and said that there would they be whereas the fight was hottest.

Now was the meeting with Harald the King in Rogaland, in that firth which is called Hafrsfirth; and both sides had many men. This was the greatest battle that has ever been fought in Norway, and hereof most Sagas tell; for of those is ever most told, of whom the Sagas are made; and thereto came folk from all the land, and many from other lands, and swarms of Vikings.

Now Onund laid his ship alongside one board of the ship of Thorir Longchin, about the midst of the fleet, but King Harald laid his on the other board, because

[1] From the translation of *The Saga of Grettir the Strong,* by Eirikr Magnússon and William Morris.

Thorir was the greatest bearserk, and the stoutest of men; so the fight was of the fiercest on either side. Then the king cried on his bearserks for an onslaught, and they were called the Wolf-coats, for on them would no steel bite, and when they set on naught might withstand them. Thorir defended him very stoutly, and fell in all hardihood on board his ship; then was it cleared from stem to stern, and cut from the grapplings, and let drift astern betwixt the other ships. Thereafter the king's men laid their ship alongside Onund's, and he was in the forepart thereof and fought manly; then the king's folk said,

"Lo, a forward man in the forecastle there, let him have somewhat to mind him how that he was in this battle."

Now Onund put one foot out over the bulwark and dealt a blow at a man, and even therewith a spear was aimed at him, and as he put the blow from him he bent backward withal, and one of the king's forecastle men smote at him, and the stroke took his leg below the knee and sheared it off, and forthwith made him unmeet for fight. Then fell the more part of the folk on board his ship; but Onund was brought to the ship of him who is called Thrand; he was the son of Biorn, and brother of Eyvind the Eastman; he was in the fight against King Harald and lay on the other board of Onund's ship.

But now, after these things, the more part of the fleet scattered in flight; Thrand and his men, with the other Vikings, got them away each as he might, and sailed west over the Sea; Onund went with him, and Balk and Hallyard Sweeping; Onund was healed, but went with a wooden leg all his life after; therefore as long as he lived was he called Onund Treefoot.

There were two Vikings called Vigbiod and Vestmar; they were South-islanders, and lay out both winter and summer; they had thirteen ships, and harried mostly in Ireland, and did many an ill deed there till Eyvind the Eastman took the land-wardship; thereafter they got them gone to the South-isles, and harried there and all about the firths of Scotland: against these went Thrand and Onund, and heard that they had sailed to that island, which is called Bute. Now Onund and his folk came there with five ships; and when the Vikings see their ships and know how many they are, they deem they have enough strength gathered there, and take their weapons and lay their ships in the midst betwixt two cliffs, where was a great and deep sound; only on one side could they be set on, and that with but five ships at once. Now Onund was the wisest of men, and bade lay five ships up into the sound, so that he and his might have back way when they would, for there was plenty of sea-room astern. On one board of them too was a certain island, and under the lee thereof he let one ship lie, and his men brought many great stones forth on to the sheer cliffs above, yet might not be seen withal from the ships.

Now the Vikings laid their ships boldly enough for the attack, and thought that the others quailed; and Vigbiod asked who they were that were in such jeopardy.

Thrand said that he was the brother of Eyvind the Eastman, "and here beside me is Onund Treefoot my fellow."

Then laughed the Vikings, and shouted:

"Treefoot, Treefoot, foot of tree,
Trolls take thee and thy company.

"Yea, a sight it is seldom seen of us, that such men should go into battle as have no might over themselves."

Onund said that they could know nought thereof ere it were tried; and withal they laid their ships alongside one of the other, and there began a great fight, and either side did boldly. But when they came to handy blows, Onund gave back toward the cliff, and when the Vikings saw this, they deemed he was minded to flee, and made towards his ship, as came as nigh to the cliff as they might. But in that very point of time those came forth on to the edge of the cliff who were appointed so to do, and sent at the Vikings so great a flight of stones that they might not withstand it.

Then fell many of the Viking-folk, and others were hurt so that they might not bear weapon; and withal they were fain to draw back, and might not, because their ships were even then come into the narrowest of the sound, and they were huddled together both by the ships and the stream; but Onund and his men set on fiercely, whereas Vigbiod was, but Thrand set on Vestmar, and won little thereby; so, when the folk were thinned on Vigbiod's ship, Onund's men and Onund himself got ready to board her: that Vigbiod saw, and cheered on his men without stint: then he turned to meet Onund, and the more part fled before him; but Onund bade his men mark how it went between them; for he was of huge strength.

Now they set a log of wood under Onund's knee, so that he stood firmly enow; the Viking fought his way forward along the ship till he reached Onund, and he smote at him with his sword, and the stroke took the shield, and sheared off all it met; and then the sword drove into the log that Onund had under his knee, and stuck fast therein; and Vigbiod stooped in drawing it out, and even therewith Onund smote at his shoulder in such wise, that he cut the arm from off him, and then was the Viking unmeet for battle.

But when Vestmar knew that his fellow was fallen, he leaped into the furthermost ship and fled with all those who might reach her. Thereafter they ransacked the fallen men; and by then was Vigbiod nigh to his death: Onund went up to him, and sang:

"Yea, seest thou thy wide wounds bleed?
What of shrinking didst thou heed
In the one-foot sling of gold?
What scratch here dost thou behold?

And in e'en such wise as this
Many an axe-breaker there is
Strong of tongue and weak of hand:
Tried thou wert, and might'st not stand."

So there they took much spoil and sailed back to Barra in the autumn.

HOW *ELLIDI,* THE DRAGON-SHIP, AT THE COMMAND OF FRITHIOF THE BOLD, DROVE DOWN UPON THE WITCHES[1]

SO WHEN Frithiof and his men were come out of the Sognfirth there fell on them great wind and storm, and an exceeding heavy sea: but the ship drave on swiftly, for sharp built she was, and the best to breast the sea.

So now Frithiof sang:

"Oft let I swim from Sogn
My tarred ship sooty-sided,
When maids sat o'er the mead-horn
Amidst of Baldur's Meadows;
Now while the storm is wailing,
Farewell I bid you maidens,
Still shall ye love us, sweet ones,
Though *Ellidi* the sea fill."

Said Biorn: "Thou mightest well find other work to do than singing songs over the maids of Baldur's Meadows."

"Of such work shall I not speedily run dry, though," said Frithiof. Then they bore up north to the sounds nigh those isles that are called Solundir, and therewith was the gale at its hardest.

Then sang Frithiof:

"Now is the sea a-swelling,
And sweepeth the rack onward;
Spells of old days cast o'er us
Make ocean all unquiet;
No more shall we be striving
Mid storm with wash of billows,
But Solundir shall shelter
Our ship with ice-beat rock-walls."

So they lay to under the lee of the isles hight Solundir, and were minded to abide

[1] From *Three Northern Love Stories.*

there; but straightway thereon the wind fell: then they turned away from under the lee of the islands, and now their voyage seemed hopeful to them, because the wind was fair awhile; but soon it began to freshen again.

Then sang Frithiof:

"In days foredone
From Foreness strand
I rowed to meet
Maid Ingibiorg;
But now I sail
Through chilly storm
And wide away
My long-worm driveth."

And now when they were come far out into the main, once more the sea waxed wondrous troubled, and a storm arose with so great drift of snow, that none might see the stem from the stern; and they shipped seas, so that they must be ever a-baling. So Frithiof sang:

"The salt waves see we nought
As seaward drive we ever
Before the witch wrought weather,
We well-famed kings' defenders:
Here are we all a-standing,
With all Solundir hull-down,
Eighteen brave lads a-baling,
Black *Ellidi* to bring home."

Said Biorn: "Needs must he who fareth far fall in with diverse hap." "Yea, certes, foster-brother," said Frithiof. And he sang withal:

"Helgi it is that helpeth
The white-head billows' waxing;
Cold time unlike the kissing
In the close of Baldur's Meadow!
So is the hate of Helgi
To that heart's love she giveth.
O would that here I held her,
Gift high above all giving!"

"Maybe," said Biorn, "she is looking higher than thou now art; what matter when all is said?"

"Well," says Frithiof, "now is the time to show ourselves to be men of avail, though blither tide it was at Baldur's Meadows."

So they turned to in manly wise, for there were the bravest of men come together in the best ship of the Northlands. But Frithiof sang a stave:

array; wherefore it seems good to me that each man of us here should have somewhat of gold on him."

Then he smote asunder the ring, Ingibiorg's gift, and shared it between all his men, and sang a stave withal:

"The red ring here I hew me
Once owned of Halfdan's father,
The wealthy lord of erewhile,
Or the sea-waves undo us,
So on the guests shall gold be,
If we have need of guesting;
Meet so for mighty men-folk
Amid Ran's hall to hold them."

"Not all so sure is it that we come there," said Biorn; "and yet it may well be so."

Now Frithiof and his folk found that the ship had great way on her, and they knew not what lay ahead, for all was mirk on either board, so that none might see the stem or stern from amidships; and therewith was there great drift of spray amid the furious wind, and frost, and snow, and deadly cold.

Now Frithiof went up to the masthead, and when he came down he said to his fellows: "A sight exceeding wondrous have I seen, for a great whale went in a ring about the ship, and I misdoubt me that we come nigh to some land, and that he is keeping the shore against us; for certes King Helgi has dealt with us in no friendly wise, neither will this his messenger be friendly. Moreover I saw two women on the back of the whale, and they it is who will have brought this great storm on us with the worst of spells and witchcraft; but now we shall try which may prevail, my fortune or their devilry, so steer ye at your straightest, and I will smite these evil things with beams."

Therewith he sang a stave:

"See I troll women
Twain on the billows,
E'en they whom Helgi
Hither hath sent.
Ellidi now
Or ever her way stop
Shall smite the backs
Of these asunder."

So tells the tale that this wonder went with the good ship *Ellidi,* that she knew the speech of man.

But Biorn said: "Now may we see the treason of those brethren against us." Therewith he took the tiller, but Frithiof caught up a forked beam, and ran into the prow, and sang a stave:

"*Ellidi*, hail!
Leap high o'er the billows!
Break of the troll wives
Brow or teeth now!
Break cheek or jaw
Of the cursed woman,
One foot or twain
Of the ogress filthy."

Therewith he drave his fork at one of the skin-changers and the beak of *Ellidi* smote the other on the back, and the backs of both were broken; but the whale took the deep and gat him gone, and they never saw him after.

Then the wind fell, but the ship lay waterlogged; so Frithiof called out to his men, and bade bale out the ship, but Biorn said:

"No need to work now, verily!"

"Be thou not afeard, foster brother," said Frithiof, "ever was it the wont of good men of old time to be helpful while they might, whatsoever should come after."

And therewith he sang a stave:

"No need, fair fellows,
To fear the death-day:
Rather be glad,
Good men of mine,
For if dreams wot aught
All nights they say
I yet shall have
My Ingibiorg."

Then they baled out the ship; and they were now come nigh unto land; but there was yet a flaw of wind in their teeth. So then did Frithiof take the two bow oars again, and rowed full mightily. Therewith the weather brightened, and they saw that they were come out to Effia Sound, and so there they made land.

The crew were exceeding weary; but so stout a man was Frithiof that he bore eight men a-land over the foreshore, but Biorn bore two, and Asmund one. Then sang Frithiof:

"Fast bare I up
To the fire-lit house
My men all dazed
With the drift of the storm:
And the sail moreover
To the sand I carried;
With the might of the sea
Is there no more to do."

relations was the most likely to have good luck on such an expedition: and Eric consented, and rode from home with Leif when they had got all ready for sea; but when they were coming near to the ship the horse on which Eric was riding stumbled, and he fell from the horse, and hurt his foot.

"It is not destined," said Eric, "that I should discover more lands than this of Greenland, on which we dwell and live; and now we must not run hastily into this adventure."

Eric accordingly returned home to Brattalid; but Leif, with his comrades, in all thirty-five men, rigged out their vessel. There was a man from the South country called Tyrker with the expedition. They put the ship in order, and went to sea when they were ready. They first came to the land which Biarne had last discovered, sailed up to it, cast anchor, put out a boat, and went on shore; but there was no grass to be seen. There were huge snowy mountains up the country; but all the way from the sea up to these snowy ridges the land was one field of snow, and it appeared to them a country of no advantages. Leif said:

"It shall not be said of us, as it was of Biarne, that we did not come upon the land; for I will give the country a name, and call it Helloland."

Then they went on board again, put to sea, and found another land. They sailed in towards it, cast anchor, put out a boat, and landed. The country was flat and overgrown with wood; and the strand far around consisted of a white sand, and low towards the sea. Then Leif said,

"We shall give this land a name according to its kind, and call it Markland."

Then they hastened on board, and put to sea again with an on-shore wind from north-east, and were out for two days, and made land. They sailed towards it, and came to an island which lay on the north side of the land, where they landed to wait for good weather. There was dew upon the grass; and having accidentally got some of the dew upon their hands and put it to their mouths, they thought they had never tasted anything so sweet as it was. Then they went on board, and sailed into a sound that was between the island and a ness which went out northwards from the land, and sailed west past the ness. There was very shallow water in ebb-tide, so that their ship lay dry; and there was a long way between their ship and the water. They were so desirous to get to the land that they would not wait till their vessel floated, but ran to the land, to a place where a river comes out of a lake. As soon as their ship was afloat, they took the boats, rowed to the ship, towed her up the river, and from thence into the lake, where they cast anchor, carried their beds out of the ship, and set up their tents. They resolved to put things in order for wintering there, and they erected a large house . . . .

It happened one evening that a man of the party was missing; and it was the South-country man, Tyrker. Leif was very sorry for it; because Tyrker had been long in his father's house, and he loved Tyrker in his childhood. Leif blamed his comrades very much, and prepared to go with twelve men on an expedition to find him; but they had gone only a short way from the station before Tyrker came to meet them, and he was joyfully received. . . .

Leif said to him:

"Why art thou so late, my foster-father? and why didst thou leave thy comrades?"

He spoke at first long in Turkish, rolled his eyes, and knit his brows; but they could not make out what he was saying. After a while and some delay, he said in Norse:

"I did not go much farther than they; and yet I have something altogether new to relate, for I found vines and grapes."

"Is that true, my foster-father?" said Leif.

"Yes, true it is," answered he; "for I was born where there is no scarcity of vines and grapes."

Now they slept all night, and next morning Leif said to his men:

"Now we have two occupations to attend to, and day about; namely, to gather grapes or cut vines, and to fell wood in the forest to load our vessel."

And this advice was followed. It is related that their stern-boat was filled with grapes, and then a cargo of wood was hewn for the vessel. There was also self-sown wheat in the fields and a tree which is called Massur. Of all these they took samples; and some of the trees were so large that they were used in houses. Towards spring they made ready and sailed away; and Leif gave the country a name from its productions, and called it Vinland.

NORWAY

THE CORMORANTS OF ANDÆR[1]

Jonas Lie
(1833-1908)

OUTSIDE Andvær lies an island, the haunt of wild birds, which no man can land upon, be the sea never so quiet; the sea-swell girds it round about with sucking whirlpools and dashing breakers.

On fine summer days something sparkles there through the sea-foam like a large gold ring; and, time out of mind, folks have fancied there was a treasure there left by some pirates of old.

At sunset, sometimes, there looms forth from thence a vessel with a castle astern, and a glimpse is caught now and then of an old-fashioned galley. There it lies as if in a tempest, and carves its way along through heavy white rollers.

Along the rocks sit the cormorants in a long black row, lying in wait for dog-fish.

But there was a time when one knew the exact number of these birds. There was never more nor less of them than twelve, while upon a stone, out in the sea-mist, sat the thirteenth, but it was only visible when it rose and flew right over the island.

The only persons who lived near the Vær at winter time, long after the fishing season was over, were a woman and a slip of a girl. Their business was to guard the scaffolding poles for drying fish against the birds of prey, who had such a villainous trick of hacking at the drying ropes.

The young girl had thick coal-black hair, and a pair of eyes that peeped at folk so oddly. One might almost have said that she was like the cormorants outside there, and she had never seen much else all her life. Nobody knew who her father was.

Thus they lived till the girl had grown up.

It was found that, in the summer time, when the fishermen went out to the Vær to fetch away the dried fish, that the young fellows began underbidding each other, so as to be selected for that special errand.

Some gave up their share of profits, and others their wages; and there was a general complaint in all the villages round about that on such occasions no end of betrothals were broken off.

But the cause of it all was the girl out yonder with the odd eyes.

---

[1] From R. Nisbet Bain's translation in *Weird Tales from Northern Seas.*

For all her rough and ready ways, she had something about her, said those she chatted with, that there was no resisting. She turned the heads of all the young fellows; it seemed as if they couldn't live without her.

The first winter a lad wooed her who had both house and warehouse of his own.

"If you come again in the summer time, and give me the right gold ring I will be wedded by, something may come of it," said she.

And, sure enough, in the summer time the lad was there again.

He had a lot of fish to fetch away, and she might have had a gold ring as heavy and as bonnie as heart could wish for.

"The ring I must have lies beneath the wreckage, in the iron chest, over at the island yonder," said she, "that is, if you love me enough to dare fetch it."

But then the lad grew pale.

He saw the sea-bore rise and fall out there like a white wall of foam on the bright warm summer day, and on the island sat the cormorants sleeping in the sunshine.

"Dearly do I love thee," said he, "but such a quest as that would mean my burial, not my bridal."

The same instant the thirteenth cormorant rose from his stone in the misty foam, and flew right over the island.

Next winter the steersman of a yacht came a wooing. For two years he had gone about and hugged his misery for her sake, and he got the same answer.

"If you come again in the summer time, and give me the right gold ring I will be wedded with, something may come of it."

Out to the Vær he came again on Midsummer Day.

But when he heard where the gold ring lay, he sat and wept the whole day till evening, when the sun began to dance north-westward into the sea.

Then the thirteenth cormorant arose, and flew right over the island.

There was nasty weather during the third winter.

There were manifold wrecks, and on the keel of a boat, which came driving ashore, hung an exhausted young lad by his knife-belt.

But they couldn't get the life back into him, roll and rub him about in the boat-house as they might.

Then the girl came in.

"'Tis my bridegroom!" said she. '

And she laid him in her bosom, and sat with him the whole night through, and put warmth into his heart.

And when the morning came, his heart beat.

"Methought I lay betwixt the wings of a cormorant, and leaned my head against its downy breast," said he.

The lad was ruddy and handsome, with curly hair, and he couldn't take his eyes away from the girl.

He took work upon the Vær.

But off he must needs be gadding and chatting with her, be it never so early and never so late.

So it fared with him as it had fared with the others.

It seemed to him that he could not live without her, and on the day when he was bound to depart, he wooed her.

"*Thee* I will not fool," said she. "Thou hast lain on my breast, and I would give my life to save thee from sorrow. Thou shalt have me if thou wilt place the betrothal ring upon my finger; but longer than the day lasts thou canst not keep me. And now I will wait, and long after thee with a horrible longing, till the summer comes."

On Midsummer Day the youth came thither in his boat all alone.

Then she told him of the ring that he must fetch for her from among the skerries.

"If thou hast taken me off the keel of a boat, thou mayest cast me forth yonder again," said the lad. "Live without thee I cannot."

But as he laid hold of the oars in order to row out, she stepped into the boat with him and sat in the stern. Wondrous fair was she!

It was beautiful summer weather, and there was a swell upon the sea: wave followed upon wave in long bright rollers.

The lad sat there, lost in the sight of her, and he rowed and rowed till the insucking breakers roared and thundered among the skerries; the groundswell was strong, and the frothing foam spurted up as high as towers.

"If thy life is dear to thee, turn back now," said she.

"Thou art dearer to me than life itself," he made answer.

But just as it seemed to the lad as if the prow were going under, and the jaws of death were gaping wide before him, it grew all at once as still as a calm, and the boat could run ashore as if there was never a billow there.

On the island lay a rusty old ship's anchor half out of the sea.

"In the iron chest which lies beneath the anchor is my dowry," said she. "Carry it up into thy boat, and put the ring that thou seest on my finger. With this thou dost make me thy bride. So now I am thine till the sun dances north-westwards into the sea."

It was a gold ring with a red stone in it, and he put it on her finger and kissed her.

In a cleft on the skerry was a patch of green grass. There they sat them down, and they were ministered to in wondrous wise, how he knew not nor cared to know, so great was his joy.

"Midsummer Day is beauteous," said she, "and I am young and thou art my bridegroom. And now we'll to our bridal bed."

So bonnie was she that he could not contain himself for love.

But when night drew nigh, and the sun began to dance out into the sea, she kissed him and shed tears.

"Beauteous is the summer day," said she, "and still more beauteous is the summer evening; but now the dusk cometh."

And all at once it seemed to him as if she were becoming older and older and fading right away.

When the sun went below the sea-margin there lay before him on the skerry some mouldering linen rags and nought else.

Calm was the sea, and in the clear Midsummer night there flew *twelve* cormorants out over the sea.

SWEDEN

THE OUTCAST

Selma Lagerlöf

(1858–)

(The following episodes are taken from Selma Lagerlof's novel, *Bannlyst,* which has been translated into English, under the title of *The Outcast,* by W. Worster, M.A., and published by Messrs Gyldendal.

Sven Elversson and his comrades, starving in the Arctic, are said to have eaten a man. Sven, in reality, had had no part in the affair, though he had no memory of it. Returning home, he finds himself outcast from all.)

I

The "Naiad"

A FEW days after Christmas, Ung-Joel came back to Grimön, with a message from Olaus, to ask if Sven would take a share in the herring-fishery on board the motor-boat *Naiad,* belonging to his crew.

"He says it's hardly likely you could get taken on with any other crew," said Ung-Joel; "but seeing that you're my brother, I was to tell you. They'll not be the best of company, I doubt, that sail with Olaus."

Mor Elversson declared at once that it was out of the question; Sven should never have any dealings with any of them. But his father thought otherwise.

"It wouldn't be a bad thing, perhaps, if Sven tried to pick up the ways of the fishery on the coast here," he said. "And it's true enough he'd hardly get taken on with any other crew."

"Joel! How can you talk so ?" cried his wife. "Who knows what they've been plotting and planning now, to send for him like that. Some new mischief, I'll be bound."

"Why, I only said 'it was a pity Sven shouldn't have a part in the fishery,'" said Joel mildly.

But Sven remembered his father's words on Christmas Eve, and it came into his mind now that perhaps it was his wish to get him away from home.

"You can tell Olaus I'll come," he said to his brother. "And thank him for offering. I'll go over to Fårön myself as soon as I can."

"Why not come back with me now?" said Ung-Joel. "Then you can get the things you want at our store. There was a telegram in this morning that the herring are shoaling thick up at Smögen. By to-morrow they'll be getting away all about."

There was a hurry of preparation for a while, and then the two brothers set off, leaving Joel and Thala alone.

For a week or so they heard no news of Sven, then one Sunday Ung-Joel came out to visit them.

Mor Thala was eager to know how matters had gone with Sven and the crew—for all she knew, they might have killed him.

"I've heard nothing but what folk say," answered the boy. "And that's this. The crew of the *Naiad* before counted one man that had helped to kill a child, and one that had starved an old woman to death, one that had burnt down a place, and one that never sold but what he'd stolen, and two that were fast drinking themselves to death—and now they'd got another help, and that a man who'd eaten human flesh, so it would be hard to find a rougher crowd on one keel. I've heard nothing from Sven himself, but, from all accounts, he seems to be getting on all right with them."

"That's foolishness," said his mother. But for all her angry looks, she was glad to learn that no ill had come to Sven. "But don't forget as soon as you've word from Sven to come here and let us know. 'Tis the best you can do for your father and me."

A fortnight later, Ung-Joel came out to the island again.

"Here's what they're saying now," he began. "That the *Naiad* men won't be able to stand much more of Sven. They say here's the dirtiest, meanest, stinking little boat all along the coast getting gradually clean and workmanlike, the motor taken to working properly instead of going on strike when it's most needed, the rags of sails they used to help now and then been patched and put in order, the faded old flag done away with and a bright new one in its place, and the name painted clean on the stern with all the letters in gold; the food on board getting that decent you wouldn't know but what you were on shore, and clean pots and pans in the galley. And the way folk look at it is this: the *Naiad* men, they might at a pinch take any sort of scoundrel on board, but clean pots and pans and all the rest, it's more than they can put up with."

"Ah! you're making fun of me," said his mother. But it was plain to see that she was glad at heart. "And don't forget," she went on, "as soon as you've any word from Sven, come out and let us know. He's done no wrong, and we must know how it is with him, that he doesn't come to any harm."

But folk that live at Grimön have need of all their patience, waiting for news. All through another two weeks Mor Thala waited, before Ung-Joel came with news of his brother.

"I haven't seen him myself yet," he explained. "But I've heard what they say, that it can't be long now before there's an end of it with Sven Elversson and the *Naiad* crew. It seems that Olaus—he's the skipper—has taken to seeing the men

apparent when the motor was started, and the two ends of the net were brought on board ready to haul.

Olaus and Corfitzson were hauling, the others stood ready to disengage the fish from the meshes as the net came in. And as the fish appeared, a full catch of splendid mackerel, glistening all colours of the rainbow, their faces brightened.

"You see, they won't have troubled us the night," said Corfitzson.

"Keep quiet, can't you!" snapped out Olaus, with an oath. "Want to tell them we're here? They'll find us soon enough without that. Feel here!"

He hoisted the net a little out of the water, and all saw, among the glittering fish, something big and dark. There was dead silence on board, and next moment the body of a man came on deck with the net.

One young fellow, who had taken Hjelmfeldt's place on board, tried to get the corpse free of the net, but the skipper's voice called to him sharply:

"Leave it alone. There's another of them here."

And a moment later a new command:

"Let them alone. There's more of them coming."

Just then Corfitzson and Olaus lifted on board a dreadful mass: two bodies twined together.

And when the last of the net was hauled in, there lay a huge mound of dead men, brown meshes, and fish in one confusion. The fish, still living, flapped and slithered about, making the whole horrible mass seem alive.

When the bodies were lifted on board, Sven Elversson was so affected that he wept. He wiped the tears away with the back of his hand, but could not stop them. He stamped his foot, but the tears still came. He was forced to leave his work at the net and walk away far astern.

There he stood until the net was in and the motor started for the homeward run. The silent crew, sullen, unwilling, and gloomy as before, had begun once more the work of clearing fish and mussels from the net, and getting loose the rest.

"All in the net to be thrown over," commanded Olaus.

When Sven Elversson heard the order, he went up to the rest. The tears still flowed from his eyes, but he did not heed them. He took his place with the crew, and set to work, helping with their dreadful task.

They came to one of the dead. Sven Elversson lifted him up, and loosened some of the meshes that had caught in the buttons of his uniform. It was an elderly man with a sailor's beard under his chin. Some one suggested that he was an Englishman. When he had got the body loose, Sven Elversson began hoisting it to the deck.

"All that's in the net to go overboard," said the skipper, bending down towards the corpse.

But Sven Elversson restrained him.

"Will you not let this be laid to rest in holy ground, Olaus ?" he said.

Olaus did not answer directly.

"Best to get these horrors away from the ship," he said.

Sven Elversson clenched his teeth in the endearour to keep back his tears, and said as firmly as he could:

"If you throw this overboard, you will have to throw me too."

He was astonished to hear himself speaking so, but he could not help it. He felt that he would stand by his word.

The others, too, saw that he meant what he said, and would never let the dead man go while he himself lived.

The skipper swore, and turned away, but made no direct refusal, and the others understood that he agreed.

Sven Elversson tried to lift the body, but it was too heavy for him. Then the young fellow newly joined came to his help, and together they laid the dead man by the bulwarks.

The next body was loosed from the net, and laid beside the first without question. Two men carried it up to where Sven Elversson stood. "This one's a German," they said.

To his surprise, Sven Elversson noted that the men on board had suddenly changed to a different expression, a different humour. They swore no longer, but spoke calmly and quietly. They no longer felt hatred towards these hosts of dead, that came and stole away their livelihood. They were accustomed to show respect and reverence to the dead, and something in their nature was more at ease to know that these drowned men of war were to be given decent burial.

Sven Elversson, too, felt strangely easier in mind. His soul felt more at rest now than ever since the first day of his misfortune.

He seemed to hear voices about him, thanking him for his charity to the bodies that once had been the dwellings of immortal souls.

"Now you are loosed from the burden that was laid upon you," said the voices. "Thus it was to come about. Your guilt is taken from you. You have risked your life to save the dead, and you have atoned for all."

His heart beat lightly and strongly, and he thought: "Let others condemn me now if they will, it will not matter, for in myself I know that I have fulfilled my penance and conquered."

THE SHIP[1]

Verner von Heidenstam

(1859–)

LUCIDLY the summer night spread its shadow, but far out among the islands at Korsö gathered armed country-folk and islanders from Sandhamn and Harö.

A winter had snowed itself away since the Sunday when in Tistedal the muskets had been presented the last time before the king. Many of the oldest Charles men and those most broken with gout had already retired with their scanty pensions to their little farms, where they knotted their fish-nets by the window or looked over their old diaries. Serious, God-fearing, respected, they met at the church on Sundays; and generals and colonels, without regard to rank, embraced with moist eyes their brothers in arms of the long campaigns. The terms of peace had not yet been signed. When the cannon of the Russian fleet thundered once more among the islands, the veterans buttoned up their worn blue coats as tightly as before and unbuckled the broadsword from the bed-post. Then they each and all went out to defend hearth and home to the uttermost.

Captain Resslöf of had appointed himself leader of the band that was assembled on Korsö. Already weary of his room, he stood among the people with a confident bearing. His razor and scissors had rested all winter in the drawer. His hair was so long, his beard was so white, and it was such a pleasure to look at him, that even the sullen and heavy islanders brightened whenever he turned toward them.

After the day's tempest, the surf was still rolling against the rocky seaward shore of the island, but in the hollow by the shining sound hardly a puff of air brushed over the pines under which the men, restless and expectant, counted the distant cannon-shots.

With shaking voice a pastor's son from Djurö stepped forward. He held his cap squeezed in his hand, and his pallor was greyer than ever in the nocturnal light:

"Captain, you have sent the sloops that brought us here to the inner islands to fetch more people. Two leaky rowboats are all we have to save ourselves in, if the enemy lands, but we are more than forty men. Conceal the truth no more! Our little band can no longer accomplish anything here. We have heard, of course, that Rika Fuchs with his Södermanlanders had already marched to Södra Stäk to beat the enemy or lose his life, and that Düker with his Dalecarlians and Westmanlanders is following soon after; but we know, too, that at Boo and along all the coast of Värmdon and Södertörn there will soon be nothing to look for on the cliffs but

[1] From Charles Wharton Stork's translation, *The Charles Men.*

black ashes. Forgive my words, but we have all heard that Trosa is sacked, and that Nyköping is burning, so that the glare is visible away up toward Stockholm. In Norrköping Swedish peasants and soldiers plunder the wagons of the fugitives in the open street. At Vikboland the peasantry give signals to the Russian ships with sheets and bleached cloth to show that they surrender and swear loyalty to the Czar, and at Marstrand Tordenskjold has hoisted the Danish flag. Whichever way we look, the air is full of conflagration and smoke. It's all over with Sweden, our home, our home."

"I conceal nothing," answered Resslöf, "but rely upon it that the Swedes always get help at the eleventh hour. They seldom get it sooner."

The pastor's son smiled with a sneer, as he departed:

"It is night now, and the tenth hour has just gone by. Let us be hopeful!"

The men pressed close about Resslöf in great uneasiness. The cannonshots were still thundering, but more faintly and farther out to sea.

Then the pale son of the pastor came once more across the rocks. He stumbled and slipped. He leaped. He pressed in among the crowd without letting himself be checked.

"Here's an uncanny thing, good people. Out at sea there a ship is coming with a lighted lantern in the bow, but with neither mast, nor sail, nor oars. And not a man can I make out on deck. Nobody is standing at the tiller. But the ship goes on just the same, though it moves slowly, slowly."

A murmur of superstitious fear ran through the peasants, but the taciturn islanders followed Resslöf to the topmost cliff by the inlet. They thought that the pastor's son had seen the ship in a vision, for they could not discover anything on the wide sea, around which glowed the nocturnal heavens.

Suddenly they all uttered a cry of astonishment, and the others, who followed them at a distance, began once more to murmur. From behind the rugged cape there drove forward heavily and slowly in the surf a brigantine, without sail and rigging, but with port-holes painted white, and at the stern under the lighted lantern stood a golden lion with paws raised as if to spring.

"That's a ghost ship," muttered the peasants.

Hesitatingly Resslöf ordered some of the bravest islanders to take their muskets and accompany him in one of the rowboats.

They neared the ship cautiously with noiseless strokes and raised muskets, but when they hailed, they received no answer. Some of the small panes in the after cabin gleamed, but that was the reflection of the night, and soon they all became equally dark. Only the bow light burned and flickered.

"God have mercy on us!" whispered Resslöf, pointing to the long strip of cloth which trailed in the water from the stern. "*There* are our colours. And now I can read the name. This is the brigantine *Swedish Lion?*"

"Yes, yes, it's the brigantine *Swedish Lion,*" murmured the peasants on the island.

They shipped the oars. They lay to by the helm and climbed up on a rope of the fallen rigging, but when they entered the empty cabin through a broken window, they had to feel their way forward in the darkness with their hands.

"Isn't there a crew of a single man here?" inquired Resslöf, raising his voice.

No one answered, however, but all remained as quiet as before.

He then shoved up the hatch to the deck. Ship rats ran freely back and forth over the planks, but along the gunwales on both sides lay pale and motionless sailors, who had fallen at their post. He went from man to man, bending down to convince himself that they were all dead.

Thereupon he said to his followers:

"The eleventh hour is come. Bring the people on board now and make the two rowboats fast at the stern, before the surf and current drive the brigantine ashore. We can both bring ourselves safe to the inner islands and salvage a vessel of the Crown that has gone bravely through its fight."

The old man went off across the deck and sat down at the highest point of the stern, alone and apart from the others.

As soon as the people had been conveyed on board, they towed the brigantine in between the islands. Under the softly gliding prow the bays and sounds, illumined by the summer night, reflected the golden lion.

The reports of the cannon no longer rolled in from the sea. More slowly than a broken veteran proceeding to his cottage on a crutch the ship glided between the rocky islets. Women and children, who had hidden there under bushes and roots of trees, stepped out of their concealment. Joyful at hearing the words of their mother tongue from the deck, they flocked upon the beaches and piers with countless importunate questions.

"This is the *Swedish Lion* coming back from the fight," answered those on board.

With that the old Charles man by the flagstaff roused himself from his melancholy and stood up.

"It is more than that. Give me your hands!" he said to the younger men, drawing them close to him. "Hats off, good people, hats off! This devastated ship is like Sweden, who conceals herself behind her islands with her last troops and her dead. How the prisoners longed for her, those who have gone hundreds of miles away beside the rivers of Siberia! Lonely, in disguise, they stood on the deck of their whale-boat with the illimitable expanse of the Arctic Ocean before their sight, calling upon God every hour in their anguish that He should not quench the flame of their life till they were under the roof of their home. The roof of their home? It lies charred upon the ground. Beaten, beaten is our people, divided is our empire, and on our coasts the ruins are smoking. O inscrutable, eternal God, will the dawn never come? Be silent, be silent, good people: the dawn is coming. The captives in Siberian cities, as they sit dumbly at their handiwork, shall one morning leap up and see in the square a rider waving a white flag as a sign that peace has been declared. Thirsty mouths shall drink from Frederick's and Ulrica's gold-rimmed goblets, and the Christmas board shall again be spread by women who are not in mourning. Yet again the hay shall diffuse its fragrance in Sweden. The church bells shall ring. For a whole year they shall ring every noontide for peace—and for the fallen. Where, indeed, are the old battalions with Grothusen's drum and the banners of Turkish silk? And he who held us together in the great strife and never would believe the sign that God had forsaken us, he in whose heroic nature all our yearning was concealed—where does he dwell? Ask the children that sing. Alas! they go hence one by one, the old brothers in arms. Wherever we fare through the country, walking or by post-chaise, we shall recognize in the mists of night the small white churches where eight or ten strong sons have laid the slabs above their graves. And where does there blossom in an alien land a field so remote that we may not sit down on the sward and whisper: 'Is this perchance the place where one of ours, one who fought and bled, is slumbering?' In their poor garments they loitered a short while before us by the bivouac fire, and then went away and fell. Such they were. So I recall them. So, too, they live in memory and say amid a grateful land: 'Beloved be the people that in the decline of their greatness made their poverty to be revered before the world!'"

DENMARK

THE LITTLE MERMAID[1]

Hans Christian Andersen

(1805-1875)

FAR out in the wide sea,—where the water is blue as the loveliest cornflower, and clear as the purest crystal, where it is so deep that very, very many church-towers must be heaped one upon another, in order to reach from the lowest depth to the surface above,—dwell the Mer-people.

Now you must not imagine that there is nothing but sand below the water: no, indeed, far from it! Trees and plants of wondrous beauty grow there, whose stems and leaves are so light, that they are waved to and fro by the slightest motion of the water, almost as if they were living beings. Fishes, great and small, glide in and out among the branches, just as birds fly about among our trees.

Where the water is deepest, stands the palace of the Mer-king. The walls of this palace are of coral, and the high, pointed windows are of amber; the roof, however, is composed of mussel-shells, which, as the billows pass over them, are continually opening and shutting. This looks exceedingly pretty, especially as each of these mussel-shells contains a number of bright, glittering pearls, one only of which would be the most costly ornament in the diadem of a king in the upper world.

The Mer-king who lived in this palace had been for many years a widower; his old mother managed the household affairs for him. She was, on the whole, a sensible sort of a lady, although extremely proud of her high birth and station, on which account she wore twelve oysters on her tail, whilst the other inhabitants of the sea, even those of distinction, were allowed only six. In every other respect she merited unlimited praise, especially for the affection she showed to the six little princesses, her grand-daughters. These were all very beautiful children; the youngest was, however, the most lovely; her skin was as soft and delicate as a rose-leaf, her eyes were of as deep a blue as the sea, but like all other mermaids, she had no feet, her body ended in a tail like that of a fish.

The whole day long the children used to play in the spacious apartments of the palace, where beautiful flowers grew out of the walls on all sides around them. When the great amber windows were opened, fishes would swim into these apartments as swallows fly into our rooms; but the fishes were bolder than the swallows, they swam straight up to the little princesses, ate from their hands, and allowed themselves to be caressed.

---

[1] From *Fairy Tales.*

In front of the palace there was a large garden, full of fiery red and dark blue trees, whose fruit glittered like gold, and whose flowers resembled a bright, burning sun. The sand that formed the soil of the garden was of a bright blue colour, something like flames of sulphur; and a strangely beautiful blue was spread over the whole, so that one might have fancied oneself raised very high in the air, with the sky at once above and below, certainly not at the bottom of the sea. When the waters were quite still, the sun might be seen looking like a purple flower, out of whose cup streamed forth the light of the world.

Each of the little princesses had her own plot in the garden, where she might plant and sow at her pleasure. One chose hers to be made in the shape of a whale, another preferred the figure of a mermaid, but the youngest had hers quite round like the sun, and planted in it only those flowers that were red, as the sun seemed to her. She was certainly a singular child, very quiet and thoughtful. Whilst her sisters were adorning themselves with all sorts of gay things that came out of a ship which had been wrecked, she asked for nothing but a beautiful white marble statue of a boy, which had been found in it. She put the statue in her garden, and planted a red weeping willow by its side. The tree grew up quickly, and let its long boughs fall upon the bright blue ground, where ever-moving shadows played in violet hues, as if boughs and root were embracing.

Nothing pleased the little princess more than to hear about the world of human beings living above the sea. She made her old grandmother tell her everything she knew about ships, towns, men, and land animals, and was particularly pleased when she heard that the flowers of the upper world had a pleasant fragrance (for the flowers of the sea are scentless), and that the woods were green, and the fishes fluttering among the branches of various gay colours, and that they could sing with a loud clear voice. The old lady meant birds, but she called them fishes, because her grandchildren, having never seen a bird, would not otherwise have understood her.

"When you have attained your fifteenth year," added she, "you will be permitted to rise to the surface of the sea; you will then sit by moonlight in the clefts of the rocks, see the ships sail by, and learn to distinguish towns and men."

The next year the eldest of the sisters reached this happy age, but the others—alas! the second sister was a year younger than the eldest, the third a year younger than the second, and so on; the youngest had still five whole years to wait till that joyful time should come when she also might rise to the surface of the water and see what was going on in the upper world; however, the eldest promised to tell the others of everything she might see, when the first day of her being of age arrived; for the grandmother gave them but little information, and there was so much that they wished to hear.

But none of all the sisters longed so ardently for the day when she should be released from childish restraint as the youngest, she who had longest to wait, and was so quiet and thoughtful. Many a night she stood by the open windows, looking up through the clear blue water, whilst the fishes were leaping and playing around her. She could see the sun and the moon; their light was pale, but they appeared larger than they do to those who live in the upper world. If a shadow passed over them, she knew it must be either a whale or a ship sailing by full of human beings, who indeed little thought that, far beneath them, a little mermaiden was passionately stretching forth her white hands towards their ship's keel.

The day had now arrived when the eldest princess had attained her fifteenth year, and was therefore allowed to rise up to the surface of the sea.

When she returned she had a thousand things to relate. Her chief pleasure had been to sit upon a sandbank in the moonlight, looking at the large town which lay on the coast, where lights were beaming like stars, and where music was playing; she had heard the distant noise of men and carriages, she had seen the high church-towers, had listened to the ringing of the bells; and just because she could not go there she longed the more after all these things.

How attentively did her youngest sister listen to her words! And when she next stood at night time, by her open window, gazing upward through the blue waters, she thought so intensely of the great noisy city that she fancied she could hear the church-bells ringing.

Next year the second sister received permission to swim wherever she pleased. She rose to the surface of the sea, just when the sun was setting; and this sight so delighted her, that she declared it to be more beautiful than anything else she had seen above the waters.

"The whole sky seemed tinged with gold," said she, "and it is impossible for me to describe to you the beauty of the clouds. Now red, now violet, they glided over me; but still more swiftly flew over the water a flock of white swans, just where the sun was descending; I looked after them, but the sun disappeared, and the bright rosy light on the surface of the sea and on the edges of the clouds was gradually extinguished."

It was now time for the third sister to visit the upper world. She was the boldest of the six, and ventured up a river. On its shores she saw green hills covered with woods and vineyards, from among which arose houses and castles; she heard the birds singing, and the sun shone with so much power, that she was continually obliged to plunge below, in order to cool her burning face. In a little bay she met with a number of children, who were bathing and jumping about; she would have joined in their gambols, but the children fled back to land in great terror, and a little black animal barked at her in such a manner that she herself was frightened at last, and swam back to the sea. She could not, however, forget the green woods, the verdant hills, and the pretty children, who, although they had no fins, were swimming about in the river so fearlessly.

The fourth sister was not so bold, she remained in the open sea, and said on her return home, she thought nothing could be more beautiful. She had seen ships sailing by, so far off that they looked like seagulls, she had watched the merry dolphins gamboling in the water, and the enormous whales, sending up into the air a thousand sparkling fountains.

The year after, the fifth sister attained her fifteenth year. Her birthday happened at a different season to that of her sisters; it was winter, the sea was of a green colour, and immense icebergs were floating on its surface. These, she said, looked like pearls; they were, however, much larger than the church-towers in the land of human beings. She sat down upon one of these pearls, and let the wind play with her long hair, but then all the ships hoisted their sails in terror, and escaped as quickly as possible. In the evening the sea was covered with sails; and whilst the great mountains of ice alternately sank and rose again, and beamed with a reddish glow, flashes of lightning burst forth from the clouds and the thunder rolled on, peal after peal. The sails of all the ships were instantly furled, and horror and affright reigned on board, but the princess sat still on the iceberg, looking unconcernedly at the blue zigzag of the flashes.

The first time that either of these sisters rose out of the sea, she was quite enchanted at the sight of so many new and beautiful objects, but the novelty was soon over, and it was not long ere their own home appeared more attractive than the upper world, for there only did they find everything agreeable.

Many an evening would the five sisters rise hand in hand from the depths of the ocean. Their voices were far sweeter than any human voice, and when a storm was coming on, they would swim in front of the ships, and sing,—oh! how sweetly did they sing! describing the happiness of those who lived at the bottom of the sea, and entreating the sailors not to be afraid, but to come down to them.

The mariners, however, did not understand their words; they fancied the song was only the whistling of the wind, and thus they lost the hidden glories of the sea; for if their ships were wrecked, all on board were drowned, and none but dead men ever entered the Mer-king's palace.

Whilst the sisters were swimming at evening time, the youngest would remain motionless and alone, in her father's palace, looking up after them. She would have wept, but mermaids cannot weep, and therefore, when they are troubled, suffer infinitely more than human beings do.

"Oh! if I were but fifteen!" sighed she, "I know that I should love the upper world and its inhabitants so much."

At last the time she had so longed for arrived.

that her little face could not be seen, and watched the prince with unremitting attention.

It was not long before one of the young girls approached. She seemed quite frightened at finding the prince in this state, apparently dead; soon, however, she recovered herself, and ran back to call her sisters. The little mermaid saw that the prince revived, and that all around smiled kindly and joyfully upon him—for her, however, he looked not, he knew not that it was she who had saved him, and when the prince was taken into the house, she felt so sad, that she immediately plunged beneath the water, and returned to her father's palace.

If she had been before quiet and thoughtful, she now grew still more so. Her sisters asked her what she had seen in the upper world, but she made no answer.

Many an evening she rose to the place where she had left the prince. She saw the snow on the mountains melt, the fruits in the garden ripen and gathered, but the prince she never saw, so she always returned sorrowfully to her subterranean abode. Her only pleasure was to sit in her little garden gazing on the beautiful statue so like the prince. She cared no longer for her flowers; they grew up in wild luxuriance, covered the steps, and entwined their long stems and tendrils among the boughs of the trees, so that her whole garden became a bower.

At last, being unable to conceal her sorrow any longer, she revealed the secret to one of her sisters, who told it to the other princesses, and they to some of their friends. Among them was a young mermaid who recollected the prince, having been an eye-witness herself to the festivities in the ship; she knew also in what country the prince lived, and the name of its king;

"Come, little sister!" said the princesses, and embracing her they rose together arm in arm, out of the water, just in front of the prince's palace.

This palace was built of bright yellow stones, a flight of white marble steps led from it down to the sea. A gilded cupola crowned the building, and white marble figures, which might almost have been taken for real men and women, were placed among the pillars surrounding it. Through the clear glass of the high windows one might look into magnificent apartments hung with silken curtains, the walls adorned with magnificent paintings. It was a real treat to the little royal mermaids to behold so splendid an abode; they gazed through the windows of one of the largest rooms, and in the centre saw a fountain playing, whose waters sprang up so high as to reach the glittering cupola above, through which the sunbeams fell dancing on the water, and brightening the pretty plants which grew around it.

The little mermaid now knew where her beloved prince dwelt, and henceforth she went there almost every evening. She often approached nearer the land than her sisters had ventured, and even swam up the narrow channel that flowed under the marble balcony. Here on a bright moonlight night she would watch the young prince,who believed himself alone.

Sometimes she saw him sailing on the water in a gaily-painted boat with many coloured flags waving above. She would then hide among the green reeds which grew on the banks, listening to his voice, and if any one in the boat noticed the rustling of her long silver veil, which was caught now and then by the light breeze, they only fancied it was a swan flapping his wings.

Many a night when the fishermen were casting their nets by the beacon's light, she heard them talking of the prince, and relating the noble actions he had performed. She was then so happy, thinking how she had saved his life when struggling with the waves, and remembering how his head had rested on her bosom, and how she had kissed him when he knew nothing of it, and could never even dream of such a thing.

Human beings became more and more dear to her every day; she wished that she were one of them. Their world seemed to her much larger than that of the mer-people; they could fly over the ocean in their ships, as well as climb to the summits of those high mountains that rose above the clouds; and their wooded domains extended much farther than a mermaid's eye could penetrate.

There were many things that she wished to hear explained, but her sisters could not give her any satisfactory answer; she was again obliged to have recourse to the old queen-mother, who knew a great deal about the upper world, which she used to call "the country above the sea."

"Do men when they are not drowned live for ever?" she asked one day. "Do not they die as we do, who live at the bottom of the sea?"

"Yes," was the grandmother's reply, "they must die like us, and their life is much shorter than ours. We live to the age of three hundred years, but when we die, we become foam on the sea, and are not allowed even to share a grave among those that are dear to us. We have no immortal souls, we can never live again, and are like the grass which, when once cut down, is withered for ever. Human beings, on the contrary, have souls that continue to live, when their bodies become dust, and as we rise out of the water to admire the abode of man, they ascend to glorious unknown dwellings in the skies which we are not permitted to see."

"Why have not *we* immortal souls?" asked the little mermaid. "I would willingly give up my three hundred years to be a human being for only one day, thus to become entitled to that heavenly world above."

"You must not think of that," answered her grandmother, "it is much better as it is; we live longer and are far happier than human beings."

"So I must die, and be dashed like foam over the sea, never to rise again and hear the gentle murmur of the ocean, never again see the beautiful flowers and the bright sun! Tell me, dear grandmother, are there no means by which I may obtain an immortal soul?"

"No!" replied the old lady. "It is true that if thou couldst so win the affections of a human being as to become dearer to him than either father or mother; if he loved thee with all his heart, and promised whilst the priest joined his hands with thine to be always faithful to thee; then his soul would flow into thine, and thou wouldst then become partaker of human bliss. But that can never be!for what in our eyes is the most beautiful part of our body, the tail, the inhabitants of the earth think hideous, they cannot bear it. To appear handsome to them, the body must have two clumsy props which they call legs."

The little mermaid sighed and looked mournfully at the scaly part of her form, otherwise so fair and delicate.

"We are happy," added the old lady, "we shall jump and swim about merrily for three hundred years; that is a long time, and afterwards we shall repose peacefully in death. This evening we have a court ball."

The ball which the queen-mother spoke of was far more splendid than any that earth has ever seen. The walls of the saloon were of crystal, very thick, but yet very clear; hundreds of large mussel-shells were planted in rows along them; these shells were some of rose-colour, some green as grass, but all sending forth a bright light, which not only illuminated the whole apartment, but also shone through the glassy walls so as to light up the waters around for a great space, and making the scales of the numberless fishes, great and small, crimson and purple, silver and gold-coloured, appear more brilliant than ever.

Through the centre of the saloon flowed a bright, clear stream, on the surface of which danced mermen and mermaids to the melody of their own sweet voices, voices far sweeter than those of the dwellers upon earth. The little princess sang more harmoniously than any other, and they clapped their hands and applauded her. She was pleased at this, for she knew well that there was neither on earth nor in the sea a more beautiful voice than hers. But her thoughts soon returned to the world above her; she could not forget the handsome prince; she could not control her sorrow at not having an immortal soul. She stole away from her father's palace, and whilst all was joy within, she sat alone lost in thought in her little neglected garden. On a sudden she heard the tones of horns resounding over the water far away in the distance, and she said to herself, "Now he is going out to hunt, he whom I love more than my father and my mother, with whom my thoughts are constantly occupied, and to whom I would so willingly trust the happiness of my life! All! all, will I risk to win him—and an immortal soul! Whilst my sisters are still dancing in the palace, I will go to the enchantress whom I have hitherto feared so much, but who is, nevertheless, the only person who can advise and help me."

So the little mermaid left the garden, and went to the foaming whirlpool beyond which dwelt the enchantress. She had never been this way before-neither flowers nor sea-grass bloomed along her path; she had to traverse an extent of bare grey sand till she reached the whirlpool, whose waters were eddying and whizzing like mill-wheels, tearing everything they could seize along with them into the abyss below. She was obliged to make her way through this horrible place, in order to arrive at the territory of the enchantress. Then she had to pass through a boiling, slimy bog, which the enchantress called her turf-moor: her house stood in a wood beyond this and a strange abode it was. All the trees and bushes around were polypi, looking like hundred-headed serpents shooting up out of the ground; their branches were long slimy arms with fingers of worms, every member, from the root to the uttermost tip, ceaselessly moving and extending on all sides. Whatever they seized they fastened upon so that it could not loosen itself from their grasp. The little mermaid stood still for a minute, looking at this horrible wood; her heart beat with fear, and she would certainly have returned without attaining her object, had she not remembered the prince—and immortality. The thought gave her new courage, she bound up her long waving hair, that the polpyi might not catch hold of it, crossed her delicate arms over her bosom, and, swifter than a fish can glide through the water, she passed these unseemly trees, who stretched their eager arms after her in vain. She could not, however, help seeing that every polypus had something in his grasp, held as firmly by a thousand little arms as if enclosed by iron bands. The whitened skeletons of a number of human beings who had been drowned in the sea, and had sunk into the abyss, grinned horribly from the arms of these polypi; helms, chests, skeletons of land animals were also held in their embrace; among other things might be seen even a little mermaid whom they had seized and strangled! What a fearful sight for the unfortunate princess!

But she got safely through this wood of horrors, and then arrived at a slimy place, where immense fat snails were crawling about, and in the midst of this place stood a house built of the bones of unfortunate people who had been shipwrecked. Here sat the witch caressing a toad in the same manner as some persons would a pet bird. The ugly fat snails she called her chickens, and she permitted them to crawl about her.

"I know well what you would ask of me," said she to the little princess. "Your wish is foolish enough, yet it shall be fulfilled, though its accomplishment is sure to bring misfortune on you, my fairest princess. You wish to get rid of your tail, and to have instead two stilts like those of human beings, in order that a young prince may fall in love with you, and that you may obtain an immortal soul. Is it not so?" Whilst the witch spoke these words, she laughed so violently that her pet toad and snails fell from her lap. "You come just at the right time," continued she; "had you come after sunset, it would not have been in my power to have helped you before another year. I will prepare for you a drink with which you must swim to land, you must sit down upon the shore and swallow it, and then your tail will fall and shrink up to the things which men call legs. This transformation will, however, be very painful; you will feel as though a sharp knife passed through your body. All who look on you after you have been thus changed will say that you are the loveliest child of earth they have ever seen; you will retain your peculiar undulating movements, and no dancer will move so lightly, but every step you take will cause you pain all but unbearable; it will seem to you as though you were walking on the sharp edges of swords, and your blood will flow. Can you endure all this suffering? If so, I will grant your request."

"Yes, I will," answered the princess, with a faltering voice; for she remembered her dear prince, and the immortal soul which her suffering might win.

"Only consider," said the witch, "that you can never again become a mermaid, when once you have received a human form. You may never return to your sisters, and your father's palace; and unless you shall win the prince's love to such a degree, that he shall leave father and mother for you, that you shall be mixed up with all his thoughts and wishes, and unless the priest join your hands, so that you become man and wife, you will never obtain the immortality you seek. The morrow of the day on which he is united to another, will see your death; your heart will break with sorrow, and you will be changed to foam on the sea."

"Still I will venture!" said the little mermaid, pale and trembling as a dying person.

"Besides all this, I must be paid, and it is no slight thing that I require for my trouble. Thou hast the sweetest voice of all the dwellers in the sea, and thou thinkest by its means to charm the prince; this voice, however, I demand as my recompense. The best thing thou possessest I require in exchange for my magic drink; for I shall be obliged to sacrifice my own blood, in order to give it the sharpness of a two-edged sword."

"But if you take my voice from me," said the princess, "what have I left with which to charm the prince?"

"Thy graceful form," replied the witch, "thy modest gait, and speaking eyes. With such as these, it will be easy to infatuate a vain human heart. Well now! hast thou lost courage? Put out thy little tongue, that may cut it off, and take it for myself, in return for my magic drink."

" Be it so!" said the princess, and the witch took up her cauldron, in order to mix her potion. "Cleanliness is a good thing," remarked she, as she began to rub the cauldron with a handful of toads and snails. She then scratched her bosom, and let the black blood trickle down into the cauldron, every moment throwing in new ingredients, the smoke from the mixture assuming such horrible forms as were enough to fill beholders with terror, and a moaning and groaning proceeding from it, which might be compared to, the weeping of crocodiles. The magic drink at length became clear and transparent as pure water; it was ready.

"Here it is!" said the witch to the princess, cutting out her tongue at the same moment. The poor little mermaid was now dumb: she could neither sing nor speak.

"If the polypi should attempt to seize you, as you pass through my little grove," said the witch, "you have only to sprinkle some of this magic drink over them, and their arms will burst into a thousand pieces." But the princess had no need of this counsel, for the polypi drew hastily back, as soon as they perceived the bright phial, that glittered in her, hand like a star; thus she passed safely through the formidable wood over the moor, and across the foaming mill-stream.

She now looked once again at her father's palace; the lamps in the saloon were extinguished, and all the family were asleep. She would not go in, for she could not speak if she did; she was about to leave her home for ever; her heart was ready to break with sorrow at the thought; she stole into the garden, plucked a flower from the bed of each of her sisters as a remembrance, kissed her hand again and again, and then rose through the dark blue waters to the world above.

The sun had not yet risen, when she arrived at the prince's dwelling, and ascended those well-known marble steps. The moon still shone in the sky when the little mermaid drank off the wonderful liquid contained in her phial, she felt it run through her like a sharp knife, and she fell down in a swoon. When the sun rose, she awoke; and felt a burning pain in all her limbs, but—she saw standing close to her the object of her love, the handsome young prince, whose coal-black eyes were fixed inquiringly upon her. Full of shame she cast down her own, and perceived, instead of the long fish-tail she had hitherto borne, two slender legs; but she was quite naked, and tried in vain to cover herself with her long thick hair. The prince asked who she was, and how she had got there; and she, in reply, smiled and gazed upon him with her bright blue eyes, for alas! she could not speak. He then led her by the hand into the palace. She found that the witch had told her true; she felt as though she were walking on the edges of sharp swords, but she bore the pain willingly; on she passed, light as a zephyr, and all who saw her, wondered at her light undulating movements.

When she entered the palace, rich clothes of muslin and silk were brought to her; she was lovelier than all who dwelt there, but she could neither speak nor sing. Some female slaves, gaily dressed in silk and gold brocade, sung before the prince and his royal parents; and one of them distinguished herself by her clear sweet voice, which the prince applauded by clapping his hands. This made the little mermaid very sad, for she knew that she used to sing far better than the young slave.

"Alas!" thought she, "if he did but know that, for his sake, I have given away my voice for ever."

The slaves began to dance; our lovely little mermaiden then arose, stretched out her delicate white arms, and hovered gracefully about the room. Every motion displayed more and more the perfect symmetry and elegance of her figure; and the expression which beamed in her speaking eyes touched the hearts of the spectators far more than the song of the slaves.

All present were enchanted, but especially the young prince, who called her his dear little foundling. And she danced again and again, although every step cost her excessive pain. The prince then said she should always be with him; and accordingly a sleeping palace was prepared for her on velvet cushions in the anteroom of his own apartment.

The prince caused a suit of male apparel to be made for her, in order that she might accompany him in his rides; so together they traversed the fragrant woods, where green boughs brushed against their shoulders, and the birds sang merrily among the fresh leaves. With him she climbed up steep mountains, and although her tender feet bled, so as to be remarked by the attendants, she only smiled, and followed her dear prince to the heights, whence they could see the clouds chasing each other beneath them, like a flock of birds migrating to other countries.

During the night, she would, when all in the palace were at rest, walk down the marble steps, in order to cool her feet in the deep waters; she would then think of those beloved ones, who dwelt in the lower world.

One night, as she was thus bathing her feet, her sisters swam together to the spot, arm in arm and singing, but alas! so mournfully! She beckoned to them, and they immediately recognized her, and told her how great was the mourning in her father's house for her loss. From this time the sisters visited her every night; and once they brought with them the old grandmother, who had not seen the upper world for a great many years; they likewise brought their father, the Mer-king, with his crown on his head; but these two old people did not venture near enough to land to be able to speak to her.

The little mermaiden became dearer and dearer to the prince every day; but he only looked upon her as a sweet, gentle child; and the thought of making her his wife never entered his head. And yet his wife she must be, ere she could receive an immortal soul; his wife she must be, or she would change into foam, and be driven restlessly over the billows of the sea!

"Dost thou not love me above all others?" her eyes seemed to ask, as he pressed her fondly in his arms, and kissed her lovely brow.

"Yes," the prince would say, "thou art dearer to me than any other, for no one is as good as thou art! Thou lovest me so much; and thou art so like a young maiden, whom I have seen but once, and may never see again. I was on board a ship, which was wrecked by a sudden tempest; the waves threw me on the shore, near a holy temple, where a number of young girls are occupied constantly with religious services. The youngest of them found me on the shore, and saved my life. I saw her only once, but her image is vividly impressed upon my memory, and her alone can I love. But she belongs to the holy temple; and thou who resemblest her so much hast been given to me for consolation; never will we be parted!"

"Alas! he does not know that it was I who saved his life," thought the little mermaiden, sighing deeply; "I bore him over the wild waves, into the wooded bay, where the holy temple stood; I sat behind the rocks, waiting till some one should come. I saw the pretty maiden approach, whom he loves more than me," — and again she heaved a deep sigh, for she could not weep — "he said that the young girl belongs to the holy temple; she never comes out into the world, so they cannot meet each other again — and I am always with him, see him daily; I will love him, and devote my whole life to him."

"So the prince is going to be married to the beautiful daughter of the neighbouring king," said the courtiers, "that is why he is having that splendid ship fitted out. It is announced that he wishes to travel, but in reality he goes to see the princess; a numerous retinue will accompany him." The little mermaiden smiled at these and similar conjectures, for she knew the prince's intentions better than any one else.

"I must go," he said to her, "I must see the beautiful princess; my parents require me to do so; but they will not compel me to marry her, and bring her home as my bride. And it is quite impossible for me to love her, for she cannot be so like the beautiful girl in the temple as thou art; and if I were obliged to choose, I should prefer thee, my little silent foundling, with the speaking eyes." And he kissed her rosy lips, played with her locks, and folded her in his arms, whereupon arose in her heart a sweet vision of human happiness and immortal bliss.

"Thou art not afraid of the sea, art thou, my sweet silent child?" asked he tenderly as they stood together in the splendid ship, which was to take them to the country of the neighbouring king. And then he told her of the storms that sometimes agitate the waters; of the strange fishes that inhabit the deep, and of the wonderful things seen by divers. But she smiled at his words, for she knew better than any child of earth what went on in the depths of the ocean.

At night time, when the moon shone brightly, and when all on board were fast asleep, she sat in the ship's gallery, looking down into the sea. It seemed to her, as she gazed through the foamy track made by the ship's keel, that she saw her father's palace, and her grandmother's silver crown. She then saw her sisters rise out of the water, looking sorrowful and stretching out their hands towards her. She nodded to them, smiled, and would have explained that everything was going on quite according to her wishes; but just then the cabin boy approached, upon which the sisters plunged beneath the water so suddenly that the boy thought what he had seen on the waves was nothing but foam.

The next morning the ship entered the harbour of the king's splendid capital. Bells were rung, trumpets sounded, and soldiers marched in procession through the city, with waving banners, and glittering bayonets. Every day witnessed some new entertainments, balls and parties followed each other; the princess, however, was not yet in the town; she had been sent to a distant convent for education, and had there been taught the practice of all royal virtues. At last she arrived at the palace.

The little mermaid had been anxious to see this unparalleled princess; and she was now obliged to confess, that she had never before seen so beautiful a creature. The skin of the princess was so white and delicate, that the veins might be seen through it, and her dark eyes sparkled beneath a pair of finely formed eye-brows. "It is herself!" exclaimed the prince, when they met, "it is she who saved my life, when I lay like a corpse on the sea-shore!" and he pressed his blushing bride to his beating heart.

"Oh, I am all too happy!" said he to his dumb foundling. "What I never dared to hope for, has come to pass. Thou must rejoice in my happiness, for thou lovest me more than all others who surround me." —And the little mermaid kissed his hand in silent sorrow; it seemed to her as if her heart was breaking already, although the morrow of his marriage day, which must inevitably see her death, had not yet dawned. Again rung the church-bells, whilst heralds rode through the streets of the capital, to announce the approaching bridal. Odorous flames burned in silver candlesticks on all the altars; the priests swung their golden censers; and bride and bridegroom joined hands, whilst the holy words that united them were spoken. The little mermaid, clad in silk and cloth of gold, stood behind the princess, and held the train of the bridal dress; but her ear heard nothing of the solemn music; her eye saw not the holy ceremony; she remembered her approaching end, she remembered that she had lost both this world and the next.

That very same evening, bride and bridegroom went on board the ship; cannons were fired, flags waved with the breeze, and in the centre of the deck stood a magiaificent pavilion of purple and cloth of gold, fitted up with the richest and softest couches. Here the princely pair were to spend the night. A favourable wind swelled the sails, and the ship glided lightly over the blue waters.

As soon as it was dark, coloured lamps were hung out and dancing began on the deck. The little mermaid was thus involuntarily reminded of what she had seen the first time she rose to the upper world. The spectacle that now presented itself was equally splendid—and she was obliged to join in the dance, hovering lightly as a bird over the ship boards. All applauded her, for never had she danced with more enchanting grace. Her little feet suffered extremely, but she no longer felt the pain; the anguish her heart suffered was much greater. It was the last evening she might see him, for whose sake she had forsaken her home and all her family, had given away her beautiful voice, and suffered daily the most violent pain—all without his having the least suspicion of it. It was the last evening that she might breathe the same atmosphere in which he, the beloved one, lived; the last evening when she might behold the deep blue sea, and the starry heavens—an eternal night, in which she might neither think nor dream, awaited her. And all was joy in the ship; and she, her heart filled with thoughts of death and annihilation, smiled and danced with the others, till past midnight. Then the prince kissed his lovely bride, and arm in arm they entered the magnificent tent, prepared for their repose.

All was now still; the steersman alone stood at the ship's helm. The little mermaid leaned her white arms on the gallery, and looked towards the east, watching for the dawn; she well knew that the first sunbeam would witness her dissolution. She saw her sisters rise out of the sea; deadly pale were their features; and their long hair no more fluttered over their shoulders, it had all been cut off. "We have given it to the witch," said they, "to induce her to help thee, so that thou mayest not die. She has given to us a pen-knife: here it is! before the sun rises, thou must plunge it into the prince's heart; and when his warm blood trickles down upon thy feet they will again be changed to a fish-like tail; thou wilt once more become a mermaid, and wilt live thy full three hundred years, ere thou changest to foam on the sea. But hasten! either he or thou must die before sun-rise. Our aged mother mourns for thee so much, her grey hair has fallen off through sorrow, as ours fell before the scissors of the witch. Kill the prince, and come down to us! hasten! hasten! dost thou not see the red streaks on the eastern sky, announcing the near approach of the sun? A few minutes more and he rises, and then all will be over with thee." At these words they sighed deeply and vanished.

The little mermaid drew aside the purple curtains of the pavilion, where lay the bride and bridegroom; bending over them, she kissed the prince's forehead, and then glancing at the sky, she saw that the dawning light became every moment brighter. The prince's lips unconsciously murmured the name of his bride—he was dreaming of her, and her only, whilst the fatal penknife trembled in the hand of the unhappy mermaid.

All at once, she threw far out into the sea that instrument of death; the waves rose like blazing flames around, and the water where it fell seemed tinged with blood. With eyes fast becoming dim and fixed, she looked once more at her beloved prince; then plunged from the ship into the sea, and felt her body slowly but surely dissolving into foam.

THE CRUISE OF THE *WILD DUCK*[1]

Holger Drachmann

(1846-1908)

I

THE old man's dead," said Daniel Vibe, putting his head in at the window, where his friend, Klaus Tommerup, sat balancing himself on two legs of his chair with a tabby cat on his knee. Klaus interrupted his caresses, let the cat go, brushed the hairs off his arm, and asked—

" When? "

"At three o'clock this morning."

"Did he suffer much?"

"Not a great deal; I thought it would have been worse. The doctor came just at the end. He said it was a good thing."

" What?"

"The doctor said it was a good thing."

" I suppose it is," said Tommerup. "When a man has lived seventynine years and has spent fifty of them in grudging and grumbling, and quarrelling with his family, and dies decently at last, I suppose the doctor is right in saying it's a good thing."

Daniel Vibe did not answer. He pulled off his black gloves—he had already provided himself with gloves—and looked at his hands which were stained purple. It was warm standing there in the sun. Tommerup looked at his watch-chain, and then he asked his friend—

" I suppose you are going to buy the *Wild Duck* now, Daniel?"

" First, there's the funeral."

" But I want to know if you mean to buy the cutter."

"I'm thinking of it," said Vibe.

"Very good. Then we'll be off in a fortnight. It's wretched work going about like a chimney-sweep in a hole like this. I have done it myself, and I know."

He stretched out his hand through the window to his friend, who pressed it and walked away with drooping head, closely observed by a good many feminine spectators whose profiles were reflected in the little window mirrors all along the street.

Tommerup looked after him, and nodded approvingly.

"He does it well," he remarked, "very well."

Then he glanced in the opposite direction, down towards the little harbour,

---

[1] From *The Cruise of the Wild Duck and Other Tales.*

where two barges were loading bricks and a yacht was flying her flag half-mast high in honour of the only ship-owner and principal merchant of the town who had that morning exchanged time for eternity.

Neither the barges nor the yacht attracted Klaus Tommerup's attention. His glance passed over the half-rotten pier-head and fell upon a cutter-rigged boat; his dark eyes rested upon her with a sort of caress in them, and as he looked he sighed. Old Tommerup, his father, had departed this life the previous year, leaving his son a soap factory, heavily encumbered with mortgages, and sorely in want of capital; and the ledger which lay on the desk before him spoke of matters far enough removed from cutter-rigged boats and pleasure cruises. And at this moment the big tabby cat sprang on his master's back and drew his attention back to the book.

II

A fortnight had passed, but young Vibe did not consider it quite correct to leave home so soon after the event, "which had deeply affected one of the principal families of the town," as the local newspaper put it. He had cut his whiskers rather short—this was also a sacrifice to propriety—and his slender figure looked very well in his black clothes; but even the most elegantly garbed grief has its drawbacks. He was very much at a loss to know how to kill time without exposing himself to the disapproval of those ever-watchful critics who had only winked at certain of his youthful follies because he was the sole heir to old Vibe's corn and coal business. Now by his father's death he was promoted to a more serious position, and expected to behave seriously in consequence.

Daniel Vibe was a young man, but by no means an imprudent one. He went to the family physician and showed him a little red spot on his cheek. The doctor lifted his eye-brows, smiled, and said "I think perhaps you want a little change. You might be the better for a breath of sea air. Don't you think so? You would not object . . . ?"

And on that Daniel Vibe bought the *Wild Duck*.

He got an old lawyer, the family factotum, who had assisted his father in a good many small matters that did not, strictly speaking, lie quite within his profession, to buy the boat for him privately. And the old *examinatus juris* was pleased to see young Vibe show so much business capacity. In the club they nodded approvingly when it came out at last that Vibe was the real purchaser; the doctor had let a word or two fall about young Vibe's health, and in that town nothing was unpardonable that was done with a good object. Klaus Tommerup went about whistling softly to himself; as his habit was when he had anything particular on his mind; and the next morning very early he was on board the boat doing sundry odds and ends of work about her. Later on in the day the owner himself arrived, wearing a short blue jacket, black trousers, a cap with a broad peak, and a bit of crape twisted round his anchor buttons. He looked on while the other worked, and so the morning passed.

III

"I suppose we ought to have a man on the boat?" asked Daniel Vibe the next day.

"It wouldn't be a bad plan to have some fellow to do the rough work," answered Tommerup, still busy on board, while his friend still stood on the pier-head and looked on.

"Who should we take, do you think?" asked the owner.

"I don't know—Hullo, what are all the people doing down there?"

Tommerup emerged from the cabin as he spoke, and a strong gust of wind blew his hair out on one side like a fan. There was really an unusual number of people—quite half a score in all-collected on the generally deserted pier. A stiff breeze sweeping down the fairway whistled and howled in the cutter's rigging.

"What is it?" asked Vibe of a man near him, setting his legs wide apart in a jaunty, nautical way, rather as if he took the pier for the deck of a rolling ship. A tradesman of the town, who was holding his tall hat on with both hands, explained that it was Prip's son who was believed to be capsizing out in the bay.

"What?" cried Tommerup, and sprang on to the jetty, "capsizing? But he has just made a new sail for the yawl, and he had plenty of ballast in her yesterday. I saw it myself."

"There is something wrong with him all the same," observed the tradesman, "and they have just sent to tell old Prip."

"I must have a nearer look at that," said Tommerup, incredulously; and he drew his friend with him to the other side of the pier under lee of the old goods-shed.

There before them lay the broad open bay, and the gusts of wind were sweeping over it, and the clouds of the clear, cool May morning were flying before the breeze above the heads of the "crowd" who held on their hats and exhausted themselves in conjectures as to the fate of the yawl.

One believed that she had capsized already: another maintained that she was still up in the wind with flapping sail, and that she must drift out to sea unless, indeed, she were caught on the Quarantine Island, or left hanging on the reef of rocks out beyond the Northern Clapper.

The question was apparently open, and so was the bay; and the yawl at that distance looked so tiny that it was possible to entertain the most contrary surmises about her. All that was actually known was that old Prip's son, Sören, had gone out into the bay that morning to try the new smack sail which he had made himself.

What had happened out there was not yet clear, but it was evident that something was wrong, and at this point in the debate Klaus Tommerup turned sharp round on his heel, and sprang back on board the *Wild Duck*, saying to his friend, "Come along."

"What do you mean?" asked Vibe, with a little hesitation.

"Cast off aft, and let us get away," answered Tommerup, shortly, as he set to work on the reef points of the mainsail.

"You go by yourself," said Vibe, adding more slowly, "I must be off on business."

Tommerup looked up and nodded at his friend with a little smile.

And the next moment the *Wild Duck* glided out into the bay.

IV

Those who stood on the pier, among them young Vibe, who had found that his business was not so pressing after all, watched the cutter speed over the smooth water like a real Wild Duck, curtseying now and then as she met the swell, lying over first by fits and starts, and then more continuously, because it was really blowing pretty hard, and young Vibe congratulated himself with great emphasis on having given his comrade a hint to take in the two reefs in time.

"She behaves very well," declared the skipper of the yacht, with a side glance at the young man. "You should have gone with him yourself, Hr. Vibe; it's just the day for a big boat like that."

But Daniel Vibe only shrugged his shoulders, and then expressed himself to the ropemaker and the tanner and the watchmaker, in the most correct nautical terms, regarding the pretty behaviour of his vessel.

" Tommerup certainly sails her very well," he added, "but after all every one can't be a skipper by trade."

" Certainly not," answered the'skipper of the yacht, rubbing his elbow.

And now as the *Wild Duck* grew gradually smaller and smaller, and the yawl was scarcely visible at all, the spectators disappeared gradually from the pier; and among the last who sauntered across the ill-paved landing-place was young Vibe.

"There's old Prip," said the tanner, pointing to a tall, thin figure leaning against a rusty anchor-stock, and holding his hand over his small grey eyes, to shade them from the sun, as he peered out across the bay.

"So it is," said Vibe; "let us hear what he has to say."

They directed their course straight towards him, but the old man did not seem to be in the least aware of their presence. It was not till Vibe's cap came directly across his line of vision that he let his hand fall, and twisted his forefinger round the bowl of the clay pipe which was jammed tight in a corner of his mouth.

"Good morning, Prip," said Vibe.

Prip grunted in reply.

"My boat has gone out to save the yawl, Prip," said Vibe, with some satisfaction.

There was no answer. The small grey eyes blinked at the sun, and the forefinger went on pressing down the ashes in the bowl of the pipe.

"It's a lucky thing for your son," said the tanner.

The old man screwed up his eyes, opened them suddenly, and looked down on the stout little leather cleaner with an expression of amused indifference.

"I think Sören will be glad to see her, old man," said Vibe, with a touch of familiarity in his tone.

"I think," said the old man, taking the pipe out of his mouth for a moment, "that Sören will pitch into them well as soon as they get near enough to him."

With that the pipe resumed its usual place, and old Prip turned and strolled homewards to the old erection—something between a house and a shed—which lay on the far side of the harbour, where a tumbledown tar-kiln brought to mind the long since abandoned dockyard, which had once been the pride of the town.

V

It was blowing hard out over the bay, and the bay was not at any time to be trifled with. There was a narrow channel and a good deal of sand. It was something like two miles across to the high land on the opposite side. In the middle there was passage for big vessels, and generally there was a strong current. Out towards the sea the bay ran up into an inlet, where it was possible to put in quite snugly when it was blowing a gale outside. In this quarter lay several islets, among them the Quarantine Island; and there, too, was the long reef of rocks known as the Northern Clapper. There were not a few of these reefs or "clappers" round about. If you had a good boat which steered well, and if you knew the channel, there was very good sailing in the bay. The skipper of the yacht always said so, and Tommerup did not contradict him. But it is to be observed that these two gentlemen had so far done very little in their lives but sail in and out and round the bay.

Klaus Tommerup on board the cutter lay up as far as he could, and so had the wind with him going free towards the high land on the opposite coast. He had lost sight of the yawl for an hour, and then perceived her behind one of the little islands. The smack sail was lowered, and the yawl lay in smooth water by a big rock; but Tommerup could see no one in her. He made straight for her, however, going as near as he dared venture into the shallow water. Then he backed his foresail and hailed her. A young man's head appeared above the gunwale of the boat and vanished again. Tommerup sounded the depth of the water, ventured a dozen fathoms nearer, and shouted once more. The head again appeared. It certainly belonged to Sören Prip.

"What's the matter?" inquired the man in the yawl.

"That's what I want to know," returned the man in the cutter.

"Go to the devil!" said the voice from the yawl.

Tommerup was slightly disconcerted. But not being of a hasty disposition, he shouted to the other again—

"Is there anything wrong? Can I do anything for you?

"It's the step of the mast that's cracked. I can't hold her to the wind," Sören answered.

"Put the yawl off then, and I'll tow you," suggested Klaus.

"Put off yourself, and let me alone," the other retorted; and the head vanished once more.

Tommerup stayed where he was full five minutes longer, but the cutter had already twice touched the bottom; and he became impatient.

"Come out, man, I say," he shouted, "and let there be an end to this foolery! I can't lie here all day knocking my boat to pieces."

Sören Prip stood straight up. "I tell you," he said, "I sailed the yawl out, and I'm going to sail her home again, if I wait ever so long for the chance."

He held a bottle of beer to his mouth for a moment, and then laid the bottle and himself down again in the bottom of the boat.

Tommerup hauled in his foresail and stood off shore. Then, making a long tack, he bore down upon the Quarantine Island, as if he meant to land there; changing his mind, he sailed for a couple of hours up and down the channel, and as by that time it was late in the afternoon, and he began to feel hungry, he fancied the man in the yawl might be in the same case, and going down to leeward of the islet, he hailed him again.

There was no answer this time; no head appeared.

"That is certainly the man for us," thought Klaus Tommerup; and full of inward admiration for such steadfastness, he put the cutter about and sailed fast homewards.

VI

"You're quite right, that's the man for the *Wild Duck*" Daniel Vibe declared emphatically the next morning. The two friends sat in the cabin of the cutter which was again moored to the pier-head. A steady, pleasant breeze had been blowing for half an hour, following a stormy night and a wet daybreak. The breeze came from the other side of the bay, and, gliding into the harbour with the breeze, the top of a new smack sail presently became visible across the pier-head.

"Hullo!" cried Tommerup, " there he is!"

"Is that the man?" asked the owner of the cutter; and taking out the silver whistle with which he had provided himself as part of the necessary apparatus for a pleasure sail, he whistled quite in a man-of-war's fashion to the yawl.

Klaus looked at him, and then over at the yawl, as she came into the harbour. The little mast was still leaning backward with hardly any sail up, but the wind was with her, and she made way. Sören sat at the helm, and peered up at the deck of the cutter, as if the performance with the whistle, though it did not in any way concern him personally, afforded him a little amusement after the monotony of the previous day and night.

"Come alongside!" shouted Vibe.

The yawl glided quietly on its way.

"We want to speak to you!" shouted Tommerup.

"Oh, was that what you were whistling for?" asked Sören, and turned the tiller.

The yawl came alongside of the cutter; Sören sat still.

"Would you like to exchange vessels?" asked Vibe, pleasantly.

Sören measured the *Wild Duck* with his eye, and said—

"What shall I give in exchange for her?"

Tommerup laughed, and Vibe looked doubtful.

"Hr. Vibe is asking if you will engage with us?" said Tommerup. Sören came a little nearer.

"Is your cargo coal?" he asked.

"What?" shouted Vibe.

"I mean, are we bound for England?"

"Are you mad?" exclaimed Vibe, looking quite startled.

Sören glanced from Vibe to Tommerup, and back again.

"Ah, well, after all," he continued, "that's dirty work, and it would be a sin to spoil the smart paint. So it's corn, then?"

"Can't you understand?" cried Daniel. "This is a pleasure boat."

"All right," said Sören, with perfect composure. "That saves the trouble of lading and unlading. It will be rather amusing to run over there just for the fun of it."

"But we are not going to England at all," Vibe announced firmly.

"Not?" said Sören, slowly, while he examined the roomy, well-fitted-out boat with critical eyes. "I thought that if Hr. Tommerup"—

"I am the owner of this vessel, not Tommerup," said Vibe, angrily.

"And now let's have no more nonsense; will you come with us, or not?"

"Here I am," said Sören.

In the meantime Tommerup had taken out of his pocket, not a silver whistle, for which there wasn't after all any particular use, but his old tobacco pipe—a short cutty—which he filled, lighted, and began to smoke with philosophic calm. It is difficult to guess the thoughts of meditative people, but as Tommerup watched the breeze playing with the smoke, there is reason to think he was wishing that his soap factory was free and unencumbered, so that he might sell it and be his own master in a boat of his own.

VII

They sailed together, the three of them. When the weather was settled and the course fairly clear, Daniel Vibe took his place at the wheel, and Tommerup sat or lay by the stern railing. Sören's post was in the fore hatchway. If any change occurred, Tommerup's hand slipped inadvertently, as it were, on to the tiller, while Vibe's hand moved away as if unconsciously, and the owner contented himself for the moment with repeating in a loud voice the words of command softly suggested by his comrade. When the squall was over, or the shoal passed, the hands changed places again by the same tacit agreement. But if the course became more difficult, and the breeze dropped; or if the squall seemed likely to last long, Klaus Tommerup's body followed his hand to the tiller, while Daniel Vibe found a temporary refuge on the companion. Sören minded his own business, and paid no attention to anyone else. But when a reef or two had been taken in, and the owner happened, once in a way, to be still at the helm, Sören put the hard knuckle of his right forefinger between his teeth, and repeated half aloud to himself a favourite sentence, "We have a fine lot of stuff on board; real good stuff on board her."

So they sailed together, and each one naturally fell in time into the part which best suited him.

It was an August day—Daniel Vibe's twenty-ninth birthday. To receive the congratulations of his family, and to drink punch at the club in the evening, was not making enough of the day according to his ideas; and a real revel, with a big dinner, and so on, was not seemly, his relations thought, so soon after the great bereavement. He therefore provisioned the *Wild Duck* particularly well, and invited some of the best people of the town to come with him for a sail, which might perhaps last till the next day. Possibly this prospect deterred them; in any case the guests failed to put in an appearance. Daniel Vibe resolved to show that he could do without them; they set sail and glided out of the harbour. The weather was extremely promising, and the tanner and the chemist who had been invited at the last moment to fill the vacant places stood on the pier and repented in their hearts that they had made it a point of honour to decline.

Away they went. The captain was now in white trousers, light blue flannel shirt under his pea-jacket, and the peaked cap; and he still wore a bit of crape over his gilt buttons. His long fair whiskers made him look quite English, and he really was a very handsome birthday figure.

Of course he steered. The wind was fair and fresh. Tommerup thought the barometer showed a tendency to fall, but Daniel declared that he wouldn't ask advice from any weather-glass on his birthday. At breakfast he was evidently in the highest spirits. Sören sat forward and stared at the horizon, with his knuckle in his mouth, putting a word now and again into the conversation. As for Tommerup, he had brought a cushion up from the cabin and had made a comfortable place for himself in the stern. Beside him he placed a basket of provisions, to which he gave his undivided attention as soon as they were clear of the harbour swell. The soap factory had now come quite to a standstill, and the old woman—the solitary remnant of his father's household—who attended to his few wants, had announced that morning that her master did not give her an adequate sum for the weekly expenses, and that if it were not increased she must leave his service. Tommerup had managed to content her for the moment, but all the same, he had left his coffee and his bread and butter almost untouched, and there was a cloud on his broad, open brow as he walked down to the harbour with his cat under his arm. Klaus had not found it in his heart to leave the animal alone at home. The low, dreary old house had looked very melancholy indeed that morning in its owner's eyes, and he did not fancy it wore a much more cheerful aspect in the eyes of the cat. Tommerup's family had died out; he had no enemies in the town, and few friends; but he had his cat, and the cat's name was Jacob.

So he lay on the cushion which was stuffed with the best cork, and Jacob lay on his knee and blinked at the sun, and devoured the occasional mouthfuls of cold chicken which his master bestowed upon him.

VIII

Daniel Vibe was, as I have said, in excellent spirits. He meant that day to get right out to sea, he said, and they made straight for the other side of the bay.

Near the inlet they passed another little vessel belonging to the town, loaded with peat and potatoes—no unusual freight. The boat was heavily laden, the piles of peat were hanging over the sides; she beat up with difficulty against the tide. Vibe scoffed at her master's seamanship.

"Faith," said he, "there's a fine trade!"

"The man gets a living for himself and his wife and child out of it, any way," remarked Sören, thoughtfully.

"What, has he got a family on board along with the peat?" laughed the captain.

"They don't live on peat," said Sören. "The man does a very good business, they say."

Tommerup said nothing, but nodded in a friendly way to the man, who responded by waving his cap.

"You ought to go in for something of that sort yourself, Tommerup," said Vibe. "Then you would have a chance of being your own master; while as it is—"

"As it is things are in a bad way," said Tommerup, stroking the cat's back. "You mean that a peat barge that goes is better than a soap factory that stands still," he went on. " You are great at logic, Daniel. Lend me your corkscrew."

"Yes, let's have a drink," said the captain.

They did have a drink. The first bottle of sherry was soon emptied, and, in spite of Tommerup's objections, another was opened. Tommerup refused to drink any more, but Vibe kept passing the bottle to Sören, who did not refuse the captain's invitation. And he was not accustomed to wine.

The Clapper was passed; the *Wild Duck* went curtseying out into the open sea. The captain's pale face was a little flushed. His cap was on the side of his head, and he looked rather rakish. Klaus sat and stroked his cat, and looked up at the sky and across the cutter's sail.

"The wind is freshening," remarked Sören.

"So much the better," cried Vibe; but he added immediately, "Shall we take in a reef?"

" It would be as well," said Tommerup. "Luff."

They took in a reef, and in the afternoon, while the *Wild Duck* kept out in the open, this is what happened.

Vibe sat at the helm, although the wind, as Sören had foretold, grew fresher and fresher. The wine was doing its work; the captain was bolder to-day. He meant to show them that he could sail his own ship. So he stayed where he was, and a new bottle was opened, of which Sören had a fair share.

Klaus Tommerup looked on for a little while and forbade the sailor presently to drink any more.

"You let him alone!" cried Vibe. "I am the captain of this boat, and it's my birthday."

Tommerup nodded. The vessel was labouring a good deal, and now and then shipped a sea. So he put his cat inside the breast of his coat, and buttoned him safely up, and then resumed his place on his cork cushion, apparently indifferent, but really keeping a sharp look-out on each of the helmsman's movements.

Sören drank, and was as happy as a child. He was wet through already, but the water did not seem to trouble him as much as it troubled Jacob. The cat sat with his head out, but whenever a wave washed over the boat he put it in and mewed. "Hold her a little off, Daniel," said Tommerup.

Sören stood upright with his hands behind him, holding on to the topmost stay.

At Tommerup's word he made a grimace, an action which, strictly speaking, overstepped the limits of discipline.

"*We* are going to sail her to-day, aren't we, Sören?" cried the captain.

"So we are," laughed Sören; and again he accepted the bottle which Tommerup himself had to pass to him.

The air became gradually more and more hazy. The sun shone red through the mist.

"I don't like the look of it," said Tommerup, glancing back at the shore, which was fading into the grey blue distance.

"Bosh!" said Vibe.

"We ought to turn back," answered his comrade. "It will be hard enough to beat up now and it will be fresher still before evening."

"Perhaps you're afraid?" cried the captain boldly.

At that moment Sören's feet slipped away from him, and he went flat down on his back on the wet deck.

Vibe grew pale. Sören was up again in a moment, but Tommerup looked severely at him, and Sören seemed a little ashamed. He had not appreciated the birthday sherry quite rightly. The drink had been stronger than the cutter's sailor.

And so came the first flash and the first peal of thunder. The sea turned purple and grey, and was specked inshore with innumerable white dots, and the wind whistled ominously. Tommerup rose to his knees, buttoned up his coat in spite of Jacob's evident objection, and put his hand on Vibe's shoulder.

"Get out of the way," he said. "We shall have the storm on us in a minute; it's no time for fooling."

But Vibe was obstinate.

"As you please," said Tommerup, and eased the mainsail. "Stand by the halyards, Sören; let go the peak halyard; let the throat halyard be!

At this moment the cutter dipped her nose under an unusually high sea, which the helmsman had not parried. Sören clung to the hoop of the mast; the water rushed foaming aft, and filled the hole in which the helmsman stood.

Vibe let go the tiller and shot up out of the hole like a cork from a bottle. The boat careened right over, so that the mainsail dipped in the water. Vibe lost his balance, slid to leeward, and went overboard.

"Let go the foresail!" shouted Tommerup, and put the helm hard over with his foot. Then, turning quick as lightning, he snatched up the cork cushion, and threw it overboard, where Vibe's head appeared above the water.

The cutter shot up into the wind.

"Is there no rope?" shouted Tommerup. "Cut the jib halyard—cut it away with your knife, man! Now a turn of the rope round the oar and over with it. He is holding on to the cushion. That's right; pay out the rope. Now he's got it. All right, haul him in—here he is!"

And Klaus Tommerup bent over the railing, hauled in his comrade and pushed him into the cabin without ceremony. Jacob, who found himself also in an uncomfortable position, was mewing miserably, and he was sent into the cabin too.

"It's no good whining about it now," remarked his master.

Sören looked at him penitently.

"I deserve a thrashing, Hr. Tommerup," he said. "I did not think that the stuff was so strong."

"You must wait for your thrashing till we come ashore," answered the other. "It remains to be seen if we ever do. Down with the sail! Down with the throat halyard! Confound you, man, look alive! Here it comes." And while the *Wild Duck* was shrouded in the sheet of rain, and lay heeling over on her side with bare poles, he muttered to himself, "It's lucky for Daniel it didn't come sooner."

IX

Just in front of the inlet that ran out of the bay, on the island that had been long known as the Quarantine Island, there stood a yellow brick building with a high tiled roof, surrounded by ruined cottages and deserted gardens. The inside of the house corresponded to its exterior; half-ruined as it was, it still retained an air of dignity—a reminiscence of the days when epidemics were in fashion, and were treated with respectful consideration by the authorities. There are on our coast many such desolate outlying stations, mouldering fortresses, decayed depots.

There is about them something of the sentiment that attaches to old castles and old soldiers.

The afternoon was passing into the evening, and there was more than a touch of autumn in the air. Right across the island, from the little harbour up to the highest rampart, there stretched a row of weather beaten trees, with all their branches growing out on one side, not unlike a worn-out comb or toothbrush. The storm—for now it was really a storm—whistled wildly among these old veterans; there was not much else left for it to do. The coarse yellow grass outside the windows of the building waved to and fro, and the gusts of wind rattled against the convex panes.

In the large room, whose scanty furniture dated from the days of Napoleon—a silhouette of the Emperor on horseback still adorned the mirror—the inspector was sitting. What he was inspector of, no one quite knew. If he had inspected himself, as he sat in the deep armchair covered with flowery tapestry, he would have discovered himself to be a respectable old ruin, like the rest of the island. He had once been a strong, broad-shouldered man, but he was now bent with rheumatism, and there was in his eye a watery gleam that might perhaps be connected with the corner cupboard behind him, whose doors stood open, revealing two or three decanters. Before him on the little table stood a steaming mixture, which he now and then sipped with trembling hand.

Some distance from the armchair, by the gable window, sat a young girl with a book before her, that looked like a family volume of sermons. She had been reading, but had paused to look attentively at the sea. Then she went back to her reading, but evidently with an effort. It might be imagined that the book was a sort of necessity to which a girl might submit in a rather hopeless position, left to herself on a dreary island with a father like the one in the armchair, not knowing what to do with her youth and health, or how to find an outlet for her longings and her strength.

Now and then , as she glanced from the printed page to the armchair, there was visible in her eyes an expression of profound melancholy, out of keeping with her years, of weary resignation to an inevitable fate.

But when she looked away from him with a little shudder, and glanced again through the casement at the world outside, her expression altered, revealing a gleam of resolution, the result possibly of continual intercourse with the sea.

Every ruin has some point round which the mouldering fragments may cling for a long time, and the sea has strength and freshness for everyday. It is not to pass away till all things pass; and that hour is long in coming.

The girl's world lay there beyond those windows. It was little or great, according as you looked at it. At this moment it contained a single boat that with reefed mainsail and close-reefed foresail, in the red flush of the sunset, was beating up towards the inlet against wind and tide, and doing her utmost apparently to clear the rocky reef, the Northern Clapper, which lay to leeward of her.

The girl knew the pilot's boat, and the few other vessels along the coast. But she could not connect this one with any owner. She knew enough to be aware that the situation was very serious, and she watched still more intently, and presently uttered an exclamation of dismay.

" What's the matter?" asked the old man in the armchair.

She did not heed the question. Like a seabird with wounded wing, the boat drifted sideways, and the breakers on the reef were near—terribly near.

" Ah! . . . thank Heaven!" she cried.

"But what is it?" asked the voice from the armchair again.

"It's a boat which . . . It was making straight for . . . Now she has righted herself again. Look for yourself!"

"Not a trace of a boat," stammered the inspector, whose window looked to the west, while the gable looked to the east.

"They can't get up to the town, father; that is impossible. I think—yes, I really think," she repeated after a few moments' anxious scrutiny, "that they are coming over to us. Poor men! how wet they must be."

"Hot water," said the inspector, "that's what they'll want. Hot water and something in it!"

X

From the little harbour of the island three men walked up to the brick building. The one in the middle was supported by his stronger friends on either side.

They opened the outer door; there was a little sound of stamping and splashing in the brick-paved entry; then they knocked at the door, and finally entered the big room.

"Good evening. Excuse me," said Tommerup.

"By your leave," said Sören.

Daniel Vibe said nothing. They led him to the hard high-backed sofa, and he dropped on to it with a groan; it seemed to him that he was still sailing.

The young girl had been standing doubtfully in the middle of the room. Now she hastened to the door, and came back immediately with a clean towel and a glass of water.

"Your friend is ill. You have been in great danger?"

She addressed her remark to Tommerup, who, dripping wet as he was, nodded with some embarrassment, and struggled with the captain as with a child. Sören assisted him; and the floor round the three of them was like a little sea.

"We have a bed all ready," said the girl. "Would that not be the best thing?"

Vibe had recovered himself a little. He sat up and threw out his arms.

"Bed!" said he; "who talks of going to bed?"

He looked wildly round, and his glance fell on the little table beside the armchair. He staggered across the room, snatched up the glass and emptied it at a draught. The old man raised his large eyes approvingly, and spoke to his daughter in his harsh voice.

"I told you so," he said, jerking his elbow in the direction of the cupboard. "Hot water and the decanter."

The girl stood again as if uncertain what to do. She looked away from her father with a sigh, and seemed silently to ask Tommerup's advice.

"Yes, let us have something hot," he answered reassuringly, "and if you had any dry clothes?"

He pointed first at Vibe, then glanced at himself and Sören; and then he apologized for the condition of the floor.

The inspector's daughter blushed, though there was apparently no particular reason why she should blush because three strangers, dripping wet and much the worse for their trip, had visited the nearest island in stress of weather. She exchanged a few words with her father about the big wardrobe in the garret, and then disappeared.

There were now three men in the room, besides the ruin in the armchair. Vibe sat down again on the sofa. He was evidently much shaken, excited, nervous, and very pale; he was the living picture of a weak character, just escaped from a great danger, and still suffering from the effects of sea-sickness. He shook with cold in his wet clothes; the hot drink had done him a little good, but only a little, and he sat there shaking his head like an owl in a cage.

Tommerup surveyed the different objects in the room as well as the fading light permitted. The attention he paid to certain things seemed to indicate an old acquaintance with them. He tried to getup a conversation with the armchair but the attempt was sadly fruitless. The inspector only uttered a few unintelligible words and disjointed sentences, and ended with the assurance that they should soon have something hot.

"Ah yes," said Sören, who was amusing himself by letting his feet squelch in his shoes as he walked across the floor, "that isn't a bad idea—unless Hr. Tommerup has anything against it."

"I have nothing against it now," answered Klaus. "What do you say, Vibe? Come, pull yourself together a bit."

But that was more than the captain was capable of doing at present. He moved his head from side to side, and uttered a broken monologue, of which fragments such as "never sail again . . ." and "the confounded cutter . . ." were alone audible.

The door opened, and the daughter of the house came in with a light in her hand.

"The gentlemen can go in now and change their things," said she. And so they did. The captain was helped in and out of his clothes like a child. To Tommerup's repeated suggestion that he should accept the bed that had been offered to him, he answered with a mixture of fretfulness and defiance—

" No, he was going to show them . . ."

In the meantime the table was laid for supper. A large jug was set steaming among the eggs and sausages and bread and butter, and what Vibe showed them was that he was thirsty rather than hungry. To the old man's evident satisfaction, he mixed himself first one glass and then another and then retreated to the sofa, and lay listening to the brief plain narrative of their expedition, which Tommerup gave on his comrade's behalf and his own.

But the simplicity with which the great events of the day were represented was not at all to Daniel Vibe's mind. Encouraged by the mixture, in the midst of concocting his third glass, he broke into Tommerup's story with such striking additions that his friend was silenced and Vibe continued alone.

They had really gone through unheard-of dangers. And if he himself had not had the confounded ill-luck to stumble and go overboard at the critical moment—an accident which however had given him a chance to display his dexterity in swimming—they would perhaps . . . Sören could not contain himself. He began to laugh with half an egg and a slice of sausage in his mouth.

The captain grew angry.

"What are you grinning at, you idiot?" said he.

Klaus Tommerup interposed to keep the peace. The young girl who sat at some distance from the table watched him intently. From the armchair there came occasionally broken expressions of surprise and approval to which no one paid any attention at all.

Then the captain was seized with another attack of giddiness; his face turned yellow-white, and when he had disposed of another glass the tears streamed from his eyes, and he declared Klaus Tommerup to be his preserver and best friend. Sören nodded assent. Tommerup asked the girl to clear the table. The captain did not want to go to bed—not at all—he wanted to drink another glass to his friend and preserver, he wanted the armchair to pledge him—he wanted every one to be cheerful.

"All right," said Tommerup, laughing. "Let us be cheerful by all means," and he smiled reassuringly at the girl as if to say, "We must let him have plenty of rope."

"That's right," cried Vibe. "I am glad you are thawing at last."

Daniel Vibe, without exactly being a musician, was fond of singing. His taste lay rather in the music-hall direction. Rich young men in small towns—and in large ones, too—frequently have a turn for this kind of music. It requires no serious preliminary study, but chiefly a readiness to applaud noisily, and a purse opened freely to stimulate the singers who, like nightingales, trill their prettiest songs after sundown.

Daniel Vibe sang. Tommerup raised his eyebrows a little and glanced at the girl. She was listening with a faint smile to the funny falsetto voice. She could not hear the first words distinctly, but suddenly she set her lips together and moved her chair.

"That's enough of that," said Tommerup.

"What's wrong?" asked Vibe, and burst into careless laughter.

The wealthy young hero of the small seaport town was not endowed with a particularly refined nature and perhaps he did not know himself how coarse his song was. A glance from his friend now seemed to make him aware of the girl's presence for the first time.

"Oh, I see," he said, "the young lady. You needn't be afraid of me, Missy. You may trust me. . ."

Here Tommerup spoke to him gravely.

"All right," Vibe went on, "just as you like. You're my preserver; . . . you're a regular brick, that's what you are. Come on, let's have a drink together, and the girl too. No one's going to hurt you, Missy; but you see, when a fellow's had such a close shave . . . and then to lie half drowned in the cabin . . . Tommerup, you're my friend, and if I'm not to sing, by Jove, you must."

Tommerup vainly endeavoured to soothe him. Nothing would do but a song. With his thoughtful air, and his good-humoured little smile, he at last agreed.

"All right," he said, "it's your birthday, and so you shall have your own way."

This is what he sang:

"I am contented with my store;
Altho' I should not be the worse
For just a very little more,
I covet not my neighbour's purse;—
For thine is thine,
And mine is mine,
Do what you will, mine it is still.

"The sun that shines as bright for me
As for the richest man I meet;
The breeze that blows as fresh and free;
Good appetite and slumbers sweet;-
No money buys
What most I prize;
Bid what you will, mine it is still.

"And while I'm roaming far away,
I'll hear perchance that one at home
Looks out for me from day to day,
And wonders why I do not come;
Then hand in hand
We two shall stand;
The world may frown, she'll be my own."

After Vibe had relieved his mind by declaring the song too sentimental for grown-up men, Sören asked leave to say something, and proceeded to make a little speech in honour of Tommerup, ending by congratulating the captain on having had one man on board fit to look after himself and the boat and the others into the bargain.

Here Vibe again grew white; and when he had got the better of his reviving recollections of the terrors of the sea, he stared coldly at Sören, and rejoined that the whole thing was wholly and solely the fault of the *Wild Duck*; she was the wretchedest *Wild Duck*, the most miserable cutter he'd ever seen; and it was a shame that his old friend Tommerup had ever palmed her off on him.

Tommerup smiled, but Sören took the remark very seriously indeed.

"You can strike my name off the list of your crew, Hr. Vibe," said he; "and you can say I'm a common sailor, and that I loaf about at home doing nothing—you can say so and welcome. I can tell you there are worse ways of putting in the time than that. My father and my grand father never did anything when they were my age but shoot, and sail, and fish, and all the same one of them's gone to his grave an honest man, and the other'll do the same; and so shall I, without cheating a soul out of a single farthing, and without letting every bad girl in the town make a fool of me. But when you begin grumbling at Hr. Tommerup, I tell you, you'd best go home and keep quiet, and it's a pity you didn't do it a good while ago."

"I say, Sören!" said Klaus.

"Oh, let him go on!" cried Vibe, flushing and turning pale, and then bursting into tears, as a weak man will at critical moments. He threw himself on the sofa, overcome with alcohol and emotion, and wept freely.

Sören looked perplexed, and Tommerup laid his hand consolingly on his friend's shoulder.

"I shall never set foot on the cutter again," he moaned, "never again."

"How are you going to get home, then?" muttered Sören.

"I'll knock a hole in her and sink her as soon as we get back," said Vibe.

"it would be better to sell her," responded the persistent Sören.

"Never!" was the answer.

"Well, then, you ought to give her to Hr. Tommerup," suggested Sören. "He has done enough to-day to earn her, and a good deal more."

Vibe did not answer at once; but presently he sat up, and extended his hand as he had seen travelling actors do and as he always did himself when he made a speech at the club.

"Tommerup, my friend, my preserver!" said he. "I owe you my life twice over to-day. First because you fished me out of the water, and then because you sailed us safely here. I give you the *Wild Duck*."

Tommerup was endeavouring to release himself from his friend's embrace.

"You'll have forgotten all about it to-morrow, Daniel," he answered, smiling.

"What!" said Vibe. "You think I'm drunk? Well, well . . . But I'll show you . . . Look here, my good girl, can you give me paper and pen and ink? I really mean it . . . and you'll be paid for it, too. . .. I'll give you a kiss afterwards. That's right . . . the old man over there shall be a witness. No, he's too far gone . . . Never mind, Sören and you shall be witnesses. There—it's a deed of gift in *optima forma*, as we lawyers say, and Tommerup can get it registered to-morrow at the office."

"I spoke just now," he said, "of my best friend. You can see by that what a fool I am, since I have made a close friend of that little creature.

"But Jacob did me a good turn just now. I was beginning to lose heart, and I should not do that. For however poor I am, there is some one here who is worse off still, and so. . . . Now give me both your hands, and promise me that you will stick to me through thick and thin. . . . Ah, don't cry—come here, come to me!"

He opened his arms, and the girl clung to him, and sobbed, with her arms round his neck—

"I will, I will. . . . Only trust me!"

It was rather late and the candle had burned very low, when Klaus Tommerup stepped into the room which had been allotted to the three companions. And he could not refrain from waking up Sören to tell him the news.

"Well, well," said Sören, and slapped his knee. "Then it's you, after all, who are keeping your birthday to-day! Anyhow, you have got a present."

"That I have," said Tommerup, with a beaming face.

Then he held up his candle-end and let the light fall on Daniel Vibe who was snoring loudly.

"He is sleeping it off," he observed. "A drunken man is an ugly sight to be sure. Just think, Sören, if that were your brother, or if either of us had a father like—"

"He is an ass," said Sören, rubbing his eyes, "but he has a good business at home yonder."

"So he has," said Tommerup; and he blew out the light.

XII

What remains to be told?

Nothing much, for everything went its natural way.

The second day from that evening Klaus went to see his friend who sat in the outer office, while the old lawyer, the pillar of the house, worked in the adjoining room.

There was a certain embarrassment in Daniel Vibe's greeting.

Tommerup took a half-sheet of paper out of his pocket-book and presented it to his friend.

Vibe coloured.

"I just wanted to give you back this paper," said Tommerup quietly.

"I fancy you wrote it rather in a hurry."

"Not at all," said Vibe, glancing a little anxiously towards the adjoining room. "You have free leave to make use of it—that's to say, you may regard the cutter quite as your own."

Tommerup looked at him and he blushed a little more.

"You know very well, Daniel," said he, "that I should never press you to keep that promise, although I would sooner sail that boat than do anything else in the world—no, not exactly anything in the world, but sooner than most things. I only want to know how we stand; because yesterday after we landed you kept out of my way the whole afternoon. Either we can go on as we have done till now, and I have your leave to use the boat when I like, while you are still her owner and her captain; or else the *Wild Duck* is mine, honestly earned and honestly paid, and you have my leave to use her as much as you like, and to put on as much sail as you please."

"Heaven forbid!" exclaimed Vibe.

"Well then," said Tommerup, with his old smile, "the boat is really mine?"

"The boat is yours, confound her!" said Vibe.

"Thanks," said Tommerup; and he shook hands with his friend.

"Don't be angry," he added, "if I ask you to exchange this bit of paper for a regular document, drawn up by the old fox in there. For this counts for nothing, as far as I can judge."

"Give me the paper," said Vibe. "I will give you a proper deed of gift this evening at the club."

They shook hands again—Tommerup, as he had always done, Vibe in a slightly altered way. But what could anyone guess from that?

The same evening Tommerup received his deed of gift. The new owner of the *Wild Duck* wished to give a punch supper, but the late owner excused himself on the ground of having a headache.

After that Tommerup often sailed with Sören across to the Quarantine Island and almost gave up going to the club. One pleasure has to make way for another. But one very wet autumn evening he came into the club again.

He did not notice anything unusual at first and was not at all aware that the other men there avoided him. But the apothecary, who was every one's friend and every one's adviser, took him aside and explained with a good deal of circumlocution that Daniel Vibe had several times told how Tommerup had taken him over to the Quarantine Island and made him drunk along with the "tipsy inspector and the little hussy his daughter," and so had tricked him out of the cutter.

Tommerup shook the rain from his coat-sleeves, looked up, asked the apothecary on his word of honour if what he said was true, and then went straight into the most select room of all, where Vibe sat among the other leading people of the place, playing high and drinking more rumpunch than was good for him.

Klaus was standing in front of Vibe before the latter had noticed his approach. Vibe grew rather pale.

"Look here, Daniel Vibe," said Tommerup, "I'm told you have played me a very dirty trick. As far as 1 could I have always been a true comrade to you. Will you say here before everyone that the apothecary lies when he says that you have said this and that about me in my absence?"

There was perfect silence in this very select room, and in those adjoining it. Vibe dropped his cards and stretched out a somewhat unsteady hand for his glass.

" Do you mean—do you mean to assault me?" he asked, looking round on his companions for assistance in case of need.

One of the other players who had been a friend of old Tommerup's spoke up.

"Vibe has told us all," he said, "that that's how Tommerup managed it."

"Good," said Tommerup, and fastened a button of his coat. "Then I invite my former friend and comrade, Daniel Vibe, here on the spot to declare that he has slandered me falsely."

Vibe bent his head without answering.

"You see, gentlemen," continued Tommerup, with a very slight quiver in his voice, "that Hr. Vibe is in an awkward position. As far as I am concerned I have time to wait; I have always had time. But no one can wait indefinitely where his honour is in question. I expect at midday to-morrow a written apology from my former friend and I shall read it aloud here to-morrow evening. Should it not come, I shall declare Daniel Vibe to be a common slanderer, and I shall suggest that you should turn him out of your society, because he is not fit to be among decent people."

And so Tommerup went away.

The next morning Tommerup received his apology. It was couched in the briefest possible terms and hit the medium between excuse and denial so neatly that the recipient bit his lip and murmured, "The cunning old fox!

None the less he went to the club and read the letter aloud—Vibe was absent—to the assembled members, and then he addressed the following little speech to them—

"This is not an excuse," said he, "such as I had a right to expect. But all the same I accept it, and I do not want to proceed any further in the matter. Hr. Vibe has a lot of people in his office, and he's a big man in this town and I am nothing. That's a fact I know I shall have to reckon with. But I part from you, gentlemen, persuaded that I have kept my good name untarnished and that is enough for me. If I stayed in the club I should necessarily be a cause of offence. My being here would always keep one man away, and you can spare me better than him. Thanks for the good times we have had here together, and farewell."

A month later the soap factory was sold, but Tommerup did not sell it himself. Some one else was kind enough to do it for him. All the outstanding claims had been collected by one person and that person proceeded to turn Klaus Tommerup into the street with nothing but a few absolutely necessary personal belongings, among them the cat Jacob.

Everything was sold—the whole property that for many generations had belonged to Tommerup's family; and so all claims were settled. Only the cutter, the *Wild Duck*, remained in his possession and in the meantime he lived on board her. The townspeople were discreet enough not to trouble him with visits.

The day after he had settled into his new quarters, old Prip, Sören's father, strolled down the pier. Tommerup put his head out of the companion. The old man stood still and tcok his pipe out of his mouth.

"Look here, Hr. Tommerup," said he, "Sören says there is room for you at home in the shed."

"I beg your pardon?"

"We have got two rooms ready for you; they are rather small, but they look west; you can see out across the bay. And we will share the kitchen; and so you can be married."

The old man replaced his pipe and walked away.

Tommerup gazed after him.

Shortly after, Sören made his appearance.

"Are you two mad?" shouted Tommerup to him.

"Not that I know of," said Sören. "You can't live with a wife on board the boat; anyhow not with children."

"Who told you I was thinking of getting married?" asked Tommerup, after a moment's despondent reflection.

Sören opened his eyes.

"Every one that has a sweetheart wants to get married. Why not let the parson arrange it? That's the easiest way."

Tommerup could not refrain from smiling.

"The question is, Sören, what shall we have to live on?"

"Peat and potatoes, of course. And you'll take me with you?"

Klaus Tommerup jumped up, sprang on the pier, and pressed Sören's hand.

"I had forgotten all about the peat," he cried.

"Yes, and the potatoes too," added the accurate Sören.

So the firm of Klaus Tommerup and Sören Prip really sailed with the above-mentioned freight, and it soon became evident that the *Wild Duck* with that freight could keep a man, and his wife and child besides. The price of peat continued to rise, while the love at home did not go down. But whether Hr. Tommerup, after the shed was pulled down and a house put up in its place, and after the *Wild Duck* had a duckling in the shape of a smaller boat, and after both of these had been replaced bv a big yacht—whether Tommerup then applied to the club for membership again, this story does not say.

JAPAN

HOW THE EMPRESS JINGO SAILED UNTO THE LAND CALLED CHOSEN[1]

THE Empress returned to the Bay of Kashihi, and loosing her hair, looked over the sea, saying:

"I, having received instructions of the Gods of Heaven and Earth, and trusting in the Spirits of the Imperial ancestors, floating across the deep blue sea, intend in person to chastise the West. Therefore do I now lave my head in the water of the sea. If I am to be successful, let my hair part spontaneously into two."

Accordingly she entered the sea and bathed, and her hair parted of its own accord. The Empress bound it up parted into bunches. Then she addressed her ministers, saying:

"To make war and move troops is a matter of the greatest concern to a country. Peace and danger, success and failure, must depend on it. If I now entrusted to you, my ministers, the duties of the expedition we are about to undertake, the blame, in case of ill-success, would rest with you. This would be very grievous to me. Therefore, although I am a woman, and a feeble woman too, I will for a while borrow the outward appearance of a man, and force myself to adopt manly counsels. Above, I shall receive support from the Spirits of the Gods of Heaven and Earth, while below I shall avail myself of the assistance of you, my ministers. Brandishing our weapons, we shall cross the towering billows; preparing an array of ships, we shall take possession of the Land of Treasure. If the enterprise succeeds, all of you, my ministers, will have the credit, while if it is unsuccessful, I alone shall be to blame. Such have been my intentions, do ye deliberate together regarding them."

The ministers all said:

"The object of the measure which the Empress has devised for the Empire is to tranquillize the ancestral shrines and the Gods of Earth and Grain, and also to protect her servants from blame. With heads bowed to the ground we receive thy commands."

The various provinces were ordered to collect ships and to practise the use of weapons. But an army could not be assembled. The Empress said:

"This is surely the will of a God."

So she erected the Shrine of Oho-miwa, and offered there a sword and a spear. Then the troops assembled freely. Hereupon a fisherman of Ahe, by name

[1] From W. G. Aston's translation of *The Nihongi*.

Womaro, was sent out into the Western sea, to spy if there was any land there. He came back and said:

"There is no land to be seen."

Again a fisherman of Shika, named Nagusa, was sent to look. After several days he returned, and said:

"To the North-West there is a mountain girt with clouds and extending crosswise. This is perhaps a country."

Hereupon a lucky day was fixed upon by divination. There was yet an interval before they should set out. Then the Empress in person, grasping her battle-axe, commanded the three divisions of her army, saying:

"If the drums are beaten out of time, and the signal-flags are waved confusedly, order cannot be preserved among the troops. If greedy of wealth and eager for much, you cherish self and have regard for your own interests, you will surely be taken prisoners by the enemy. Despise not the enemy, though his numbers may be few; shrink not from him, though his numbers may be many. Spare not the violent, slay not the submissive. There will surely be rewards for those who ultimately conquer in battle, and of course punishments for those who turn their backs and flee."

After this a God gave instructions, saying:

"A gentle spirit will attach itself to the Empress's person, and keep watch over her life: a rough spirit will form the vanguard and be a guide to the squadron."

So when she had received the divine instructions she did worship, and for this purpose appointed Otarimi, Yosama no Ahiko to be the Director of the ceremonies in honour of the God.

Sail was set from the harbour of Wani. Then the Wind-God made a breeze to spring up, and the Sea-God uplifted the billows. The great fishes of the ocean, every one, came to the surface and encompassed the ships. Presently a great wind blew from a favourable quarter on the ships under sail, and following the waves, without the labour of the oar or helm, they arrived at Silla. The tide-waves following the ships reached far up into the interior of the country. Hereupon the King of Silla feared and trembled, and knew not what to do, so he assembled all his people and said to them:

" Since the State of Silla was founded, it has never yet been heard that the water of the sea has encroached upon the land. Is it possible that the term of existence granted to it by Heaven has expired, and that our country is to become a part of the ocean?"

Scarce had he spoken when a warlike fleet overspread the sea. Their banners were resplendent in the sunlight. The drums and fifes raised up their voices, and the mountains and rivers all thrilled to the sound. The King of Silla beholding this from afar, felt that his country was about to be destroyed by this extraordinary force, and was terrified out of his senses. But presently, coming to himself, he said:

"I have heard that in the East there is a divine country named Nippon, and also that there is there a wise sovereign called the Tenno. This divine force must belong to that country. How can we resist them by force of arms?"

So he took a white flag, and of his own accord rendered submission, tying his hands behind his back with a white rope. He sealed up the maps and registers, and coming down before the Royal vessel, bowed his head to the ground, and said:

"Henceforward, as long as Heaven and Earth endure, we will obediently act as thy forage-providers, not allowing the helms of our ships to become dry, every spring and every autumn, we will send tribute of horse-combs and whips. And, without thinking the sea-distance a trouble, we will pay annual dues of male and female slaves." He confirmed this by repeated oaths, saying, "When the sun no longer rises in the East, but comes forth in the West; when the river Arinare turns its course backward, and when the river pebbles ascend and become stars—if before this we fail to pay homage every spring and every autumn, or neglect to send tribute of combs and whips, may the Gods of Heaven and Earth both together punish us."

HOW HIKO-HOHO-DEMI-NO MIKOTO MARRIED THE SEA-KING'S DAUGHTER[1]

THE elder brother, Ho-no-susori-no Mikoto, was endowed with a sea-gift, and was therefore called Umi no sachi-hiko:[2] the younger brother, Hiko-hoho-demi-no Mikoto, was endowed with a mountain gift, and was therefore called Yama no sachi-hiko. Whenever the wind blew and the rain fell, the elder brother lost his gain, but in spite of wind and rain the younger brother's gain did not fail him. Now the elder brother spoke to the younger brother, saying:

"I wish to make trial of an exchange of gifts with thee."

The younger brother consented, and the exchange was accordingly made. Thereupon the elder brother took the younger brother's bow and arrows, and went a-hunting to the mountain; the younger brother took the elder brother's fish-hook, and went on the sea a-fishing. But neither of them got anything, and they came back empty-handed. The elder brother accordingly restored to the younger brother his bow and arrows, and demanded back his own fish-hook.

Now the younger brother had lost the fish-hook in the sea, and he knew not how

[1] From W. G. Aston's translation of *The Nihongi*.

[2] Sea-gift-prince.

to find it. Therefore he made other new fish-hooks, several thousands in number, which he offered to his elder brother. The elder brother was angry, and would not receive them, but demanded importunately the old fish-hook.

"These are not my old fish-hook: though they are many, I will not take them."

And he continued repeatedly to demand it vehemently. Therefore Hiko-hoho-demi-no Mikoto's grief was exceedingly profound, and he went and made moan by the shore of the sea. Now there was an old man, who suddenly came forward, and gave his name as Shiho-tsuchi no Oji. He asked him, saying:

"Who art thou, my lord, and why dost thou grieve thee?"

Hiko-hoho-demi-no Mikoto answered and told him the matter from first to last.

The old man said:

"Grieve no longer. I will devise a plan." So he unfolded his plan, saying: "The courser on which the Sea-God rides is a sea-monster eight fathoms in length, who with fins erect stays in the small orange-tree house. I will consult with him."

So he took Hiko-hoho-demi-no Mikoto with him, and went to see the sea-monster.

The sea-monster then suggested a plan, saying:

"I could bring the Heavenly Grandchild to the Sea-palace after a journey of eight days, but my King has a courser, a sea-monster of one fathom, who will without doubt bring him thither in one day. I will therefore return and make him come to thee. Thou shouldst mount him, and enter the sea. When thou enterest the sea, thou wilt in due course find there the Little Shore of Delight. Proceed along this shore and thou wilt surely arrive at the palace of my King. Over the well at the palace gate there is a multitudinous branching cassia tree. Do thou climb up on to this tree and stay there."

Having so said, he entered into the sea, and departed.

Accordingly, the Heavenly Grandchild, in compliance with the sea-monster's words, remained there, and waited for eight days, when there did indeed appear to him a sea-monster of one fathom. He mounted on it, and entered the sea, where he followed in every particular the former sea-monster's advice.

At this time Toyo-tama-hime, the daughter of the God of the Sea, came with a jewel-bowl in her hand and was about to draw water, when she saw in the well the reflection of a man. She looked up and was startled, so that she let fall the bowl, which was broken to pieces. But without regard for it, she returned within and told her parents, saying:

"I have seen a man on the tree which is beside the well. His countenance is very beautiful, and his form comely. He is surely no ordinary person."

When the God, her father, heard this, he wondered. Having prepared an eight-fold cushion, he went to meet him, and brought him in. When they were seated, he asked the reason of his coming, upon which he answered and told him all his case. Now the God of the Sea at once conceived pity for him, and summoning all the broad of fin and narrow of fin, made inquiry of them. They all said:

"We know not. Only the Red-woman has an ailment of the mouth and has not come."

So she was sent for in all haste, and on searching her mouth, the lost fish-hook was at once found. Upon this the God of the Sea chid her, saying:

"Thou Kuchime! Hence forward thou shalt not be able to swallow a bait, nor shalt thou be allowed to have a place at the table of the Heavenly Grandchild." This is the reason why the fish Kuchime is not among the articles of food set before the Emperor.

After this, Hiko-hoho-demi-no Mikoto took to wife the Sea God's daughter, Tovo-tama-hime, and dwelt in the sea palace. For three years he enjoyed peace and pleasure, but still had a longing for his own country, and therefore sighed deeply from time to time. Toyo-tama-hime heard this and told her father, saying:

"The Heavenly Grandchild often sighs as if in grief. It may be that it is the sorrow of longing for his country."

The God of the Sea thereupon drew to him Hiko-hoho-demi-no Mikoto, and addressing him in an easy, familiar way, said:

"If the Heavenly Grandchild desires to return to his country I will send him back."

So he gave him the fish-hook which he had found, and in doing so, instructed him, saying:

"When thou givest this to thy elder brother thou must recite the following: 'A big hook, and eager hook, a poor hook a silly hook.' After saving all this, fling it to him with a back-handed motion."

Then he summoned together the sea monsters, and inquired of them, saying:

"The Grandchild of the Heavenly Deity is now about to take his departure homewards. In how many days will you accomplish this service?"

Then all the sea-monsters fixed each a number of days according to his own length. Those of them which were one fathom long of their own accord said:

"In the space of one day we will accomplish it."

The one-fathom sea-monsters were accordingly sent with him as his escort. Then he gave him two precious objects, the tide-flowing jewel and the tide-ebbing jewel, and taught him how to use them. He further instructed him, saying:

"If thy elder brother should make high fields, do thou make puddle fields; if thy elder brother make puddle fields, do thou make high fields. Moreover, when thy elder brother goes to sea a-fishing, let the Heavenly Grandchild stand on the sea-shore and do that which raises the wind. Now that which raises the wind is whistling. If thou doest so, I will forthwith stir up the wind of the offing and the wind of the shore, and will overwhelm and vex him with scurrying waves." And he taught him, saying: "If thy elder brother is angry and has a mind to do thee hurt, then produce the tide-flowing jewel and drown him therewith. As soon as he is in peril and appeals for mercy, bring forth the tide-ebbing jewel and therewith save him. If thou dost vex him in this way, he will of his own accord become thy submissive vassal."

When the Heavenly Grandchild was about to set out on his return journey, Toyo-tama-hime addressed him, saying:

"Thy handmaiden is already pregnant, and the time of her delivery is not far off. On a day when the winds and waves are raging, I will surety come forth to the sea-shore, and I pray thee that thou wilt make for me a parturition house, and await me there."

Thereupon the Sea-God placed Hiko-hoho-demi-no Mikoto on the back of a great sea-monster, and so sent him back to his own country.

Now Hiko-hoho-demi-no Mikoto followed implicitly the teaching of the Sea-God. First of all he offered his elder brother the fish-hook. His elder brother was angry and would not receive it. Accordingly the younger brother produced the tide-flowing jewel, upon which the tide rose with a mighty overflow, and the elder brother was drowning. Therefore he besought his younger brother, saying:

"I will serve thee as thy slave. I beseech thee, spare my life."

The younger brother then produced the tide-ebbing jewel, whereupon the tide ebbed of its own accord, and the elder brother was restored to tranquillity. After this the elder brother changed his former words, and said:

I am thy elder brother. How can an elder brother serve a younger brother?"

Then the younger brother produced the tide-flowing jewel, which his elder brother seeing, fled up to a high mountain. Thereupon the tide also submerged the mountain. The elder brother climbed a lofty tree, and thereupon the tide also submerged the tree. The elder brother was now at an extremity and had nowhere to flee to. So he acknowledged his offence, saying:

"I have been in fault. In future my descendants for eighty generations shall serve thee as thy dog-men. I pray thee, have pity on me."

Then the younger brother produced the tide-ebbing jewel, whereupon the tide ceased of its own accord. Hereupon the elder brother saw that the younger brother was possessed of marvellous powers, and at length submitted to serve him.

After this Toyo-tama-hime fulfilled her promise, and bringing with her her younger sister, Tama-yori-hime, bravely confronted the winds and waves, and came to the sea-shore, riding on a great tortoise, and throwing a splendour over the sea. Now the months of her pregnancy were already fulfilled, and the time of her delivery was urgent. Then she spake quietly to the Heavenly Grandchild, saying:

"Thy handmaid is about to be delivered. I prav thee do not look on her."

The Heavenly Grandchild wondered at these words, and peeped in secretly, when behold, she had become changed into a great sea-monster of eight fathoms. Now she was aware that the Heavenly Grandchild had looked in upon her privacy, and was deeply ashamed and resentful. When the child was born the Heavenly Grandchild approached and made inquiry, saying: "By what name ought the child to be called?"

She answered and said:

"Let him be called Hiko-nagisa-take-u-gava-fuki-ahezu no Mikoto. Hadst thou not disgraced me, I would have made the sea and land communicate with each other, and for ever prevented them from being sundered. But now that thou hast disgraced me, wherewithal shall friend-feelings be knit together?"

So she wrapped the infant in rushes, and abandoned it on the seashore. Then she barred the sea-path, and passed away.

Then Hiko-hoho-demi-no Mikoto made a song, saying:

"Whatever befalls me,
Ne'er shall I forget my love
With whom I slept
In the island of wild-ducks—
The birds of the offing."